Eccentric Chuck with the Rose Engine.

Rose Engine

Each Specimen on the other side is the result of a different Apparatus.

This page shows the effect of the same Apparatus, when employed in conjunction with the Rose Engine.

Although only one Specimen of each individual Apparatus is given, yet the Patterns, which may be considered almost endless, depend on the skill and taste of the Operator.

Geometric Chuck combined with the Rose Engine

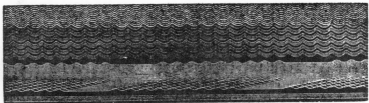

Straight Line Chuck combined with the Rose Engine.

Two Eccentric Movements.

One Oval and one Eccentric Movement.

HOLTZAPFFEL & CO.'s *Compound Oval and Eccentric Chuck with the Rose Engine.*

TURNING

AND

MECHANICAL MANIPULATION.

INTENDED AS

A WORK OF GENERAL REFERENCE AND PRACTICAL INSTRUCTION

ON THE LATHE,

AND THE VARIOUS MECHANICAL PURSUITS

FOLLOWED BY AMATEURS.

———•———

BY

CHARLES HOLTZAPFFEL,

ASSOCIATE OF THE INSTITUTION OF CIVIL ENGINEERS, LONDON ;
HONORARY MEMBER OF THE ROYAL SCOTTISH SOCIETY OF ARTS, EDINBURGH ;
CORRESPONDING MEMBER OF THE AMERICAN INSTITUTE OF NEW YORK ;
ALSO OF THE FRANKLIN INSTITUTE, PHILADELPHIA,
ETC., ETC.

TO BE COMPRISED IN SIX VOLUMES.

VOL. II.

THE PRINCIPLES OF CONSTRUCTION, ACTION, AND APPLICATION, OF CUTTING TOOLS USED BY HAND ; AND ALSO OF MACHINES DERIVED FROM THE HAND TOOLS.

Illustrated by upwards of Seven Hundred Woodcuts.

TEE Publishing
Warwickshire
England

Published in England by
TEE Publishing
The Fosse,
Fosse Way,
Radford Semele,
Warwickshire, CV31 1XE

First published 1847
Reprinted 1993

ISBN 1-85761-032-6

Printed and bound in England by WBC Ltd., Bridgend.

GENERAL SKETCH

OF THE

CONTENTS OF THE WORK.

** The First, Second, and Third Volumes of this work, are written as accompanying books, and will have one Index in common, so as to constitute a general and preliminary work, the addition to which of any of the other volumes, will render the subject complete for the three classes of Amateurs referred to in the Introductory Chapter.

ADDRESS.

It is a source of extreme gratification to H. & Co., to notice the extent to which the Mechanical Arts, and more particularly that of Turning, are pursued; the Turning Lathe, in its various modifications, assisted by its appendages of mechanism, being at present absolutely essential to some stage of every manufacture.

The cultivation of Mechanics by Gentlemen who have the advantages of general acquirements and of leisure, has given rise to many ideas and suggestions on their part, which have led to valuable practical improvements. H. & Co. have a large share of these obligations to acknowledge, but it would obviously be extremely difficult to particularise them, as the ultimate form of any successful piece of mechanism is commonly the result of *many* successive modifications.

In some cases H. & Co. have been furnished by Gentlemen with the theoretical and general sketch of machines, the details of construction being entrusted partially, or wholly, to themselves; and in others they have merely carried into practical effect the finished designs.

To each of the Gentlemen by whom they have been favoured with communications, as well as to those whose names appear in this Catalogue, they beg to return their most sincere thanks, with the assurance that it would give them great pleasure to make further additions to this list under similar circumstances.

The public is respectfully invited to inspect H. & Co.'s ware-rooms, where may be seen the principal part of the tools and machines specified in this list; but of these numerous apparatus, some few are only made to order, and others cannot be always in readiness; consequently, drawings of nearly the whole are in preparation, to supply this inevitable deficiency. The drawings are often found to assist foreign Gentlemen, and others, who experience inconvenience from being unacquainted with the technical names of the various apparatus.

Amateurs who desire to receive instruction in Turning or Mechanical Manipulation generally, can receive lessons from H. & Co.'s experienced workmen, either in rooms fitted up for the purpose at Charing Cross, or at their private residences, in town or country.

No. 64, Charing Cross,
October, 1844.

PREFACE TO THE SECOND VOLUME.

In submitting the second volume of the work on Turning and Mechanical Manipulation to public scrutiny, two subjects call for the Author's especial notice; the delay in its appearance, and the reason for the proposed augmentation of the number of the volumes, intended to constitute the work, from five to six.

The delay has been caused principally, by the unexpected manner in which the subject matter of this volume has been extended by additional examples and illustrations—also by great and unavoidable interruptions caused by the Author's general engagements—and by some domestic calamities, the most severe of which has been the loss of the Author's eldest son.

The division of the matter that was originally meant to compose the second volume, has been mainly caused by a desire to lessen the disappointment, which has been repeatedly expressed at the delay in the progress of the work. This division although it has increased the number of the volumes from five to six, has not caused any further departure from the original scheme of the work, as will be seen on the perusal of the titles of the distinct treatises of which it is proposed to consist.

A few unimportant errors in the references to the several volumes, will naturally ensue from this augmentation in their number, but as the references to the pages, to the woodcuts, and to the appendix notes, will be consecutive throughout the three preliminary volumes, it is hoped that no confusion will be experienced in consequence.

In conclusion the Author has to repeat his former request, that any omissions, errors, or ambiguities may be pointed out for correction in the subsequent appendices; and as he has bestowed an equal amount of care on the production of this, as on the first volume, a second edition of which is also this day published, the Author hopes to be again rewarded with some measure of public approval. He promises to use his best exertions in the furtherance of the work, and as some of the matter is in preparation, and none of the remaining volumes are expected to exceed the first in extent, he hopes not to be again.compelled to trespass so long on the patience of his readers.

CHARING CROSS, LONDON,
November, 10, 1846.

TABLE OF CONTENTS OF THE SECOND VOLUME.

CHAP. XXV.—BORING TOOLS.

CHAP. XXVI.—SCREW CUTTING TOOLS.

CHAP. XXVII.—SAWS.

APPENDIX.

NOTES REFERRING TO THE FIRST VOLUME.

NOTES REFERRING TO THE SECOND VOLUME.

THE END OF THE TABLE OF CONTENTS.

TURNING

MECHANICAL MANIPULATION.

VOL. II.

THE PRINCIPLES OF CONSTRUCTION, ACTION, AND APPLICATION
OF CUTTING TOOLS USED BY HAND ; AND ALSO OF
MACHINES DERIVED FROM THE HAND TOOLS.

——•——

CHAPTER XXII.

GENERAL REMARKS UPON CUTTING TOOLS.

INTRODUCTION.

THE title of the present volume appears to be sufficiently descriptive without additional explanation, consequently the author
will alone offer a few words on the notions which led to the division of the volume into the eight chapters enumerated in the
table of contents, and on their particular arrangement.

The chisel was selected as the subject of the first chapter, as
from the simplicity of its form and action, it may be viewed as a
keen wedge, sometimes employed with quiet pressure, at other
times used with percussion, as in tools of the character of axes
and adzes ; and the straight chisel mounted in a stock for its
guidance becomes the plane. Further, the carpenter's chisel may
be used as a turning tool, and many tools of this kind, the second
in the classification, follow the condition of chisels and planes, if
we imagine the tool to be held at rest, and the work to revolve
against it, on a fixed axis. The practice of turning is naturally
associated with that of boring holes, although in most cases, the
boring tool revolves whilst the work remains at rest. Turning
and boring, each circulatory processes, led to the selection of the
screw as the subject of the next chapter, for revolution combined

with rectilinear advance, are exhibited in all the numerous modes of producing screws.

Saws were ideally compared with some of the scraping chisels, but with a multiplication of points, and these sometimes arranged in continuous order as in the circular saw. The file from its vast assemblage of scraping teeth, was likened to a multiplication of the saw; but unfortunately the file has not been engrafted upon any machine, embodying the manipulation of the unassisted instrument. Shears and punches are next considered in great measure as parallel subjects, and the rectilinear edges of shears although mostly duplicated, nevertheless bear some resemblance to simple chisels, although from their duplication they act on both sides of the material; and lastly the ordinary punch, is comparable with the rectilinear edges of the shears and chisels, if we do but conceive these to be bent into the circular form.

Should these grounds for the arrangement adopted be deemed fanciful or visionary, it may be added that some order or selection was imperative, and it is hoped the present will serve as efficiently as any other that could be selected.

SECT. I.—THE ANGLES AND POSITIONS OF TOOLS, AS REGARDS THE ACT OF CUTTING.

THE section now to be commenced, refers exclusively to the principles and construction of cutting tools, which will be considered in a general manner, and without reference to any particular branches of mechanical art, the tools and applications being selected by their characters and principles alone.

All edged tools may be considered to be wedges formed by the meeting of two straight, or of two curvilinear surfaces, or of one of each kind, meeting at angles varying from about 20 to 120 degrees.

Some few tools are pointed, from the meeting of three or more planes or surfaces.

Occasionally, as in the hatchet, the chipping chisel, and the turner's chisel for soft wood, the tool is ground from both sides, or with two bevils or chamfers; at other times, as in the carpenter's chisels and plane irons, the tool is ground from one side only, and in such cases, the general surface or shaft of the tool constitutes the second plane of the wedge; this difference does not affect the principle.

The general characters of cutting tools, namely, their angles, and their relations to the surfaces to be produced, depend upon the hardness of the opposed substances, and the direction and nature of their fibres ; these primary characters, require especial consideration.

The particular or specific characters of cutting tools, namely, the forms of their blades, stocks, or handles, are adapted to the convenience of the individual, or the structure of the machine by which they are guided ; these secondary characters, the less require or admit of generalization.

It will be now attempted to be shown that, granting the latitude usual in all classifications, cutting tools may be included in three groups, namely, Paring Tools, Scraping Tools, and Shearing Tools.

First—Paring or splitting tools, with thin edges, the angles of which do not exceed sixty degrees ; one plane of the edge being nearly coincident with the plane of the work produced, (or with the tangent, in circular work). These tools remove the fibres principally in the direction of their length, or longitudinally ; and they produce large coarse chips or shavings, by acting like the common wedge applied as a mechanical power.

Secondly—Scraping tools with thick edges, that measure from sixty to one hundred and twenty degrees. The planes of the edges form nearly equal angles with the surface produced ; or else the one plane is nearly or quite perpendicular to the face of the work, (or becomes as a radius to the circle). These tools remove the fibres in all directions with nearly equal facility, and they produce fine dust-like shavings by acting superficially.

Thirdly—Shearing, or separating tools, with edges of from sixty to ninety degrees, generally duplex, and then applied on opposite sides of the substances. One plane of each tool, or of the single tool, coincident with the plane produced.

In explanation of these views, the diagram, fig. 316, is supposed to represent seven different tools, the bevils or edges of which are all at the angle of sixty degrees, this may be considered as the medium angle of the paring, scraping, and shearing tools.

The cutting and scraping tools are supposed to be moving from A to B, which line represents the face of the work ; or the tools may be considered to be at rest, and the work to be moving from B to A.

Or, in turning, the tool may be supposed to remain fixed, and the circle to represent the moving surface of the work; one plane of the tool then becomes a tangent or radius.

The shearing tools, if in pairs, are proceeding towards each other on the line C D, whilst A B still represents the face of the work. The single tools act on the same principle, but the body of the material, or the surface of the bench or support, supplies the resistance otherwise offered by the second tool.

The tools *a, c, f*, are bevelled or chamfered on both sides, the others from one side only; in these latter, the general face of the tool forms the second side of the angle, and allowing for exaggeration, both as to excess and deficiency, the diagram may be considered to represent the edges of the following tools.

[*a, b, c, d, Splitting and Paring Tools, proceeding from* A *to* B.]

a—The axe, or the cleaver for splitting.

b—The side hatchet, adze, paring and drawing knives, paring chisels, and gouges, the razor, pen-knife, spokeshave, the engraver's graver, and most of the engineer's cutting, turning, and planing tools for metal.

Fig. 316.

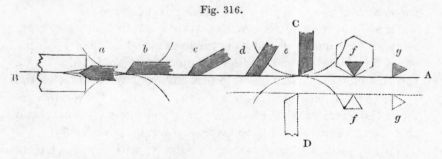

c—The turning chisel for soft wood, the chipping chisels, for iron, stone, &c.

d—The joiner's chisels, and carving tools, used with the bevils downwards, the joiner's planes, the cross-cut chisel for metal, and some other metal tools.

[*e, f, Scraping Tools, proceeding from* A *to* B.]

e—When single, the scraping tools for turning the hardwoods, ivory, and brass, the hand-plane for metal, and when multiplied, the various saws, and files.

f—When single, a triangular scraper for metal, and when multiplied, the cross-cut saw for wood, and also polygonal broaches or rimers with any number of sides, for metal.

[*e, f, Shearing Tools, proceeding from* C *to* D.]

e—When duplex, shears with edges from eighty to ninety degrees, commencing with delicate lace scissors for single threads, and ending with the engineer's shears for cutting iron bars and plates upwards of one inch thick; also duplex punches with rectangular edges, for punching engines and fly-presses.

e—When single, the carpenter's firmer and mortise-chisels, the paring-knife moving on a hinge, and cutting punches for gun wadding and thin materials.

f—When duplex, common nippers for wire, more generally however, the blades are inclined, so that one bevil of each blade lies in one and the same plane, and which is vertical to A B, as at *g g*.

f—When single, the smith's cutting-off chisel.

In practice, the tools differ from the constant angle of sixty degrees assumed in the diagram for the convenience of explanation, as the angles of all tools are determined by the hardness, and the peculiarity of fibre or structure, of the several substances upon which they are employed. The woods and soft fibrous materials, require more acute angles than the metals and hard bodies ; and the greater or less degree of violence to which the tools are subjected, greatly influences likewise the angles adopted for them.

Thus, under the guidance of a little mechanism, the thin edge of a razor, which is sharpened at an angle of about 15 degrees, is used to cut minute slices or sections of woods, in all directions of the grain, for the purpose of the microscope. But the carpenter and others require more expeditious practice, and the first change is to thicken the edges of the tools to range from about 20 to 45 degrees, to meet the rough usage to which they are then exposed, whether arising from the knots and hard places in the woods, or the violence applied.

In tools for iron and steel from 60 to 70 will be found a very common angle, in those for brass 80 to 90, in hexagonal broaches for metal it increases to 120, and in the octagonal broach sometimes employed the angle is still greater ; in the circular broach required by clock and watchmakers, the angle disappears and the tool ceases either to cut or scrape, it resolves itself into an instrument acting by pressure, or becomes a burnisher.

To a certain extent, every different material may be considered to demand tools of a particular angle, and again the angle is somewhat modified by the specific mode of employment: these conditions jointly determine the practical angles suited to every case, or the angles of greatest economy, or most productive effect.

The diagram shows that, independently of the measure of the angle of the tool, we have to consider its position as regards the surface of the work, the broad distinction being that, in the paring tools, the one face of the wedge or tool, is applied nearly parallel with the face of the work; and in the scraping tools, it is applied nearly at right angles, as explained in the foregoing definitions. Indeed the paring tools, if left to themselves, will in some cases assume the position named; thus for example, if we place a penknife at an elevated angle upon a cedar pencil, and attempt to carry it along as a carpenter's plane, the penknife if held stiffly will follow the line of its lower side and dig into the wood; but if it be held slenderly, it will swing round in the hand until its blade lies flat on the pencil, and it will even require a little twisting or raising to cause it to penetrate the wood at all. This disposition appears to be equally true, in the thin edges of the penknife or razor, and in the thick edges of the strong paring tools for metal.

The action of a cutting-tool in motion is twofold. The moving force is first exerted on the point of the wedge, to sever or divide the substance particle from particle; the *cohesion of the mass* now directly opposes the entry of the tool, and keeps it back. But the primary motion impressed on the tool having severed a shaving, proceeds to bend or curl it out of the way; the shaving ascends the slope of the wedge, and the *elasticity of the shaving* confines the tool in the cleft, presses it against the lower side, disposes it to pursue that line, and therefore to dig into the substance.

In pursuing the more detailed examination of different cutting tools employed in the mechanical arts, amongst the several classifications which might be adopted, it appears to the author to be the more generally useful to consider the various tools in separate

chapters under the following heads, namely, Chisels and Planes
— Turning tools — Boring tools — Screw-cutting tools — Saws —
Files — Shears and Punches — as some of all these kinds of tools
may be found in every work-room.

The several chapters and sections will be commenced with the
tools for the woods, which are perhaps the more commonly used
by the amateur, the corresponding tools for metal will generally
be then considered, and lastly some illustrations will be given of
the same tools applied to various machines, still further to prove
the uniformity of principle upon which they act, throughout these
several circumstances.

These comparative views may serve to show the similitude of
principle in tools for like purposes, whether the tools be large or
small, whether they be used for wood or metal, and either by
hand or machinery; and in cases of indecision or difficulty, a
glance through any one section or chapter may denote, either
the most appropriate of the ordinary tools, or may occasionally
suggest some new modification to suit a particular case, in imitation of the numerous conversions which will be already found to
exist amongst the tools used in the constructive arts.

SECT. II.—THE FORMS AND MOTIONS OF TOOLS, AS REGARDS THE
PRODUCTION OF LINES, SUPERFICIES, AND SOLIDS.

THE principles of action of all cutting tools, and of some
others, whether guided by hand or by machinery, resolve themselves into the simple condition, that the work is the combined
copy of the form of the tool, and of the motion employed. Or
in other words, that we exactly put into practice the geometrical
definitions employed to convey to us the primary ideas of lines,
superficies, and solids; namely, that the line results from the
motion of a point, the superficies from the motion of a line,
and the solid from the motion of a superficies.

It therefore follows, as will be shown, that when the tool is a
point having no measurable magnitude, that two motions must
be impressed upon it, one equivalent to the breadth, and another
equivalent to the length of the superficies. When the tool is
wide, so as to represent the one dimension of the superficies,
say its breadth, then only one motion is to be impressed, say a
motion equivalent to the length of the superficies; and these two
are either rectilinear or curvilinear, accordingly as straight or
curved superficies are to be produced.

To illustrate this in a more familiar way than by the ideal mathematical conceptions, that a point is without magnitude, a line is without breadth, and a superficies without thickness; we will suppose these to be materialised, and to become pieces of wood, and that the several results are formed through their agency on soft clay.

Fig. 317.

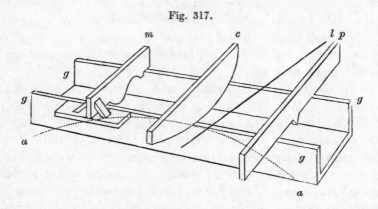

Thus supposing *g g*, to be two boards, the edges of which are parallel and exactly in one plane, and that the interval between them is filled with clay; by sliding the board *p*, along the edges of *g g*, the point in *p*, would produce a line, and if so many lines were ploughed, that every part of the clay were acted upon by the point, a level surface would at length result. The line *l*, such as a string or wire, carried along *g g*, would at one process reduce the clay to the level of the edges of the box.

Either the point or the line, might be applied in any direction whatever, and still they would equally produce the plane, provided that every part of the material were acted upon; and this, because the section of a plane is everywhere a right line, and which conditions are fulfilled in the elementary apparatus, as the edges of *g g* are straight and give in every case the longitudinal guide; and with *l*, the second line is formed at once, either with a string, a wire, or a straight board; but in *p*, the point requires a second or transverse guide, and which is furnished by the straight parts of the board *p*, rubbing on the edges of *g g*, and therefore the point obtains both a longitudinal and a transverse guide, which were stated to be essential.

The board *c*, with a circular edge, and *m*, with a moulding, would respectively produce circular and moulded pieces, which would be straight in point of length in virtue of *g g*, the line of motion, and curved in width in virtue of *c*, or *m*, the lines of the tools. But now *c*, and *m*, must always advance parallel with their starting positions, or the width of the moulding would vary; and this is true, whenever curved guides or curved tools are employed, as the angular relation of the tool must be then constantly maintained, which it is supposed to be by the external piece or guide attached to *m*.

Supposing *g y*, each to have circular edges, as represented by the dotted arc *a a*, or to be curved into any arbitrary moulding, the same boards *p, l, c, m*, would produce results of the former transverse sections, but the clay would in each case present, longitudinally, the curved figure of the curved longitudinal boards *a a;* here also the line of the tool and the line of the motion would obtain in the result.

If, to carry out the supposition, we conceive the board *a a*, to be continued until it produced the entire circle, we should obtain a cylinder at one single sweep, if the wire *l*, were carried round at right angles to *a a*. But to produce the same result with the point *p*, it must be done either by sweeping it round to make circular furrows very near together, or by traversing the point from side to side, to make a multitude of contiguous lines, parallel with the axis of the cylinder. In either case we should apply the point to every part of the surface of the cylinder, which is the object to be obtained, as we copy the circle of *a a*, (which is supposed to be complete,) and the line *l*; or the transverse motion of *p*, which is equivalent to a line.

But it is obvious that, in every case referred to, there is the choice of moving either the clay or the tool, without variation in the effect. If in respect to the circular guide *a a*, we set the clay to rotate upon its center, we should produce all the results without the necessity for the guide boards *a a*, as the axis being fixed, and the tool also fixed, the distance from the circumference to the center would be everywhere alike, and we should obtain the condition of the circle by *motion alone*, instead of by the *guide;* and such, in effect, is turning.

An every-day example of this identical supposition is seen in the potter's wheel; and the potter also, instead of always describing the lines of his works with his hands, as in sketching, occasionally resorts to curved boards or templets, as for making

H H

the mouldings for the base of a column, or any other circular ornament. But here, as also in ordinary turning, we have choice, either to employ a figured tool, or to impress on a pointed tool a path identical with the one section; for example, the sphere is turned either by a semicircular tool applied parallel with the axis, or else by sweeping a narrow or pointed tool around the sphere, in the same semicircular path.

Having shown that in every case, the superficies is a copy of the tool and of the one motion, or of the point and the two motions, it will be easily conceived that the numerous superficies and solids, emanating from the diagonal, spiral, oval, cycloid, epicycloid, and other acknowledged lines, which are mostly themselves the compositions of right lines and of circles, may be often mechanically produced in three different ways.

First, by the employment of tools figured to the various shapes, and used with only one motion or traverse; secondly, by the use of figured guides, *cams*, or *shaper-plates*, by which the motion is constrained, just the same as *p* makes a right or a curved line, in virtue of its straight or curved guide; and thirdly, by the employment of a point actuated by two motions, by the composition of which most geometric lines are expressed.

Thus when *uniform* motions are employed, two rectilinear motions produce a diagonal to themselves; one circular and one continued right-line motion, give the spiral, the screw, and the cycloid; also if during *one* circular revolution, either the circle or the point make *one* oscillation in a right line, we obtain the oval; by two circular movements we obtain the epicycloid, by three motions the compound or double epicycloid, and so on. And when one or both of the rectilinear or circular generating motions, are *variable* as to velocity, we obtain many different kinds of curves, as the parabola, hyperbola, and others; and thence the solids, arising from the revolutions of some of these curves upon an axis.

We produce the practical *composition* of any two lines or movements, whether regular or irregular, by impressing these movements on the opposite extremities of an inflexible line or rod; from which rod we obtain a compounded *line*, if we trace the motion of a point inserted in any part of the rod, and we obtain a compounded *superficies*, if we copy the motion of the entire line. This may need explanation.

Supposing that in fig. 317, the back guide $g\,g$, to remain a straight line, the front to become the circular arc $a\,a$, the board p, being now traversed in contact both with the straight and curved edges, the point p would describe a line if it were close against the line $g\,g$; or an arc if close against the arc $a\,a$; midway it would describe an arc of about half the original curvature. On the other hand, the line b would cut off the clay in a superficies, possessing at the three parts these same conditions, and merging gradually from the right line to the arc $a\,a$.

But a similar composition of the two lines or motions would occur, were the lines $g\,g$, $a\,a$, to be exchanged for any others, similar or dissimilar, parallel or oblique, or irregular in two directions; and in mechanical practice we combine, in like manner, two motions to produce a compound line or a compound superficies. Indeed in many cases there is no alternative but to impart to two edges $g\,a$ of a block, the marginal outlines of the superficies, and then, generally by *hand-labour*, to reduce all the intermediate portions under the guidance of a straight edge applied at short intervals upon the two edges, which thus become compounded or melted together in the superficies. Numbers of irregular surfaces can be produced by this mode alone.

In fine, in mechanical processes, we translate the mathematical *conceptions* of the rectilinear, circular, and mixed motions of points and lines, into the mechanical *realities* of rectilinear, circular, and mixed motions of pointed or linear tools.

It is not imperative, however, that the tools should have but one fixed point or edge, as without change of principle a succession of similar points may be arranged in a circle, to constitute a revolving cutter, which by its motions will continually present a new point, and multiply the rapidity of the effect. In most cases, the introduction of a tool with a figured outline, cancels the necessity for the means otherwise required to generate such figured line by the motion of a point; and a tool with a figured superficies, cancels also the remaining motion required to produce the superficies, and the tool is simply impressed as a stamp or die.

In tracing the method of applying these theoretical views, to the explanation of the general employment of cutting tools, or the practice of the workshop, we may safely abandon all apprehension of complexity, notwithstanding the almost bound-less variety of the elements of machinery, and other works of cutting tools. For although all the regular figures and solids referred to, are in reality met with, besides a still greater number of others of an irregular or arbitrary character, still by far the greater majority of pieces resolve themselves into very few and simple parts, namely, solids with plane superficies, such as *prisms, pyramids,* and *wedges,* and solids with circular superficies, such as *cylinders, cones,* and *spheres.* These are frequently as it were strung together in groups, either in their entire or dissected states; but as they are only wrought one surface at a time, the whole inquiry may be considered to resolve itself into the production of superficies.

And it may be further stated that, the difference between the modes of accomplishing the same results, by hand tools or by machinery, bears a very close resemblance to the difference between the practices, of the artist who draws the right line and circle by aid of the unassisted hand, and of the mechanical draftsman, who obtains the same lines with more defined exactness, under the *guidance* of the rule and compasses.

The *guide principle* is to be traced in most of our tools. In the joiner's plane it exists in the form of the stock or sole of the plane, which commonly possesses the same superficies as it is desired to produce. For instance, the carpenter's plane used for flat surfaces is itself flat, both in length and width, and there-fore furnishes a double guide. The flat file is somewhat under the same circumstances, but as it cuts at every part of its surface, from thousands of points being grouped together, it is more treacherous than the plane, as regards the surface from which it derives its guidance, and from this and other reasons, it is far more difficult to manage than the carpenter's plane.

In many other cases the cutting instrument and the guide are entirely detached; this is strictly the case in ordinary turning, in which the circular guide is given by the revolution of the lathe mandrel which carries the work, the surface of which becomes the copy of the tool, or of the motion impressed upon the tool, either by the hand of the workman under the guidance of his eye alone, or by appropriate mechanism.

When the lathe is employed under the most advantageous circumstances to produce the various geometrical solids or figures, the tool is placed under the guidance of a ruler or rather of a slide, by which its path is strictly limited to a rectilinear motion. Thus for a cylinder, the slide is placed exactly parallel with the rotary axis of the mandrel, and for a plain flat surface the tool is moved on a slide at right angles to the axis. Generally two slides fixed in these positions are attached to the lathe to carry and guide the tool, the machine being known as the sliding rest; but mostly the one slide only is used as a traversing or directional slide for guiding the tool, the other as an adjusting or position slide, for regulating the penetration of the tool into the work.

Sometimes the two slides are moved simultaneously for the production of cones, but more generally the one slide is placed oblique and used alone. The lathe is employed with great effect in producing plane surfaces, but the more modern engine, the planing-machine, the offspring of the slide or traversing lathe recently adverted to, is now also very much employed for all kinds of rectilinear works.

The planing-machine being intended principally for rectilinear solids of all kinds, its movements are all rectilinear, and these are in general restricted to three, which are in the same relation to each other as the sides of a cube; namely, two are horizontal and at right angles to each other, and the third is vertical, and therefore perpendicular to the other two. The general outline of the machine will be conceived by imagining a horizontal railway to take the place of the revolving axis of the lathe, and the slide rest of the lathe to be fixed vertically against the face of a bridge stretching over the railway.

In the general structure of this most invaluable machine, the railway is the cutting slide, upon which the work is slid to and fro. For producing a horizontal surface, the horizontal slide is employed for traversing the tool across the face of the work, which is thus reduced by ploughing a series of parallel grooves, not exceeding in distance the width of the pointed tool, so that first the line, and then the surface arise, exactly as in the geometrical suppositions. For vertical planes, the vertical is the traversing slide, the horizontal the adjusting; and for oblique planes, the vertical slide is swivelled round to the assigned angle, the imaginary railway being employed in all cases to give the cutting motion.

To advance into greater detail would be to encroach on the subject of the succeeding chapters; although it may be added, that when we examine into almost any machine employed in cutting, it will be found that the end to be obtained is always a superficies, either plane or curved, and which superficies reduced to its elementary condition, presents length and breadth.

When therefore, we have put on one side the mechanism required for connecting and disconnecting the engine with the prime mover, whether animal, steam, or other power; it will be found that when the superficies is produced by a pointed tool, the primary motions resolve themselves into two, which may be considered representative of length and breadth. The velocity of the one primary motion, is suited to the speed proper for cutting the material with the most productive effect, which for the metals is sometimes as low as ten or twenty feet per minute, measured at the tool, and for the woods, the speed is above ten or twenty times as great.* The velocity of the other primary motion is generally very small, and often intermittent; and it becomes a mere creep or traverse motion, by which the pointed tool is gradually moved in the second direction of the superficies, under formation.

In producing circular bodies, one of these primary motions becomes circulating or rotary, and in complex or irregular forms, an additional movement, making in all three, or *sometimes* four are compounded; and lastly, when linear or figured tools are employed, one of the motions is generally expunged.

---

* The principal limit of velocity in cutting machines, appears to be the greatest speed the *tool* will safely endure, without becoming so heated by the friction of separating the fibres, as to lose its *temper* or proper degree of hardness.

The cohesion of iron being very considerable, a velocity materially exceeding ten to twenty feet per minute, would soften and discolour the tool, whereas in general the tools for iron are left nearly or quite hard. Brass having much less cohesion than iron, allows a greater velocity to be used, lead and tin admit of still more speed, and the fibrous cohesion of the soft woods is so small, that when the angles of the tools are favourable, there is hardly a limit to the velocity which may be used. Water, soap and water, oil, milk, and other fluids, are in many cases employed, and especially with the more fibrous metals, for the purpose of lubricating the cutting edges of the tools to keep down the temperature, the fluids reduce the friction of separating the fibres, and cool both the tool and work, thereby allowing an increase of velocity ; and at the same time they lessen the deterioration of the instrument, and which when blunted, excites far more friction, and is likewise more exposed to being softened, than when keen and in perfect working order. There are, however, various objections to the constant use of lubricating fluids with cutting tools.

The other movements of cutting machines may be considered as secondary, and introduced either to effect the adjustment of position at starting, or the changes of position during the progress of the work; or the resettings by which the same superficies is repeated, as in the respective sides of a prism, or the teeth of a spur wheel, which may be viewed as a complex prism.

The above two or three movements may in general be impressed wholly upon the tool, wholly upon the work, or partly upon each; and which explains the very many ways which, in cases of simple forms, may be adopted to attain the same result.

In numerous instances likewise, all the movements are as it were linked together in a chain, so that they may recur at proper intervals, without the necessity for any other adjustment, than that which is done prior to the first starting, such are very appropriately called *self-acting machines,* and these, in many cases, give rise to very curious arrangements and combinations of parts, quite distinct from the movements abstractedly required to produce the various superficies and solids, in which the mathematician and mechanician from necessity exactly agree, when their respective speculations are sifted to their elementary or primary laws, which are few, simple, and alike for all.

Mr. Nasmyth has written an interesting paper entitled "Remarks on the Introduction of the Slide Principle, in Tools and Machines employed in the production of Machinery."*

This principle, although known for a far greater period, has within less than half a century, and in many respects even within less than the fourth of a century, wrought most wonderful changes in the means of constructing mechanism, possessed of nearly mathematical accuracy. The whole of this is traced to the employment of the two, or the three *slide movements,* to which method Mr. Nasmyth has judiciously applied the term " *Slide Principle,*" but the object in this place is rather to examine in detail the principles and practices, than to refer to the influence these have had on manufacturing industry, and thence on the general condition of mankind, and upon our own nation in particular.

---

* See Buchanan's Mill Work, by G. Rennie, F.R.S. 1841. Page 393.

CHAPTER XXIII.

CHISELS AND PLANES.

SECT. I.—INTRODUCTION; BENCH PLANES.

IF we drive an axe, or a thin wedge, into the center of a block of wood, as at *a*, fig. 318, it will split the same into two parts through the natural line of the fibres, leaving rough uneven surfaces, and the rigidity of the mass will cause the rent to precede the edge of the tool. The same effect will partially occur, when we attempt to remove a stout chip from off the side of a block of wood with the hatchet, adze, paring or drawing knife, the paring chisel, or any similar tool. So long as the chip is too rigid to bend to the edge of the tool, the rent will precede the edge; and with a naked tool, the splitting will only finally cease, when the instrument is so thin and sharp, and it is applied to so small a quantity of the material, that the shaving can bend or ply to the tool, and then only will the work be *cut* or will exhibit a true copy of the smooth edge of the instrument, in opposition to its being *split* or *rent*, and consequently showing the natural disruption or tearing asunder of the fibres.

In fig. 318 are drawn to one scale several very different paring-tools, which agree however in similitude with the type, *b*, fig. 316, page 460, and also corroborate the remark on page 462, that "in the paring-tools, the one face of the wedge or tool is applied nearly parallel with the face of the work." In tools ground with only one chamfer, this position not only assists in giving direction to the tool, but it also places the strongest line of the tool exactly in the line of resistance, or of the work to be done.

For example, the axe or hatchet with two bevils *a*, fig. 318, which is intended for hewing and splitting, when applied to *paring* the surface of a block, must be directed at the angle *á*, which would be a much less convenient and less strong position than *b*, that of the *side hatchet* with only one chamfer; but for paring either a very large or a nearly horizontal surface, the side hatchet in its turn is greatly inferior to the adze *c*, in which the handle is elevated like a ladder, at some 60 or 70 degrees from the ground, the preference being given to the horizontal position for the surface to be wrought. The instrument is held in both hands, whilst the operator stands upon his work in a stooping position, the handle being from twenty-four to thirty inches long, and the weight of the blade from two to four pounds.

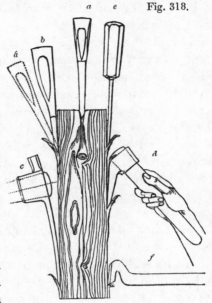

Fig. 318.

The adze is swung in a circular path almost of the same curvature as the blade, the shoulder-joint being the center of motion, and the entire arm and tool forming as it were one inflexible radius; the tool therefore makes a succession of small arcs, and in each blow the arm of the workman is brought in contact with the thigh, which thus serves as a stop to prevent accident. In coarse preparatory works, the workman directs the adze through the space between his two feet, he thus surprises us by the quantity of wood removed; in fine works, he frequently places his toes over the spot to be wrought, and the adze penetrates two or three inches beneath the sole of the shoe, and he thus surprises us by the apparent danger yet perfect working of the instrument, which in the hands of the shipwright in particular, almost rivals the joiner's plane; it is with him the nearly universal paring instrument, and is used upon works in all positions.

The small Indian adze or Bassōōlăh *d*, fig. 318, in place of being circular like the European adze, is formed at a direct angle of about 45 or 50 degrees; its handle is very short, and it is used with great precision by the nearly exclusive motion of the elbow joint.* In order to grind either of these adzes, or *percussive*

* "This very useful instrument, (says Sir John Robison,) varies a little in different districts, in weight and in the angle which the cutting face forms with the line of the handle, but the form shown is the most general, and the weight averages about

chisels, it is necessary to remove the handle, which is easily accomplished as the eye of the tool is larger externally as in the common pickaxe, so that the tool cannot fly off when in use, but a blow on the end of the handle easily removes it.

The chisel e, admits of being very carefully placed, as to position, and when the tool is strong, very flat, and not tilted up, it produces very true surfaces as seen in the mouths of planes.   The chisel when applied with *percussion,* is struck with a wooden mallet, but in many cases it is merely *thrust* forward by its handle.   It will shortly be shown that various other forms of the handle or stock of the chisel, enable it to receive a far more defined and effective thrust, which give it a different and most important character. The *paring-knife,* fig. 8, p. 26, Vol. 1, exhibits also a peculiar but most valuable arrangement of the chisel, in which the thrust obtains a great increase of power and control; and in the *drawing-knife,* the narrow transverse blade and its two handles form three sides of a rectangle, so that it is actuated by *traction,* instead of by violent percussion or steady thrust.

The most efficient and common paring-tool for metal, namely *f,* has been added to fig. 318 for comparison with the paring-tools for wood; its relations to the surface to be wrought are exactly the same as the rest of the group, notwithstanding that the angle of its edge is doubled on account of the hardness of the material, and that its shaft is mostly at right angles, to meet the construction of the slide rest of the lathe or planing machine.

The chisel, when inserted in one of the several forms of stocks or guides, becomes the plane, the general objects being, to limit the extent to which the blade can penetrate the wood, to provide a definitive guide to its path or direction, and to restrain the splitting in favour of the cutting action.

In general, the sole or stock of the plane is in all respects an

---

1lb. 12oz.   The length of handle is about twelve or thirteen inches, and in use it is grasped so near the head, that the forefinger rests on the metal, the thumb nearly on the back of the handle, the other fingers grasp the front of it, the nails approaching the ball of the thumb.   The wrist is held firmly, the stroke being made principally from the elbow, the inclination of the cutting face being nearly a tangent to the circle described by the instrument round the elbow joint as a center, the exact adjustment being made by the grasp and the inclination of the wrist, which is soon acquired by a little practice   In this way very hard woods may be dressed for the lathe with a degree of ease and accuracy not attainable with the small axe used in this country."

accurate counterpart of the form it is intended to produce, and it therefore combines in itself the longitudinal and the transverse sections, or the two guides referred to in the theoretical diagram, page 464, and the annexed figure 319, the parts of which are all drawn to one scale, may be considered a parallel diagram to 317, page 464, so far as regards planes.

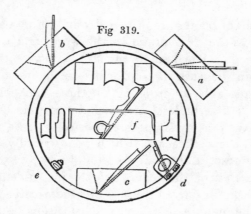

Fig 319.

Thus, although convex surfaces, such as the outside of a hoop, may be wrought by any of the straight planes, applied in the direction of a tangent as at *a*, it is obvious the concave plane, *b*, would be more convenient. For the inside of the hoop, the radius of curvature of the plane must not exceed the radius of the work : thus *c*, the *compass plane*, would exactly suit the curve, and it might be used for larger diameters, although in a less perfect manner. For the convenience of applying planes to very small circles, some are made very narrow or short, and with transverse handles such as *d*, the plane for the hand-rails of staircases, the radius of its curvature being three inches ; it resembles the spokeshave *e*, as respects the transverse handles, although the hand-rail plane has an iron, wedge, and stop, much like those of other planes.

The sections of planes, are also either straight, concave, convex, or mixed lines, and suited to all kinds of specific mouldings, but we have principally to consider their more common features, namely, the circumstances of their edges and guides ; first, of those used for flat surfaces, called by the joiners, *bench planes* ; secondly, the *grooving* planes ; and thirdly, the *moulding* planes.

The various surfacing planes are nearly alike, as regards the arrangement of the iron, the principal differences being in their magnitudes. Thus the maximum width is determined by the average strength of the individual, and the difficulty of maintaining with accuracy the rectilinear edge. In the ordinary bench planes the width of the iron ranges from about 2 to $2\frac{1}{2}$ inches.*

The lengths of planes are principally determined by the degree of straightness that is required in the work, and which may be thus explained. The joiner's plane is always either balanced upon *one* point beneath its sole, or it rests upon *two* points at the same time, and acts by cropping off these two points, without descending to the hollow intermediate between them. It is therefore clear, that by supposing the work to be full of small undulations, the spokeshave, which is essentially *a very short plane,* would descend into all the hollows whose lengths were greater than that of the plane, and the instrument is therefore commonly used for curved lines. But the greater the length of the plane, the more nearly would its position assimilate to the general line of the work, and it would successively obliterate the minor errors or undulations; and provided the instrument were itself *rectilinear*, it would soon impart that character to the edge or superficies submitted to its action. The following table may be considered to contain the ordinary measures of surfacing planes.

Names of Planes.	Lengths, in inches.	Widths, in inches.	Widths of Irons.
Modelling Planes, like Smoothing Planes .	1 to 5	$\frac{1}{4}$ to 2	$\frac{3}{16}$ to $1\frac{1}{2}$
Ordinary Smoothing Planes	$6\frac{1}{2}$ to 8	$2\frac{3}{8}$ to $3\frac{1}{4}$	$1\frac{3}{4}$ to $2\frac{3}{8}$
Rebate Planes	$9\frac{1}{2}$	$\frac{3}{8}$ to 2	$\frac{3}{8}$ to 2
Jack Planes	12 to 17	$2\frac{1}{2}$ to 3	2 to $2\frac{1}{4}$
Panel Planes	$14\frac{1}{2}$	$3\frac{1}{2}$	$2\frac{1}{2}$
Trying Planes	20 to 22	$3\frac{1}{4}$ to $3\frac{3}{8}$	$2\frac{3}{8}$ to $2\frac{1}{2}$
Long Planes	24 to 26	$3\frac{5}{8}$	$2\frac{5}{8}$
Jointer Planes	28 to 30	$3\frac{3}{4}$	$2\frac{3}{4}$
Cooper's Jointer Planes . . .	60 to 72	5 to $5\frac{1}{4}$	$3\frac{1}{2}$ to $3\frac{3}{4}$

The succession in which they are generally used, is the jack plane for the coarser work, the trying plane for finer work and trying its accuracy, and the smoothing plane for finishing.

---

* The "iron," is scarcely a proper name for the *plane-iron*, which is a *cutter* or *blade*, composed partly of iron and steel; but no confusion can arise from the indescriminate use of any of these terms.

The diagram, fig. 320, is one quarter the full size, and may be considered to represent the ordinary surfacing planes, the mouths of which are alike, generally about one-third from the front of the plane, and thus constituted. The line *a*, *b*, is called the *sole; c, d,* upon which the blade is supported, is the *bed,* and this ,in planes of common pitch, is usually at an angle of 45° with the perpendicular.

Fig. 320.

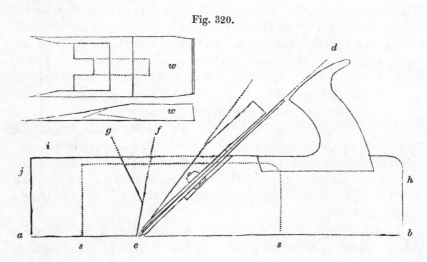

The *mouth* of the plane is the narrow aperture between the face of the iron, and the line *c, f,* which latter is called the *wear :* the angle between these should be as small as possible, in order that the wearing away of the sole, or its occasional correction, may cause but little enlargement of the mouth of the plane ; at the same time the angle must be sufficient to allow free egress for the shavings, otherwise the plane is said to *choke.* The line *g,* is called the *front,* its angle is unimportant, and in practice it is usually set out one quarter of an inch wider on the upper surface than the width of the iron.

The *wedge* of the plane which fixes the iron is commonly at an angle of 10°, and it is slightly driven between the face of the iron and the shoulder or *abutment, c e.* It is shown by the two detached views, that the wedge *w,* is cut away at the central part, both to clear the screw which connects the double iron, and to allow room for the escape of the shavings. The wedge is loosened by a moderate blow, either on the end of the plane at *h,* on the top at *i*, or by tapping the side of the wedge, which may be then pulled out with the fingers; a blow on the front of the plane at *j*, sets the iron forward or deeper, but it is not resorted to.

In all the bench planes, the iron is somewhat narrower than the stock, and the mouth is a wedge-formed cavity; in some of the narrow planes the cutting edge of the iron extends the full width of the sole, as in the rebate plane *f*, fig. 319, page 475; in these and others, the narrow shaft of the iron and the thin wedge alone proceed through the stock, and there is a curvilinear mouth extending through the plane; the mouth is taper, to turn the shavings out on the more convenient side. When the planes only cut on the one part of the sole, as in fig. 332, page 485, the angular mouth extends only part way through the plane, and the curvilinear perforation is uncalled for.

In the diagram, fig. 320, when the stock terminates at the dotted line, *s, s,* it represents the smoothing plane; when it is of the full length, and furnished with the handle or *toat*, it is the jack plane or panel plane; the still longer planes have the toat further removed from the iron, and it is then of the form shown in fig. 330 page 483.

Fig. 321 represents, one-eighth the full size, a very effective plane, which is commonly used on the continent for roughing

Fig. 321.

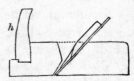

out, or as our jack plane, the *horn h,* being intended for the left hand, whilst the right is placed on the back of the stock. The Indians and Chinese bore a hole through the front of the plane for a transverse stick, by which a boy assists in pulling the plane across the work. When the plane is very large, it is by the Chinese, and others, placed at the end of the bench at an angle, and allowed to rest on the ground, whilst the work is slid down its face; and a similar position is employed by the coopers in our own country, for planing the staves of casks, the plane being in such cases, five or six feet long and very unwieldy, the upper part is supported on a prop, and the lower rests on a transverse piece of wood or sleeper.

The amount of force required to work each plane is dependent on the angle and relation of the edge, on the hardness of the material, and on the magnitude of the shaving; but the required force is in addition greatly influenced by the degree in which the shaving is *bent* for its removal in the most perfect manner.

The diagrams 322 to 326 represent, of their full size, parts of the irons and mouths of various planes, each in the act of removing a shaving. The sole or surface of the plane rests upon the face of the work, and the cutter stands as much in advance of the sole of the plane, as the thickness of the shaving, which is in each case so bent, as to enable it to creep up the face of the inclined iron, through the narrow slit of the plane, called its mouth, the width of which determines the extent to which the fibre of the wood can tear up or split with the grain.

The spokeshave, fig. 322, cuts perhaps the most easily of all the planes, and it closely assimilates to the penknife; the angle of the blade is about 25 degrees, one of its planes lies almost in contact with the work, the inclination of the shaving is slight, and the mouth is very contracted. The spokeshave works very easily in the direction of the grain, but it is only applicable to small and rounded surfaces and cannot be extended to suit large flat superficies, as the sole of the plane cannot be cut away for such an iron, and the perfection of the mouth is comparatively soon lost in grinding the blade.

Fig. 322.   Fig. 323.

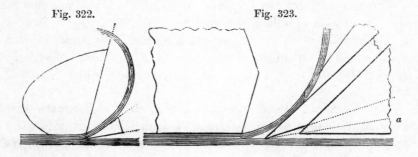

The diagrams, figs. 323, 4, and 5, suppose the plane irons to be ground at the angle of 25°, and to be sharpened on the more refined oilstone at 35°, so as to make a second bevil or slight facet, as shown by the dotted lines *a*, in each of the figures; the irons so ground are placed at the angle of 45°, or that of *common pitch ;* it therefore follows, that the ultimate bevil which should be very narrow, lies at an elevation of 10° from the surface to be planed.

Fig. 323 represents the mouth of an old jack plane, from the sole of which about half an inch of wood has been lost by wear and correction, which is no uncommon case. The wide mouth allows a partial splitting of the fibres before they creep up the face of the single iron; this plane works easily, and does not greatly alter the shavings, which come off in spiral curls, but the work is left rough and torn.

Fig. 324.   Fig. 325.   Fig. 326.

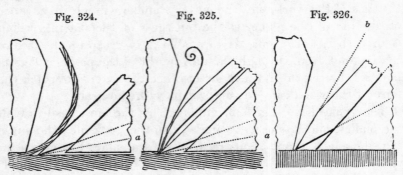

Fig. 324, a similar but less worn plane with a closer mouth, allows less of the splitting to occur, as the shaving is more suddenly bent in passing its narrower mouth, so that the *cutting* now begins to exceed the splitting, as the wood is held down by the closer mouth; the shaving is more broken and polygonal, but the work is left smoother.

The same effects are obtained in a much superior manner in the planes with double irons, such as in fig. 325, the top iron is not intended to cut, but to present a more nearly perpendicular wall for the ascent of the shavings, the top iron more effectually *breaks* the shavings, and is thence sometimes called the *break* iron.

Now therefore, the shaving being very thin, and constrained between two approximate edges, it is as it were bent out of the way to make room for the cutting edge, so that the shaving is removed by absolute *cutting*, and without being in any degree split or rent off.

The compound or double iron is represented detached, and of half size in fig. 327 ; in this figure the lower piece *c*, is the one

Fig. 327.

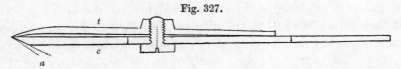

used for cutting, the upper piece *t* or the top iron, has a true edge, which is also moderately sharp, the top iron is placed from one-sixteenth to one-fiftieth of an inch from the edge of the cutter, the two are held together so closely by the screw which passes through a long mortise in c, and fits in a tapped hole in t, that no shaving can get between them.

The constant employment of the top iron in all available cases, shows the value of the improvement; and the circumstances of the plane working the smoother, but harder when it is added, and the more so the closer it is down, demonstrate that its action is to *break* or *bend* the fibres. This is particularly observable in the coarse thick shavings of a double-iron jack plane, compared with those of the same thickness from a single-iron plane; the latter are simply spiral and in easy curves, whereas those from the double-iron are broken across at short intervals, making their character more nearly polygonal; and the same difference is equally seen in thinner shavings, although of course less in degree.

Fig. 326 represents the iron of a plane intended " for the use of cabinet-makers and others, who require to cut either hard or coarse-grained wood," the upper bevil given to the iron, being considered to dispense with the necessity for the top-iron; but it is obviously much more difficult to produce a true right-lined edge, by the meeting of two planes, each subject to error in sharpening, than when one exists permanently flat as in the broad surface of the blade.*

The same edge may be obtained by a blade with a single chamfer, the flat side of which is placed in either of the dotted positions of fig. 326. The first, or b, is that previously in common use in the ordinary moulding planes for mahogany, and c is almost the position of the bed for the iron of the mitre-plane, also previously common; in all three planes, the ultimate angle of the face of the cutter is just 60 degrees from the horizontal.

Fig. 328 represents the mouth of the mitre plane full size, and fig. 329 the entire instrument one-eighth size. The stock is much less in height than in ordinary planes, and the iron lies at an angle of about 25°, and is sharpened at about the ordinary angle of 35°, making a total elevation of 60°, which, together with the delicate metallic mouth, render the absence of the top

---

* See Transactions of the Society of Arts, 1825, vol. xliii. p. 85.

iron unimportant, even when the plane is used lengthways of the fibres, although its ostensible purpose is to plane obliquely across their ends, as in the formation of mitre joints.

Figs. 328.   329.

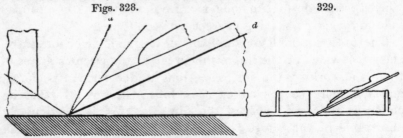

In all ordinary planes the mouth gets wider as the iron is ground away, because of the unequal thickness or taper form of the blade as seen at *c*, fig. 327. In the mitre-plane this is avoided by placing the chamfer upwards, now therefore the position of the blade is determined by its broad flat face which rests on the bed of the instrument *d*, and maintains one constant position as regards the mouth, uninfluenced by the gradual loss of thickness in the iron.

The smoothing and trying planes are also made with metal soles, and with single irons of ordinary angles, as one great purpose of the top iron is to compensate for the enlargement of the mouth of the plane by wear, this defect is almost expunged from those with iron soles, and which are gradually becoming common, both with single and with double irons. See Appendix, Note A.H., page 978.

Some variation is made in the angles at which plane irons are inserted in their stocks. The spokeshave is the lowest of the series, and commences with the small inclination of 25 to 30 degrees; and the general angles, and purposes of ordinary planes, are nearly as follows. *Common pitch*, or 45 degrees, from the horizontal line, is used for all the bench planes for deal, and similar soft woods. *York pitch*, or 50 degrees from the horizontal, for the bench-planes for mahogany, wainscot, and hard or stringy woods. *Middle pitch*, or 55 degrees, for moulding planes for deal, and smoothing planes for mahogany, and similar woods. *Half pitch*, or 60 degrees, for moulding planes for mahogany, and woods difficult to work, of which bird's-eye maple is considered one of the worst.

Boxwood, and other close hard woods, may be smoothly *scraped,* if not cut, in any direction of the grain, when the angle constituting the pitch entirely disappears; or with a common smoothing-plane, in which the cutter is perpendicular, or even leans slightly forward; this tool is called a *scraping plane,* and is used for scraping the ivory keys of piano-fortes, and works inlaid with ivory, brass, and hardwoods; this is quite analogous to the process of turning the hardwoods.

The cabinet-maker also employs a scraping-plane, with a perpendicular iron, which is groved on the face, to present a series of fine teeth instead of a continuous edge; this, which is called a *toothing plane,* is employed for roughing and *scratching* veneers, and the surfaces to which they are to be attached, *to make a tooth* for the better hold of the glue.

The smith's-plane for brass, iron, and steel, fig. 330, has likewise a perpendicular gutter, ground to 70 or 80 degrees; it is adjusted by a vertical screw, and the wedge is replaced by an end screw and block, as shown in the figure, which is one-eighth size. In the planes with vertical irons, the necessity for the narrow mouth ceases; and in the smith's plane some of the irons, or more properly cutters, are also grooved on the faces, by which their edges are virtually divided into several narrow pieces; this enables the instrument to be more easily employed in roughing-out works, by abstracting so much of the width

Fig. 330.

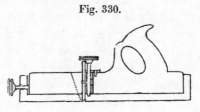

of the iron, and by giving it a greater degree of penetration, but the finishing is done with smooth-edged cutters, and those not exceeding from five-eighths of an inch to one inch wide.

It is well known that most pieces of wood will plane better from the one end than from the other, and that when such pieces are turned over, they must be changed end for end likewise; the necessity for this will immediately appear, if we consider the shade-lines under the plane-irons *a, b,* fig. 331, to represent the natural fibres of the wood, which are rarely parallel with the face of the work. The plane *a,* working *with the grain,* would cut smoothly, as it would rather press down the fibres than otherwise; whereas *b* would work *against the grain*, or would meet the fibres cropping out, and be liable to tear them up.

It was explained in Chap. IV., Vol. I., that the handsome characters of showy woods, greatly depend on all kinds of ir- regularities in the fibres; so that the conditions *a* and *b*, fig. 331, continually

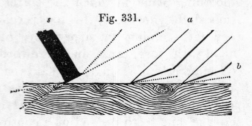

Fig. 331.

occur in the same piece of wood, and in which we can therefore scarcely produce one straight and smooth cut in any direction. Even the most experienced workman will apply the smoothing-plane at various angles across the different parts of such wood according to his judgment; in extreme cases, where the wood is very curly, knotty, and cross-grained, the plane can scarcely be used at all, and such pieces are finished with the steel scraper.

This simple tool was originally a piece of broken window-glass, and such it still remains in the hands of some of the gun-stock makers; but as the cabinet-maker requires the rectilinear edge, he employs a thin piece of saw-plate, which is represented black and highly magnified at *s*, fig. 331. The edge is first sharpened at right angles upon the oilstone, and it is then mostly bur-nished, either square or at a small angle, so as to throw up a trifling burr, or wire-edge. The scraper is held on the wood at about 60°, and as the minute edge takes a much slighter hold, it may be used where planes cannot be well applied. The scraper does not work so smoothly as a plane in perfect order upon ordinary wood, and as its edge is rougher and less keen, it drags up some of the fibres, and leaves a minute roughness, inter-spersed with a few longer fibres.

SECT. II.—GROOVING PLANES.

We may plane *across the grain* of hard mahogany and box-wood with comparative facility, as the fibres are packed so closely, like the loose leaves of a book when squeezed in a press, that they may be cut in all directions of the grain with nearly equal facility, both with the flat and moulding planes. But the weaker and more open fibres of deal and other soft woods, cannot withstand a cutting edge applied to them *parallel with them-selves*, or laterally, as they are torn up, and leave a rough unfinished surface. The joiner uses therefore, *for deal and soft woods*, a very keen plane of low pitch, and slides it across obliquely, so as to attack the fibre from the one end, and virtually to remove it in the direction of its length; so that the force is divided and applied to each part of the fibre in succession.

The moulding planes cannot be thus used, aud all mouldings made in deal, and woods of similar open soft grain, are con-sequently always planed lengthways of the grain, and added as separate pieces. As however many cases occur in carpentry, in which rebates and grooves are required directly across the grain of deal, the obliquity is then given to the *iron*, which is inserted at an angle, as in the skew-rebate and fillister, and the stock of the plane is used in various ways to guide its transit.

Many of these planes present much ingenuity and adaptation to their particular cases: for example fig. 332 is the side view, and fig. 333 the back of the *side-fillister*, which is intended to

Figs. 332.   333.   334.

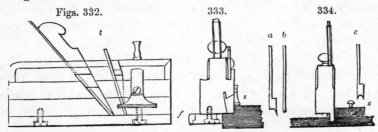

plane both with and across the grain, as in planing a rebate around the margin of a panel. The loose slip, or the fence *f,* is adjusted to expose so much of the oblique iron as the width of the rebate; the screw-stop *s,* at the side, is raised as much above the sole of the plane as the depth of the rebate, and the little tooth *t,* or scoring point, (shown detached, in two views *a, b,*) precedes the bevelled iron, so as to shear or divide the fibres as with the point of a penknife, to make the perpendicular edge keen and square. This plane is therefore a four-fold combina-tion of two measures and two cutters. The oblique iron, and the tooth or cutter, are pretty constantly met with in the planes used across the grain.

Others of these planes have less power of adjustment; for

instance the grooving-plane fig. 334, for planing across the
grain, has two separate teeth, or else a single tooth with two
points *c*, in addition to the cutting-iron which is commonly placed
square across the face of the plane; the groove is only used for
the reception of a shelf, its sides are therefore the more important parts, and the obliquity of the iron may be safely omitted.
The fence can no longer be a part of the instrument, as it is
often used in the middle of a long piece, a wooden straight-edge
s, is therefore temporarily nailed down to guide the plane; and
the stop is sometimes a piece of boxwood, fitted stiffly in a mortise through the stock, at other times it is adjusted by a thumb-
screw, as in the figure 334.

The *plough*, fig. 335, is a grooving-plane, to work *with the
grain;* it has similar powers to the fillister, but with a greater
horizontal range.   The width of the groove is determined by
that of the blade, of which each plough has several; they are
retained in the perpendicular position by a thin iron plate,
which enters a central angular groove in the back of the blade.
The teeth or scoring points are now uncalled for, as the iron
works perfectly well the lengthway of the fibre.   The screw-stop
is the same as before; but the *fence f,* is built upon two transverse *stems s s*, one only seen, passing through mortises in the
body of the plane, and fixed by wedges.   In the German plough
the position of the fence *f,* is determined and maintained by two
wooden screws, instead of the stems *s s*, and there are two wooden
nuts to each screw, one on each side of the stock of the plough.

Figs. 335.   336.   337.   338.

339.

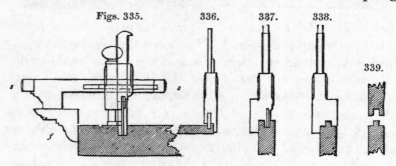

Other grooving-planes for working with the grain are also
made without teeth, examples of which may be seen in the
drawer-bottom plane 336, and the slit deal planes, of which 337
makes the groove, and 338 the tongue, used for connecting

boards for partitions and other purposes, with the groove and tongue-joint 339. The planes of this class being generally used for one specific purpose and measure, are unprovided with loose parts, as they are worked until the sole of the plane, or some of its edges come in contact with the wood, and stop the further progress of the cutter.

Fig. 340, the reglet plane, is of this kind, it derives its name from being employed in making the parallel slips of wood, or *reglet*, used by the printer for the wide separation of the lines of metal type; the adjustable fences are screwed fast, as much in advance of the sole of the plane as the required thickness of the reglets or rules, which are then planed away until, from the slips resting on the bench, the tool will cut no longer.

Figs. 340.

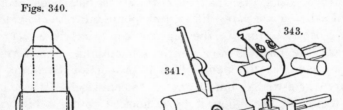

Fig. 341 is a router plane, it has a broad surface carrying in its center one of the cutters belonging to the plough, it is used for levelling the bottoms of cavities, the stock must be more than twice the width of the recess, and the projection of the iron determines the depth, the sides of the cavities are prepared before-hand with the chisel and mallet. The ordinary name for this plane is not remarkable for its propriety or elegance, it is generally called the " *old woman's tooth.*" See Appendix, Note A. I., page 979.

The carpenters' gages, for setting out lines and grooves parallel with the margin of the work, are closely associated with the system of fences or rails. The *stem* of the gage, fig. 842, is retained in the *head*, or stock, by means of a small wedge, and the cutter is fixed in a hole at right angles to the face of the stem, by another wedge. The *marking-gage*, for setting out lines, has a simple conical point; the *cutting-gage*, for cutting veneers and thin wood, has a lancet-shaped knife, and is a very effective tool; the *router-gage*, for inlaying small lines of wood and brass, has a tooth like a narrow chisel.

There are other forms of gages, some of these have screw adjustments; in the most simple, the stem is a wooden screw flattened on one side, and the head of the gage consists of two wooden nuts, which become fixed when screwed fast against each other. The *mortise-gage*, which is much used, has two points that may be adjusted to scribe the widths of mortises and tenons. In the *bisecting* gage there are two sliding pieces or heads, which are made to embrace the object to be bisected, and the scribing point is in the center of two equal arms jointed respectively to the two sliding heads.*

The *cooper's croze* is used for making the grooves for the heading of casks, after the ends of the staves have been levelled by a tool called a *sun plane*, like a jack-plane but of a *circular* plan. The croze is similar to the gages, except that it is very much larger; the head is now nearly semicircular, and terminates in two handles; the stem, which is proportionally large, is also secured by a wedge, but the cutter is composed of three or four saw-teeth, closely followed by a hooked router, which sweeps out the bottom of the groove.

The *banding plane* † is allied to the gages, and is intended for cutting out grooves, and inlaying strings and bands in straight and circular works, as in the rounded corners of piano-fortes and similar objects. It bears a general resemblance to the plough, fig. 335, but it is furnished in addition with the double tooth *c*, of the grooving plane, fig. 334. In the banding plane, the central plate of the plough is retained as a guide for the central positions of the router and cutter, which are inserted, so as to meet in an angle of about 80 degrees, between two short projections of the central plate; the whole of the parts entering the groove are compressed within the length of one inch, to pass through curvatures of small radius; there are various cutters and fences, both straight and circular, according to the nature of the work. See Appendix, Note A. J., page 979.

Fig. 343 is a plane which is the link betwixt carpentry and

---

* See H. R. Palmer's gage for marking center lines.—Trans. Soc. of Arts, 1813, vol. xxxi. p. 248.

† Mr. R. Onwin's banding plane.—Trans. Soc. of Arts, 1817, vol. xxxv. p. 122.

turning; the conical hole in the plane is furnished with a cutter placed as a tangent to the circle, so that the wood enters in the rough octagonal form, and leaves it rounded, fit for a broom, an umbrella handle, or an office ruler: sometimes either the work or plane is driven by machinery, with the addition of one or two preparatory gouges, for removing the rougher parts.

SECT. III.—MOULDING PLANES.

All the planes hitherto considered, whether used parallel with the surfaces as in straight works, or as tangents to the curves as in curved works, are applied under precisely the same circumstances as regards the angular relation of the mouth, because the edge of the blade is a right line parallel with the sole of the plane; but when the outline of the blade is curved, some new conditions arise which interfere with the perfect action of the instrument.   It is now proposed to examine these conditions in respect to the semicircle, from which the generality of mouldings may be considered to be derived.

In the astragal, *a, b, c, d, e,* fig. 344, a small central portion at *c,* may be considered to be a horizontal line; two other small portions at *b,* and *d,* may be considered as parts of the vertical dotted lines, *b, f,* and *d, g;* and the intermediate parts of the semicircle are seen to merge from the horizontal to the vertical line.

The reason why one moulding plane figured to the astragal cannot, under the usual construction, be made to work the vertical parts of the moulding with the same perfection as the horizontal, exists in the fact, that whereas the ordinary plane iron presents an angle of some 45 to 60 degrees to the *sole* of the plane, which part is meant to cut, it presents a right angle to the *side* of the plane, which part is not meant to cut.   Thus if the parts of the iron of the square rebate plane, which protrude through the sides of the stock, were sharpened ever so keenly, they would only *scrape* and not *cut,* just the same as the scraping plane with a perpendicular iron.

When, however, the rebate plane is meant to *cut at the side,* it is called the *side-rebate plane,* and its construction is then just reversed, as shown in the three views, fig. 346 ; that is, the iron is inserted perpendicularly to the sole of the plane, but at an horizontal angle *x x,* or *obliquely to the side of the plane,* so that the cut is now only on the one side *z z*, of the plane, and which side virtually becomes the sole. A second plane sloped

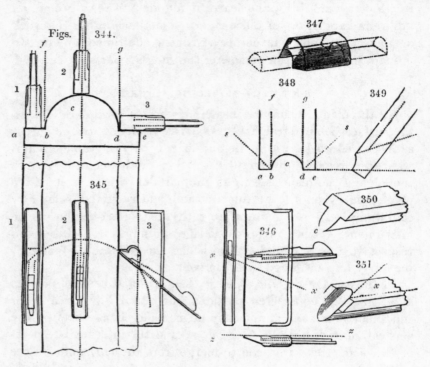

the opposite way, is required for the opposite side, or the planes are made in pairs, and are used for the sides of grooves, and places inaccessible to the ordinary rebate plane.

In the figures 344 and 345, the square rebate planes 1 and 2, will cut the horizontal surfaces *a b*, and *c*, perfectly, because the irons present the proper slopes to these surfaces, but in attempting to plane the vertical line *b f*, with the side of 1, we should fail, because the cutter is at right angles to that superficies, and it would only scrape, or be said to *drag*. The plane 3, when laid on its side, would act perfectly on the vertical face; but now it would be ineffective as regards the horizontal. The square rebate plane, if applied all around the semicircle, would be everywhere effective so long as its shaft stood as a radius to the curve, in fact as at 2, and 3, as then the angle of the iron would be in the right direction in each of its temporary situations. But in this mode a plane to be effective throughout, demands either numerous positions of the plane, or an iron of such a kind as to combine these several positions.

Theoretically speaking therefore, the face of the cutter suitable to working the entire semicircle or bead, would become a cone, or like a tube of steel bored with a hole of the same diameter as the bead, turned at one end externally like a cone, and split in two parts. Fig. 347 would represent such a cutter, and which just resembles a half round gouge applied horizontally and sharpened externally. But this theoretical cutter would present all the difficulties of the spokeshave iron; as to the trouble of fixing it, its interference with the sole of the plane, and the difficulty of maintaining the form of the mouth of the instrument, if made as a spokeshave, owing to the reduction of the cutter in sharpening.*

But as the iron 3, and also the side-rebate, fig. 346, work perfectly well in their respective positions, or when the cutters are inclined *horizontally*, whilst the central iron 2, only requires to be inclined *vertically*, it occurred to me that by employing a cutter *in all respects as usual*, except that its face should be *curved as in the arc connecting the three irons* in fig. 345, the one tool would cut equally well at every point of the curve; and experience proved the truth of the supposition. The precise form of the iron will be readily arrived at, by cutting out in card the diagram, fig. 348, and bending it to a circular sweep until the parts exterior to the dotted lines *b f,—d g*, just meet the spring of the bead, at about the angle of half or middle pitch, or 30 or 35 degrees from the right angle, and it will be then found necessary to cut away the corners to the lines *b s,—d s*, or so much of them as dip below the straight surface of the fillet, as seen in fig. 349.

The author had a plane constructed exactly in agreement with the above particulars, that is, with an iron curved to about the third of a circle, the mouth of the plane was curved to correspond, and in every other respect the instrument was as usual; it was found entirely successful.

The inclination of the tool to each part of the work is very

---

* The cutter 347, is used for making the cylindrical rollers upon which ribbons are wound; the cutter is fixed at the end of a slide, and is worked by a lever, the cylinders are made at two cuts in lengths of 8 or 10 inches, and afterwards divided.

nearly alike, and it assimilates at different parts to each of the ordinary rebate planes, all of which work well. Namely, at the crown of the moulding c, to the square rebate plane; at the spring b and d, to the side rebate planes; and at the fillets a b, d e, to the skew rebate. And notwithstanding the fluted form of the iron, no greater difficulty is experienced in sharpening the iron in the new form like a gouge, than in the old like a chisel, the figure of the end being nearly alike in each case.*

As all the imperfections in the actions of moulding-planes occur at the vertical parts, there is a general attempt to avoid these difficulties by keeping the mouldings flat or nearly without vertical lines. For example, concave and convex planes, called *hollows and rounds*, include generally the fifth or sixth, sometimes about the third of the circle; and it is principally in the part between the third and the semicircle that the dragging is found to exist; and therefore, when a large part of the circle is wanted, the plane is applied at two or more positions in succession.

In a similar manner large complex mouldings often require to be worked from two or more positions with different planes, even when none of their parts are undercut, but in which latter case this is of course indispensable. And in nearly all mouldings the plane is not placed perpendicularly to the moulding, but at an angle so as to remove all the nearly vertical parts, as far towards the horizontal position as circumstances will admit.

---

* The above forms of cutters suggested for mouldings, are each applicable to most mouldings, but from their nature they are too troublesome for ordinary use.

For instance, we may employ a cutter such as 347, the lower surface of which, as in 350, is the astragal or any other moulding, the general slope or chamfer, will cause the tool to cut at the fillets and at c, which parts are horizontal ; but the lines of the mouldings, which are vertical, require the tool to be fluted to obtain the horizontal angle, x, shown in dotted lines in 351, and there is all the inconvenience of the nearly horizontal position of the spokeshave iron.

The iron, when sloped at the accustomed angle of pitch, requires to be convex for a convex moulding, and to be sharpened behind ; and by the converse, for a concave moulding the tool must be also concave and sharpened in front, and all-vertical lines in the moulding require the cutter to be fluted as in fig. 351, at x. Mixed or flowing mouldings will require, on the same principle, the cutter to have nearly the sections of the mouldings, and to be sharpened always in front, in the spokeshave form of iron ; but partly in front and partly behind in the sloping irons ; but these conditions are far too complex except in some favourable cases. The cutters are always made flat on the face, and to lessen the difficulty, the mouldings are drawn shallow, with but few or no vertical parts, or else they are wrought by two or more different planes.

Thus the plane for the moulding, fig. 352, would have its stock perpendicular to the dotted line *a b*, connecting the extreme parts of the moulding, the angular deviation being generally called the *spring*. The spring is also partly determined by the position which is most favourable to the maintenance of the form of the cutter in sharpening it; as the obliquity of the sole of the plane causes the cutter, when advanced through it, also to shift sideways, and cause a disagreement between their figures.

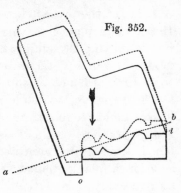

Fig. 352.

In the act of working, or as it is called in *sticking* the moulding, the wood is always first accurately squared to its dimensions to serve as a guide, and it is then sometimes roughly bevelled nearly to the line *a b;* the plane is applied in the dotted position, the blank edge *o*, of the plane, rests against the edge of the prepared wood, and determines what is called the "*on*" of the moulding, that is, how far the plane can proceed upon the wood; and the planing is continued vertically until the blank edge *d*, stops the further action, or determines the "*down*," by resting upon the solid wood beneath it. In some cases where the planes are unprovided with fences or blank edges, or that they are applied in places where fences in the ordinary form are inapplicable, a slip of wood is nailed down for their guidance, as in fig. 334, page 485.

Wide moulding planes have been occasionally worked by two individuals, one to guide and thrust as usual, the other to pull with a rope. The top iron is however absent from the whole of the group, if we except the *capping plane* used for the upper surfaces of staircase rails, which are faintly rounded. The absence of the top iron is partly compensated for, by the pitch of moulding planes being as stated on page 482, about 10 degrees more upright than in bench planes for the same materials. The angles and edges of many of the small planes are *box slipped*, that is, slips of boxwood are inlaid in the beechwood, in order that the projecting edges or the *quirks*, may possess greater durability.

SECT. IV.—REMARKS ON THE BENCH, AND USE OF THE PLANE.

It is not the present intention to resume the consideration of the joiner's planes in this work, it therefore appears desirable before quitting the subject to add a few instructions respecting the modes of keeping them in order, and of using them, in which some kind of bench or support for the work is always required.

The benches are made in various ways, from a few rough boards nailed together, to the structure shown in fig. 353, which represents one of the most complete kind of cabinet-makers' benches, carefully connected by screw-bolts and nuts : its surface is a thick plank planed very flat and true, with a trough to receive small tools, without interfering with the surface of the bench.

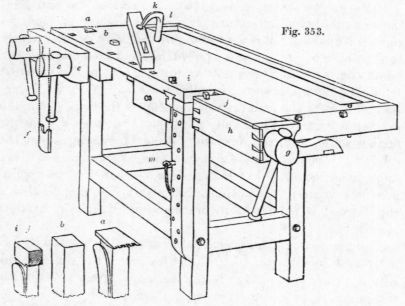

Fig. 353.

The wood to be planed is laid on the bench, and is stayed by an iron bench-hook *a*, which is fitted in a mortise, so that it may be placed at any required elevation, or flush with the surface of the bench. The bench-hook has teeth projecting from its face, intended to stick into the wood, and retain it from moving sideways; but to avoid the injury which would be inflicted by the teeth on nearly finished works, there is also a square wooden stop *b*, fitted tight into a square mortise. These are shown removed, and on a much larger scale, at the foot of the engraving, the same letters of reference being repeated.

The two side screws c, d, constitute with the chop e, a kind of vice; the screw c, simply compresses, the screw d, has a piece f, called a *garter*, (shown detached,) which enters a groove in the cylindrical neck of the screw d, so that when the screws are both opened d serves to bring the chop e outwards. The chops are greatly used for fixing work by the sides or edges, and as they open many inches, small boxes, drawers, and other works may be pinched between them.

There are other constructions of benches which it is unnecessary to describe; some have only one of the screws c, d, the other being replaced by a square bar fixed in e, and many are not furnished with the end screw g, which draws out the sliding piece h, that is very carefully fitted. The end screw serves also as a vice for thin works which are more conveniently held at right angles to the position of the side screws; but its more valuable purpose is for holding work by the two ends, which mode is exceedingly convenient, especially in making grooves, rebates, and mouldings, as the work is in no danger of slipping away from the tools. There are several square holes along the front of the bench, for an iron stop i, which has a perpendicular and slightly roughened face, and a similar stop j, is also placed in h; and as the latter slides a quantity not less than the interval between the holes, pieces of any length below the longest may be securely held.

For holding squared pieces of wood upon the bench, as in making mortises or dovetails, the holdfast k, is used in the manner shown, it is an ∟ formed iron, the straight arm of which fits loosely in a hole in the bench; the work is fixed by driving on the top at k, and it is released by a blow on the back at l. Sometimes also the holdfast is made in two parts jointed together like the letter ⊤, with a screw at the one end of the transverse piece, by which the work can be fixed without the hammer, but the former mode is far more common and is sufficiently manageable. And m is a pin which is placed in any of the holes in the leg of the bench, to support the end of long boards, which are fixed at their other extremity by the screws c, d. We will now proceed to the management of the planes. See Appendix, notes A K, A L, and A M, pp. 978 and 980.

Of the bench planes enumerated in the list on page 476, the following are most generally used, namely, the jack plane for the coarser work, the trying plane for giving the work a better figure or trying its straightness and accuracy, and the smoothing plane for finishing the surface, without detracting from the truth obtained by the trying plane. Sometimes when the wood is very rough and dirty, two jack planes are used still more to divide the work, and these instruments are managed in the following manner.

The remarks on page 477-8 explain that, for long planes, the iron is released by a blow of the hammer on the top of the plane at the front; the smoothing, and all short planes, are struck at the back of the plane, and never on the top, or the wedge may be tapped sideways, and pulled out with the fingers.

The top iron is then removed, by loosening the screw, and sliding it up the mortise, until its head can pass through the circular hole in the cutting iron.

The plane-iron having been ground to an angle of some 25 degrees, with the stone running towards the edge, it is next sharpened at an angle of about 35 degrees on the oilstone. The iron is first grasped in the right hand, with the fore finger only above and near the side of the iron, and with the thumb below; the left hand is then applied with the left thumb lapping over the right, and the whole of the fingers of that hand on the surface of the iron; the edge should be kept nearly square across the oilstone, as when one corner precedes the other, the foremost angle is the more worn.

When the iron is required to be very flat, as for the finishing planes, the surface of the oilstone should be kept quite level, and the blade must be held at one constant angle, but when it is required to be round on the edge, a slight roll of the blade is required edgeways; lastly, the flat face of the iron is laid *quite flat* on the oilstone, to remove the wire edge, and if required, the edge is drawn through a piece of wood to tear off this film, after which the iron is again touched on the oilstone, both on the chamfer and flat surface, as the edge when finished should be perfectly keen and acute.

The iron is frequently held too high to expedite the sharpening; it is clear, that should it be elevated above 45°, or the pitch of the plane, the bevil would be in effect reversed, and it could only act as a burnisher; exactly at 45° the keen edge would be soon worn away, and the condition of the burnisher would remain; and, within certain limits, the lower or thinner the edge is sharpened the better. Perhaps the angle of 35° which is assumed, is as favourable as any, as if the edge be too acute the durability greatly decreases, and therefore some regard is also shown to the degree of wear and fatigue, the iron is called upon to endure*.

The edge of the iron is likewise ground to different *forms* according to the work; thus, the jack plane is found to work more easily when the iron is rounded as an arc, so that whether it project in the center more or less than one-sixteenth of an inch, the common measure, the angles of the iron should sink down to the sole of the plane at the corners of the mouth.

The ease thus afforded appears more or less due to three causes. The rounded iron makes its first penetration more easily, as it commences as it were with a point, or very narrow edge: the iron has to penetrate the wood as a wedge, first to *cut* and then to *bend* the shaving; and it is likely that the reduction of labour in the *cutting*, by the narrow portion of the edge being employed, is greater than the increase, in *bending* a thicker but narrower shaving: and lastly, the curved iron distantly approaches the condition of the skew-iron, and in all inclined blades there is a partial sliding or saw-like motion, which is highly favourable to cutting. The irons for the finishing planes, although sharpened as flat as possible at other parts, are faintly rounded at the corners to prevent their leaving marks upon the wood.

The cutting iron having been sharpened, the top-iron is screwed fast at the required distance from the edge, say for coarse works one-sixteenth, and for fine work, one-fortieth or fiftieth of an inch. The compound iron is placed in the mouth of the plane, and the eye is directed from the front along the sole, to see that it projects uniformly and the required quantity; the wedge is then put in with the right hand, and slightly tapped with the hammer. If this should by chance carry forward the iron also, a blow on the back of the plane at *h*, fig. 320, p. 477, or on the upper surface

---

* When the minute chamfer of the plane-iron is almost parallel with the sole of the plane, it will for a short time be entirely effective. Thus, as an experiment, drive the iron a very small quantity through the sole, and sharpen it by allowing the oilstone to rub both on the edge and on the wood behind; this will produce a very accurate edge, and the iron when set back, will cut beautifully.

of the long planes at *i*, partially withdraws the iron, and in this manner, by a few slight blows on the end or either edge of the iron, and on the end of the wedge, the adjustment is readily effected. Violence should be avoided, as the wedge if overdriven might split the plane, and long before that it would distort the sole and *drive the back wood up*, which means, that the wood behind the iron would be driven so as to stand slightly in advance of that before the iron, the two parts of the sole becoming slightly discontinuous or out of line. The iron should be always so slenderly held, that one or two moderate blows would release the iron and wedge.

There is a very ingenious modification of the double iron plane *, in which the cutter is a thin unperforated blade of steel, placed between a brass bed and an iron top-piece; the cutter, instead of being fixed and adjusted in the ordinary manner by taps of the hammer, is managed by the quiet action of various screws.

In a plane patented in America, in 1832, the bottom or cutting iron is made as usual, but without any mortise; the top iron has a thumb-screw at its upper end, and moves on two lateral pins or fulcrums ¾-inch from its lower edge; the pins fit into two grooved pieces of metal let into the sides of the plane, the lengths of the grooves exactly determine the situation of the top iron. When therefore the cutter is placed in its required position, the thumb-screw is turned, it bears on the upper part of the cutter, and tilts the top iron, until its lower edge also bears hard against the usual part of the cutter, and thereby fixes it without a wedge.

The main hindrances to the general employment of these constructions appear to be their increased cost, and the great dexterity with which the required adjustments are accomplished by the accustomed hand with the apparently rude, yet sufficient, means of the hammer †.

The planes being respectively in good working condition, the board to be planed is laid on the bench, and if it should be obviously higher, either at the opposite corners from being " *in winding*," or in the middle, or at the edges from being " *cast and*

---

* Invented by Mr. H. Bellingham. See Trans. Soc. of Arts, 1836, vol. li.

† The same remark applies to Mr. F. E. Franklin's Screw Bench Hook, (idem, vol. liii,) intended to supersede *a* or *j*, fig. 353, page 494.

rounding," these partial prominences are first removed with the jack plane; but in general the shavings should be of the full length of the work, or at any rate a yard long.

The toat of the plane is held in the right hand, the front being grasped with the left hand, the thumb towards the workman; the planes require to be pressed down on the work during the cut, this is done less by an exertion of the muscles, than by slightly inclining the body, to cause its weight to rest partly upon the plane. During the return stroke, the pressure should be discontinued to avoid friction on the edge, which would be thereby rounded, and there is just an approximation to lifting the heel of the plane off the work; or in short pieces it is entirely lifted. The general attempt should be to plane the work somewhat hollow, an effect which cannot however really occur, when the plane is proportionally long and quite straight.

The sole of a long plane is in a great measure the test of the straightness of the work; thus when the rough outside has been removed with the jack-plane, the trying-plane is employed, which is set with a much finer cut, and the workman will in a great measure tell the condition of the surface by the continuity and equality of the shavings. It is however also needful to examine its accuracy with a straight-edge; the edge of the plane applied obliquely across the board is in general the primary test, but as the work approaches to perfection, the straight-edge is laid parallel with the sides of the work, and also diagonally across it; and towards the last, the work if small is raised to the level of the eye, or in large pieces, the workman stoops to attain the same relative position.

In using the straight-edge the workman is partly guided by the eye, or the line of light that is observable between the instrument and the work, and partly by the sense of touch, as he tries whether the straight-edge, when it is very slightly rotated as on a center, bears hardest at the ends or in the middle, and he applies the plane accordingly *.

---

* The straight-edge is simply a wide thin bar of wood or metal, made as accurately straight as possible; the truth of a straight-edge can be only proved by the examination of a series of at least three. Thus, supposing A to be perfect, B to be slightly concave, and C to be slightly convex; it might happen that B and C exactly agreed, but A could not agree with either of them.

Or supposing A to be concave exactly like B, or to become B', then B and C

The foregoing mode refers to surfaces of moderate width, but when the pieces are narrow, or two or more distant parts alone are required to be in one level, the winding sticks are employed. These are two straight-edges, say twenty to thirty inches long, which are placed transversely upon the ends of the work and parallel with each other, they receive their direction from the respective ends or transverse sections, and should these be inclined to each other, or *in winding* instead of parallel, the winding sticks would magnify the error. This is explained by the diagram fig. 354, the eye placed on the level of the imaginary plane, bounded by the edges $a\,b,\,c\,d,$ of the winding sticks, would find the edge of $a\,b$ exactly parallel with that of $c\,d,$ but if $c\,d$ were situated as in the dotted lines, the disagreement of position arising from the twist or inclination of the edge would be immediately apparent. It is important that the winding sticks should be parallel, as then the eye may be directed to their upper edges, thereby avoiding the interference of the work itself. If the work be perfect, the two sticks appear in exact parallelism, when from the foreshortening, $c\,d,$ is nearly eclipsed.

Figs. 354.   355.

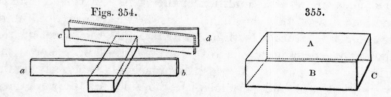

Nearly all the works in carpentry are first prepared as parallelograms of various proportions, whether they are to be subsequently used in that simple form, or to be worked with grooves, rebates, or mouldings; or to be connected by joints of various kinds. We will now follow up the formation of one flat surface, by explaining the order in which to produce the three pairs of parallel rectangular surfaces in fig. 355, namely, $A\,a,$ the two faces, $B\,b,$ the two sides, and $C\,c,$ the two ends; and in this and every work possessing flat surfaces, it is of the utmost consequence that one face A, should be first wrought in the most careful and exact manner as above described, to serve

---

would also agree, but B and B' would disagree; therefore the rectilinear form can only be proved to exist when A, B, and C will bear a strict comparison in each binary combination.

as the foundation or base, from which all the other measures are to be successively derived.

The works are generally sawn out a trifle above the required sizes, and the subsequent modes of proceeding, depend upon the proportions of the pieces, or whether they are thick as in carpentry, or thin as in joinery and cabinet making. In thick pieces, after the face A, has been planed quite flat, the side B is next wrought, and a short square is used to examine whether the two are exactly at right angles, for this purpose the stock of the square is rested against A, and the blade on B at various parts of the work; or indeed the square is slowly traversed to ascertain that the angle is everywhere in agreement with the square. The angle A B, is then marked with pencil lines extending on the face and side, to denote that this angle is to serve as the foundation for the subsequent measures.

Before proceeding to plane the second face a, the marking gage, fig. 342, p. 487, is adjusted until its point stands exactly as far from the head of the gage as the intended thickness of the work. The gage is then rubbed forcibly against the finished face A, so as to scratch a line on the edges of $B\ b$, indicative of the intended new surface a, and which is then worked with the same care and precaution as its companion A. After this b, is similarly worked, when the width of the faces $A\ a$, have been also scored by the marking gage applied against the true side B. In planing a and b, the square is applied from B and A respectively, to ensure the rectangular forms of the edges, and the gage is also used together with the square to test the parallelism of the work; and lastly, the ends $C\ c$ are marked on all four sides with the square, preparatory to the use of the saw, or the formation of the tenons, mortises, or dovetails by which the parts are attached. When the works are planed with rebates, grooves, or mouldings, the squaring up of the four sides is always the preliminary step, although in some cases the principal attention is devoted to the two surfaces $A\ B$, especially when they are only required to serve for the attachment of other parts of the work.

In squaring up works cut out of thin plank, the mode is different, the pit-saw leaves the board nearly parallel, and when the piece has been cut out with the hand-saw, the face A is first *tried up*, that is, corrected with the trying plane, the piece is next *gaged to thickness*, either at the ends only, or on all four edges,

and the second face *a*, is planed up. The rectangular piece is
next fixed in the screw clamp of the bench, with the edge *B*
upwards, and which is made quite straight with the trying plane
in its ordinary position, and tested with the square; the two
ends *C c*, are next marked off with the square, and planed from
the corrected edge *B*, and lastly *b* is gaged and shot down to
the width. By these means, should the fibres have been split,
or *spalled off* in shooting the ends, the removal of the edge *b*, as
the last process would correct the evil. There are some very
useful contrivances employed in planing the edges of thin works,
and which will be next adverted to.

In squaring or *shooting* the edges of boards, the *shooting
board* drawn in figs. 356 and 357, is very much used; it is a
contrivance to enable the side *A*, of the work, (the ends of which
are shaded in each of these views,) to be laid flat on a bed *e*,
whilst the plane lies on its side, either·on the bench, or upon the
additional piece *f*; and provided the shooting board is parallel
and straight, and that the sole of the plane is at right angles to
its side, the rectangular forms of the edges are much more readily
attained. The work is, nevertheless, examined with the square,
as if the set of the iron be imperfect it will introduce a little
error, and which is corrected by tapping the iron sideways, to
correct its position.

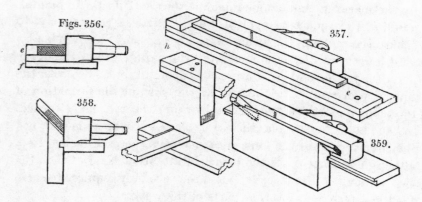

Figs. 356.

In squaring the ends *C c*, the traverse block *g* of the shooting board, is the rectangular gage, and the cross piece also
partly supports the fibres from tearing away; for bevils, corresponding blocks are fitted to it as represented at *h*, but the

mitre, or the angle of forty-five degrees there shown, is the one principally required. To plane the edges, *B* or *C*, to the mitre or other angle, the respective beds upon which the work and plane are supported, are required to be to each other in that particular angular relation, as in figs. 358 and 359 which represent the mitre block for angles of forty-five degrees.

These contrivances of *external* fences materially assist in pieces much narrower than the face of the plane, and the order in which the six faces are dressed, is very closely followed, although with different tools, in other arts, in which the works consist of like surfaces requiring a similarly strict relation to each other.

SECT. V.— PLANING MACHINES FOR WOOD.

In using hand-tools the instrument rests immediately upon the face of the work under formation; and in repeating any one result, the same careful attention is again required in every successive piece. But it was explained in the last chapter, that in the machines acting by cutting, the accuracy is ensured far more readily, by running either the work or the tool, upon a straight slide, an axis, or other guide, the perfection of which has been carefully adjusted in the first formation of the machine; and the slide or movement copies upon the work, its own relative degree of perfection. The economy of these applications is therefore generally very great, and they are frequently most interesting, on account of the curious transitions to be observed from the hand-processes to the machines, in some cases with but little, in others with considerable change in the general mode of procedure.

The first planing machine for wood is supposed to have been that invented by General Bentham, who took out a patent for it in 1791; it was based on the action of the ordinary plane, the movements of which it closely followed. This contrivance reduced the amount of skill required in the workman, but not that of the labour; it appears to have been but little used. The board to be planed was sometimes laid on a bench, at other times fixed by long cheeks having teeth which penetrated its edges; the iron of the plane extended the full width of the board, and the stock of the plane had slips to rest on the bench and check the cutting action, when the board was reduced to the intended thickness, much the same as in the reglet plane, fig. 340.

For feather-edged boards, the two slips were of unequal

thicknesses; for those intended to be taper in their length, the guide rails had a corresponding obliquity, and were fixed to the bench. The plane was moved to and fro by a crank, it was held down to its work by weights, and the plane was lifted up in the back stroke to remove the friction against the cutter *.

The *scale-board plane*, abbreviated into *scabbard-plane*, for cutting off the wide chips used for making hat and bonnet boxes, is, in like manner, a plane exceeding the width of the board; it is loaded with weights, and dragged along by a rope and windlass, the projection of the iron determines the thickness of each shaving or scale-board. This construction is also reversed, by employing a fixed iron, drawing the wood over it, and letting the scale-board descend through an aperture in the bench; each of these modes is distinctly based on the common plane. See Appendix, Note A. N., page 981.

The late Mr. Joseph Bramah took out a patent in 1802 for a planing machine for wood; one of which may be seen in the Gun Carriage Department, Woolwich Arsenal. The timber is passed under a large horizontal wheel, driven by the steam-engine at about ninety revolutions per minute; the face of the wheel is armed with a series of twenty-eight gouges, placed horizontally and in succession around it; the first gouge is a little more distant from the center, and a little more elevated than the neand so on. The finishing tools are two double irons, just like those of the joiner, but without the advantage of the mouth.

Mr. Bramah employed the principle of his famous hydrostatic press, (patented in 1791,) both for raising the cutter wheel to suit the different thicknesses of wood, and also for traversing the timber under the cutters upon guide rails; the latter, by means of an endless chain connected with the piston of the pump, by a rack, pinion, and drum. The bottom of the axis of the cutter wheel is cylindrical to the extent of its vertical adjustment, and is fitted in a tube terminating at its upper part, in a cupped leather collar, impervious to oil or water, as in the hydrostatic press. The injection of water into the tube by a small force-pump, lengthens the column of fluid, upon which the wheel is supported as on a solid post; the descent of the wheel is effected by allowing a portion of water to escape by a valve †.

---

* See the Encyclopedia Metropolitana, &c. &c.

† Mr. Bramah's patent includes many modifications of fixed and revolving

A more recent machine for planing flooring boards, and other wood works, consists of a series of knives placed parallel with, and around the axis of, a small cylinder; the board is passed underneath the cutter whilst it is in rapid motion; this may be called an adzing machine, and the knives are of the full width of the board.

In Mr. Muir's patent planing machine for flooring boards, a rotary adze roughly planes the bottom, another operates on the top of the board; afterwards, two oblique fixed cutters, like the skew-rebate irons, but with top irons, remove each a shaving of the full length and width of the deal; two cutters make the sides parallel, and two others groove the edges for the tongues, or in fact, these are four revolving planes or saws in order to expedite their effect.   The board enters the machine as left from the saw-mill, it is thrust forward by the engine, and comes out very speedily in a condition nearly ready for fixing, the eight operations being simultaneous; but sometimes a little finishing with the hand-smoothing plane, is required at those parts where the grain is unfavourable to smooth cutting. Other machines, by Paxton, by Burnett and Poyer, and others, are used for preparing sash bars, and similar works *.   See Appendix, Notes A.O., & A.P., pages 981 & 982.

The preceding machines are mostly intended to work *with* the grain; and I am only acquainted with one rectilinear planing machine that is exclusively intended for cutting *across* the grain, namely, the mortising engine, one of the series of machines erected at Portsmouth in 1807, by Mr. Brunel, for the manufacture of ships' blocks †.

A hole is first bored through the block at the commencement of the intended groove for the sheave, and it is extended by the successive action of a mortising or paring tool, which rides per-

---

cutters, for planing and cutting wood and metal works ; also a machine for turning spheres, and for cutting wooden bowls one out of the other, and likewise other mechanical contrivances.   See Specification, Gregory's Mechanics, vol. ii. p. 415.

* See the description of Paxton's machine, Trans. Soc. of Arts, vol. liii. p. 97 ; see also specification of Burnett and Poyer's patent.

The reader is likewise referred to the foot note, page 32, vol. i, on Taylor's patent machine for chopping out the staves for casks ; a similar mode was previously employed for chipping into fragments the dye-woods, the logs of which fell against the revolving disk through an inclined shoot.

† Now Sir Mark Isambard Brunel.

pendicularly up and down; just before the tool descends, the block is traversed a quantity equal to each cut or shaving.

The cutter is made cylindrical, and is formed just like a quill pen, but solid and with an elliptical cutting edge instead of the points. " The chisels are provided with small teeth, which are fitted into dove-tailed notches formed in the blade of the chisel. These are called scribers, they have a sharp edge projecting a short distance beyond the inside edge of the chisel, and therefore in descending through the mortise, the scribers cut the sides of the mortise fair, and make two clefts which separate the chip, (which will be cut out at the next stroke,) at its edges from the inside of the mortise, so that the chip comes out clean without splitting at the edges, and this makes the inside of the mortise as clean and smooth as possible "*. A hole is drilled nearly in the axis of the cylinder, for the insertion of a pin, by which the shavings are thrust out when they happen to clog the hole.

By forming the tool of a semicircular section and with two small fins, or edges projecting at right angles from the ends of the diameter, and then sharpening it so that the diameter becomes a straight chisel-edge, the scribing points are formed in the solid with the chisel, and are continually restored as the tool is sharpened. The tool is then perfectly analogous to fig. 334, page 485, if we suppose the plane condensed into a long chisel of semicircular section, equal to the diameter of the hole, the progressive elongation of which it has to effect.

There are many useful applications of revolving *figured* planes, moving through *curved* paths, by which we obtain figures of double curvature, as explained in the theoretical diagram, fig. 317, page 464. Mr. Brunel introduced an example of this in the scoring engine, one of the machines recently adverted to, for the manufacture of ships' blocks.

It is intended to form the groove around the block, for the rope by which it is attached to the rigging. The revolving plane is a disk of brass with a round edge and two cutters, inserted at an angle of about 30° with the radius; it traverses around the one side of the block, and receives its direction from a shaper plate or pattern placed parallel with the block, by which arrange-

---

* Rees's Cyclopedia, article " Machinery for manufacturing Ships' Blocks."

ment the cutter makes the groove deep at the ends, but shallow where it passes the pin or axis of the sheave. The same method has been subsequently extended to shaping the entire block with cutters of the full width, applied at four times *.

These several machines are compounds of slides and guides, and of fixed or revolving planes: the relative degrees of perfection attained, depend on the stability of the machines, and their respective agreement with the principles of the ordinary hand tools, which are generally themselves, the last stages of a long series of gradual improvements.

But the absence of some of the true characters of the plane, in nearly the whole of the machines for wood, namely, the proper obliquities of the iron, the frequent want of the *mouth* of the plane, and of the top or breaker iron, which so greatly restrains the splitting and tearing up of the fibres, prevent the machines from producing, in the softer woods, the smooth finished work of hand tools, in the management of which the judgment of the operator can be employed to combat the peculiarities of fibre. But the enormous productive powers of such machines, outweigh these drawbacks, and the more especially so, as the general forms or outlines are repeated by them in a most exact manner, and a little after-trimming by hand imparts the necessary finish.

In speaking of the apparatus for ornamental turning, there will be occasion to show that these same principles are strictly embodied in miniature, in the various parts of the complex lathe for ornamental turning; but as the hardwood and ivory therein generally used, admit of the employment of scraping-tools, not requiring either the obliquity of the cutter, or the mouth of the plane, the above objections do not apply to them, and their several results exhibit a much nearer approach to perfection.

---

* In revolving planes for wood, the cutters should always present an obliquity of about 30° to the radius, otherwise, or when the cutters are placed radially, they only scrape, or act like saws. Some of these planes are made of one disk of steel, in which case there are four, five, or six openings, like the mouths of rebate planes; the one side of each wedge or cutter is now a part of the circumference, the other is elevated some 20 or 30 degrees, thereby resembling the spokeshave iron. This form of cutter, although nearly perfect, is very expensive, and difficult to maintain in order.

CHAPTER XXIV.

TURNING-TOOLS.

SECT. I.—FACILITY OF TURNING COMPARED WITH CARPENTRY.

THE process of turning is accomplished with considerably more facility, truth, and expedition, than any other process requiring cutting tools, because in the most simple application of the art, the *guide principle* is always present, namely that of *rotation.* The expedition of the process is due to its being uninterrupted or continuous, except as regards the progressive changes of the tool, and which is slowly traversed from part to part, so as to be nearly always in action.

To choose the most simple condition, let us suppose the material to be in rotation upon a fixed axis, and that a cutting tool is applied to its surface at fifty places. Provided the tool remain quiescent at *one* place, for the period of *one* revolution of the material, the parts acted upon will each become *one* circle; because the space between the tool and the axis is for a period constant, and the revolution of the material converts the distance of the tool from the center, into the radius of one circle; and the same is equally true of the fifty positions.

The fifty circles will be concentric, or parallel with each other, because the same axis, extended or continued as a line, remains constant, or is employed for each of them, and therefore conceiving the fifty circles to be as many parts of the outline of a vase or other object, simple or complex, it will be strictly symmetrical, or equidistant from the central line at corresponding parts.

Each of the fifty circles will also become the margin of a plane at right angles to the axis, and which axis being a straight line, the whole of the circles will be parallel, and therefore the top and bottom of the vase will be also exactly parallel. And yet all these accurate results must inevitably occur, and that without any measurement, provided the material revolve on one fixed axis, and that the tool is for a short period constant or stationary at each part of the surface; conditions inseparable from the turner's art.

The principle of rotation upon a fixed axis, removes the necessity for many of the steps and measurements required to produce with accuracy the various angular solids employed in carpentry and many other arts. For example, at page 501 the methods were explained by which the joiner produces the three pairs of parallel surfaces *A a, B b, C c*, of fig. 355, and which are generally required in each separate piece of his work. And in making a box he has to combine six such pieces with the same relations of parallelism, and therefore thirty-six various surfaces have to be operated upon, to obtain the hollow cube, or the carpenter's box.

The turner's box consists of two pieces, in place of six; as the bottom and its four sides are resolved into one piece; when of wood, by nature in the forest; when of metal, by man in the crucible. The surfaces are therefore reduced from thirty-six to eight, namely, the inner and outer surfaces of the bottom and lid amounting to four, and the inner and outer sides or margins, amounting to four also, and the revolution of the work upon one axis, places the eight in exact and true relation with extreme rapidity.

For example, the ends or terminal planes of the box, are from necessity at right angles to the axis of rotation, and parallel with each other. In each of these superficies the question of being *in or out of winding* ceases; as if straight, they can only be planes or cones, and which the one straight-edge immediately points out.

The principle of rotation ensures circularity in the work, and perpendicularity or equality as regards the central line; it only remains therefore, to attend to the outline or contour. The right line serves to produce the cylinder, which is a common outline for a box; and the employment of mixed, flowing, and arbitrary lines, produces vases and ornaments of all kinds, the beauty of which demands attention alone to one single element, or conception, namely, that of form; and in the choice and production of which a just appreciation of drawing and proportion greatly assist.

In the art of drawing, it is almost essential to the freedom of the result, that the lines should be delineated at once, and almost without after correction; in the art of turning, it is always desirable to copy a drawing or a sketch, but having nearly attained the end, the tool may be continually re-applied, partially to remove any portions which may appear redundant, until the most scrupulous eye is satisfied.

The combining of the several parts of turned objects, as the separate blocks of which a column or other work is composed, is greatly facilitated from the respective parallelism of the ends of the pieces of which turned objects consist; and the circular tenons and mortises, whether plain or screwed, place the different pieces perpendicular and central with very little trouble.

These several, and most important facilities in the art of turning, are some amongst the many reasons, for its having obtained so extensive and valuable an employment in the more indispensable arts of life, as well as in its elegances.

———————

The relative advantages of the different sections of the tree, as regards the works of the turner and carpenter, were explained with figures in the fifth chapter of Vol. I., at pages 49 and 50, where it is shown that, from various reasons, the transverse section of the entire tree or branch is the most generally proper for the lathe; and therefore, in turning the tops and bottoms of works, as in figs. 13 and 14, page 49, Vol. I., we are cutting across the ends of the fibres, and in turning the sides of the same we are, as it were, proceeding across the width of a plank or board.

The tools used in turning the woods act much in the manner of the blades of the carpenter's planes; but as we have now, at all times, a *circular guide* in the lathe-mandrel, we do not require the stock of the plane or its *rectilinear guide*. Although if we conceive the sole of the plane applied as the tangent to the circle, the position it would give is nearly retained, but we are no longer encumbered with the stock or guide. In turning-tools for soft woods, the elevation of the tool, and the angle of its edge, are each of them less than in ordinary planes, and in those for the hard woods both angles are greater.

For example, the softest woods are turned with tools the acute edges of which measure about 20 to 30 degrees, and are applied nearly in coincidence with the tangent, as in fig. 360.

These tools closely assimilate to the spokeshave, which is the plane of the lowest pitch and keenest edge. On the contrary, the hardest woods may be turned with the above soft-wood tools, applied just as usual; but on the score of economy and general

Figs. 360.

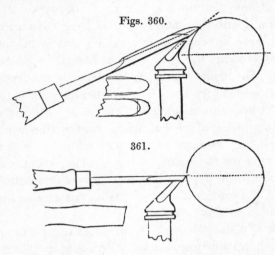

361.

convenience, the edges are thickened to from 60 to 80 degrees, and the face of the tool is applied almost horizontally on the lathe-rest, or as a radius to the circle, as in fig. 361, thus agreeing with the opposite extreme of the planes, in which the cutter is perpendicular and much less acute, as in the scraping and toothing-planes, which are only intended to scrape, and not to cut.

The hard-wood tools may be figured, and employed as scrapers in turning the members of the capital or the base of a column, or similar object in hard wood or ivory; but if we try the same tools on deal, ash, and other soft woods, we shall in vain attempt to produce the capital of a column, or even its cylindrical shaft, with a thick horizontal tool as in hard wood; for the fibres would not be cut, but forcibly torn asunder, and the surface would be left coarse and ragged.

But a reference to the planes with which the joiner proceeds *across* the fibres of deal, will convey the particulars suited to the present case; the iron is always thin and sharp, and applied in an oblique manner, so as to attack the fibre from the one end, and virtually to remove it in the direction of its length.

It is proposed now to describe some of the more important of the turning-tools, commencing with those employed on the soft grained woods, but it would be both hopeless and unnecessary to attempt the notice of all the varieties which are to be met with in the hands of different individuals; and as their practical applications will be entered upon in detail in the succeeding volume, only so much will be here advanced as, it is hoped, may serve to explain the modifications of the general principles of cutting tools, to some of the more usual purposes of turning. To avoid repetition, it may be observed, that in general the position of the tool for turning the cylinder, and secondly that for the flat surface or plane, will be alone described. For works of intermediate angles, whether curves or flowing lines, the position of the tool slides from that for the cylinder to that for the plane, or the reverse; and these changes will be readily made apparent, when the reader gradually moves either a tool or even a rod of wood, from the one to the other of the described positions.

It may be added, that most of the tools for metal are applied direct from the grindstone, the oilstone being used for such tools only as are employed for the more delicate metal works, or for the last finish of those of stronger kinds; all the tools for wood, ivory, and similar materials, are invariably sharpened on the oilstone. It may be desirable to remark, in addition, that the rough exterior faces of all works should be turned with narrow or pointed tools, and only a narrow portion at a time, until the surfaces are perfectly true or concentric; as wide flat tools, applied to rough irregular surfaces, especially of metal, would receive a vibratory, or rather an endlong motion, quite incompatible with truth of work.

SECT. II.—TURNING TOOLS FOR SOFT WOOD.

Angle 20° to 30°.—Figures generally half-size.

The tools most generally used for turning the soft woods, are the gouge and chisel, figs. 362 to 365, wherein they are shown of one-fourth their medium size; they vary from one-eighth to two inches wide; and as they are never driven with the mallet, they do not require the shoulders of the carpenter's tools, they are also ground differently. The turning-gouge is ground externally and obliquely, so as to make the edge elliptical, and it is principally the middle portion of the edge which is used; the chisel is ground from both sides, and with an oblique edge, and figs. 366 and 367 represent the full thickness of the chisel and its ordinary angles, namely, about 25 to 30 degrees for soft, and 40 for hard woods. The gouges and chisels wider than one inch are almost invariably fixed in long handles, measuring with the blades from 15 to 24 inches; the smaller tools have short handles, in all from 8 to 12 inches long.

Fig. 360 shows the position of the gouge in turning the cylinder; the bevil lies at a tangent, and the tool generally

Figs. 362.   363.   364.   365.   366.

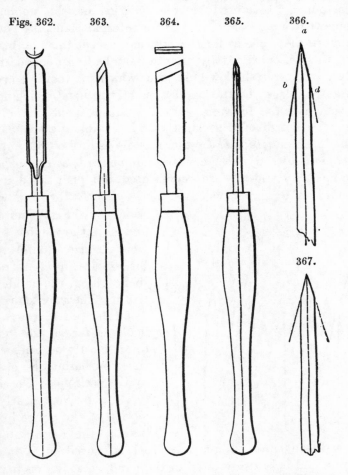

367.

rests on the middle of the back, or with the concave side upwards, the extremity of the handle is held in the right hand

L L

close to the person, and the left hand grasps the blade, with the fingers folded beneath it, and in this manner the gouge is traversed along the cylinder.

For turning the flat surface, the gouge is supported on its edge, that is, with the convex side towards the plane of the work, and with the handle nearly horizontal, to bring the center of the chamfered edge in near coincidence with the plane; the tool is inclined rather more than the angle at which its chamfer is ground, and it is gradually thrust from the margin to the center of the work.

The gouge is also used for hollow works, but this application is somewhat more difficult. For the internal plane, the position is almost the same as for the external, except that the blade is more inclined horizontally, that it may be first applied in the center, to bore a shallow hole, after which the tool is traversed across the plane, by the depression of the hand which moves the tool as on a fulcrum, and it is also rotated in the hand about the fourth of a circle, so that in completing the margin, or the internal cylinder, the tool may lie as in fig. 360, but with the convex instead of the concave side upwards as there shown.

In figs. 368 and 370 are represented the plans, and in 369 and 371 the elevations, of the *hook-tools* for soft wood,

Figs. 368.   369.   370.   371.

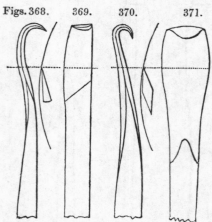

which may be called internal gouges; they differ somewhat in size and form, the blades are from 6 to 12 inches long, the handles 12 to 15. They are sharpened from the point around the hook as far as the dotted lines, mostly on one, sometimes on both sides, as seen by the sections. The hook tools follow very nearly the motion of the gouge in hollowing, the rest is placed rather distant and oblique; the tool is moved upon it as a fulcrum, and it is also rotated in the hand, so as always to place the bevil of the tool at a very small inclination to the tangent.

The finishing tools used subsequently to the gouges or hook-tools have straight edges; the chisel, fig. 364, is the most common, its position closely resembles that of the gouge, subject to the modifications called for by its rectilinear edge. If, for example, the edge of the chisel were just parallel with the axis of the cylinder, it would take too wide a hold; there would be risk of one or other corner digging into the work, and the edge, from its parallelism with the fibres, would be apt to tear them out. All these inconveniences are avoided by placing the edge oblique, as in fig. 364, in which the tool may be supposed to be seen in plan, and proceeding from right to left, fig. 360 being still true for the other view; the tool is turned over to proceed from left to right, and both corners of the tool are removed from the work, by the obliquity of the edge. The tool may be ground square across, but it must be then held in a more sloping position, which is less convenient.

Turning a flat surface with the chisel is much more difficult. The blade is placed quite on edge, and with the chamfer in agreement with the supposed plane *a, b, c*, fig. 366; the point of the chisel then cuts through the fibres, and removes a thin slice which becomes dished in creeping up *a, d*, the bevil of the tool; it then acts something like the scoring point of the planes, or the point of a penknife. Flat surfaces, especially those sunk beneath the surface, as the insides of boxes, are frequently smoothed with an ordinary firmer chisel, which is ground and sharpened with one bevil, but rather thicker than for carpentry. The edge is then burnished like the scraper, p. 484, and it is applied horizontally like a hardwood tool, as in fig. 361, but against the face or plane surface. The wire edge then lies in the required position, but it must be frequently renewed.

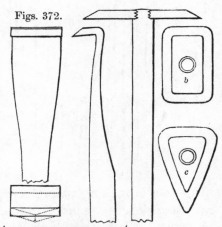

Figs. 372.   373.

The *broad*, represented in three views in fig. 372 endures much longer, but it requires to be held downwards or *underhand*, at about an angle of 40 to 50 degrees from the horizontal, in order to bring its edge into the proper relation to the plane to be turned.   Another form of the broad is also represented in fig. 373, it is a cylindrical stem, upon the end of which is screwed a triangular disk of steel, sometimes measuring 3 inches on the sides, and sharpened externally on each edge, this tool requires the same position as the last.   Broads of the forms *b, c,* are also used, but principally for large works the plank way of the grain*.

For the insides of cylinders, the side-tool, fig. 374, which is represented in three views, is sometimes used ; it is sharpened on both edges, and applied horizontally. The tool fig. 375, also shown in three views, serves both for the sides and the bottoms of deep works, but it does not admit of being turned over ; and 376 is another form of the same tool for shallower works, the cranked form of which is considered to give it a better purchase.

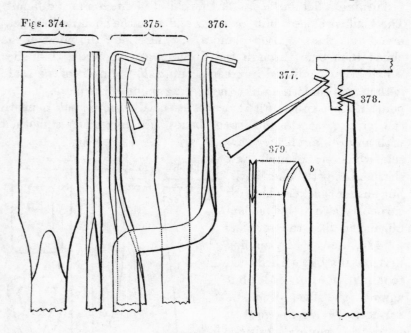

Figs. 374.   375.   376.   377.   378.   379.

The tools used for cutting screws in soft wood, by aid of the traversing or screw mandrel lathe, partake of the same general characters as the others, and are represented in their relative positions ; fig. 377 is for the outside, and 378 for the inside

---

* Similar tools are also used for turning pewter wares.

screw. To conclude the notice of tools of this class, the parting
tool, fig. 379, has an angular notch or groove on its upper
surface, from which it results that when the tool is sharpened
on the bevil *b*, the upper face *f*, presents two points, which separate the fibres by a double incision. This method wastes only
as much wood as equals the thickness of the tool, and it leaves
the work smooth and flat; whereas, when the angle of the
chisel is used for the same purpose, several cuts are required,
and the gap must present a greater angle than the bevil of the
tool, and which consumes both more time and wood.

The various turning tools for soft woods which have been
described are, with the exception of the gouge and chisel, nearly
restricted to the makers of Tunbridge-ware, toys, and common
turnery; with them they are exceedingly effective, but to others
somewhat difficult. The amateur turner scarcely uses more than
the common gouge and chisel, and even these but insufficiently,
as much may be done with them; it has been shown, for instance, that moulding tools cannot be used for the soft woods,
but they are efficiently replaced by the gouge for the concave,
and the chisel for the convex mouldings, which proceedings will
however, be detailed in the fourth volume.

A good fair practice on the soft woods would be found very
greatly to facilitate the general manipulation of tools, as all
those for the soft woods, demand considerably more care as to
their positions and management than those next to be described.

SECT. III.—TURNING TOOLS FOR HARDWOOD AND IVORY.

Angles 40° to 80°.—Figures generally half size.

The gouge is the preparatory tool for the hard as well as for
the soft woods, but it is then ground less acutely; the soft-wood
chisel may indeed be employed upon the hardest woods, but
this is seldom done, because the tools with single bevils, held in
a horizontal position, as in fig. 361, page 511, are much more
manageable, and on account of the different natures of the

Figs. 380.   381.

materials they are thoroughly suitable, notwithstanding that
their edges are nearly as thick again as those of soft-wood tools.

In general, also, the long handles of the latter are replaced by shorter ones, as in figs. 380 and 381, measuring with the tools from 8 to 12 inches; but these give in general an abundant purchase, as from the nearly horizontal position of the tool, the lathe rest or support can be placed much nearer to the work.

The hard-wood tools are often applied to a considerable extent of the work at one time, and the finishing processes are much facilitated by selecting instruments the most nearly in correspondence with the required shapes. Rectilinear surfaces, such as cylinders, cones, and planes, whether external or internal, necessarily require tools also with rectilinear edges, which are sloped in various ways as regards their shafts, they are made both large and small, and of proportionate degrees of strength to suit works of different magnitudes : the following are some of the most usual kinds.

Figs. 382. 383.　　384.　　385.　　386. 387. 388.　　389.　　390.　　391.

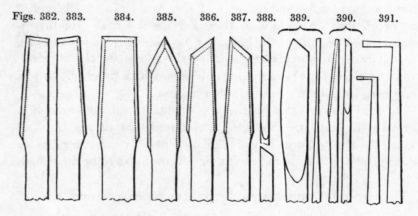

The *right side tool,* fig. 382, cuts on the side and end, the dotted lines being intended to indicate the undercut bevil of the edge; it is thus named beeause it cuts *from the right hand* towards the left. The *left side tool,* fig. 383, is just the reverse. The *flat-tool,* fig. 384, cuts on both sides, and on the end likewise; and in all three tools the angle seen in plan, is less than a right angle, to allow them to be applied in rectangular corners. The *point-tool,* fig. 385, is also very convenient; and *bevil-tools,* figs. 386 and 387, the halves of the former, are likewise employed; figs. 388 show the general thicknesses of these tools. When any of them are very narrow they are made proportionally deep to give sufficient strength, the extreme case being the *parting-tool,* fig. 389, which is no longer required to be fluted, as in the corresponding tool for soft wood; but the side tools, when used for small and deep holes, necessarily require to be small in both respects, as in fig. 390. The application of the *inside parting-tool*, fig. 391, has been previously shown on page 151, Vol. I., in respect to the removal of rings of ivory from the interior of solid works, in preference to turning the materials into shavings; it is also useful in some other undercut works.

Some of the curvilinear tools for hard wood are represented in the annexed group; the simicircular or *round tool*, fig. 392,

Figs. 392. 393. 394. 395. 396. 397. 398. 399. 400. 401.

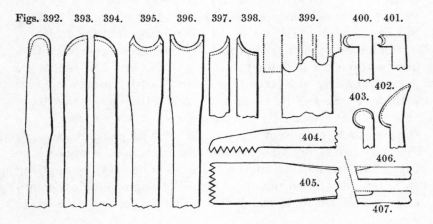

403. 402.

404.

406.

405.

407.

is the most general, as concave mouldings cannot be made without it, and it is frequently divided, as in the *quarter round tools*, figs. 393 and 394; it is convenient that these should be exact counterparts of the mouldings, but they may also be used for works larger than themselves, by sweeping the tools around the curves. Convex mouldings are frequently made by rectilinear tools, which are carried round in a similar manner, so as to place the edge as a tangent to the curve, but the *bead*, fig. 395, the *astragal*, fig. 396, or the *quarter hollows*, figs. 397 and 398, facilitate the processes, and complete the one member of the moulding at one sweep, and enable it to be repeated any number of times with exact uniformity.

Frequently the tools are made to include several members, as the entire base or capital of a column, as in fig. 399. Similar figured tools, have been applied to turning profiles of about one or one and a half inches high, by employing four different tools, embracing each about a quarter of the profile, and applied at four radial positions, around a ring of some three to five inches diameter; the rings are cut up into radial slices, and turned flat on each face prior to being glued upon tablets. Profiles have been likewise successfully and more skilfully turned, by the ordinary round, point, and flat tools, which processes will be proposed as examples in the practical part of the fourth volume.

Figs. 400 to 403 represent some of the various kinds of *inside* tools, which are required for hollowing vases and undercut works; and 404 the *inside screw* tool, and 405 the *outside screw* tool for hard wood, ivory, and the metals, these tools are made with many points, and are bevilled like the rest of the group, they will be further noticed in the chapter on screw-cutting tools.

The hollow tools, figs. 395 to 398, may be sharpened with a narrow slip of oilstone used almost as a file; but their sweeps are more accurately sharpened by conical metal grinders, supplied with emery, as will be explained; most other moulding tools, and the screw tools, are only sharpened upon the face. The ends of these tools may be whetted at a slope, if it be more gradual, than in fig. 406, this however, increases the angle of the edge; but by nicking in the tools, as in fig. 407, by applying them transversely on the grindstone, the original angle is maintained, and which is the better mode for screw tools more especially.

SECT. IV.—TURNING TOOLS FOR BRASS.

Angles 70° to 90°.—Figures generally the same as the tools for hard wood.

The turning-tools for brass are in general simple, and nearly restricted to round, point, flat, right and left side tools, parting tools, and screw tools; they closely resemble the hard-wood tools, except that they are generally ground at angles of about 60° or 70°, and when sharpened it is at an angle of 80° or 90°; some few of the finishing or planishing tools, are ground exactly at 90°, upon metal laps or emery wheels, so as to present a cutting edge at every angle and on both sides of the tools.

It is not a little curious that the angles which are respectively suitable to brass and to iron, are definitively shown to be about 90 and 60 degrees. For turning brass, a worn-out square file is occasionally ground on all sides to deprive it of its teeth, it is used as a side tool, and is slightly tilted, as in

fig. 408, just to give one of the edges of the prism sufficient penetration; but applied to iron, steel, or copper, it only scrapes
with inconsiderable effect.   A triangular file, fig. 409, similarly
ground, cuts iron with great avidity and effect, but is far less

Figs. 408.   409.   410.

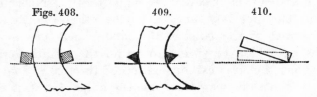

suited to brass; it is too penetrative, and is disposed to dig
into the work.   It appears indeed, that each different substance
requires its own particular angle, from some circumstances of
internal arrangement as to fibre or crystallization not easily
accounted for.

A stout narrow round tool, fig. 392, in a long handle, serves
as the gouge or roughing out tool for brass-work, others prefer
the point, fig. 385, with its end slightly rounded, which combines, as it were, the two tools with increased strength; a small
but strong right side tool 382, is also used in rough-turning;
the *graver*, figs. 411 and 412, although occasionally employed
for brass, is more proper for iron, and is therefore described in
the next section.

The wide finishing tools should not be resorted to under any
circumstances until the work is roughed out nearly to the shape,
and reduced to perfect concentricity or truth, with narrow tools
which only embrace a very small extent of the work.

It is the general impression that in taking the finishing cuts
on brass it is impolitic, either to employ wide tools, or to support
them in a rigid solid manner upon the rest, as it is apt to make
the work full of fine lines or striæ. This effect is perhaps jointly
attributable to the facility of vibration which exists in brass and
similar alloys, to the circumstance of their being frequently
used in thin pieces on the score of economy, and to their being
rotated more rapidly in the lathe than iron and steel, to expedite
the progress of the work.

When a wide flat tool is laid close down on the rest, and
made to cut with equal effect throughout its width, lines are
very likely to appear on the metal, and which if thin, rings like
a bell from the vibration into which it is put; but if the one

corner of the tool penetrate the work to the extent of the thickness of the shaving, whilst the other is just flush with the surface, or out of work, the vibration is lessened, and that whether the penetrating angle or the other move in advance.

The brass turner frequently supports the smoothing tool upon the *one edge only*, and keeps the other slightly elevated from the rest by the twist of the hand, which thus appears to serve as a cushion or spring to annul the vibrations, fig. 410 shows about the greatest inclination of the tool. Some workmen with the same view interpose the finger between the tool and the rest, in taking very light finishing cuts. The general practice, however, is to give the tool a constant rotative shuffling motion upon the supported edge, never allowing it to remain strictly quiet, by which the direction of the edge of the tool is continually changed, so as not to meet in parallelism any former striæ which may have been formed, as that would tend to keep up the exciting cause, namely, the vibration of the metal. The more the inclination of the tool, the greater is the disposition to turn the cylinder into small hollows.

Some workmen burnish the edges of the finishing tools for brass, like the joiners' scraper, or the firmer chisel used in softwood turning. On account of the greater hardness and thickness of the edge of the tool, it cannot be supposed that in these cases any very sensible amount of burr or wire edge is thrown up. The act appears chiefly to impart to the tool the smoothness and gloss of the burnisher, and to cause it, in its turn, to burnish rather than cut the work; the gas-fitters call it a planishing tool, but such tools should never be used for accurate works until the surface is perfectly true and smooth.

The hard-wood and brass turners avoid the continual necessity for twisting the lathe rest in its socket to various angular positions, as they mostly retain it parallel with the mandrel, and in turning hollow works they support the tool upon an arm-rest; this is a straight bar of iron, which resembles a long-handled tool, but it has a rectangular stud at the end, to prevent the cutting tool from sliding off.

The position of the arm-rest and tool, as seen in plan, are therefore nearly that of a right angle; the former is held under the left arm, the latter in the right hand of the workman, the fore-fingers of each hand being stretched out to meet near the end of the tool. This may appear a difficult method, but it is in all respects exceedingly commodious, and gives considerable freedom and choice of position in managing the tool, the advantage of which is particularly felt in guiding the first entry of the drill, or the path of the screw-tool; and in brass work it likewise renders the additional service of associating the tool with the elastic frame of the man. But when particular firmness and accuracy are required the tool should be supported upon the solid rest as usual.

SECT. V.—TURNING TOOLS FOR IRON, STEEL, ETC.

Angles 60° to 90°.—Figures generally one-sixth the full size.

The *triangular* tool is one of the most effective in turning these metals, as was adverted to at page 521; the triangular tool is also used by the engravers and others for scraping the surfaces of the metals, and it is then applied nearly perpendicular, or as a penknife in erasing; but when the triangular tool is placed nearly as a tangent against the inner or outer edge of a ring or cylinder, as in fig. 409, it seems almost to devour the metal, and instead of scratching, it brings off coarse long shavings. In turning the flat sides of the ring, the face of the tool is placed almost in agreement with the plane to be turned.

The *graver*, which is also an exceedingly general tool, is a square bar of steel ground off at the end, diagonally and obliquely, generally at an angle of from 30 to 50 degrees. The parts principally used are the two last portions of the edge close to the point, and to strengthen the end of the tool a minute facet is sometimes ground off, nearly at right angles to the broad chamfer, or principal face.

The proper position of the tool, in turning a cylinder, will be most readily pointed out by laying the chamfer of the tool in exact contact with the flat end of such cylinder; it will be then found that one of the lateral angles of the tool will touch the rest, and the obliquity in the shaft of the tool, would be the angle, at which the graver is ground, instead of which it is held square and slightly elevated above the horizontal position, as shown in fig. 411. The graver is rotated upon the supporting angle, which sticks into the rest, much the same as the edge of the triangular tool; in fact, the two tools, although different in form, remove the shaving in a very similar manner.

In using the graver and other tools for the metals, it is the aim to avoid exposing the end of the tool to the rough gritty surface of the material. This is done by cleaning the surface, espe-

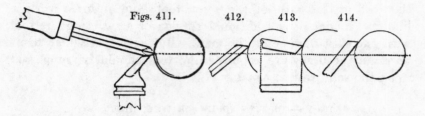

Figs. 411.　　412.　　413.　　414.

cially the extreme edge, with an old file, and beginning at that edge, the work is at one sweep reduced nearly to its required diameter by a wide thin cut, which may be compared with a chamfer, or a conical fillet, connecting the rough external surface with the smooth reduced cylinder. Therefore after the first entry, the point of the tool is buried in the clean metal below the crust, and works laterally, which is indeed the general path of pointed tools for metal.

When the graver is used in the turn-bench with intermittant motion, as for the pivots of watches, the axes for sextants, and other delicate works; it is applied *overhand,* or inverted, as in fig. 412, but it is then necessary to withdraw the tool during each back stroke of the bow, to avoid the destruction of the acute point, and which alone is used. The graver, when thus applied in lathes with continuous motion, is only moved on the rest as on a fulcrum, and in the plane in which it lies, rather as a test of work done, than as an active instrument.

The edge of the graver is afterwards used for smoothing the stronger kinds of work, it is then necessary to incline the tool horizontally, to near the angle at which it is ground, in order to bring the sloping edge parallel with the surface. But the smoothing is better done by a thick narrow flat tool, ground at about sixty degrees, the handle of which is raised slightly above the horizontal, as in fig. 413, in order that its edge may approach the tangential position; here also the tool is rotated on one edge, after the manner of the brass tools or the graver.

For many slight purposes requiring rather delicacy than strength, as in finishing the rounded edge of a washer, the flat tool is inverted or placed bevil upwards, as in fig. 414; the lower side then becomes the tangent, and the edge the axis of rotation of the tool, the same as in turning convex mouldings with the soft-wood chisel. Indeed, many analogies may be traced between the tools respectively used for soft woods and iron, except that the latter are ground at about twice the angle to meet the increased resistance of the hard metal, and the tools are mostly sustained by the direct support of the rest, instead of resting in great measure against the hands of the individual.

For instance, the *heel-tool*, which is used for rough turning the metals, is represented of the full size in the side-view, fig. 415, and the front-view, fig. 416, and also on a smaller scale in figs. 417 and 418. The dotted lines *a*, fig. 417, denote the relative

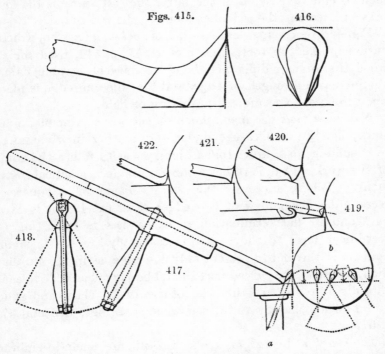

Figs. 415. 416.

422. 421. 420.

419.

418.

417.

position of the fluted gouge, and although the heel or hook-tool occupies nearly the same spot, its edge is of double the thickness, and the entire resistance of the cut is sustained by the heel of the tool, which is poised upon the flat horizontal surface of the rest; the shaft of the tool is bent nearly at right angles, that it may be held either above or below the shoulder of the workman as preferred. Some variation is made in the form and size of the heel-tools, and they are occasionally pointed instead of round upon the cutting edge.

The heel-tool is slightly rotated upon its heel in its course along the work, so that, as seen at *b*, its edge travels in short arcs, and when its position becomes too inclined, a fresh footing is taken; on this account the straight handle, employed in ordinary tools, is exchanged for the transverse handle represented. In the best form of heel-tools the square shaft lies in a groove in the long handle, and is fixed by an eye-bolt and nut, passing through the transverse handle, as seen in the section 418. Notwithstanding the great difference between the materials upon which the gouge and heel-tool are employed, their management is equally easy, as in the latter the rest sustains the great pressure, leaving the guidance alone to the individual.

Fig. 419 represents another kind of *hook-tool* for iron, which is curiously like the tools, figs. 368 to 371, p. 514, used for soft wood, the common differences being here also observable, namely the increased strength of edge, and that the one edge is placed upon the rest to secure a firm footing or hold.

Nail-head tools are made much on the same principle, one of these, fig. 420, is like a cylinder, terminating in a chamfered overhanging disk, to be rolled along so as to follow the course of the work, but it is rather a theoretical than practical instrument. When, however, the tool is made of a square or rectangular bar, and with two edges as at fig. 421, it is excellent, and its flat termination greatly assists in imparting the rectilinear form to the work. Occasionally the bar is simply bent up at the end to present only one edge, as in fig. 422, it is then necessary the curved part should be jagged as a file to cause it to dig into the rest like the others of its class, and which present some analogy to the soft-wood tools, figs. 372 and 373, p. 515.

The *cranked*, or *hanging* tools, fig. 423, are made to embrace the rest, by which they are prevented from sliding away, without the necessity for the points and edges of the heel-tools; the escape of the cranked tool sideways is prevented by the pin inserted in one of the several holes of the rest. The direct penetration is caused by the depression of the hand; the sideway motion by rotating the tool by its transverse handle, which is frequently a hand-vice temporarily screwed upon the shaft.

To save the trouble of continually shifting the lathe-rest, an iron wedge, (not represented,) is generally introduced at *a*, between the rest and the back of the tool; when the wedge is advanced at intervals it sets the tool deeper into the work, when it is withdrawn it allows more room for the removal of the tool.

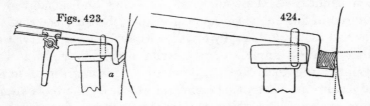

Figs. 423.   424.

The succeeding figure, 424, represents a tool of nearly similar kind, the stock is of iron, and it carries a piece of steel, about three or four inches long, and one inch square, which is forged hollow on the faces by means of the fuller, to leave less to be ground away on the stone. The rectilinear edges of this tool are used for smoothing iron rollers, iron ordnance, and other works turned by hand, and to preserve the edge of the tool, thin spills of hard wood are sometimes placed between the cutter and the bar. Under favourable arrangements these tools also are managed with great facility; indeed it occasionally happens that the weight of the handle just supplies the necessary pressure to advance the tool, so that they will rest in proper action without being touched by the hand; a tolerable proof of the trifling muscular effort occasionally required, when the tools are judiciously moulded and well applied.

These hand tools and various others of the same kinds, although formerly much used by the millwrights, are now in a great measure replaced by the fixed tools applied in the sliding rest, some account of which will be given in the next section.

SECT. VI.—FIXED OR MACHINE TOOLS FOR TURNING AND PLANING.

Angles as in the hand-tools.—Figures generally one-fourth to one-eighth the full-size.

THE performance of fixed tools is, in general, much more effective than that of hand tools; as the rigid guides and slides now employed, do not suffer the muscular fatigue of the man, nor do they experience those fluctuations of position to which his hand is liable. Therefore, as the tool pursues one constant undeviating course, the corresponding results are obtained both more economically and more accurately by the intervention of the *guide-principle,* or the *slide-rest,* from which we derive the *slide-lathe,* and thence the *planing-machine,* and many other most invaluable tools.

The cutting edges of machine tools mostly follow the same circumstances as those of hand tools, but additional care is required in forming them upon principle; because the shafts of the fixed tools are generally placed, with little power of deviation, either at right angles to, or parallel with, the surfaces to be wrought; the tools are then held in the iron grasp of screws and clamps, in mortises, staples, and grooves. The tools do not, therefore, admit of the same accommodation of position, to compensate for erroneous construction, or subsequent deterioration from wear, as when they are held in the hand of the workman, and directed by his judgment.

It must also be additionally borne in mind that, however ponderous, elaborate, or costly the *machine* may be, its effectiveness *entirely depends* upon the proper adaptation and endurance of the *cutting-tool,* through the agency of which it produces its results.

The usual position of the fixed turning tools is the horizontal

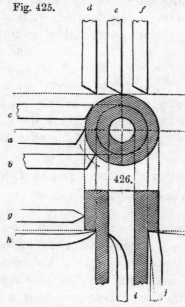

Fig. 425.

line, as at *a,* fig. 425; and unless the tools always lie on the radius, (or any other predetermined line,) various interferences occur. For instance, the tool proceeding in either of the lines *b* or *c,* could not reach the center of the work, and a portion would then escape being wrought; the curvature of the circle at *b,* would sacrifice the proper angle, and expose the tool to fracture from the obliquity of the strain; and at *c,* the edge would be altogether out of contact, and the tool could only rub and not cut. These evils increase with the diminution of the circle; and although the diagram is greatly exaggerated for illustration, the want of centrality is in truth

an evil of such magnitude that various contrivances are resorted to, by which either the entire slide-rest, or the cutter
alone, may be exactly adjusted for height of center.

The planing tools for metal are in general fixed vertically, and
the path of the work being, in the majority of planing machines,
rectilinear and horizontal, the tool may be placed at d, e, or f,
indifferently, there being no interference from curvature as in
turning.

In those modifications of the planing machine, in which as in
Brunel's mortising engine, the cutter travels perpendicularly,
and is also fixed perpendicularly, as in the key groove or slotting
engines, and the paring engines, the general form of the tool f,
or that of a strong paring chisel, is retained, but the blade is
slightly inclined in its length as at j, fig. 426, to avoid touching
the surface to be wrought except with its cutting edge, and the
length of the tool supplies a little elasticity to relieve the friction
of the back stroke.

Although all the various forms of hand-turning tools are more
or less employed as fixed tools, still the greater part of the work
is done with the point tool, (such as y, in the plan fig. 426,) the
angle of which should be slightly rounded; but for working
into an angle, the point of the tool is thrown off as at h, so that
its shaft may avoid either side of the angle, and it is then called
a side-tool. For internal works, and in small apertures especially, the abrupt curvature requires particular attention to the
central position of the tool i, and a frequent sacrifice of the
most proper form of the chamfer or edge. I will now describe
a few of the slide-rest tools in the previous order, namely, those
for soft wood, for hard wood, for brass, and for iron.

The fixed tools for soft wood require the same acute edges, and
nearly tangential positions, as those used by hand; and if these
conditions exist, it is quite immaterial whether the tool touch

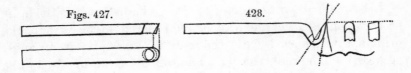

Figs. 427.   428.

the work above or below the center; but the central line, or a,
fig. 425, is the most usual. The soft-wood gouge, or hook-tool, is

successfully imitated by making an oblique hole in the end of a bar of steel, as seen in two views in fig. 427, but it is not very lasting ; or a bar of steel may be bent to the form of fig. 428, and sharpened internally, either rounded to serve as a gouge, or straight and inclined as a chisel, but neither of these tools admits in itself of adjustment for center.

The difficulty of center is combated by the use of a tool exactly like a common gouge or chisel, but only an inch or two long, and with a cylindrical stem also an inch or two long, by which it may be retained at any height, in the end of a bar of iron, having a nearly perpendicular hole and an appropriate side screw for fixing the tool ; this construction is abundantly strong for wood.

The fixed tools for hard wood and ivory, follow the several forms of the hand-tools, figs. 382 to 405, pp. 518-19, except in having parallel stems ; they are always placed horizontally, and are treated in all respects just as before. Care should be taken, however, that the *end* of the tool is its widest part ; in order that, if it be sent in below the surface of the work, as in cutting a groove, it may clear well, and not rub against the sides.

In sharpening the tools intended for hard wood and ivory, the oil-stone should be applied principally at the end, or on the chamfer of the tool, as this will not reduce the height of center, which it is always important to retain. If, however, the tools should eventually become chamfered off, after the manner of fig. 406, p. 519, they may be annealed, and thrown up to place the chamfered part in the line of the general face; they are then re-hardened, and ground up as at first. But as most of the slide-rests for wood-turning are fitted into pedestals by means of a cylindrical stem with a vertical screw adjustment, the tools may be at all times accurately centered when particular care is required ; and this provision is of still greater importance, with the several revolving cutters applied to the slide-rest, which will be hereafter adverted to.

The fixed tools for brass and for iron, whether used in the lathe or the planing machine, will be considered in one group, the principal difference is, that the tools for brass present an angle of nearly 90 degrees, the tools for iron an angle of 60, to the superficies to be wrought. Indeed the angles or edges of the cube, may be considered as the generic forms of the tools for brass, and the angles or edges of the tetrahedron, as the generic forms of the tools for iron; that is, supposing the edges or planes of these solids, to be laid almost in contact with the line of motion or of the cut, in order that they may fulfil the constant conditions of the paring tools, described at page 462, and again referred to at pages 472 to 474.

The fixed tools for brass and similar alloys resemble, as in hand-turning, the more simple of the hardwood tools, except that they are sharpened a trifle thicker on the edge; they are, however, nearly restricted to the point tool, the narrow round tool, and to the side tool, which is represented at *j*, fig. 426. It is ground so that the two cutting edges meet at an angle not exceeding about 80 degrees, that in proceeding into rectangular corners it may clear each face by about five degrees, and it will then cut in either direction, so as to proceed into the angle upon the cylindrical line, and to leave it upon the plane surface, or it may be applied just in the reverse manner without intermission.

When the tool is used for rough work the corner is slightly rounded, but in finishing it is usually quite sharp; and as it differs only some ten degrees from the solid angle of a cube, it is abundantly strong. If the tools acted upon a considerable extent or width of the brass, they would be liable to be set in vibration; but as the paths of the cutters are determined by the guide principle employed, the point fulfils all that can be desired.

The fixed tools for iron, present more difficulties than the generality of the foregoing kinds; first, the edges of the tools are thinner, and more interfered with in the act of grinding, as the vertical height of the cutting edge is reduced when either face of the wedge is ground; and secondly, they are exposed to far more severe strains from the greater hardness of the material, and the less sparing manner in which it is reduced or wrought, owing to its smaller price and other circumstances; and therefore, the most proper and economic forms of the tools for iron are highly deserving of attention.

The fracture of a tool when it is overloaded, commonly points out the line of greatest resistance or strain. The tool fig. 429, on next page, although apparently keen, is very weak, and it is besides disposed to pursue the line at which its wedge-formed extremity meets the work, or to penetrate at an angle of some 30 degrees, (see page 462). Figure 429, would probably break through a line drawn nearly parallel with the face *a b*, of the work under formation; that portion should therefore be made very nearly parallel with *a, b*, the line of resistance, in order to impart to the tool the strength of the entire section of the steel; so that should it now break, it will have a much longer line of fracture. The tool thus altered is very proper for brass, an alloy upon which acute tools cannot be favourably employed.

Figs. 429.   430.   431.   432.   433.

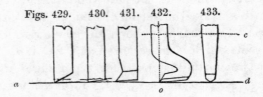

But with the obtuse edge of fig. 430, other metals will be only removed with considerable labour, as it must be remembered the tool is a wedge, and must insinuate itself as such amongst the fibres of the material. To give the strengthened tool the proper degree of penetration, the upper face is next sloped as in 431, to that angle in which the minimum of friction and the maximum of durability of the edge most nearly meet; and which, for iron, is shown to be about 60 degrees, as in the triangular tool fig. 409. The three planes of pointed tools for iron, meeting at 60 degrees, constitute the angle of the tetrahedron, or the solid with four equilateral planes, like a triangular pyramid, the base and sides of which are exactly alike.

But the form of 431 would be soon lost in the act of grinding; therefore to conclude, the tool is made in the bent form of fig. 432, in which the angles of 431 are retained, and the tool may be many times ground without departing from its most proper form. This is in effect extending the angle of the tetrahedron, into the triangular prism ground off obliquely, or rather, as seen in the front view fig. 433, into a prism of five sides, the front angle of which varies from 60 degrees to 120 degrees, and is slightly rounded, the latter being most suitable for rough work, sometimes the front of the prism is half-round, at other times quite flat, these forms are shown in fig. 439.

The extremities of figs. 431 and 432, approach very closely to the form of the graver, used for engraving on steel and copperplates, than which, no instrument works more perfectly. The slender graver, whether square or lozenge, is slightly bent, and has a flattened handle, so that the ridge behind the point may lie so nearly parallel with, and so completely buried in, the line or groove under formation, as to be prevented or checked, by the surface contact, from digging into the work. This is another confirmation of the fact, that the line of penetration is that of the lower face of the cutter or wedge, or that touching the work.

In adopting the crank-formed tools 432, the principle must not be carried into excess, as it must be remembered, we can never expunge *elasticity* from our materials, whether viewed in relation to the machine, the tool, or the work.

The tool should be always grasped as near the end as practicable, therefore the hook or crank should occupy but little length; as the distance from the supposed line of the fixing screw c, to the edge of the tool, being doubled, the flexure of the instrument will be fourfold; when trebled, ninefold; in fact as the square. And also as the flexure may be supposed to occur from near the center of the bar, (that is neglecting the crook,) the point of the tool should not extend beyond the central line o; otherwise when the tool bends, its point would dig still deeper into the work from its rotation on the intersection of c and o; the point situated behind the central line would spring *away from*, or *out of*, instead of *into* the work. To extend the wear of the cranked tools, they are commonly forged so that the point is nearly level with the upper surface of the shaft, as in fig. 438; they then admit of being many times ground before they reach the central line, and they are ultimately ground, (always at the end of the prism and obliquely,) until the hook

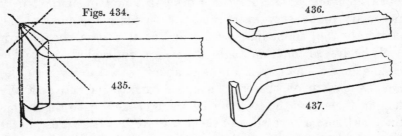

Figs. 434.   436.

435.   437.

is entirely lost. This avoids such frequent recurrence to the forge fire, but it is a departure from the right principle, to allow the point to extend beyond the center line o. See Appendix, Note A Q, page 983.

The works of the lathe and planing-machine frequently present angles or rebates, chamfers, grooves, and under-cut lines, which require that the tool should be bent about in various ways, in order that their edges may retain as nearly as possible the same relations to all these surfaces, as the ordinary surfacing tools figs. 431 and 432 have to the plane *a b*. For instance, the shaft of the tool 431, when bent at about the angle of 45 degrees, becomes a side cutting and facing tool, as shown in plan in fig. 434, in elevation in 435, and in perspective in 436 ; and in like manner, the cranked tool 432, when also bent as in 434, becomes 437, and is also adapted to working into angular corners upon either face.

Mr. Nasmyth's tool gage, shown in elevation in 438, and in plan in 439, entirely removes the uncertainty of the angles given

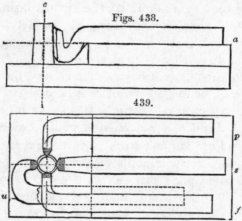

Figs. 438.

439.

to these irregular bent tools ; for instance, when the shaft of the tool is laid upon the flat surface and applied to the iron cone *c*, whose side measures about 3° with the perpendicular, it serves with equal truth for *s*, the tool for surfaces; *p, f*, the side-cutting tools, used also for perpendicular cuts and fillets ; and *u* for undercut works.

In applying tools to lathe works of small diameters, it is necessary to be very exact, and not to place them *above* the center, or they immediately rub ; and as this soon occurs with tools having so small an angle, it appears desirable to make the cone gage for small lathe works of about twice the given angle, and to mark upon the cone, a circle exactly indicative of the height of center; the tool can be then packed up to the center line, with one or two slips of sheet iron, to be afterwards placed beneath the tool when it is fixed in the lathe rest. In small hollow works, the most lasting or the crank-formed tools, are entirely inapplicable, indeed so much attention is required to prevent the tool from rubbing against the interior surfaces, that the ordinary angles cannot be employed, and the cone gage ceases to be useful, but in every other case it should be constantly resorted to ; the additional thickness *a*, is required to make it applicable to the crank-formed tools*.

Fig. 440, represents a cutter introduced in the Block Machinery at Portsmouth, to lessen the difficulty of making and restoring the tools, for turning the wrought-iron pins for the sheaves; it consists of a cylindrical wire which, from being ground off obliquely, presents an elliptical edge ; the tool is fixed in a stock of iron, terminating in an oblique hole, with a binding screw. The tool, when used for iron, in the "pin turning lathes," was made solid, when used for turning the surfaces of the wooden shells, in the "shaping engine," it was pierced with a central hole ; the latter could only facilitate the process of sharpening, without altering the character of the edge, which continued under the same circumstances as when solid.

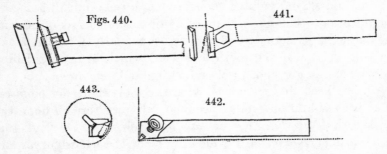

Figs. 440.   441.   443.   442.

About sixteen years back, the author made for his own use, a tool such as fig. 440, but found that with rough usage the cutter was shivered away, on account of its breadth, and he was soon led to substitute for the solid cylinder, a triangular cutter, the final edge of which was slightly rounded, and placed more nearly perpendicular, in a split socket with a side screw, as in fig. 441. The strength of the edge was greatly increased, and it became, in fact, an exact copy of the most favourable kind of tool for the lathe, or planing-machine, retaining the advantage that the

---

* The general similitude between some of the author's figures, 429 to 439, (engraved in Jan. 1840,) and part of those in Mr. James Nasmyth's article on Tools, in Buchanan's Mill Work, (published in Dec. 1841,) is solely due to their being each indebted to the same individual, (namely, to Mr. Joseph Clement,) for the general theory advanced, and which associates the principles of machine tools for metal, that are of comparatively modern date, with those of cutting tools generally, even of the most primitive kinds.

original form could be always kept, with the smallest expenditure of time, and without continually re-forging the blade, to the manifest deterioration of the steel from passing so frequently through the fire; it being only requisite to grind its extremity like a common graver, and to place it so much higher in the stock as to keep the edge at all times true to the center.

A right and a left hand side tool for angles, the former seem in figs. 442 and 443, were also made; the blade and set screw were placed at about 45°, and at a sufficient vertical angle, to clear both the inside of a cylinder of three inches diameter, and also to face the bottom or surface. These side tools answered very well for cast iron; but fig. 441, the ordinary surfacing tool, is excellent for all purposes, and has been employed in many extensive establishments*.

In turning heavy works to their respective forms, a slow motion and strong pointed tools are employed; but in finishing these works with a quicker rate of motion, there is risk of putting the lathe in a slight tremor, more particularly from the small periodic shocks of the toothed wheels, which in light finishing cuts are no longer kept in close bearing as in stronger cuts.

Under these circumstances, were the tools rigid and penetrative, each vibration would produce a line or scratch upon the surface, but the *finishing* or *hanging* tools, figs. 444 and 445, called also *springing* tools, which are made of various curves and degrees of strength, yield to these small accidental motions. The first resembles in its angles the rest of the tools used for brass, the second those for iron, their edges are rectilinear, and

---

* The prismatic cutters admit of the usual variations of shape : sometimes two binding screws are used, and occasionally a tail screw, to receive the direct strain of the cut. When the blades are only used for cutting in the one direction, say from right to left, they may, with advantage, be ground with a double inclination; for as all these pointed tools work *laterally*, the true inclination of some 60° to the narrow facet or fillet operated upon, is then more strictly attained.

Considerable economy results from this and several other applications, in which the cutter and its shaft are distinct parts. The small blades of steel admit of being formed with considerable ease and accuracy, and of being hardened in the most perfect manner. And when the cutters are fixed in strong bars or shafts of iron, they receive any required degree of strength, and the one shaft or carriage will serve for any successive number of blades.

The blades are sometimes made flat, or convex in the front, and ground much thinner, to serve for soft wood ; the tools for hard wood and ivory, being more easily ground, do not call for this application of detached blades.

sometimes an inch wide. The width and elasticity of these finishing tools, prevent their acting otherwise than as scrapers, for removing the slight superficial roughness, without detracting from the accuracy of form previously given. In a somewhat similar manner the broad hand flat tool, rendered elastic by its partial support, as in fig. 410, page 521, is frequently used for smoothing brass works, and others turned with the slide rest.

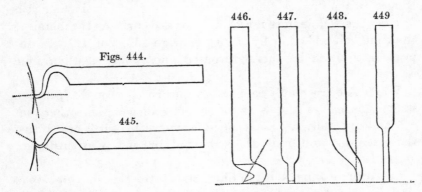

Figs. 444.

445.

446.   447.   448.   449.

Figs. 446 and 447 represent a very excellent finishing tool, introduced by Mr. Clement, for planing cast and wrought iron, and steel; it resembles the cranked tools generally, but is slighter, it is made smooth and flat upon the extremity ; or rather in a very minute degree rounded. This tool is sharpened very keenly upon the oilstone, and is used for extremely thin cuts, generally one quarter of an inch wide, and when the corners just escape touching, the work is left beautifully smooth ; the edge should on no account stand in advance of the center line. But to avoid the chatters so liable to occur in brass works, Mr. Clement prefers for that material the elastic planing tool, fig. 448 and 449, its edge is situated considerably behind the center.

In concluding the notice of the turning tools, it may be necessary to add a few words on those used for lead, tin, zinc, copper, and their ordinary alloys. The softest of these metals, such as lead, tin, and soft pewter, may be turned with the ordinary tools for soft wood; but for the harder metals, such as zinc, and hard alloys containing much antimony, the tools resemble those used for the hard woods, and they are mostly employed dry.

Copper, which is much harder and tougher, is turned with tools similar to those for wrought-iron, but in general they are sharpened a little more keenly, and water is allowed to drop upon the work to lessen the risk of *dragging* or tearing up the face of the copper, a metal that neither admits of being turned or filed with the ordinary facility of most others. Silver and gold, having the tenacious character of copper, require similar turning tools, and they are generally lubricated with milk.

In the above, and nearly all the metals except iron and those of equal or superior hardness, there seems a disposition to adhere, when by accident, the recently removed shaving gets forcibly pressed against a recently exposed surface, (the metals at the time being chemically clean, see page 432, Vol. I.,) this disposition to unite is nearly prevented when water or other fluid is used.

Water is occasionally resorted to in turning wrought iron and steel; this causes the work to be left somewhat smoother, but it is not generally used, except in heavy work, as it is apt to rust the machinery, oil fulfils the same end, but is too expensive for general purposes.—See Appendix, Note AR., page 983.

Cast-iron having a crystalline structure, the shavings soon break, without causing so much friction as the hard ductile metals; cast-iron is therefore always worked dry, even when the acute edges of 60 degrees are thickened to those of 80 or 90, either from necessity, as in some of the small boring tools, or from choice on the score of durability, as in the largest boring tools and others. Brass and gun-metal are also worked dry, although the turning tools are nearly rectangular, as the copper becomes so far modified by the zinc or tin, that the alloys, although much less crystalline than cast iron, and less ductile than copper, yield to the turning tools very cleanly without water.

But when tools with rectangular edges are used for wrought iron and steel, on account of the greater cohesion of these materials, they must be lubricated with oil, grease, soap and water, or other matter, to prevent the metals from being torn. And the screw cutting tools, many of which present much surface friction, and also rectangular or still more obtuse edges, almost invariably require oil or other unctuous fluids, for all the metals.

It will be shown in the practice of metal turning, that the diamond point, figs. 64 and 65, page 178, Vol. I., is occasionally used in turning *hardened* steel and other substances; figs. 72 to 74 are constantly used in engraving by machinery, and in graduating mathematical instruments.—See Appendix, Notes AS. to AV. pages 983 to 1001.

CHAPTER XXV.

BORING TOOLS.

SECT. I.—BORING BITS, FOR WOOD.

THE process of boring holes may be viewed as an inversion of that of turning; generally the work remains at rest, and the tool is revolved and advanced. Many of the boring and drilling tools have angular points, which serve alike for the removal of the material, and the guidance of the instrument; others have blunt guides of various kinds for directing them, whilst the cutting is performed by the end of the tool.

Commencing as usual with the tools for wood, the brad-awl fig. 450, may be noticed as the most simple of its kind; it is a cylindrical wire with a chisel edge, which rather displaces than removes the material; it is sometimes sharpened with three facets as a triangular prism. The awl, fig. 451, used by the wire-workers, is less disposed to split the wood; it is square and sharp on all four edges, and tapers off very gradually until near the point, where the sides meet rather more abruptly.

The generality of the boring instruments used in carpentry are fluted, like reeds split in two parts, to give room for the shavings, and they are sharpened in various ways as shown by figures 452 to 456. Fig. 452 is known as the *shell-bit*, and also as the *gouge-bit*, or *quill-bit*, it is sharpened at the end like a gouge, and when revolved it shears the fibres around the margin of the hole, and removes the wood almost as a solid core. The shell-bits are in very general use, and when made very small, they are used for boring the holes in some brushes.

Fig. 453, the *spoon-bit*, is generally bent up at the end to make a taper point, terminating on the diametrical line; it acts something after the manner of a common pointed drill, except that it possesses the keen edge suitable for wood. The spoon-bit is in very common use, the *coopers' dowel-bit*, and the *table-bit*, for making the holes for the wooden joints of tables, are of this kind; occasionally the end is bent in a semicircular form, such are called *duck-nose-bits* from the resemblance, and also *brush-bits* from their use; the diameter of the hole continues undiminished for a greater depth than with the pointed spoon-bit.

Figs. 450. 451. 452. 453. 454. 455. 456.

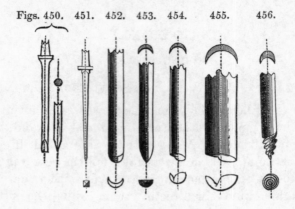

The *nose-bit*, fig. 454, called also the *slit-nose-bit*, and *auger-bit*, is slit up a small distance near the center, and the larger piece of the end is then bent up nearly at right angles to the shaft, so as to act like a paring chisel; and the corner of the reed, near the nose also cuts slightly. The form of the nose-bit, which is very nearly a diminutive of the *shell-auger*, fig. 455, is better seen in the latter instrument, in which the transverse cutter lies still more nearly at right angles, and is distinctly curved on the edge instead of radial. The augers are sometimes made three inches diameter, and upwards, and with long removable shanks, for the purpose of boring wooden pump-barrels, they are then called *pump-bits*.

There is some little uncertainty of the nose-bits entering exactly at any required spot, unless a small commencement is previously made with another instrument, as a spoon-bit, a gouge, a brad-awl, a center-punch or some other tool; with augers a preparatory hole is invariably made, either with a gouge, or with a center-bit exactly of the size of the auger. When the nose-bits are used for making the holes in sash bars, for the wooden pins or dowels, the bit is made exactly parallel, and it has a square brass socket which fits the bit; so that the work and socket being fixed in their respective situations, the *guide principle* is perfectly applied. A "*guide tube*" built up as a tripod which the workman steadies with his foot, has been recently applied by Mr. Charles May, of Ipswich, for boring the auger holes in railway sleepers exactly perpendicular*.

The gimlet fig. 456 is also a fluted tool, but it terminates in a sharp worm or screw, beginning as a point and extending to the full diameter of the tool, which is drawn by the screw into the wood. The principal part of the cutting is done by the angular corner intermediate between the worm and shell, which acts much like the auger, the gimlet is worked until the shell is full of wood, when it is unwound and withdrawn to empty it.

The center-bit, fig. 457, shown in three views, is a very beautiful instrument, it consists of three parts, a center point or *pin*, filed triangularly, which serves as a guide for position; a thin shearing point or *nicker*, that cuts through the fibres like the point of a knife; and a broad chisel edge or *cutter*, placed obliquely to pare up the wood within the circle marked out by the point. The cutter should have both a little less radius and less length than the nicker, upon the keen edge of which last the correct action of the tool principally depends.

Many variations are made from the ordinary center-bit, fig. 457; sometimes the centerpoint is enlarged into a stout cylindrical plug, so that it may exactly fill a hole previously made, and cut out a cylindrical countersink around the same, as for the head of a screw bolt. This tool, known as the *plug center-bit*, is much used in making frames and furniture, held together by screw-bolts. Similar tools but with loose cutters inserted in a diametrical mortise, in a stout shaft, are also used in ship-building for inlaying the heads of bolts and washers, in the timbers and planking.

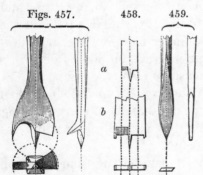

Figs. 457.   458.   459.

The *wine-cooper's center-bit* is very short, and is enlarged behind into a cone, so that immediately a full cask has been bored, the cone plugs up the hole until the tap is inserted. The center-bit deprived of its chisel-edge, or possessing only the pin and nicker, is called a *button-tool*, it is used for boring and

* See Minutes of Conversation Inst. Civil Engineers. 1842, page 76.

cutting out at one process, the little leather disks or *buttons*, which serve as nuts for the screwed wires in the mechanism connected with the keys of the organ and piano-forte.

The *expanding center-bit*, shown on a much smaller scale in fig. 460, is a very useful instrument ; it has a central stem with a conical point, and across the end of the stem is fitted a transverse bar, adjustable for radius. When the latter carries only a lancet-shaped cutter it is used for making the margins of circular recesses, and also for cutting out disks of wood and thin materials generally ; when, as in Mr. James Stone's modification, the expanding center-bit has two shearing points or nickers, and one chisel-formed cutter, it serves for making grooves for inlaying rings of metal or wood in cabinet work, and other purposes *. See Appendix, note A W., p. 1001.

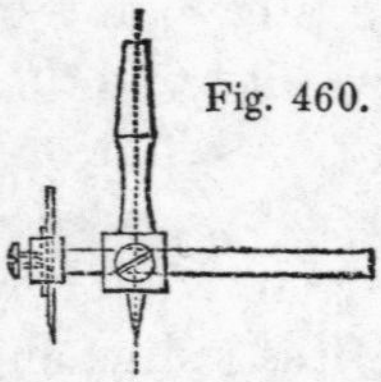

Fig. 460.

The above tools being generally used for woods of the softer kinds, and the plankway of the grain, the shearing point and oblique chisel of the center-bit, fig. 457, are constantly retained, but the corresponding tools used for the hard woods assume the characters of the hard wood tools generally. For instance, *a*, fig. 458, has a square point, also two cutting edges, which are nearly diametrical, and sharpened with a single chamfer at about 60 degrees; this is the ordinary *drill* used for boring the finger-holes in flutes and clarionets, which are afterwards chamfered on the inner side with a stout knife, the edge of which measures about 50 degrees. The key-holes, are first scored with the *cup-key tool*, *b*, and then drilled, the tools *a*, and *b*, being represented of corresponding sizes, and forming between them the annular ridge which indents the leather of the valve or key.

When *a*, fig. 458, is made exactly parallel and sharpened up the sides, it cuts hard mahogany very cleanly in all directions of the grain, and is used for drilling the various holes in the small machinery of piano-fortes; this drill, (and also the last two,) is put in motion in the lathe; and in fig. 459, the lathe-drill for hard woods, called by the French *langue de carpe*, the center point and the two sides melt into an easy curve, which is sharpened all the way round and a little beyond its largest part.

Various tools for boring wood have been made with spiral

---

* See Trans. Soc. of Arts, vol. xxxi. p. 250.

stems, in order that the shavings may be enabled to ascend the hollow worm, and thereby save the trouble of so frequently withdrawing the bit.   For example, the shaft of fig. 461, the *single-lip auger*, is forged as a half-round bar, nearly as in the section above; it is then coiled into an open spiral with the flat side outwards, to constitute the cylindrical surface, and the end is formed almost the same as that of the shell auger, fig. 455. The *twisted gimlet*, fig. 462, is made with a conical shaft, around which is filed a half-round groove, the one edge of which becomes thereby sharpened, so as gradually to enlarge the hole after the first penetration of the worm, which, from being smaller than in the common gimlet, acts with less risk of splitting.

Figs. 461.   462.   463.   464.   465.   466.   467.   468.

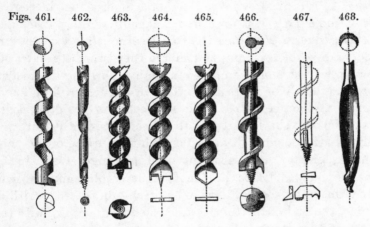

The ordinary screw auger, fig. 463, is forged as a parallel blade of steel, (seen in the section, fig. 464, which also refers to 463 and 465,) it is twisted red-hot, the end terminates in a worm by which the auger is gradually drawn into the work, as in the gimlet, and the two angles or lips are sharpened to cut at the extreme ends, and a little up the sides also.

The same kind of shaft is sometimes made as in fig. 464, with a plain conical point, with two scoring cutters and two chisel edges, which receive their obliquity from the slope of the worm: it is as it were a double center-bit, or one with two lips 'grafted on a spiral shaft. The same shaft has been also made, as in fig. 465, with a common drill point, and proposed for metal, but this seems scarcely called for; but it is in this form very effective in Hunter's patent stone-boring machine, intended for stones not harder than sandstones; the drill is worked by a cross, guided by a tube, and forced in by a screw cut upon the shaft carrying the drill; so that the stone is not ground to powder, but cast off in flakes with very little injury to the drill.

Another screw auger, which is perhaps the most general after the double-lipped screw auger, fig. 463, is known as the *American screw auger*, and is shown in fig. 466; this has a cylindrical shaft, around which is brazed a single fin or rib; the end is filed into a worm as usual, and immediately behind the worm a small diametrical mortise is formed for the reception of a detached cutter, which exactly resembles the nicking point and chisel edge of the center-bit; it may be called a center-bit for deep holes. The parts are shown detached in fig. 467. The loose cutter is kept central by its square notch, embracing the central shaft of the auger; it is fixed by a wedge driven in behind, and the chisel edge rests against the spiral worm. Spare cutters are added in case of accident, and should the screw be broken off, a new screw and mortise may be made by depriving the instrument of so much of its length. This instrument will be found on trial extremely effective; and on account of the great space allowed for the shavings, they are delivered perfectly, until the worm is buried a small distance beneath the surface of the hole·

The Americans have also invented an auger, said to be thoroughly applicable to producing square holes, and those of other forms : the tool consists of a steel tube, of the width of the hole, the end of the tube is sharpened from within, with the corners in advance or with four hollowed edges. In the center of the square tube works a screw auger, the thread of which projects a little beyond the end of the tube, so as first to penetrate the wood, and then to drag after it the sheath, and thus complete the hole at one process ; the removed shavings making their escape up the worm and through the tube. For boring long mortises, two or more square augers are to be placed side by side, but they must necessarily be worked one at a time *.

Fig. 468, the last of this group of spiral drills, is used in

---

* This is described in Gill's Technical Repository, vol. xi. page 317. The author has never seen one; it seems far too complex an instrument for general purposes, and its success appears to be overrated. The tools, figs. 461 to 466, are also ascribed to America ; whether truly or not it is impossible to say. Fig. 461 is in partial use. The twisted gimlet is a good tool, but as it is somewhat more expensive than the common kind, it is less used. These several instruments are probably derived from the common screw auger, fig. 463, which is, I believe, English.

Germany, and two of the instruments were brought from that country and deposited in the Museum of the Society of Arts, by Mr. Bryan Donkin＊. The tool acts as a hollow taper bit or rimer, and the screw-form point and shaft, assist in drawing it into the wood; but the instrument must pass entirely through for making cylindrical holes †.

The most usual of the modes of giving motion to the various kinds of boring bits, is by the ordinary carpenter's brace with a crank-formed shaft. The instrument is made in wood or metal, and at the one extremity has a metal socket, called the *pad*, with a taper square hole, and a spring catch used for retaining the drills in the brace when they are withdrawn from the work, and at the other, it has a swivelled head or shield, which is pressed forward horizontally by the chest of the workman; or when used vertically, by the left hand, which is then commonly placed against the forehead ‡.

The ordinary carpenter's brace is too familiarly known to require further description, but it sometimes happens, that in corners and other places there is not room to swing round the handle, *the angle brace,* fig. 469, is then convenient. It is made entirely of metal, with a pair of bevil pinions, and a winch handle that is placed on the axis

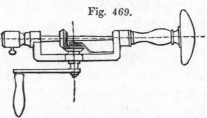

Fig. 469.

of one of these, at various distances from the center, according to the power or velocity required. Sometimes the bevil wheel attached to the winch handle, is three or four times the diameter of the pinion on the drill; this gives greater speed but less power §.

The augers, which from their increased size require more power, are moved by transverse handles; some augers are made with *shanks,* and are rivetted into the handles just like the

---

＊ See Trans., vol. xliv., p. 75.

† The coopers' bit is sometimes made with a gimlet worm, a semi-conical shell, and a conical plug to stop the hole until the tap is inserted.

‡ The carpenters' brace is sometimes fixed vertically, with the power of revolving and of being depressed by a lever, in some respects like the smith's press drill, fig. 494, page 558. See also Manuel du Tourneur, 1816, Plate IX., vol. ii.

§ Fig. 469 is reduced from Plate IX. of the Manuel du Tourneur.

gimlet; occasionally the handle has a socket or pad, for receiving several augers, but the most common mode, is to form the end of the shaft into a ring or eye, through which the transverse handle is tightly driven. The brad awls, and occasionally the other tools requiring but slight force, are fitted in straight handles; many of the smaller tools are attached to the lathe mandrel by means of chucks, and the work is pressed against them, either by the hand, or by a screw, a slide, or other contrivance; figs. 458 and 459, are always thus applied.

SECT. II.—DRILLS FOR METAL, USED BY HAND.

The frequent necessity in metal works, for the operation of drilling holes, which are required of all sizes and various degrees of accuracy, has led to so very great a variety of modes of performing the process, that it is difficult to arrange with much order the more important of these methods and apparatus.

It is, however, intended to proceed from the small to the large examples: in the present section some of the general forms of the drills for metal will be first noticed; in the next section will be traced the modes of applying hand power to drills, commencing with the delicate manipulation of the watchmaker, proceeding gradually to those requiring the different kinds of braces, and ending with the various apparatus for driving large drills by hand power. In the fourth section the machine processes will be adverted to, commencing with the ordinary lathe, and ending with the boring apparatus for the largest cylinders; the concluding section of this chapter will be devoted to the various drills, cutters, and broaches required for making conical or taper holes.

The ordinary piercing drills for metal do not present quite so much variety as the wood drills recently described, the drills for metal are mostly pointed, they consequently make conical holes, which cause the point of the drill to pursue the original line, and eventually to produce the cylindrical hole. The comparative feebleness of the drill-bow, limits the size of the drills employed with it to about one-quarter of an inch in diameter; but as some of the tools used with the bow, agree in kind with those of much larger dimensions, it will be convenient to consider as one group, the forms of the edges of those drills, which cut when moved in *either* direction.

Figs. 470, 471, and 472, represent, of their largest sizes, the usual forms of drills proper for the reciprocating motion of the drill bow, because their cutting edges being situated on the line

Figs. 470.   471.   472.   473.   474.   475.

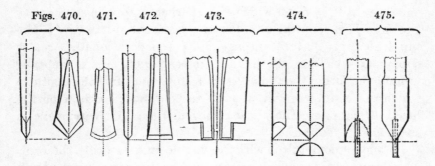

of the axis, and chamfered on each side, they cut, or rather *scrape*, with equal facility in both directions of motion.

Fig 470, is the ordinary double cutting drill, the two facets forming each edge meet at an angle of about 50 to 70 degrees, and the two edges forming the point, meet at about 80 to 100; but the watchmakers who constantly employ this kind of drill, sometimes make the end as obtuse as an angle of about 120 degrees; the point does not then protrude through their thin works, long before the completion of the hole. Fig. 471, with two circular chamfers, bores cast-iron more rapidly than any other reciprocating drill, but it requires an entry to be first made with a pointed drill; by some, this kind is also preferred for wrought iron and steel. The flat ended drill, fig. 472, is used for flattening the bottoms of holes. Fig. 473 is a duplex expanding drill, used by the cutlers for inlaying the little escutcheons and plates of metal in knife handles; the ends are drawn full size, and the explanation will be found at page 135 of the first volume.

Fig. 474 is also a double cutting drill; the cylindrical wire is filed to the diametrical line, and the end is formed with two facets. This tool has the advantage of retaining the same diameter when it is sharpened; it is sometimes called the Swiss drill, and was employed by M. Le Rivière, for making the numerous small holes, in the delicate punching machinery for manufacturing perforated sheets of metal and pasteboard; these drills are sometimes made either semicircular or flat at the extremity, and as they are commonly employed in the lathe, they will be further noticed in the fourth section, under the title of *half-round boring bits*.

The square countersink, fig. 475, is also used with the drill-bow; it is made cylindrical, and pierced for the reception of a small central pin, after which, it is sharpened to a chisel edge, as shown. This countersink is in some measure a diminutive of the pin drills, fig. 482 to 485, page 550; and occasionally circular collars are fitted on the pin for its temporary enlargement, or around the larger part to serve as a stop, and limit the depth to which the countersink is allowed to penetrate, for inlaying the heads of screws. The pin is removed when the instrument is sharpened.

By way of comparison with the double cutting drills, the ordinary forms of those which only cut in *one* direction, are shown in figs. 476, 477, and 478. Fig. 476 is the common single-cutting

Figs. 476.   477.   478.   479.   480.   481.

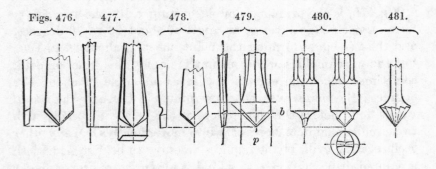

drill, for the drill bow, brace, and lathe; the point, as usual, is nearly a rectangle, but is formed by only two facets, which meet the sides at about 80° to 85°; and therefore lie very nearly in contact with the extremity of the hole operated upon, thus strictly agreeing with the form of the turning tools for brass. Fig. 477 is a similar drill, particularly suitable for horn, tortoise-shell, and substances liable to agglutinate and clog the drill; the chamfers are rather more acute, and are continued around the edge behind its largest diameter, so that if needful, the drill may also cut its way *out* of the hole.

Fig. 478, although never used with the drill bow, nor of so small a size as in the wood-cut, is added to show how completely the drill proper for iron, follows the character of the turning tools for that metal; the flute or hollow filed behind the edge, gives the hook-formed acute edge required in this tool, which is in other respects like fig. 476 ; the form proper for the cutting edge is shown more distinctly in the diagram *a*, fig. 482.

Care should always be taken to have a proportional degree of strength in the shafts of the drills, otherwise they tremble and chatter when at work, or they occasionally twist off in the neck ; the point should be also ground exactly central, so that both edges may cut.   As a guide for the proportional thickness of the point, it may measure at *b*, fig. 479, the base of the cone, about one-fifth the diameter of the hole, and at *p*, the point, about one-eighth, for easier penetration : but the fluted drills are made nearly of the same thickness at the point and base.

In all the drills previously described, except fig. 474, the size of the point is lessened each time of sharpening ; but to avoid this loss of size, a small part is often made parallel, as shown in fig. 479.   In fig. 480, this mode is extended by making the drill with a cylindrical lump, so as to fill the hole ; this is called the *re-centering drill*.   It is used for commencing a small hole in a flat-bottomed cylindrical cavity ; or else, in rotation with the common piercing drill, and the half-round bit, in drilling small and very deep holes in the lathe : see sect. iv. p. 567. Fig. 480 may be also considered to resemble the *stop drill*, upon which a solid lump or shoulder is formed, or a collar is temporarily attached by a side screw, for limiting the depth to which the tool can penetrate the work.

Fig. 481, the *cone countersink*, may be viewed as a multiplication of the common single-cutting drill.   Sometimes, however, the tool is filed with four equi-distant radial furrows, directly upon the axis, and with several intermediate parallel furrows sweeping at an angle around the cone.   This makes a more even distribution of the teeth, than when all are radial as in the figure, and it is always used in the spherical cutters, or countersinks, known as *cherries*, which are used in making bullet-moulds.

On comparison, it may be said the single chamfered drill, fig. 476, cuts more quickly than the double chamfered, fig. 470, but that the former is also more disposed of the two, to swerve or *run* from its intended position.   In using the double cutting drills, it is also necessary to drill the holes at once to their full sizes, as otherwise the thin edges of these tools stick abruptly into the metal, and are liable to produce jagged or groovy surfaces, which

destroy the circularity of the holes; the necessity for drilling
the entire hole at once, joined to the feebleness of the drill bow,
limits the size of these drills.

In using the single chamfered drills, it is customary, and on
several accounts desirable, to make large holes by a series of two
or more drills; first the run of the drill is in a measure proportioned to its diameter, therefore the small tool departs less from
its intended path, and a central hole once obtained, it is followed
with little after-risk by the single cutting drill, which is less
penetrative. This mode likewise throws out of action the less
favourable part of the drill near the point, and which in large
drills is necessarily thick and obtuse; the subdivision of the
work enables a comparatively small power to be used for drilling
large holes, and also presents the choice of the velocity best
suited to each progressive diameter operated upon. But where
sufficient power can be obtained, it is generally more judicious
to enlarge the holes previously made with the pointed drills, by
some of the group of pin drills, figs. 482 to 485, in which the
guide principle is very perfectly employed: they present a close
analogy to the plug center-bit, and the expanding center-bit,
used in carpentry.

The ordinary *pin drill*, fig. 482, is employed for making countersinks for the heads of screw-bolts inlaid flush with the surface,
and also for enlarging holes commenced with pointed drills, by

Figs. 482.   483.   484.   485.

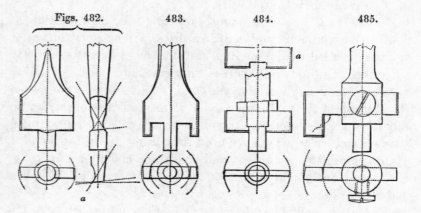

a cut parallel with the surface; the pin drill is also particularly
suited to thin materials, as the point of the ordinary drill would
soon pierce through, and leave the guidance less certain. When

this tool is used for iron, it is fluted as usual, and *a*, represents the form of the one edge separately.

Fig. 483 is a pin drill principally used for cutting out large holes in cast-iron and other plates. In this case the narrow cutter removes a ring of metal, which is of course a less laborious process than cutting the whole into shavings. When this drill is applied from both sides, it may be used for plates half an inch and upwards in thickness; as should not the tool penetrate the whole of the way through, the piece may be broken out, and the rough edges cleaned with a file or a broach.

Fig. 484 is a tool commonly used for drilling the *tube-plates* for receiving the tubes of locomotive boilers; the material is about ¾ inch thick, and the holes 1¾ diameter. The loose cutter *a*, is fitted in a transverse mortise, and secured by a wedge; it admits of being several times ground, before the notch which guides the blade for centrality is obliterated. Fig. 485 is somewhat similar to the last two, but is principally intended for sinking grooves; and when the tool is figured as shown by the dotted line, it may be used for cutting bosses and mouldings on parts of work not otherwise accessible.

Many ingenious contrivances have been made to ensure the dimensions and angles of tools being exactly retained. In this class may be placed Mr. Roberts's pin drill, figs. 486 and 487; in action it resembles the fluted pin drill, fig. 482, but the iron

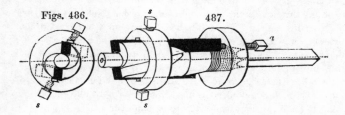

Figs. 486.   487.

stock is much heavier, and is attached to the drilling machine by the square tang; the stock has two grooves at an angle of about 10 degrees with the axis, and rather deeper behind than in front. Two steel cutters, or nearly parallel blades represented black, are laid in the grooves; they are fixed by the ring and two set screws, *s s*, and are advanced as they become worn away, by two adjusting screws, *a a*, (one only seen,) placed at the angle of 10° through the second ring; which, for the convenience of construction, is screwed upon the drill shaft just beyond the square tang whereby it is attached to the drilling machine. The cutters are ground at the extreme ends, but they also require an occasional touch on the oilstone, to restore the keenness of the outer angles, which become somewhat rounded by the friction. The diminution from the trifling exterior sharpening, is allowed for by the slightly taper form of the blades.

The process of drilling, generally gives rise to more friction than that of turning, and the same methods of lubrication are used, but rather more commonly and plentifully; thus oil is used for the generality of metals, or from economy, soap and water; milk is the most proper for copper, gold, and silver; and cast iron and brass are usually drilled without lubrication, as described at page 538. For all the above-named metals, and for alloys of similar degrees of hardness the common pointed steel drills are generally used; but for lead and very soft alloys, the carpenters' spoon bits, and nose bits, are usually employed, with water. For hardened steel, and hard crystalline substances, copper or soft iron drills, such as fig. 67 or 71, page 178, Vol. I. supplied with emery powder and oil are needed; or the diamond drill points 66, 68, and 70 are used for hardened steel, with oil alone.*

Having considered the most general forms of the cutting parts

---

* The boring tools used for the mineral substances, are partly adverted to in the ninth chapter of Vol. I; beginning with the bits used for the softest materials, those for boring through earth, sand, and clay, in order to obtain water, are enlarged copies of the shell, nose, and spiral bits used in carpentry, attached to long vertical rods which are screwed together like jointed gun rods, and are worked by a cross at the earth's surface. The rods are drawn up by a windlass, and joint after joint is unscrewed, until the bit, with its contained earth, is brought to the surface. Various attempts have been made to avoid the tedious necessity for raising the rods, by the employment of a hollow cylinder or magazine resting on the bit, to receive the borings, and to be drawn up occasionally to be emptied.

In boring large holes, the earth is generally excavated by the process of " *misering up.*" The rods terminate in the " *miser,*" which is a cylindrical iron case sometimes two to three feet diameter, with a slightly conical bottom, in which there is a slit much like the mouth of a plane, and covered with a leather flap to prevent the escape of the earth that has been collected.

In sinking the Artesian wells, lined with cast-iron tubes attached end to end by internal flanges and screws, a spring tool is used, which expands when it is thrust beneath the lower end of the series of pipes. See the Account of sinking the Artesian well at Messrs. Truman, Hanbury & Co.'s Brewery, Minutes of Conversation, Inst. of Civil Eng., 1842, p. 192.

The common pointed drill, is used for mineral substances not exceeding in hardness those enumerated under the terms, 1, 2, 3, of the Table of hardness, p. 158, Vol. I., of drills, we will proceed to explain the modes in which they are put in action by hand-power, beginning with those for the smallest diameters, and proceeding gradually to the largest.

SECT. III.—METHODS OF WORKING DRILLS BY HAND POWER.

The smallest holes are those required in watch-work, and the general form of the drill is shown on a large scale in fig. 488; it is made of a piece of steel wire, which is tapered off at the one end, flattened with the hammer, and then filed up in the form shown at large in fig. 470, p. 547; lastly, it is hardened in the candle. The reverse end of the instrument is made into a conical point, and is also hardened; near this end is attached a little brass sheave for the line of the drill bow, which in watchmaking is sometimes a fine horse-hair, stretched by a piece of whalebone of about the size of a goose's quill stripped of its feather.

Fig. 488.

The watchmaker holds most of his works in the fingers, both for fear of crushing them with the table vice, and also that he may the more sensibly feel his operations; drilling is likewise performed by him in the same manner. Having passed the bow-string around the pulley in a single loop, (or with a *round turn*,) the center of the drill is inserted in one of the small center holes in the sides of the table vice, the point of the drill is placed in the mark or cavity made in the work by the center punch; the object is then pressed forward with the right hand, whilst the bow is moved with the left; the Swiss workmen apply the hands in the reverse order, as they do in using the turn-bench*.

---

and which include some of the marbles. Glass may also be drilled with fig. 470 or 471, lubricated with turpentine. The sandstones are readily bored in Hunter's patent stone boring-machine, (see p. 543, also Conv. Civ. Eng. 1842, p. 146,) and the granites are not bored, but crushed by the jumper, or chisel point, see p. 170, Vol. I.

For the compact minerals, such as 4, 5, 6 of the table, the grinding tools may be used with sand, but emery is more effective; this powder may be also employed for minerals not exceeding the hardness of 7 and 8; but emery being somewhat inferior in hardness to the ruby, this gem and the diamond, marked 9 and 10 in the table, require either diamond dust, or splinters of the diamond, the outside skin and natural angles of which, are much harder than the inside substance. See the ninth chapter of Vol. I. generally, especially pages 178 to 180.

* See Vol. IV., page 16.

Clockmakers, and artisans in works of similar scale, fix the object in the tail-vice, and use drills, such as fig. 488, but often larger and longer; they are pressed forward by the chest which is defended from injury by the breast-plate, namely, a piece of wood or metal about the size of the hand, in the middle of which is a plate of steel, with center holes for the drill. The breast-plate is sometimes strapped round the waist, but is more usually supported with the left hand, the fingers of which are ready to catch the drill should it accidentally slip out of the center.

As the drill gets larger, the bow is proportionably increased in stiffness, and eventually becomes the half of a solid cone, about 1 inch in diameter at the larger end, and 30 inches long; the catgut string is sometimes nearly an eighth of an inch in diameter, or is replaced by a leather thong. The string is attached to the smaller end of the bow by a loop and notch, much the same as in the archery bow, and is passed through a hole at the larger end, and made fast with a knot; the surplus length is wound round the cane, and the cord finally passes through a notch at the end, which prevents it from uncoiling.

Steel bows are also occasionally used; these are made something like a fencing foil, but with a hook at the end for the knot or loop of the cord, and with a ferrule or a ratchet, around which the spare cord is wound. Some variations also are made in the sheaves of the large drills; sometimes they are cylindrical with a fillet at each end; this is desirable, as the cord necessarily lies on the sheave at an angle, in fact in the path of a screw; it pursues that path, and with the reciprocation of the drill bow, the cord traverses, or screws backwards and forwards upon the sheave, but is prevented from sliding off by the fillet. Occasionally indeed, the cylindrical sheave is cut with a screw coarse enough to receive the cord, which may then make three or four coils for increased purchase, and have its natural screw-like run without any fretting whatever; but this is only desirable when the holes are large, and the drill is almost constantly used, as it is tedious to wind on the cord for each individual hole. The structure of the bows, breast-plates, and pulleys, although often varied, is sufficiently familiar to be understood without figures. See Appendix, Note AY, page 1002.

When the shaft of the drill is moderately long, the workman can readily observe if the drill is square with the work as regards

the horizontal plane ; and to remove the necessity for the observation of an assistant as to the vertical plane, a trifling weight,
is sometimes suspended from the drill shaft by a metal ring or
hook, the joggling motion shifts the weight to the lower extremity; the tool is only horizontal when the weight remains central*.

In many cases, the necessity for repeating the shaft and pulley
of the drill is avoided, by the employment of holders of various
kinds, or *drill-stocks,* which serve to carry any required number of drill-points.   The most simple of the drill-stocks is shown
in fig. 489; it has the center and pulley of the ordinary drill.

Figs. 489.

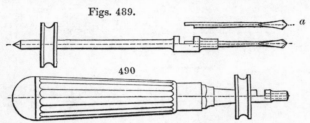

490

but the opposite end is pierced with a nearly cylindrical hole,
just at the inner extremity of which a diametrical notch is
filed.   The drill is shown separately at *a*; its shank is made
cylindrical, or exactly to fit the hole, and a short portion is
nicked down also to the diametrical line, so as to slide into the
gap in the drill-stock, by which the drill is prevented from
revolving ; the end serves also as an abutment whereby it may be
thrust out with a lever.   Sometimes a diametrical transverse
mortise, narrower than the hole, is made through the drill-stock,
and the drill is nicked in on both sides ; and Mr. Gill proposes
that the cylindrical hole of 489, should be continued to the
bottom of the notch, that the end of the drill should be filed off
obliquely, and that it should be prevented from rotating, by a pin
inserted through the cylindrical hole parallel with the notch ; the
taper end of the drill would then wedge fast beneath the pin†.

Drills are also frequently used in the *drilling-lathe;* this is a
miniature lathe-head, the frame of which is fixed in the table
vice; the mandrel is pierced for the drills, and has a pulley for

---

* This is analogous to the level of the Indian masons and carpenters ; they
squeeze a few drops of water on the upper surface of the straight edge, which is
made exactly parallel, and the escape of the fluid from either end, denotes that to
be the lower of the two.

† See Technical Repos., 1822, vol. ii., p. 149 ; also Rees's Cyclopedia.

the bow, therein resembling fig. 490, except that it is used as a fixture.

The figure 490 just referred to, represents one variety of another common form of the drill-stock, in which the revolving spindle is fitted in a handle, so that it may be held in any position, without the necessity for the breast-plate; the handle is hollowed out to serve for containing the drills, and is fluted to assist the grasp.

Fig. 491 represents the socket of an *"universal drill-stock"* invented by Sir John Robison; it is pierced with a hole as large

Figs. 491.

492.

493.

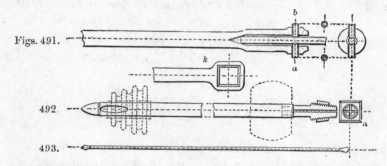

as the largest of the wires of which the drills are formed, and the hole terminates in an acute hollow cone. The end of the drill-stock is tapped with two holes, placed on a diameter; the one screw a, is of a very fine thread, and has at the end two shallow diametrical notches; the other b, is of a coarser thread and quite flat at the extremity. The wire-drill is placed against the bottom of the hole, and allowed to lean against the adjusting-screw a, and if the drill be not central, this screw is moved one or several quarter-turns, until it is adjusted for centrality; after which the tool is strongly fixed by the plain set-screw b.

Fig. 492 is a drill-stock, contrived by Mr. William Allen: it consists of a tube, the one end of which has a fixed center and pulley much the same as usual; the opposite end of the tube has a piece of steel fixed into it, which is first drilled with a central hole, and then turned as a conical screw, to which is fitted a corresponding screw nut n; the socket is then sawn down with two diametrical notches, to make four internal angles, and lastly, the socket is hardened. When the four sections are compressed by the nut, their edges stick into the drill and retain it fast, and provided the instrument is itself concentric, and the four parts are of equal strength, the centrality of the drill is at once ensured. The outside of the nut, and the square hole in the key *k*, are each taper, for more ready application; and the drills are of the most simple kind, namely, lengths of wire pointed at each end, as in fig. 493*.

The sketch, fig. 492, is also intended to explain another useful application of this drill-stock, as an *upright* or *pump-drill*, a tool little employed in this country, (except in drilling the rivet holes for mending china and glass, with the diamond drill, fig. 70, vol. I.,) but as well known among the oriental nations as the breast-drill. The pump-drill is figured and explained on page 3 of the fourth volume of this work, to which the reader is referred; occasionally the pump-drill and the common drill-stock are mounted in frames, by which their paths are more exactly defined; but these contrivances are far from being generally required, and enough will be said, in reference to the use of revolving braces, to lead to such applications, if considered requisite, for reciprocating drills. See Appendix, Notes A Z. to BB. page 1003.

Holes that are too large to be drilled *solely* by the breast-drill and drill-bow, are frequently commenced with those useful instruments, and are then enlarged by means of the hand-brace, which is very similar to that used in carpentry, except that it is more commonly made of iron instead of wood, is somewhat larger, and generally made without the spring-catch.

Holes may be extended to about half an inch diameter, with the hand-brace; but it is much more expeditious to employ still larger and stronger braces, and to press them into the work in various ways by weights, levers, and screws, instead of by the muscular effort alone.

Fig. 494 represents the old smith's press-drill, which although cumbrous, and much less used than formerly, is nevertheless simple and effective. It consists of two pairs of wooden standards, between which works the beam *a b*, the pin near *a* is placed at any height, but the weight *w* is not usually changed, as the greater or less pressure for large and small drills, is obtained by placing the brace more or less near to the fulcrum *a*; and this part of the beam is shod with an iron plate, full of small center holes for the brace. The weight is raised by the second lever *c d*, the

---

* See Technical Repository, vol. ii., 1822, p. 147.

two being united by a chain, and a light chain or rope is also suspended from *d*, to be within reach of the one or two men engaged in moving the brace. It is necessary to relieve the weight when the drill is nearly through the hole, otherwise, it might suddenly break through, and the drill becoming fixed, might be twisted off in the neck.

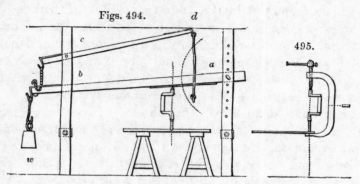

Figs. 494.

495.

The inconveniences in this machine are, that the upper point of the brace moves in an arc instead of a right line; the limited path when strong pressures are used, which makes it necessary to shift the fulcrum *a*; and also the necessity for re-adjusting the work under the drill for each different hole, which in awkwardly shaped pieces, is often troublesome.

A portable contrivance of similar date, is an iron bow frame or clamp, shown in fig. 495; the pressure is applied by a screw, but in almost all cases, whilst the one individual drills the hole, the assistance of another is required to hold the frame; 495 only applies to comparatively thin parallel works, and does not present the necessary choice of position. Another tool of this kind, used for boring the side holes in cast-iron pipes for water and gas, is doubtless familiarly known; the cramp or frame divides into two branches about two feet apart, and these terminate like hooks, which loosely embrace the pipe, so that the tool retains its position without constraint, and it may be used with great facility by one individual.

Fig. 496 will serve to show the general character, of various constructions of more modern apparatus, to be used for supplying the pressure in drilling holes with hand braces. It consists of a cylindrical bar *a*, upon which the horizontal rectangular rod *b*, is fitted with a socket, so that it may be fixed at any height, or in any angular position, by the set-screw *c*. Upon *b* slides a socket, which is fixed at all distances from *a*, by its set-screw *d*, and lastly, this socket has a long vertical screw *e*, by which the brace is thrust into the work.

The object to be drilled having been placed level, either upon the ground, on trestles, on the work bench, or in the vice, according to circumstances, the screws *c* and *d* are loosened, and the brace is put in position for work. The perpendicularity of the brace is then examined with a plumb-line, applied in two positions, (the eye being first directed as it were along the north and south line, and then along the east and west,) after which the whole is made fast by the screws *c* and *d*. The one hole having been drilled, the socket and screws present great facility in re-adjusting the instrument for subsequent holes, without the necessity for shifting the work, which would generally be attended with more trouble, than altering the drill-frame by its screws.

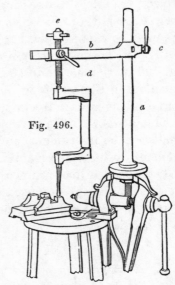

Fig. 496.

Sometimes the rod *a* is rectangular, and extends from the floor to the ceiling; it then traverses in fixed sockets, the lower of which has a set screw for retaining any required position. In the tool represented, the rod *a*, terminates in a cast-iron base, by which it may be grasped in the tail-vice, or when required it may be fixed upon the bench; in this case the nut on *a* is unscrewed, the cast-iron plate, when reversed and placed on the bench, serves as a pedestal, the stem is passed through a hole in the bench, and the nut and washer when screwed on the stem beneath, secure all very strongly together. Even in establishments where the most complete drilling machines driven by power are at hand, modifications of the press drill are among the indispensable tools: many are contrived with screws and clamps, by which they are attached directly to such works as are sufficiently large and massive to serve as a foundation.

Various useful drilling tools for engineering works, are fitted with left hand screws, the unwinding of which elongate the tools; so that for these instruments which supply their own pressure, it is only necessary to find a solid support for the center.   They apply very readily in drilling holes within boxes and panels, and the abutment is often similarly provided by projecting parts of the castings; or otherwise the fixed support is derived from the wall or ceiling, by aid of props arranged in the most convenient manner that presents itself.

Fig. 497 is the common brace, which only differs from that in fig. 496 in the left hand screw; a right hand screw would be unwound in the act of drilling a hole when the brace is moved round in the usual direction, which agrees with the path of a left hand screw.   The cutting motion produces no change in the length of the instrument, and the screw being held at rest for a moment during the revolution, sets in the cut; but towards the last, the feed is discontinued, as the elasticity of the brace and work, suffice for the reduced pressure required when the drill is nearly through, and sometimes the screw is unwound still more to reduce it.

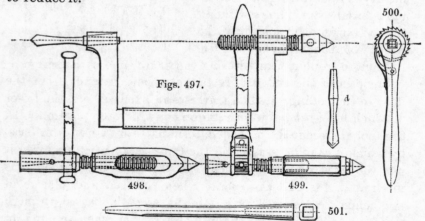

Figs. 497.

498.   499.   500.   501.

The *lever-drill*, fig. 498, differs from the latter figure in many respects, it is much stronger, and applicable to larger holes; the drill socket is sufficiently long to be cut into the left-hand screw, and the piece serving as the screwed nut, is a loop terminating in the center point.   The increased length of the lever gives much greater purchase than in the crank formed brace, and in addition the lever-brace may be applied close against a surface where the crank-brace cannot be turned round; in this case the lever is only moved a half circle at a time, and is then slid through for a new purchase, or sometimes a spanner or wrench is applied directly upon the square drill socket.

The same end is more conveniently fulfilled by the *ratchet-drill*, fig. 499, apparently derived from the last; it is made by cutting ratchet teeth in the drill shaft, or putting on the ratchet as a separate piece, and fixing a pall or detent to the handle; the latter may then be moved backward to gather up the teeth, and forward to thrust round the tool, with less delay than the lever in fig. 498, and with the same power, the two being of equal length. This tool is also peculiarly applicable to reaching into angles and places in which neither the crank-form brace, nor the lever-drill will apply. Fig. 500, the *ratchet-lever*, in part resembles the ratchet-drill, but the pressure-screw of the latter instrument must be sought in some of the other contrivances referred to, as the ratchet-lever has simply a square aperture to fit on the tang of the drill d, which latter must be pressed forward by some independent means.

Fig. 501, which is a simple but necessary addition to the braces and drill tools, is a socket having at the one end a square hole to receive the drills, and at the opposite, a square tang to fit the brace; by this contrivance the length of the drill can be temporarily extended for reaching deeply seated holes. The sockets are made of various lengths, and sometimes two or three are used together, to extend the length of the brace to suit the position of the prop; but it must be remembered, that with the additional length the tortion becomes much increased, and the resistance to end-long pressure much diminished, therefore the sockets should have a bulk proportionate to their length.

The French brace, fig. 469, page 545, is also constructed in iron, with a pair of equal bevil pinions, and a left-hand center screw like the tools, figs. 497, 498, and 499; it is then called the *corner-drill*. Sometimes also, as in the succeeding figures 502 and 503, the bevil wheels are made with a hollow square or axis, as in the ratchet-lever, fig. 500; the driver then hangs loosely on the square shank of the drill tool, or cutter bar, and when the pinion on the handle is only one-third or fourth of the size of the bevil wheel with the square hole, it is an effective driver for various uses: the long tail or lever serves to prevent the rotation of the driver, by resting against some part of the work or of the work-bench.

All the before-mentioned tools are commonly found in a variety of shapes in the hands of the engineer, but it will be

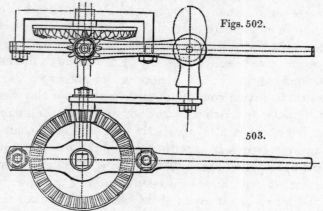

Figs. 502.

503.

observed they are all driven by hand power, and are carried to the work. I shall conclude this section with the description of a more recent drill tool of the same kind, invented by Mr. A. Shanks of Glasgow.

This instrument is represented of one-eighth size, in the side view, fig. 504, in the front view, 505, and in the section 506; it

Figs. 504.   505.   506.

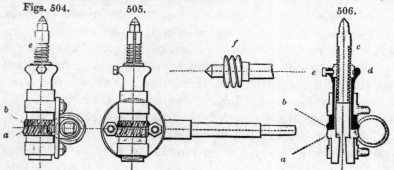

is about twice as powerful as fig. 503, and has the advantage of feeding the cut by a differential motion. The tangent screw moves at the same time the two worm wheels a and b *; the former has 15 teeth, and serves to revolve the drill; the latter has 16 teeth, and by the difference between the two, or the *odd*

---

* A principle first introduced in Dr. Wollaston's Trochiometer, for counting the turns of a carriage wheel.

tooth, advances the drill slowly and continually, which may be thus explained.

The lower wheel *a*, of 15 teeth, is fixed on the drill shaft, and this is tapped to receive the center-screw *c*, of four threads per inch. The upper wheel of 16 teeth is at the end of a socket *d*, (which is represented black in the section fig. 506,) and is connected with the center-screw *c*, by a collar and internal key, which last fits a longitudinal groove cut up the side of the screw *c*; now therefore the internal and external screws travel constantly round, and nearly at the same rate, the *difference* of one tooth in the wheels serving continually and slowly to project the screw *c*, for feeding the cut. To shorten or lengthen the instrument rapidly, the side screw *e* is loosened; this sets the collar and key, free from the 16 wheel, and the center-screw may for the time be moved independently by a spanner.

The *differential screw-drill,* having a double thread in the large worm, shown detached at *f*, requires $7\frac{1}{2}$ turns of the handle to move the drill once round, and the feed is one 64th of an inch for each turn of the drill; that being the sum of 16 by 4. See Appendix, Note B C, page 1004.

SECT. IV.—DRILLING AND BORING MACHINES.

The motion of the lathe mandrel is particularly proper for giving action to the various single cutting drills referred to; they are then fixed in square or round hole drill-chucks which screw upon the lathe mandrel. The motion of the lathe is more uniform than that of the hand tools, and the popit-head, with its flat boring flange and pressure screw, form a most convenient arrangement, as the works are then carried to the drill exactly at right angles to the face. But in drilling very small holes in the lathe, there is some risk of unconsciously employing a greater pressure with the screw, than the slender drills will bear. Sometimes the cylinder is pressed forward by a horizontal lever fixed on a fulcrum; at other times the cylinder is pressed forward by a spring, by a rack and pinion motion, or by a simple lever, and the best arrangement of this latter kind is that next to be described.

In the manufacture of harps there is a vast quantity of small drilling, and the pressure of the cylinder popit-head is given by means of a long, straight, double-ended lever, which moves horizontally, (at about one-third from the back extremity,) upon a fixed post or fulcrum erected upon the back-board of the lathe. The front of the lever is connected with the sliding cylinder by a link or connecting rod, and the back of the lever is pulled towards the right extremity of the lathe, by a cord which passes over a pulley at the edge of the back board, and then supports a weight of about twenty pounds.

Both the weight and the connecting rod, may be attached at various distances from the fixed fulcrum between them. When they are fixed at equal distances from the axis of the lever, the weight, if twenty pounds, presses forward the drill with twenty pounds, less a little friction; if the weight be two inches from the fulcrum and the connecting rod eight inches, the effect of the weight is reduced to five pounds; if, on the other hand, the weight be at eight and the connecting rod at two inches, the pressure is fourfold, or eighty pounds.

The connecting rod is full of holes, so that the lever may be adjusted exactly to reach the body of the workman, who, standing with his face to the mandrel, moves the lever with his back, and has therefore both hands at liberty for managing the work. Sometimes a stop is fixed on the cylinder, for drilling holes to one fixed depth; gages are attached to the flange, for drilling numbers of similar pieces at any fixed distance from the edge: in fact, this very useful apparatus admits of many little additions to facilitate the use of drills and revolving cutters.

Great numbers of circular objects, such as wheels and pulleys, are chucked to revolve truly upon the lathe mandrel, whilst a stationary drill is thrust forward against them, by which means the concentricity between the hole and the edge is ensured.

The drills employed for boring works chucked on the lathe, have mostly long shafts, some parts of which are rectangular or parallel, so that they may be prevented from revolving by a hook wrench, (page 218, Vol. I.,) a spanner or a hand-vice, applied as a radius, or by other means. The ends of the drill shafts are pierced with small center holes, in order that they may be thrust forward by the screw of the popit-head, either by hand or by self-acting motion; namely, a connection between either the mandrel or the prime mover of the lathe, and the screw of the popit-head, by cords and pulleys, by wheels and pinions, or other contrivances.

The drills, figs. 476 and 478, p. 548, are used for boring
ordinary holes; but for those requiring greater accuracy, or a
more exact repetition of the same diameter, the lathe drills, figs.
507 to 509 are commonly selected. Fig. 507, which is drawn in
three views and to the same scale as the former examples, is called
the *half-round bit*, or the *cylinder bit*. The extremity is ground a
little inclined to the right angle, both horizontally and vertically,
to about the extent of three to five degrees. It is necessary to
turn out a shallow recess exactly to the diameter of the end of
the bit as a commencement; the circular part of the bit fills
the hole, and is thereby retained central, whilst the left angle
removes the shaving. This tool should never be sharpened on
its diametrical face, or it would soon cease to deserve its appellation of *half-round* bit: some indeed give it about one-thirtieth
more of the circumference. It is generally made very slightly
smaller behind, to lessen the friction; and the angle, not intended to cut, is a little blunted half-way round the curve, that
it may not scratch the hole from the pressure of the cutting
edge. It is lubricated with oil for the metals generally, but is
used dry for hard woods and ivory, and sometimes for brass.

Figs. 507.   508.   509.   510.

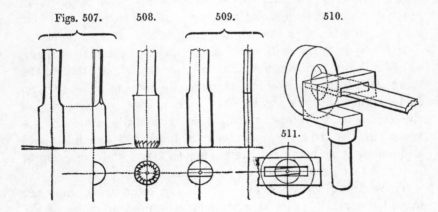

511.

The rose-bit, fig. 508, is also very much used for light finishing
cuts, in brass, iron, and steel; the extremity is cylindrical, or in
the smallest degree less behind, and the end is cut into teeth
like a countersink; the rose-bit, when it has plenty of oil, and
but very little to remove, will be found to act beautifully, but
this tool is less fit for cast-iron than the bit next to be described.
The rose-bit may be used without oil for the hard woods and

ivory, in which it makes a very clean hole; but as the end of the tool is chamfered, it does not leave a flat-bottomed recess the same as the half-round bit, and is therefore only used for thoroughfare holes.

The drill, fig. 509, is much employed, but especially for cast-iron work; the end of the blade is made very nearly parallel, the two front corners are ground slightly rounding, and are chamfered, the chamfer is continued at a reduced angle along the two sides, to the extent of about two diameters in length; this portion is not strictly parallel, but is very slightly largest in the middle or barrel-shaped: this drill is used dry for cast-iron.

Fig. 509, in common with all drills that cut on the side, may, by improper direction, cut sideways, making the hole above the intended diameter; but when the hole has been roughly bored with a common fluted drill, the end of the latter is used as a turning tool, to make an accurate chamfer, the bit 509 is then placed through the stay as shown in fig. 510, and is lightly supported between the chamfer upon the work and the center of the popit-head; the moment any pressure comes on the drill, its opposite edges stick into the inner sides of the loop, (as more clearly explained in fig. 511,) which thus restrains its position; much the same as the point and edges of the turning tools for iron dig into the rest, and secure the position of those tools.

It is requisite the drill and the loop should be exactly central, fig. 510 shows the common form of the stay when fitted to the lathe rest, but it is sometimes made as a swing gate, to turn aside, whilst the piece which has been drilled is removed, and the next piece to be operated upon is fixed in the lathe. Sometimes also the drill 509, has blocks of hardwood attached above and below it, to complete the circle; this is usual for wrought iron and steel, and oil is then employed.

These three varieties are exclusively lathe-drills, and are intended for the exact repetition of a number of holes of the particular sizes of the bits, and which, on that account, should remove only a thin shaving to save the tools from wear.

The cylinder bits, however, may be used for enlarging holes below half an inch, to the extent of about one-third their diameter at one cut; and for holes from half an inch to one inch, about one fourth their diameter or less, and as the bits increase in size, the proportion of the cut to the diameter should decrease.

The cylinder bit is not intended to be used for drilling holes in the solid material, and as the piercing drills are apt to swerve, in drilling small and very deep holes, the following rotation in the tools is sometimes resorted to. A drill, fig. 476, p. 548, say three-sixteenths diameter, is first sent in to the depth of an inch or upwards, and the hole is enlarged by a cylinder bit of one quarter inch diameter. The center at the end of the hole, is then restored to exact truth, by fig. 480 a re-centering drill, the plug of which exactly fits the hole made by the cylinder bit; the extremity of the re-centering drill then acts as a fixed turning tool, and should the first drill have run out of its position, 480 corrects the center at the end of the hole. Another short portion is then drilled with 476, enlarged with the half-round bit, and the conical extremity is again corrected with the re-centering drill; the three tools are thus used in rotation until the hole is completed, and which may be then cleaned out with one continued cut, made with a half-round bit a little larger than that previously used.

Some of the large half-round bits are so made, that the one stock will serve for several cutters of different diameters. In the bit used for boring out ordnance, the parallel shaft of the boring bar slides accurately in a groove, exactly parallel with the bore of the gun; the cutting blade is a small piece of steel affixed to the end of the half-round block, which is either entirely of iron, or partly of wood; and the cut is advanced by a rack and pinion movement, actuated either by the descent of a constant weight, or by a self-acting motion derived from the prime mover. For making the spherical, parabolical or other termination to the bore, cutters of corresponding forms are fixed to the bar*. See Appendix, Notes B D to B I, pages 1005 to 1010.

There are very many works which from their weight or size, cannot be drilled in the lathe in its ordinary position, as it is scarcely possible to support them steadily against the drill; but these works are readily pierced in the drilling machine, which may be viewed as a lathe with a vertical mandrel, and

* The outside of the gun is usually turned, whilst the boring is going on, by the hand tools, figs. 423 and 424, page 527. A plug of copper is screwed into the brass guns to be perforated for the touch-hole, copper being less injured by repeated discharges, than the alloy of 9 parts copper and 1 part tin, used for the general substance of the gun; the curved bit smooths off the end of the plug.

with the flange of the popit-head, enlarged into a table for the work, which then lies in the horizontal position simply by gravity, or is occasionally fixed on the table by screws and clamps. The structure of these important machines admits of almost endless diversity, and in nearly every manufactory some peculiarity of construction may be observed*.

Figs. 512 and 513 exhibit Nasmyth's "Portable Hand-drill," which is introduced as a simple and efficient example, that may

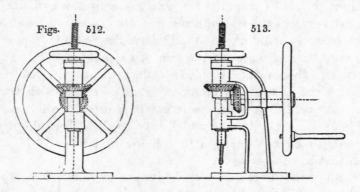

Figs.   512.   513.

serve to convey the general characters of the drilling machines. The spindle is driven by a pair of bevil pinions, the one is attached to the axis of the vertical fly wheel, the other to the drill shaft, which is depressed by a screw moved by a small hand-wheel.

Sometimes, as in the lathe, the drilling spindle revolves without endlong motion, and the table is raised by a treadle or by a hand lever; but more generally the drill-shaft is cylindrical and revolves in, and also slides through, fixed cylindrical bearings. The drill spindle is then depressed in a variety of ways; sometimes by a simple lever, at other times, by a treadle which either lowers the shaft only one single sweep, or by a ratchet that brings it down by several small successive steps, through a greater distance; and mostly a counterpoise weight restores the parts to their first position when the hand or foot is removed. Friction clutches, trains of differential wheels, and other modes, are also used in depressing the drill spindle, or in elevating the table by self-acting motion. Frequently also the platform admits of an

---

* Probably no individual has originated so many useful varieties of drilling-machines, as Mr. Richard Roberts, of the firm of Sharp, Roberts, and Co., Manchester.

adjustment independent of that of the spindle, for the sake of admitting larger pieces; the horizontal position of the platform is then retained by a slide, to which a rack and pinion movement, or an elevating screw, is added*.

Drilling machines of these kinds are generally used with the ordinary piercing drills, and occasionally with pin drills; the latter instrument appears to be the type of another class of boring tools, namely, *cutter bars*, which are used for works requiring holes of greater dimensions, or of superior accuracy, than can be attained by the ordinary pointed drills.

The small application of this principle, or of cutter bars, is shown on the same scale as the former drills, in fig. 514; the cutter *c*, is placed in a diametrical mortise in a cylindrical boring bar, and is fixed by a wedge; the cutter *c* extends equally on both sides, as the two projections or ears embrace the sides of the bar, which is slightly flattened near the mortises.

Cutter bars of the same kind, are occasionally employed with cutters of a variety of forms, for making grooves, recesses, mouldings, and even screws, upon parts of heavy works, and those which cannot be conveniently fixed in the ordinary lathe. Fig. 515 represents one of these, but its application to screws will be found in the chapter on the tools for screw cutting.

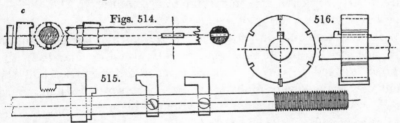

Figs. 514.   516.

515.

The larger application of this principle is shown in fig. 516, in which a cast-iron cutter-block is keyed fast upon a cylindrical bar, the block has four, six, or more grooves in its periphery.

---

* The platform in a drilling-machine, at Messrs. Peen's, Greenwich, is placed between two side frames, with fillets a few inches apart, so that it is supported at any height, like a single drawer in an empty tier. The traverse of the drill-shaft is rather more than equal to the space between the fillets.

Figures 512 and 513 are transcribed from plate 29 of "Buchanan's Mill Work," by Rennie, 1841; and plates 29 to 33 *a*, of that work, contain various other drilling machines, similar to, and explanatory of, those in general use.

Sometimes, the work is done with only one cutter, and should the bar vibrate, the remainder of the grooves are filled with pieces of hard wood, so as to complete the bearing at so many points of the circle; occasionally cutters are placed in all the grooves, and carefully adjusted to act in succession, that is, the first stands a little nearer to the axis than the second, and so on throughout, in order that each may do its share of the work; but the last of the series takes only a light finishing cut, that its keen edge may be the longer preserved. In all these cutters the one face is radial, the other differs only four or five degrees from the right angle, and the corners of the tools are slightly rounded.

These cutter bars, like the rest of the drilling and boring machinery, are employed in a great variety of ways, but which resolve themselves into three principal modes:

First, the cutter bar revolves without endlong motion, in fixed centers or bearings, in fact, as a spindle in the lathe; the work is traversed, or made to pass the revolving cutter in a right line, for which end the work is often fixed to a traversing slide rest. This mode requires the bar to measure between the supports, twice the length of the work to be bored, and the cutter to be in the middle of the bar, it is therefore unfit for long objects.

Secondly, the cutter bar revolves, and also slides with endlong motion, the work being at rest; the bearings of the bar are then frequently attached in some temporary manner to the work to be bored, and are often of wood *.

In another common arrangement, the boring bar is mounted in headstocks, much the same as a traversing mandrel, the work is fixed to the bearers carrying the headstocks, and the cutter bar is advanced by a screw. The screw is then moved either by the hand of the workman; by a star-wheel, or a ratchet wheel, one tooth only in each revolution; or else by a system of differential wheels, in which the external screw has a wheel say of 50 teeth, the internal screw a wheel of 51 teeth, and a pair of equal wheels or pinions drives these two screws continually, so that the advance of the one-fiftieth of a turn of the screw, or their difference, is equally divided over each revo-

---

* Cylinders of forty inches diameter for steam engines, have been thus bored, by attaching a cast-iron cross to each end of the cylinder ; the crosses are bored exactly to fit the boring bar, one of them carries the driving gear, and the bar is thrust endlong by means of a screw, moved by a ratchet or star wheel.

lution of the cutter-bar, much the same as in the differential motion of the screw drill, fig. 504, page 562.

This second method only requires the interval between the fixed bearings of the cutter bar, to be as much longer than the work, as the length of the cutter block; but the bar itself must have more than twice the length of the work, and requires to slide through the supports.

Cutter bars of this kind are likewise used in the lathe; in the act of boring, the end of the bar then slides like a piston into the mandrel. Such bars are commonly applied to the vertical boring machines of the larger kinds, which are usually fitted with a differential apparatus, for determining the progress of the cut; the bar then slides through a collar fixed in the bed of the machine.

In some of the large boring machines either one or two horizontal slides are added, and by their aid, series of holes may be bored in any required arrangement. For instance, the several holes in the beams, or *side levers*, and cranks of steam engines, are bored exactly perpendicular, in a line, and at any precise distances, by shifting the work beneath the revolving spindle upon the guide or railway; in pieces of other kinds, the work is moved laterally during the revolution of the cutters, for the formation of elongated countersinks and grooves.

Thirdly. In the largest applications of this principle, the boring bar revolves upon fixed bearings without traversing; and it is only needful that the boring bar should exceed the length of the work, by the thickness of the cutter block, of which it has commonly several of different diameters. The cutter block, now sometimes ten feet diameter, traverses as a slide down a huge boring bar, whose diameter is about thirty inches. There is a groove and key to couple them together, and the traverse of the cutter-block down the bar, is caused by a side screw, upon the

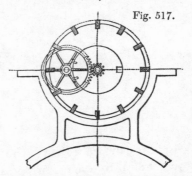

Fig. 517.

end of which is a large wheel, that engages in a small pinion, *fixed* to the stationary center or pedestal of the machine. With every revolution of the cutter bar, the great wheel is *carried around the fixed pinion,* and supposing these be as 10 to 1, the great wheel is moved one-tenth of a turn, and therefore moves the screw one-tenth of a turn also, and slowly traverses the cutter block.

The contrivance may be viewed as a huge, self-acting, and revolving sliding-rest, and the diagram 517 shows that the cutter bars are equally applicable to portions of circles, such as the D valves of steam engines, as well as to the enormous interior of the cylinder itself*.   See Appendix, Note B J, page 1010.

All the preceding boring tools cut almost exclusively upon the end alone.   They are passed entirely through the objects, and leave each part of their own particular diameter, and therefore cylindrical; but I now proceed to describe other boring tools, that cut only on their sides, go but partly through the work, and leave its section a counterpart of the instrument.   These tools are generally conical, and serve for the enlargement of holes to sizes intermediate between the gradations of the drills, and also for the formation of conical holes, as for valves, stopcocks, and other works.   The common pointed drill, or its multiplication in the rose countersink, is the type of the series; but in general the broaches have sides which are much more nearly parallel.

SECT. V.—BROACHES FOR MAKING TAPER HOLES.

The tools for making taper holes are much less varied than the drills and boring tools for cylindrical holes.   Thus the carpenter employs only the rimer, which is a fluted tool like the generality of his bits; it is sharpened from within, as shown in fig. 518, so as to act like a paring tool.   Flutes and clarionets

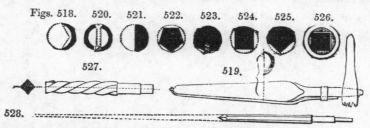

Figs. 518.   520.   521.   522.   523.   524.   525.   526.

527.   519.

528.

are first perforated with the nose-bit, and then broached with taper holes, by means of tools of this kind, which are very care-

---

* There is generally a small intermediate wheel between the two represented ; many other details of the large boring machines will also be found in " Buchanan's Mill Work," as already noticed.

fully graduated as to their dimensions.   Fig. 519 represents a German rimer, used by wheelwrights for inlaying the boxes of axletrees; the loose blade is separated from the shell of the instrument, by introducing slips of leather or wood between the two; the detached cutter fits on a pin at the front, and is fixed by a ring or collar against the shaft.

A curious rimer for the use of wine-coopers, was invented by the late Mr. John Hilton, by which the holes were made more truly circular, and the shavings were prevented from dropping into the cask.   The stock of the instrument consisted of a hollow brass cone, seen in section in fig. 520; down one side there was a slit for containing a narrow blade or cutter, fixed by three or four screws placed diametrically.   The tube was thus converted into a conical plane; the shavings entered within the tube, and were removed by taking out a cork from the small end of the cone*.

The broaches for metal are made solid, and of various sections; as half-round, like fig. 521, the edges are then rectangular, but more commonly the broaches are polygonal, as in fig. 522, except that they have 3, 4, 5, 6, and 8 sides, and their edges measure respectively 60, 90, 108, 120, and 135 degrees. The four, five, and six-sided broaches are the most general, and the watchmakers employ a round broach in which no angle exists, and the tool is therefore only a burnisher, which compresses the metal and rounds the hole.

Ordinary broaches are very acute, and fig. 528 may be considered to represent the general angle at which their sides meet, namely, less than one or two degrees; the end is usually chamfered off with as many facets as there are sides, to make a penetrating point, and the opposite extremity ends in a square *tang*, or shank, by which the instrument is worked.

Square broaches, after having been filed up, are sometimes twisted whilst red hot; fig. 527, shows one of these, the rectangular section is but little disturbed, although the faces become slightly concave.   The advantage of the tool appears to exist in its screw form : when it is turned in the direction of the spiral, it cuts with avidity and requires but little pressure, as it is

----

* See Trans. Soc. of Arts, 1830, vol. xlviii. page 125.

almost disposed to dig too forcibly into the metal: when turned
the reverse way, as in unscrewing, it requires as much or more
pressure than similar broaches not twisted.   This instrument, if
bent in the direction of its length, either in the act of twisting
or hardening, does not admit of correction by grinding, like
those broaches having plane faces.   It is not much used, and is
almost restricted to wrought iron and steel.

Large countersinks that do not terminate in a point, are
sometimes made as solid cones; a groove is then formed up one
side, and deepest towards the base of the cone, for the insertion
of a cutter, see fig. 523.   As the blade is narrowed by sharpening, it is set a little forward in the direction of its length, to
cause its edge to continue slightly in advance of the general
surface, like the iron of a plane for cutting metal.

Fig. 529 represents Mr. Richard Roberts' broach, in which
four detached blades are introduced, for the sake of retaining

Fig. 529.

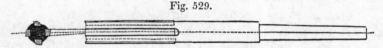

the cone or angle of the broach with greater facility.   The bar
or stock has four shallow longitudinal grooves, which are nearly
radial on the cutting face, and slightly undercut on the other.
The grooves are also rather deeper behind, and the blades
are a little wedge-form both in section and in length, to constitute the cone, and the cutting edges.   In restoring the edges
of the blades, they are removed from the stock, and their angles
are then more easily tested: when replaced, they are set nearer
to the point, to compensate for their loss of thickness.

Broaches are also used for perfecting cylindrical holes, as well
as for making those which are taper.   The broaches are then
made almost parallel, or a very little the highest in the middle;
they are filed, with two or three planes at angles of 90 degrees,
as in figs. 524 or 525.   The circular part not being able to cut,
serves as a more certain base or foundation, than when the tool
is a complete polygon; and the stems are commonly made

small enough to pass entirely through the holes, which then agree very exactly as to size. Such tools are therefore rather entitled to the name of finishing drills, than broaches.

The size of the parallel broaches is often slightly increased, by placing a piece or two of paper at the convex part; leather and thin metal are also used for the same purpose. Gun-barrels are broached with square broaches, the cutting parts of which are about eight to ten inches long; they are packed on the four sides with slips or spills of wood, to complete the circle, as in fig. 526, in which the tool is supposed to be at work. The size of the bit is progressively enlarged by introducing slips of thin paper, piece by piece between two of the spills of wood and the broach; the paper throws the one angle more towards the center of the hole, and causes a corresponding advance in the opposite or the cutting angle. Sometimes, however, only one spill of wood is employed.

A broach used by the philosophical instrument makers in finishing the barrels of air pumps, consisted of a thin plate of steel inserted diametrically between two blocks of wood, the whole constituting a cylinder with a scraping edge slightly in advance of the wood; slips of paper were also added.

According to the size of the broaches, they are fixed in handles like brad-awls, they are used in the brace, or the tap wrench, namely a double-ended lever with square central holes. Sometimes also broaches are used in the lathe just like drills, and for large works, broaching machines are employed; these are little more than driving gear terminating in a simple kind of universal joint, to lead the power of the steam-engine to the tool, which is generally left under the guidance of its own edges, according to the common principle of the instrument.

In drills and broaches, the penetrating angles are commonly more obtuse than in turning tools; thus in drills of limited dimensions, the hook-form of the turning tool for iron is inapplicable, and in the larger examples, the permanence of the tool is of more consequence than the increased friction. But on account of the additional friction excited by the nearly rectangular edges, it is commonly necessary to employ a smaller velocity in boring than in turning corresponding diameters, in order to avoid softening the tool by the heat generated; and in the ductile fibrous metals, as wrought iron, steel, copper and others, lubrication with oil, water, &c., becomes more necessary than in turning.

The drills and broaches form together a complete series. First the cylinder bit, the pin drills, and others with blunt sides, produce cylindrical holes by means of cutters at *right angles* to the axis; then the cutter becomes *inclined* at about 45 degrees, as in the common piercing drill and cone countersink; the angle becomes much less in the common taper broaches; and finally disappears in the parallel broaches, by which we again produce the cylindrical hole, but with cutters *parallel* with the axis of the hole.

Still considering the drills and broaches as one group, the drills have comparatively thin edges, always less than 90 degrees, yet they require to be urged forward by a screw or otherwise, the resistance being sustained in the line of their axes. The broaches have much more obtuse edges, never less than 90, and sometimes extending to 135 degrees; and yet the greater force required to cause the penetration of their obtuse edges into the material, is supplied without any screw, because the pressure in all these varied tools is at right angles to the cutting edge.

Thus supposing the sides of the broach extended until they meet in a point, as in fig. 528, we shall find the length will very many times exceed the diameter, and by that number will the force employed to thrust forward the tool be multiplied, the same as in the wedge, whether employed in splitting timber or otherwise; and the broach being confined in a hole, it cannot make its escape, but acts with great lateral pressure, directed radially from each cutting edge; and the broach under proper management leaves the holes very smooth and of true figure.

CHAPTER XXVI.

SCREW-CUTTING TOOLS.

SECT. I.—INTRODUCTORY REMARKS.

An elementary idea of the form of the screw, or helix, is obtained by considering it as a continuous circular wedge; and it is readily modelled by wrapping a wedge-formed piece of paper around a cylinder; the edge of the paper then represents the line of the screw, and which preserves one constant angle to the axis of the contained cylinder, namely that of the wedge.

The ordinary wedge, or the diagonal, may be produced by the composition of two *uniform* rectilinear motions, which, if equal, produce the angle of 45°, or if unequal, various angles more or less acute; and in an analogous manner, the circular wedge or the screw, may be produced of every angle or coarseness, by the composition of an uniform circular motion, with an uniform rectilinear motion. And as either the rectilinear or the circular motion, may be given to the work or to the tool indifferently, there are four distinct modes of producing screws, and which are all variously modified in practice.

The screw admits of great diversity: it may possess any diameter; it may also have any angle, that is, the interval between the threads may be either coarse or fine, according to the angle of the wedge, or the ratio of the two motions; and the wedge may be wound upon the cylinder to the right hand or to the left, so as to produce either right or left hand screws.

The idea of double, triple, or quadruple screws, will be conveyed by considering two, three, or four black lines drawn on the uncovered edge of the wedge-formed paper, or likewise by two, three, or four strings or wires placed in contact, and coiled as a flat band around the cylinder, the angle remains unaltered, it is only a multiplication of the furrows or threads; and lastly, the screw may have any section, that is the section of the worm or thread may be angular, square, round, or of any arbitrary form. Thus far as to the variety in screws.

The importance of this mechanical element, the screw, in all works in the constructive arts, is almost immeasurable. For instance, great numbers of screws are employed merely for connecting together the different parts of which various objects are composed, no other attachment is so compact, powerful, or generally available; these *binding* or *attachment* screws require, by comparison, the least degree of excellence. Other screws are used as *regulating* screws, for the guidance of the slides and the moving parts of machinery, for the screws of presses and the like; these kinds should possess a much greater degree of excellence than the last. But the most exact screws that can be produced, are quite essential to the good performance, of the engines employed in the graduation of right lines and circles, and of astronomical and mathematical instruments; in these delicate *micrometrical* screws, our wants ever appear to outstrip the most refined methods of execution.

The attempt to collect and describe *all* the ingenious contrivances which have been devised for the construction of screws, would be in itself a work of no ordinary labour or extent: I must therefore, principally restrict myself to those varied processes now commonly used in the workshops, for producing with comparative facility, screws abundantly exact for the great majority of purposes. It has been found rather difficult to arrange these extremely different processes in tolerable order, but that which seems to be the *natural order* has been adopted, thus:

There appears to be no doubt, but that in the earliest production of the apparatus for cutting screws, the external screw was the first piece made; this plain circular metal screw was serrated and thus converted into the *tap,* or cutting tool, by which internal screws of corresponding size and form were next produced; and one of these *hollow screws* or *dies* became in its turn the means of regenerating, with increased truth and much greater facility, any number of copies of the original external screw. In these several stages there is a progressive advance towards perfection, as will be hereafter adverted to.

These hand processes, are mostly used for screws, which are at least as long, if not longer than their diameters. The rotatory and rectilinear guides, and the one or several series of cutting points, are then usually combined within the tool. This first group will be considered in three sections, namely:

II. On originating screws.

III. On cutting internal screws, with screw taps.

IV. On cutting external screws, with screw dies.

Subsequent improvements have led to the employment of the lathe, in producing from the above, and in a variety of ways, still more accurate screws. These methods are sometimes used for screws which possess only a portion of a turn, at other times for screws twenty or thirty feet long and upwards. The rotatory guide is always given by the mandrel, the rectilinear guide is variously obtained, and the detached screw tool or cutter, may have one single point, or one series of points which touch the circle at only one place at a time. This second group will be also considered in three sections, namely:

V. On cutting screws, in the common lathe by hand.

VI. On cutting screws, in lathes with traversing mandrels.

VII. On cutting screws, in lathes with traversing tools.

It may be further observed that the modes described in the six sections are in general applied to very different purposes, and are only to a limited extent capable of substitution one for the other; it is to be also remarked that it has been considered convenient, in a great measure to abandon, or rather to modify, the usual distinction between the tools respectively used for wood and for metal. The eighth and concluding section of this chapter describes some refinements in the production of screws which are not commonly practised, and it is in some measure a sequel to the second section.

SECT. II.—ON ORIGINATING SCREWS.

It appears more than probable, that in the earliest attempts at making a screw, a sloping piece of paper was cemented around the iron cylinder; this oblique line was cut through with a stout knife or a thin-edged file, and was then gradually enlarged by hand until it gave a rude form of screw. Doubtless, as soon as the application of the lathe was generally known, the work was mounted between centers, so that the progress of filing up the groove could be more easily accomplished, or a pointed turning tool could be employed to assist. Such, in fact, is one of the modes recommended by Plumier, for cutting the screw upon a lathe mandrel for receiving the chucks, even in preference to the use of the die-stocks, which he urged were liable to bend the mandrel in the act of cutting the screw*.

Nearly similar modes have been repeatedly used for the production of original screws; one account differing in several respects from the above, is described as having been very successfully resorted to, above fifty years back, at the Soho works Birmingham, by a workman of the name of Anthony Robinson, before the introduction of the screw-cutting lathe.

The screw was seven feet long, six inches diameter, and of a square triple thread; after the screw was accurately turned as a cylinder, the paper was cut parallel exactly to meet around the same, and was removed and marked in ink with parallel oblique lines, respresenting the margins of the threads; and having been replaced on the cylinder, the lines were pricked through with a center punch. The paper was again removed, the dots were connected by fine lines cut in with a file, the spaces were then cut out with a chisel and hammer and smoothed with a file, to a sufficient extent to serve as a lead or guide.

The partly formed screw, was next temporarily suspended in the center of a cast-iron tube or box strongly fixed against a horizontal beam, and melted lead mixed with tin, was poured into the box to convert it into a guide nut; it then only remained to complete the thread by means of cutters fixed against the box or nut, but with the power of adjustment, in fact in a kind of slide-rest, the screw being handed round by levers†.

Another very simple way of originating screws, and which is sufficiently accurate for some purposes, is to coil a small wire, around a larger straight wire as a nucleus; this last is frequently the same wire, the one end of which is to be cut into the screw. The covering wire, whose diameter is equal to the space required between the threads of the screw, is wound on close and tight, and made fast at each end. The coiled screw, being enclosed between two pieces of hard wood, indents a hollow or counterpart thread, sufficient to guide the helical traverse, and a fixed cutter completes this simple apparatus. See Appendix, Note B K, page 1010.

---

* *L'Art du Tourneur*, by Plumier, 1701, pages 15—19.

† This mode, which is described in Gill's Tech. Repos., vol. vi., p. 261, is said to have excited at the time great admiration from its success. It is probable a gun-metal nut was cast upon this screw for use, after the screw was finished.

Common screws, for some household purposes, have been made of tinned iron wire; two covering wires are rolled on together, the one being removed leaves a space such as the ordinary hollow of the thread, and when these screws are dipped in a little melted tin, the two wires become soldered together.

Other modes have been resorted to for making original screws, by indenting a smooth cylinder, with a sharp-edged cutter placed across the same at the required angle; and trusting to the surface or rolling contact, to produce the rotation and traverse of the cylinder, with the development of the screw. In the most simple application of this method, a deep groove is made along a piece of board, in which a straight wire is buried a little beneath the surface; a second groove is made, nearly at right angles across the first, exactly to fit the cutter, which is just like a table knife, and is placed at the angle required in the screw. The cutter when slid over the wire, indents it, carries it round, and traverses it endways in the path of a screw; a helical line is thus obtained, which, by cautious management, may be perfected into a screw sufficiently good for many purposes.

The late Mr. Henry Maudslay employed a cutter upon cylinders of wood, tin, brass, iron, and other materials, mounted to revolve between centers in a triangular bar lathe; the knife was hollowed to fit the cylinder, and fixed at the required angle on a block adapted to slide upon the bar; the oblique incision carried the knife along the revolving cylinder. Some hundreds of screws were thus made, and their agreement with one another was in many instances quite remarkable; on the whole he gave the preference to this mode of originating screws*.

Mr. Allan's apparatus for originating screws for astronomical and other purposes is represented in plan in fig. 530, in side elevation in fig. 531, and 532 is the front elevation of the cutter frame alone. The piece intended for the screw, namely, a a fig. 530, is turned cylindrical, and with two equal and cylindrical necks; it is supported in a metal frame with two semi-circular

---

* The reader is also referred to the Trans. Soc. of Arts, vol. xlii., page 127, for the description of Mr. Walsh's method of making original screws by rolling contact, or with a short screw mounted as a milling tool, to act only by pressure, (see also figs. 587 and 588, page 604 of this volume), the method appears, however, to be circuitous, difficult, and very questionable. The instrument, fig. 30, page 124, vol. i., for cutting snakes in horn, is virtually an originator of screws.

bearings, *b b,* which are fixed on a slide moved by an adjusting
screw *c ;* speaking of the apparatus the inventor says :

" The instrument generates original screws perfectly true, of
any number of threads, and right or left handed. In this case,
the stock and cutter are made as in figs. 530, 531, and 532 ; the
back of the stock is made into the segment of a circle, *s ;* and
the top of the cutter is continued into an index, *t.* The cutter
is a single thread, and moves on its edge, *v,* as a center. This
must fit true, and the stock fit close to the cutter, to keep it perfectly steady : *u, u,* two screws, to adjust and fasten the cutter to
any required angle. The cutter should be rather elliptical, for
it is best to fit well to the cylinder at the greatest angle it will
be ever used. When one turn has been given to the cylinder

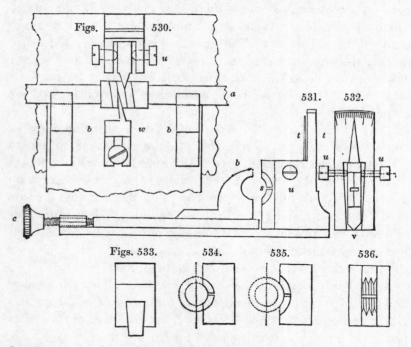

fig. 530, a tooth, *w,* is put into the cut, and screwed fast ; this
tooth secures the lead, and causes every following thread to be a
repetition of the first ; and, though it might do without, yet this
is a satisfactory security *."

---

* See Trans. Soc. of Arts, 1816, vol. xxxiv., p. 206. The engravings are copied
from figs. 6 to 12 of plate 23. An instrument based on the same general plan is
described in the Mech. Mag., 1836, vol. xxv., p. 377 ; but it is greatly inferior to
the above.

In cutting ordinary screws, the dies, shown separately in figs. 533 to 536, the consideration of which is for the present deferred, take the place of the oblique cutter in the former figures.

The screw is also originated, by traversing the tool in a right line alongside a plain revolving cylinder. Sometimes the tool has many points, and is guided by the hand alone; at other times the tool has but one single point, and is guided mechanically so as to proceed, say one inch or one foot in a right line, whilst the cylinder makes a definite number of revolutions. The tool is then traversed either by a wedge placed transversely to the axis, by a chain or metallic band placed longitudinally, or by another screw, connected in various ways with the screw to be produced, by wheel-work and other contrivances.

It would be injudicious to attempt at this place the explanation of these complex methods of originating screws; some of them will, however, be introduced in the course of this chapter, whilst, for greater perspicuity, others will be deferred unto its latter pages. The next section will be now proceeded with, on the supposition that a screw of fair quality has been originated by some of the means referred to.

SECT III.—ON CUTTING INTERNAL SCREWS, WITH SCREW TAPS.

The screw is converted into the tap, by the removal of parts of its circumference, in order to give to the exposed edges a cutting action; whilst the circular parts which remain, serve for the guidance of the instrument within the helical groove, or hollow thread, it is required to form.

In the most simple and primitive method, four planes were filed upon the screw as in fig. 537, but this exposes very obtuse edges which can hardly be said to cut, as they form the thread partly by indenting, and partly by raising or burring up the metal; and as such they scarcely produce any effect in cast iron or other crystalline materials. Conceiving, as in fig. 537, only a very small portion of the circle to remain, the working edges of squared taps, form angles of (90 + 45 or) 135 degrees with the circumference, and the angle is the greater, the more of the circle that remains. It is better to file only three planes as in fig. 538, but the angle is then as great as 120 degrees even under the most favourable circumstances.

In taps of the smallest size it is imperative to submit to these conditions, and to employ the above sections. Sometimes small intermediate facets or planes, are tipped off a little obliquely with the file, to relieve the surface friction ; this gives the instrument partly the character of a six or eight sided broach, and improves the cutting action.

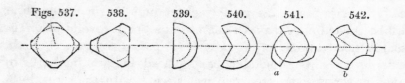

Figs. 537.   538.   539.   540.   541.   542.

There appears to be no doubt, but that for general purposes, the most favourable angle for the edges of screw taps and dies, is the radial line, or an angle of 90 degrees. This condition manifestly exists in the half-round tap fig. 539, which is advocated in the annexed quotation from Sir John Robison, who in speaking of the tap, says, " I propose that this should be made half-round, as it will be found that a tap formed in this way will cut a full clear thread, (even if it may be of a sharp pitch,) without making up any part of it by the burr, as is almost universally the case, when blunt-edged or grooved taps are used."

" It has sometimes been objected to me by persons who had not seen half-round taps in use, that, from their containing less substance than the common forms do, they must be very liable to be broken by the strain required to turn them in the work. It is proved however by experience, that the strain in their case is so much smaller than usual, that there is even less chance of breaking them than the stouter ones. Workmen are aware that a half-round opening bit makes a better hole and cuts faster than a five sided one, and yet that it requires less force to use it*."

Fig. 540, in which two-thirds of the circle are allowed to remain, has been also employed for taps ; this, although somewhat less penetrative than the last, is also less liable to displacement with the tap wrench. It is much more usual to employ three radial cutting edges instead of one only ; and as in the best forms of

---

* Select Papers read before the Soc. of Arts for Scotland, vol. i., page 41.

taps, they are only required to cut in the one direction, or when they are screwed into the nut, the other edges are then chamfered to make room for the shavings; thereby giving the tap a section somewhat like that of a ratchet wheel, with either three, four, or five teeth, as in figs. 541 and 549.

It is more common, however, either to file up the side of the tap, or to cut by machinery, three concave or elliptical flutes, as in 542; this form sufficiently approximates to the desideratum of the radial cutting edges, it allows plenty of room for the shavings, and is easily wiped out. What is of equal or greater importance, it presents a symmetrical figure, little liable to accident in the hardening, either of distortion from unequal section, as in figs. 539 and 540, or of cracking from internal angles, as in 540 and 541 *.

Still, considering alone the transverse section of the tap, it will be conceived that before any of the substance can be removed from the hole that is being tapped, the circular part of the instrument must become embedded into the metal a quantity equal to the thickness of the shaving; and in this respect figs. 537 and 538, in which the circular parts are each only the tenth or twelfth of the circumference, appear to have the advantage over the modern taps 541 and 542, in which each arc is twice as long. Such, however, is not the case, as the first two act more in the manner of the broach, if we conceive that instrument to have serrated edges; but figs. 541 and 542 act nearly as turning tools, as in general the outer or the circular surface is slightly relieved with a file, so as to leave the cutting edges *a*, somewhat in advance of the general periphery; which is equivalent to chamfering the lower plane of the turning tool some 3 degrees (see page 534,) to produce that relief which has been appropriately named the *angle of separation*.

But in the tap fig. 543, patented by Mr. G. Bodmer of Manchester, this is still more effectually accomplished. The instrument, instead of being turned of the ordinary circular section

---

* In fluting taps, as in cutting the teeth of wheels, the tap or wheel is frequently chucked in the lathe, just as in turning; but the mandrel is held at rest by the dividing plate, and the tool is a cutter, revolving horizontally, and traversed through the groove by the slide-rest screw. The round flutes are made with cutters having semicircular edges and placed centrally; the ratchet-form flutes are made with thick saws or square-edged cutters, the one edge of these is placed to intersect the center of the tap, and leave the radial edge.

in the lathe, (or as the outer dotted line,) is turned with three slight undulations, by means of an alternating radial motion given to the tool. From this it results, that when the summits of these hills are converted into the cutting edges, that not only are the extreme edges or points of the teeth made prominent, but the entire serrated surface becomes inclined at about the three degrees to the external circle, or the line of work, so as exactly to assimilate to the turning tool; and therefore there is little doubt but that, under equal circumstances, Mr. Bodmer's tap would work with less friction than any other.

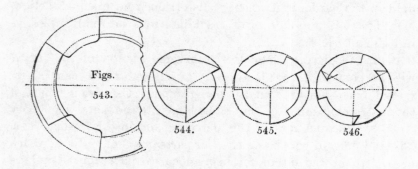

The principle of chamfering, or relieving the taps, must not however, be carried to excess, or it will lead to mischief; in explanation of which the diagrams 544, 545, and 546 may be considered parallel with the forms 429, 430, and 431, of page 532. For example, the tap, if sloped behind the teeth as in 544, would be much exposed to fracture; and the instrument being entirely under its own guidance, the three series of keen points would be apt to stick irregularly into the metal, and would not produce the smooth, circular, or helical hole, obtained when the tool 545 is used, which may be considered parallel with the turning tool fig. 430. The relief should be slight, and the surfaces of the teeth then assimilate to the condition of the graver for copperplates, (see page 532,) and thereby direct the tap in a very superior manner.

The teeth sloped in front, as in figs. 546, would certainly cut more keenly than those of 545, but they would be much more exposed to accident, as the least backward motion or violence would be liable to snip off the keen points of the teeth; and therefore, on the score of general economy and usefulness, the radial and slightly relieved teeth of fig. 545, or rather of 542, are proper for working taps.

It appears further to be quite impolitic, *entirely* to expunge the surface-bearing, or *squeeze*, from the taps and dies, when these are applied to the ductile metals; as not only does it, when slight, greatly assist in the more perfect guidance of the instrument, but it also serves somewhat to condense or compress the metal *.

The *transverse* sections hitherto referred to, are always used for those taps employed in screwing the inner surfaces of the nuts, and holes required in general mechanism. The *longitudinal* section of the working tap, is taper and somewhat like a broach, the one end being small enough in external diameter to enter the blank hole to be screwed, and the other end being as large as the screw for which the nut is intended.

Fig. 547.

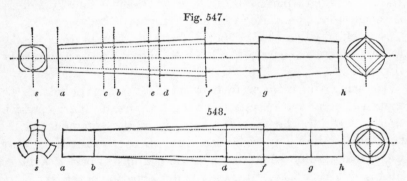

548.

In many cases a series of two three or four taps must be used instead of only one single conical tap, and the modifications in their construction are explained by the above diagrams; namely, fig. 547, the tap formerly used for nuts and thorough-fare holes, and fig. 548 the modern tap for the same purposes; the dotted lines in each represent the bottoms of the threads.

---

* Unless the taps cut very freely, it is the general aim to avoid the necessity for tapping cast-iron, which is a granular and crystalline substance, apt to crumble away in the tapping, or in the after use. The general remedy is the employment of bolts and nuts made of wrought-iron, or fixing screwed wrought-iron pins in the work, by means of transverse keys and other contrivances, and sometimes by the insertion of plugs of gun-metal, to be afterwards tapped with the screw-threads. In general also, the *small* screws for cast-iron, are coarse and shallow in the thread compared with those for wrought-iron, steel, and brass.

In the former kind, the thread was frequently finished of a taper figure, with the screw tool in the lathe ; after which either the four or three plane surfaces were filed upon it, as shown by the section at *s ;* the neck from *f* to *g* was as small as the bottom of the thread, and the tang from *g* to *h* was either square or rectangular for the tap wrench. The tang, if square was also taper, the tap wrench then wedged fast upon the tap ; the sides of the tang, if parallel, were rectangular, and measured as about one to two, and there were shoulders on two sides to sustain the wrench.

In the modern thoroughfare taps for nuts, drawn to the same scale in fig. 548, the thread is left cylindrical, from the screw tool or the dies; then from *a* to *b*, or about one diameter in length, is turned down cylindrical until the thread is nearly obliterated; from *d* to *f*, also nearly one diameter in length at the other end, is left of the full size of the bolt, and the intermediate part, *b* to *d* equal to three or four diameters, is turned to a cone, after which the tap is fluted as seen at *s*. The neck *f g*, as before is as small as the bottom of the thread, and the square *g h*, measures diagonally the same as the turned neck.

In using the modern instrument fig. 548, the hole to be tapped is bored out exactly to fit the cylindrical plug *a b*, which therefore guides the tap very perfectly in the commencement ; the tool is simply passed once through the nut without any retrograde motion whatever, and the cylindrical part *d f*, takes up the guidance when the larger end of the cone enters the hole; at the completion, the tap drops through, the head being smaller than the bottom of the thread. The old four square taps could not be thus used, for as they rather squeezed than cut, they had much more friction; it was necessary to move them backwards and forwards, and to make the square for the wrench larger, to avoid the risk of twisting off the head of the tap. In taps of modern construction of less than half an inch diameter, it is also needful to make the squares, larger than the proportion employed in fig. 548.

In tapping shallow holes, as only a small portion of the end of the tap can be used, the screwed part seldom exceeds two diameters in length, and as they will not take hold when made too conical, a succession of three or four taps is generally required. The screwed part of the first may be considered to extend from *a* to *b* of fig. 547, of the second, from *c* to *d*, of the third from *e* to *f*; so that the prior tap may, in each case, prepare for the reception of the following one. The taps are generally made in sets of three; the first, which is also called the *entering* or *taper* tap, is in most cases regularly taper throughout its length; the second, or the *middle* tap, is sometimes taper, but more generally cylindrical, with just two or three threads at the end tapered off; the third tap, which is also called the *plug* or *finishing* tap, is always cylindrical, except at the two or three first threads, which are slightly reduced.

Taps are used in various ways according to the degree of strength required to move them. The smallest taps should have considerable length, and should be fixed exactly in the axis of straight handles; the length serves as an index by which the true position of the instrument can be verified in the course of work; with the same view as to observation, and as an expeditious mode, taps of a somewhat larger size are driven round by a hand brace, whilst the work is fixed in the vice. Still larger taps require tap wrenches, or levers with central holes to fit the square ends of the taps; for screw taps from one to two inches diameter, the wrenches have assumed the lengths of from four to eight feet, although the recent improvements in the taps have reduced the lengths of the wrenches to one-half.

Notwithstanding that the hole to be tapped may have been drilled straight, the tap may by improper direction proceed obliquely, the progress of the operation should be therefore watched; and unless the eye serve readily for detecting any falseness of position, a square should be laid upon the work, and its edge compared with the axis of the tap in two positions.

In tapping deeply seated holes, the taps are temporarily lengthened by sockets, frequently the same as those used in drilling, which are represented in fig. 501, page 560; the tap wrench can then surmount those parts of the work which would otherwise prevent its application.

Sometimes for tapping two distant holes exactly in one line, the ordinary taper tap, fig. 548, is made with the small cylindrical part *a b* exceedingly long, so as to reach from the one hole to the other and serve as a guide or director. This is only an extension of the short plug *a b*, fig. 548, which it is desirable to leave on most taps used for thoroughfare holes.

Some works are tapped whilst they are chucked on the lathe mandrel; in this case the shank of the tap, if in false position, will swing round in a circle whilst the mandrel revolves, instead of continuing quietly in the axis of the lathe. Sometimes the center point of the popit-head is placed in the center hole in the head of the tap; in those which are fixed in handles it is better the handle of the tap should be drilled up to receive the cylinder of the popit-head, as in the lathe taps for making chucks; this retains the guidance more easily.

Taps of large size, as well as the generality of cutting instruments, have been constructed with detached cutters. For those exceeding about 1½ inch diameter, Mr. Richard Jones recommends two steel plugs *a a*, to be inserted within taper holes in the body of the tap, as represented in fig. 549, and in the two sections *b* and *c*; the whole is then screwed and hardened.

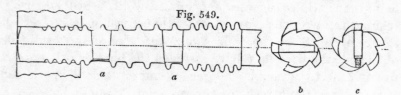

Fig. 549.

The advance of the cutters slightly beyond the general line of the thread, is caused by placing a piece of paper within the mortises *a b*, and to relieve the surface friction, each alternate tooth in the middle part of the length of the tap is filed away. Sometimes the cutters are parallel, and inserted only partway through, and are then projected by set-screws placed also on the diameter as in the section *c* *.

The cutter bar, fig. 515, p. 569, may also be viewed as a tap with detached cutters. The cylindrical bar is supported in temporary fixed bearings, one of which embraces the thread, (sometimes by having melted lead poured around the same,) the bar moves therefore in the path of a screw. In cutting the external

---

* See Trans. Soc. of Arts, 1829, vol. xlvii., p. 135.

thread, the cutter represented is shifted inwards with the progress of the work; or a straight cutter shifted outwards, serves for making an internal screw: pointed instead of serrated cutters may be also used, they are frequently adjusted by a set screw instead of the hammer, and are worked by a wrench.

This screw cutter bar, independently of its use for large awkward works, is also employed for cutting, in their respective situations, screws required to be exactly in a line with holes or fixed bearings, as the nuts of slides, presses, and similar works.

Some taps or cutters are made cylindrical, and are used for cutting narrow pieces and edges, such as screw-cutting dies, screw tools, and worm wheels; therefore it is necessary to leave much more of the circle standing, and to make the notches narrower than the width of the smallest pieces to be cut. But the grooves should still possess radial sides, and when these are connected by a curved line, as in fig. 550, there is less risk of accident in the hardening. The number of the notches increases with the diameter, but the annexed figure would be better proportioned if it had one or two less notches, as inadvertently the teeth have been drawn too weak.

Figs. 550.   551.

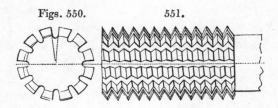

When the tool, figs. 550 and 551, is used for cutting the dies of die-stocks it is called an *original tap*, of which further particulars will be given in the succeeding section; the tool is then fixed in the vice, and the die-stock is handed round, as in cutting an ordinary screw. When 551 is used for cutting up screw tools, or the chasing-tools for the use of the turning lathe, (figs. 404 and 405, page 519,) the cutter is then called a *hob*, or a *screw-tool* cutter, and its diameter is usually greater; it is now mounted to revolve in the lathe, and the screw tool to be cut, is laid on the rest as in the process of turning, and is pressed forcibly against the cutter *.   Fig. 551 is also used as a *worm-wheel* cutter, that is, for cutting or for finishing the hollow screw-form teeth, of those wheels which are moved by a tangent screw; as in the dividing-engine for circular lines, and many other cases in ordinary mechanism. The worm wheel cutter is frequently set to revolve in the lathe, and the wheel is mounted on a temporary axis so as to admit of its being carried round horizontally by the cutter; sometimes the wheel and cutter are connected by gear †.

Attention has been hitherto exclusively directed to the forms of the taps used for metal, but those for wood are very similar, the tap fig. 542, p. 584, with three or four flutes, being the most common; those of largest size are cast in iron, and require only a little filing up to sharpen the teeth.

Different taps with loose teeth, have been adopted for wood screws of moderately large size, say exceeding 1½ or 2 inches diameter.   In the one case, shown in fig. 552, an ordinary wood screw *t*, is first made, and at the bottom of the angular thread, a narrow parallel groove is cut in the lathe with a parting tool; the screw is then turned down to the size of the hole to be tapped, leaving it as a plain cylinder with the square helical groove represented in the piece *t*.

The next process is to insert a pointed cutter *c*, in a diametrical mortise, and when the wooden tap is in use, it is guided by the block *g*, which is bored to fit, and has two iron plates *p*, which enter the groove.   The guide *g* is fixed to the work *w*, which is to be tapped; the bar glides forward in virtue of

---

* In cutting up the inside screw tool, fig. 404, in which the slope and the curvature of the teeth should be *reversed*, an *internal* screw cutter has been recommended ; it is made like a screwed nut, notched longitudinally on its inner surface.

Another method is proposed ; the inside screw tool is laid in a lateral groove in a cylindrical piece of iron, and the tool and cylinder are cut up with the diestocks as a common screw ; by which mode the inside screw tool obviously becomes the exact counterpart of the hollow thread of that particular diameter. See Technological Repository, 1821, vol. vi., p. 292. The *right hand* inside screw tool is sometimes cut over a *solid left hand hob*, which is a more simple way of reversing the angle.

† The contact of the ordinary tangent screw with the worm-wheel, resembles that of the tangent to the circle, whence the name ; but Hindley, of York, made the screw of his dividing engine to touch 15 threads of the wheel perfectly, by giving the screw a curved section derived from the edge of the wheel, and smallest in the middle. See Smeaton's *Miscellaneous Papers*, p. 183. Prof. Willis, in his *Elements of Mechanism*, 1841, p. 163—5, explains the mode of cutting such a tangent screw, but shows that its advantages are more apparent than real.

the screw thread, and at each succeeding passage the cutter is advanced a small distance, until the work is tapped of the full diameter; the hollow space between the guide g, and the work w, allows the cutter to pass entirely through the latter, the space being wider than the cutter.

Another structure is shown in the *Manuel du Turneur*. A hollow iron screw is made like fig. 553, and a hole is drilled at the termination of the thread, the extreme end of which is chamfered on the inner surface with a file, to make a keen angular edge of the shape of the thread; in its action the tool therefore somewhat assimilates to the plane, and the shavings escape through the center of the tube.

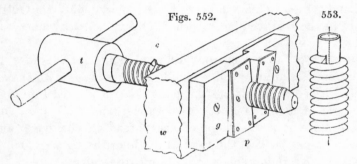

Figs. 552. 553.

This appears to be much less serviceable than the contrivance fig. 552, in which the helical guidance is perfectly at the commencement, and continues so until the end, notwithstanding the gradual formation of the thread, which may be cut at several repetitions instead of in one single cut, or in two cuts when two teeth are on opposite sides of the tube, fig. 553. The arrangement of fig. 552 may be considered as quite analogous to that of the screw cutter bar, (fig. 515, page 569,) whereas the hollow tap, fig. 553, is just the converse of the screw box described at the beginning of the following section.

SECT. IV.—ON CUTTING EXTERNAL SCREWS, WITH SCREW DIES, ETC.

For the convenience of arrangement, this section will be commenced with the description of the instrument which is commonly employed for making long screws in the soft woods, namely, the screw box, of which fig. 554 is the section, fig. 555 the plan of the principal piece through the line a, and fig. 556 the cutter, shown the full size for a two-inch screw.

The screw box consists of two pieces of wood, accurately attached by two steady pins and two screws, so as to admit of separation and exact replacement; the ends of the thicker piece, are frequently formed into handles by which the instrument is worked. A perforation is made through the two pieces of wood; the hole in the thinner piece is cylindrical, and exactly agrees with the external diameter of the screw, or of the prepared cylinder; and the hole in the thicker piece is screwed with the same tap that is to be used for the internal screws or nuts, and which is shown in three views in fig. 557. The cutter or V, has a thin cutting edge sloped externally to the angle of the thread, usually about 60 degrees, and thinned internally by a notch made with a triangular file; the cutter is inlaid in the thicker piece of wood, and fastened by a hook-form screw bolt and nut.

In placing the cutter, four different conditions require strict attention. Its angular ridge should lie as a tangent to the inner circle; its edge should be sharpened on the dotted line *b*, or at an angle of about 100 degrees with the back; its point should exactly intersect the ridge of the thread in the box; and it should lie precisely at the rake or angle of the thread, for which purpose it is inlaid deeper at its blunt extremity.

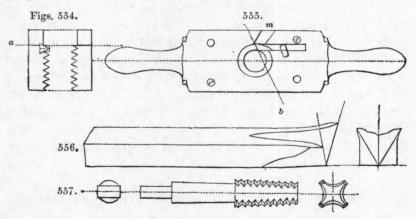

The piece of wood for the screw is turned cylindrical and a little pointed; it is then twisted into the screw box, the cutter makes a notch, which catches upon the ridge of the wooden worm immediately behind the cutter, and this carries the work forward, exactly at the rate of the thread. The whole of the material is removed at one cut, and the shavings make their escape at the aperture or mouth *m*.

In cutting the smallest screws, with this well-contrived and effective instrument, the screw box is held in the left hand, and the work is screwed in with the right; or the box is applied whilst the work remains upon the mandrel of the lathe. When the thread is required to be continued close up to a shoulder, the screw is cut up as far as the entire instrument will allow: the screw box is then removed, in order that the loose piece may be taken off from it, after which the screw is completed without impediment.

Screws of half an inch diameter and upwards, are generally fixed in the vice, whilst the screw-box is handed round just like the die-stock. For large screws exceeding two or three inches diameter, two of the V's or cutters are placed in the box, so as to divide the work; thereby lessening the risk of breaking the delicate edge of the cutter, the exact position of which is a matter of great nicety. The screw-box has been occasionally used for wooden screws of 4, 6, and 8 inches diameter, and upwards, and such large screws have been also made by hand, with the saw, chisel, mallet, and ordinary tools; but these large screws are now almost entirely superseded by those of metal, which, for most purposes, are greatly superior in every point of view.

In cutting the metal screw, or the bolt, the tools are required to be the converse of the tap, as they must have internal instead of external threads, but the radial notches are essential alike in each. For small works, the internal threads are made of fixed sizes and in thin plates of steel, such are called *screw plates;* for larger works, the internal threads are cut upon the edges of two or three detached pieces of steel, called dies, these are fitted into grooves within *diestocks,* and various other contrivances which admit of the approach of the screwed dies, so that they may be applied to the decreasing diameter of the screw, from its commencement to the completion.

The thickness of the screw plate is in general from about two-thirds to the full diameter of the screw, and mostly several holes are made in the same plate; from two to six holes are intended for one thread, and are accordingly distinguished into separate groups by little marks, as in fig. 558. The serrating of the edges, is sometimes done by making two or three small holes and connecting them by the lateral cuts of a thin saw, as in fig. 559. The notches alone are sometimes made, and when the holes are arranged as in fig. 560, should the screw be broken short off by accident, it may be cut in two with a thin saw, and thus removed from the plate.

In making small screws, the wire is fixed in the hand-vice, tapered off with a file, and generally filed to an obtuse point; then, after being moistened with oil, it is screwed into the one or several holes in the screw plate, which is held in the left hand. At other times, the work fixed in the lathe is turned or filed into form, and the plate is held in the right hand; but the force then applied is less easily appreciated. The harp-makers and some others, attach a screw plate with a single hole to the sliding cylinder of the popit-head. See page 564.

Figs 558.   559.   560.

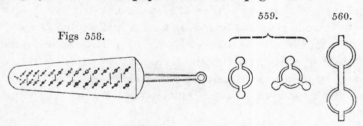

The screw plate is sometimes used for common screws as large as from half to three-quarters of an inch diameter; such screws are fixed in the tail vice, and the screw plate is made from about 15 to 30 inches long, and with two handles; the holes are then made of different diameters, by means of a taper tap, so as to form the thread by two, three, or more successive cuts, and the screw should be entered from the large side of the taper hole. It is, however, very advisable to use the diestocks, in preference to the screw plates, for all screws exceeding about one-sixteenth of an inch diameter, although the unvarying diameter of the screw plate has the advantage of regulating the equal size of a number of screws, and as such, is occasionally used to follow the diestocks, by way of a gage for size.

The diestock, in common with other general tools, has received a great many modifications that it would be useless to trace in greater detail, than so far as respects the varieties in common use, or those which introduce any peculiarity of action in the cutting edges. A notion of the early contrivances for cutting metal screws will be gathered from the figures 561 to 564, which are copied half-size from Leupold's Theatrum Machinarum Generale, 1724 *. For instance, fig. 561 is the screw plate divided in two, and jointed together like a common rule; the inner edges are cut with threads, the larger of which is judiciously placed near the joint, that it may be more forcibly compressed; there is a guide *a, a,* to prevent the lateral displacement of the edges, which would be fatal to the action. Similar instruments are still used, but more generally for screws made in the turning lathe.

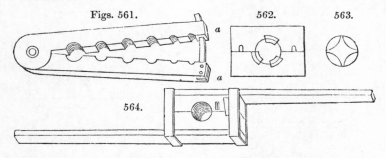

Figs. 561. 562. 563.

564.

In one of these tools, the frame or stock is made exactly like a pair of flat pliers, but with loose dies cut for either one or two sizes of threads. Plier diestocks are also made in the form of common nut-crackers, or in fact, much like fig. 561, if we consider it to have handles proceeding from *a a,* to extend the tool to about two or three times its length; the guide *a a* is retained, and removable dies are added, instead of the threads being cut in the sides of the instrument. Screwing tools are also made of one piece of steel, and to spring open, something like fig. 134, page 232, Vol. I., but shorter and stronger; the threads are cut on the sides or ends of the bosses, which are flat externally, for the convenience of compression in the tail vice.

In general, however, the two dies are closed together in a straight line, instead of the arc of a circle: one primitive method, fig. 564, extracted from the work referred to, has been thus remodelled; the dies are inserted in rectangular taper holes in

* Moxon, Plumier, and others, describe similar tools, and also the screw box.

the ends of two long levers, which latter are connected by two cylindrical pins, carefully fitted into holes made through the levers, and the ends of the pins are screwed and provided with nuts, which serve more effectually to compress the dies than the square rings represented in fig. 564.

The diestock in its most general form has a central rectangular aperture, within which the dies are fitted, so as to admit of compression by one central screw; the kinds most in use being distinguished as the *double chamfered diestocks,* figs. 565 and 566;

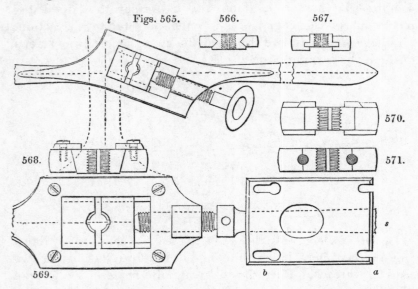

Figs. 565.   566.   567.

570.

568.   571.

569.   *b*   *a*

and the *single chamfered diestock,* figs. 568 and 569, the handles of which are partly shown by dotted lines. In the former, the aperture is about as long as three of the dies; about one-third of the length of the chamfer is filed away at the one end, for the removal of the dies laterally, and one at a time. In the single chamfered diestock 569, which is preferable for large threads, the aperture but little exceeds the length of two dies, and these are removed by first taking off the side plate *b a,* which is either attached by its chamfered edges as a slide, or else by four screws; these, when loosened, allow the plate to be slid endways, and it will be then disengaged, as the screws will leave the grooves at *a,* and the screw heads will pass through the holes at *b.*

Sometimes dies of the section of fig. 567 are applied after the manner of 566, and occasionally the rectangular aperture of fig.

569 is made parallel on its inner edges, and without the side plate *b a*; the dies are then retained by steel plates either riveted or screwed to the diestock, as represented in fig. 570, or else by two steel pins buried half-way in the sides of the stock, and the remaining half in the die, as shown in fig. 571. These variations are of little moment, as are also those concerning the general form of the stock; for instance, whether or not the handles proceed in the directions shown, (the one handle *s*, being occasionally a continuation of the pressure screw,) or whether the handles are placed as in the dotted position *t*. In small diestocks, a short stud or handle is occasionally attached at right angles to the extremity, that the diestock may be moved like a winch handle; and sometimes graduations are made upon the pressure screw, to denote the extent to which the dies are closed. These and other differences are matters comparatively unimportant, as the accurate fitting of the dies, and their exact forms, should receive the principal attention.

In general only two dies are used, the inner surface of each of which includes from the third to nearly the half of a circle, and a notch is made at the central part of each die, so that the pair of dies present four arcs, and eight series of cutting points or edges ; four of which operate when the dies are moved in the one direction, and the other four when the motion is reversed; that is when the curves of the die and screw are alike.

The formation of these parts has given rise to much investigation and experiment, as the two principal points aimed at require directly opposite circumstances. For instance, the *narrower* the edges of the dies, or the less of the circle they contain, the more easily they penetrate, the more quickly they cut, and the less they compress the screw by surface friction or squeezing, which last tends to elongate the screw beyond its assigned length. But on the other hand, the *broader* the edges of the dies, or the more of the circle they contain, the more exactly do they retain the true helical form, and the general truth of the screw.

The action of screw cutting dies is rendered still more difficult, because in general, one pair of dies, the curvatures and angles of which admit of *no change*, are employed in the production of a screw, the dimensions of which, during its gradual transit from the smooth cylinder to the finished screw, *continually change*.

For instance, the thread of a screw necessarily possesses two

magnitudes, namely, the top and bottom of the groove, and also
two angles at these respective diameters, as represented by the
dotted lines in the diagrams, figs. 572, 574, and 576, (which are
drawn with straight instead of curved lines). The angles are nearly
in the inverse proportion of the diameters; or if the bottom were
half the diameter of the top of the thread, the angle at the bottom
would be nearly *twice* that at the top. (The mode of calculating
the angles, is subjoined to figs. 614—618, page 657.)

The figures show the *original* taps, *master* taps, or *cutters*, from
which the dies, figs. 573, 575, and 577, are respectively made;
and in each of the three diagrams, the dies *a* are supposed to
be in the act of commencing, and the dies *b* in finishing, a screw
of the same diameter throughout, as that in fig. 572.

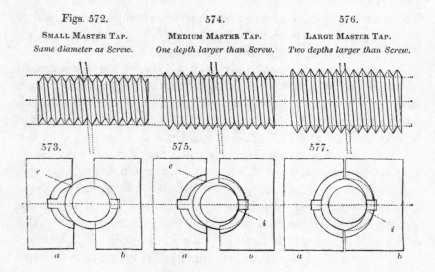

Figs. 572.	574.	576.
SMALL MASTER TAP.	MEDIUM MASTER TAP.	LARGE MASTER TAP.
Same diameter as Screw.	*One depth larger than Screw.*	*Two depths larger than Screw.*

573.   575.   577.

Of course the circumstances become the more perplexing the
greater the depth of the thread, whereas in shallow threads the
interference may be safely overlooked. As the dies cannot have
both diameters of the screw, it becomes needful to adopt that
curvature which is least open to objection. If, as in fig. 573, the
curved edges of the dies *a* and *b* have the same radii as the
finished screw, in the commencement, or at *a*, the die will only
touch at the corners, and the curved edges being almost or quite
out of contact, there will be scarcely any guidance from which to
get the *lead,* or first direction of the helix, and the dies will be

likely to cut false screws, or else parallel grooves or rings *.   In addition to this, the curved edges present, at the commencement, a greater angle than that proper for the top of the screw, but at the completion of the screw, or at *b*, the die and screw will be exact counterparts, and will be therefore perfectly suitable to each other.

If, as in fig. 577, the inner curvature of the dies *a* and *b* be the same as in the blank cylinder, *a* will exactly agree both in diameter and angle at the commencement of the screw, but at the conclusion, or as at *b*, each will be too great, and the die and screw will be far from counterparts, and therefore ill adapted to each other.

The most proper way of solving the difficulty in dies made in two parts, is by having two pairs of dies, such as 577 and 573, and which is occasionally done in very deep threads, a mode that was first published by Mr. Allan, see figs. 535 and 536, page 582. But it is more usual to pursue a medium course, and to make the original tap or cutter, fig. 574, used in cutting the dies, not of the same diameter as the bolt, as in figs. 572 and 573, not to exceed the diameter of the bolt by twice the depth of the thread, as in figs. 576 and 577, but with only one depth beyond the exact size, or half-way between the extremes, as in figs. 574 and 575, in which latter it is seen the contact although not quite perfect either at *a* or *b*, is sufficiently near at each for general practice.

The obvious effect of different diameters between the die and screw, must be a falsity of contact between the surfaces and angles of the dies; thus, in 573, the whole of the cutting falls upon *e*, the external angles, until the completion of the screw in *b*, when the action is rather compressing than cutting.   In fig. 577, the first act is that of compressing, and all the work is soon thrown on *i*, the internal angles of the die, which become

* Sometimes the dies cut a fine, single-thread screw, of one-half or one-third the coarseness of that of the dies ; at other times, a fine double or triple screw, of the same rake or velocity as the dies ; and occasionally the dies cut concentric rings. These accidental results are mainly to be attributed to the diestocks being closed upon the screw-bolt obliquely, instead of at right angles ; the edges of the dies do not then approach in the required relationship, and the two dies each cut a distinct thread, instead of one thread in common.   In the act of placing the dies the stock should be slightly " wriggled," or moved vertically, to allow the dies to select their true position on the bolt to be cut.

gradually more penetrative, but eventually too much so, being in all respects the reverse of the former. In the medium and most common example, fig. 575, the cut falls at first upon the external angles *e*, it gradually dies away, and it is during the brief transition of the cut from the external to the internal angles, *i*, that is when the screw is exactly half formed, that the com pression principally occurs.

The compression or squeezing, is apt to enlarge the diameter of the screw, (literally by swaging up the metal,) and also to elongate it beyond its assigned length, and that unequally at different parts. Sometimes the compression of the dies, makes the screw so much coarser than its intended pitch, that the screw refuses to pass through a deep hole cut with the appropriate tap ; not only may the total increase in length be occasionally detected by a common rule, but the differences between twenty or thirty threads, measured at various parts with fine pointed compasses, are often plainly visible.

Other and vastly superior modes for the formation of long screws, or those requiring any very exact number of threads in each inch or foot of their length, will be shortly explained. Yet notwithstanding the interferences which deprive the die-stocks of the refined perfection of these other methods, they are a most invaluable and proper instrument for their intended use; and the disagreement of curvature and angle is more or less remedied in practice, by reducing the circular part of the dies in various ways ; and also in some instances, by the partial sepa-ration of the guiding from the cutting action.

The most usual form of dies is shown in fig. 578, but if every measure be taken at the mean, as in fig. 579, the tool possesses a fair, average, serviceable quality ; that is, the dies should be cut over an original tap of medium dimensions, namely, one depth larger than the screw, such as fig. 574 ; the curved surface should be halved, making the spaces and curves as nearly equal as may be ; and the edges should be radial. Fig. 580, nearly transcribed from Leupold's figure 562, has been also used, but it appears as if too much of the curve were then removed.

Sometimes the one die is only used for guiding, and the other only for cutting: thus *a*, fig. 581, is cut over two different diameters of master taps, which gives it an elliptical form. A large master tap, fig. 576, is first used for cutting the pair of dies, this leaves the large parts of the curve in a; the dies are subsequently cut over a small master tap, 572.

Figs. 578.   579.   580.   581.   582.

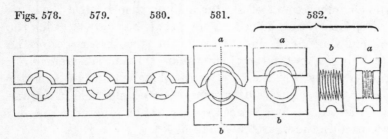

In beginning the screw, the die a, serves as a bed with guiding edges, these indent without cutting, and also agree at the first start, with the full diameter of the bolt; with the gradual reduction of the bolt, it sinks down to the bottom of a, which continually presents an angular ridge, nearly agreeing in diameter, and therefore in angle with the nascent screw. The inconveniences of the dies, fig. 581, are, that they require a large and a small master tap for the formation of every different sized pair of dies, and which latter are rather troublesome to repair. The dies also present more friction than most others, apparently from the screw becoming wedged within the angular sides of the die a.

In fig. 582, a construction advocated by Sir John Robison, the dies are first cut over a small master tap, fig. 573, the threads are then partially filed or turned out of b, to fit the blank cylinder; which therefore rests at the commencement upon blunt, triangular, curved surfaces, instead of upon keen edges; and as the screw is cut up, its thread gradually descends into the portions of the thread in b, which are not obliterated. About one-third of the thread is turned out from each side of the cutting die a, leaving only two or three threads in the center, as shown in the last view; and the surface of this die is left flat, that it may be ground up afresh when blunted, and which is also done with other dies having plane surfaces *.

Mr. Peter Keir and Mr. William Jones have each proposed to assist the action of dies for large screws, by means of cutters; their plans will be sufficiently explained by the diagrams, figs. 583 and 584. Mr. Keir applied this mode to large screws of *square* threads for gun carriages; the dies were cut very shallow,

---

* Select Papers of the Society of Arts for Scotland, vol. i., p. 41.

say one-third of the full depth, and they were serrated on their
inner faces to act like saws or files.   The dies were used to cut
up the commencement of the thread, but when it filled the shallow dies, their future office was not to cut, but only to guide the
ascent and descent of the stocks, by the smooth surfaces of the
dies rubbing upon the top of the square thread.   The remaining
portion of the screw, was afterwards ploughed out by a cutter
like a turning tool, the cutter being inserted in a hole in the one
die, and advanced by a set screw, somewhat after the manner
represented in the figures 583 and 584 *.

Mr. Jones employed a similar method for *angular* thread screws,
and the cutter was placed within a small frame fixed to the one
die.   The screw bolt was commenced with the pair of dies which
were closed by the set screw *a*, 583, the cutter being then out of
action.   When the cutter was set to work by its adjusting
screw *b*, it was advanced a little beyond the face of the die, and
not afterwards moved; but the advance of *a*, closed the dies upon
the decreasing diameter of the screw, the cutter always continuing prominent and doing the principal share of the work †.

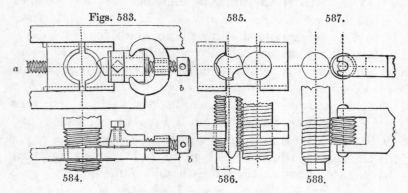

Figs. 583.   585.   587.
584.   586.   588.

Fig. 585 is the plan, and 586 the side elevation, of an old
although imperfect expedient, for producing a left-handed screw
from a right-handed tap.   It will be remembered the right and
left hand screws only differ in the *direction* of the angle, the
thread of the one coils to the right, of the other to the left hand;
and on comparing a corresponding tap and die, the inclinations
of the external curve of the one, and the internal curve of the

---

* Technical Repos., vol. viii., pages 182 and 193.
† Trans. Soc. of Arts, 1829, vol. xlvii., p. 135

other, necessarily differ in like manner as to direction. The mode employed therefore, is to carry a right-hand tap *around* the screw to be cut; the temporary screw-cutter possesses the same interval or thread as before, but the cutting angles of the tap, having the reverse direction of those of the die, the screw becomes left-handed.

The one die in 585 and 586 is merely a blank piece of brass or iron without any grooves, the other is a brass die in which the tap is fixed; as may be expected, the thread produced is not very perfect, but in the absence of better means, this mode is available as the germ for the production of a set of left-hand taps and dies. Figs. 587 and 588 represent a different mode of originating a left-handed screw, proposed by Mr. Walsh; the tool is to be a small piece of a right-handed screw, which is hardened and mounted in a frame like an ordinary *milling* or *nurling* tool, and intended to act by pressure alone; the diameter of the tool and cylinder should be like *.

The screw stock first patented by the Messrs. Whitworth of Manchester, is represented in fig. 589 : three narrow dies were fitted in three equidistant radial grooves in the stock, the ends of the dies came in contact with an exterior ring, having on its inner edge three spiral curves, (equivalent to three inclined planes,) and on its outer surface a series of teeth into which worked a tangent screw, so that on turning the ring by the screw, the three dies were simultaneously and equally advanced towards the center.

These screw stocks were found to cut very rapidly, as every circumstance was favourable to that action. For instance, on the principle of the triangular bearing, all the three dies were constantly at work; the original tap being slightly taper, every thread in the length of the die was performing its part of the work, the same as in a taper tap every thread of which removes its shaving, or share of the material; and the dies were narrow, with radial edges, which admitted of being easily sharpened.

This diestock has been abandoned by the Messrs. Whitworth,

---

* See Trans. Soc. of Arts, vol. xliii., p. 127 ; this scheme is referred to likewise in the foot-note on page 581 of this volume.

Some methods of making the *same* taps and dies, serve for cutting *either* right or left hand screws, will be found in Trans. Soc. of Arts, vol. xli., p. 115 ; *Manuel du Tourneur*, vol. i., plate 23 ; and Mechanic's Magazine, 1836, vol. xxv., p. 376. These contrivances appear, however, to possess little or no value.

in favour of their screw stock subsequently patented, which is
represented in fig. 590. The one die embraces about one-third
of the circle, the two others much less; the latter are fitted into
grooves which are not radial, but lead into a point situated near
the circumference of the screw-bolt; the edges of the dies are
slightly hooked or ground respectively within the radius, and
they are simultaneously advanced by the double wedge and nut:
the dies are cut over a large original, such as fig. 576, that is,
two depths larger than the screw. The large die serves to line
out or commence the screw, and the two others act alternately;
the one whilst the stock descends down the bolt, the other
during its ascent.

Figs. 589.   590.   591.

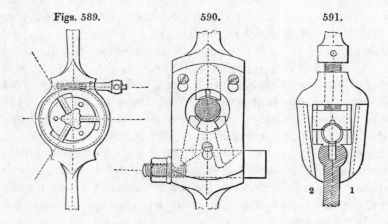

The last screw stock that will be here noticed is Mr. G. Bodmer's of Manchester, for which he also has obtained a patent.
It is seen that the one die embraces about one-third the screw,
the other is very narrow; the peculiarity of this construction is
that a circular recess is first turned out of the screw stock, and a
parallel groove is made into the same, the one handle of the stock,
(which is shaded,) nearly fills this recess, and receives the small
die. If the handle fitted mathematically true, it is clear it
would be immovable, but the straight part of the handle is narrower than the width of the groove; when the stock is turned
round, say in the direction from 2 to 1, the first process is to
rotate the handle in the circle, and to bring it in hard contact
with the side 1, this slightly rotates the die also, and the one
corner becomes somewhat more prominent than the other. When

the motion of the stock is reversed, the handle leaves the side 1, of the groove, and strikes against the other side 2, and then the opposite angle of the die becomes the more prominent; and that without any thought or adjustment on the part of the workman, as the play of the handle in the groove 1, 2, is exactly proportioned to cause the required angular change in the die.

The cutting edges of the die act exactly like turning tools, and therefore they may very safely be bevilled or hooked as such; as when they are not cutting, they are removed a little way out of contact, and therefore out of danger of being snipped off, or of being blunted by hard friction. The opposite die affords during the time an efficient guidance for the screw, and the broad die is advanced in the usual manner, by the pressure screw made in continuation of the second handle of the diestock; the dies are kept in their places by a side plate, which is fitted in a chamfered groove in the ordinary manner.

There is less variety of method in cutting external screws with the diestocks, than internal screws with taps, but it is desirable in both cases, to remove the rough surface, the work acquires in the foundry or forge, in order to economise the tools; and the best works are either bored or turned cylindrically to the true diameters corresponding with the screwing tools.

The bolt to be screwed is mostly fixed in the tail vice vertically, but sometimes horizontally, the dies are made to apply fairly, (see foot-note, page 601,) and a little oil is applied prior to starting. As a more expeditious method suitable to small screws, the work is caused to revolve in the lathe, whilst the diestock is held in the hand; and larger screws are sometimes *marked* or *lined out* whilst fixed in the vice, the principal part of the material is then removed with the chasing tool or handscrew tool, fig. 405, p. 519, and the screw is concluded in the diestocks. In cutting up large screw bolts, two individuals are required to work the screw stocks, and they walk round the standing vice or screwing clamp, which is fixed to a pedestal in the middle of the workshop.

For screwing large numbers of bolts, the engineer employs the *bolt-screwing machine*, which is a combination of the ordinary taps and dies, with a mandrel, driven by steam power. In the machine invented by Mr. Fox, the mandrel revolves, traverses, and carries the bolt, whilst the dies are *fixed* opposite to the mandrel; or else the mandrel carries the tap, and the nut to be screwed is grasped opposite to it. In the machine invented by Mr. Roberts, the mandrel does not traverse, it carries the bolt, and the dies are mounted on a slide; or else the mandrel carries the nut, and the tap is fixed on the slide. The tap or die gives the traverse in every case, and the engine and strap supply the muscle; of course the means for changing the direction of motion and closing the dies, as in the hand process, are also essential*.

Mr. Roberts' *screwing table* is a useful modification of the bolt machine, intended to be used for small bolts, and to be worked by hand. The mandrel is replaced by a long spindle running loosely in two bearings; the one end of the spindle terminates in a small wheel with a winch-handle, the other in a pair of jaws closed by a screw, in other respects like fig. 85, p. 201, vol. I. The jaws embrace the head of the bolt, which is presented opposite to dies that are fixed in a vertical frame or stock, and closed by a loaded lever to one fixed distance. In tapping the nut, it is fixed in the place before occupied by the dies, and the spindle then used, is bored up to receive the shank of the tap, which is fixed by a side screw. This machine ensures the rectangular position of the several parts, and the power is applied by the direct rotation of a hand wheel.

It will be gathered from the foregoing remarks, that the die-stock is an instrument of most extensive use, and it would indeed almost appear as if every available construction had been tried, with a general tendency to foster the cutting, and to expunge the surface friction or rubbing action; by the excess of which latter, the labour of work is greatly increased, and risk is incurred of stretching the thread.

---

* See Buchanan's Mill Work, by Rennie, 1841. Plates 38 to 38 c.

In Wright's Patent Machine for making " wood screws" for joinery work, the traverse of the mandrel is assisted by a screw guide of the same degree of coarseness as the fixed dies, and the blanks are advanced to the latter through the hollow mandrel, at the end of which they are retained by nippers, until the machine has screwed the former, and supplies a new blank. In a former machine the traversing mandrel and a fixed turning tool were used ; the thread is cut from base to point, whilst the screw is supported in a back stay. For other modifications, see Lardner's Cyclopedia, Manufactures in metal, vol. i., pp. 201—9.

In the patent diestocks the cutting is so much facilitated, that the labour is reduced perhaps to less than the half of that required with the old-fashioned and nearly semicircular dies, fig. 578 ; but when the guidance is too far sacrificed, the greedy action of the dies is a source of mischief. For instance, the instrument, fig. 589, with three dies moving simultaneously, has been superseded because of its risk of cutting irregular or " drunken " screws : for if, from the dies being improperly placed, the thread does not exactly meet, or lead into itself in the first revolution of the dies, but finds its way in with a break in the curve, this break continues unto the end ; as the three points of *bearing*, so to speak, being narrow, they may pursue the irregular line, thus giving to the diestock a rolling or " wabbling " motion, instead of a steady quiet descent. This fault is also liable to occur in every diestock, in which there is any risk of the blank cylinder not being placed truly axial, from the dies touching only by points or narrow edges, instead of against a fair proportion of the curve ; but, when the dies are moderately broad, there is more chance of the defect being afterwards corrected.

Subsequently to the introduction, by Messrs. Whitworth, of their screw-stock, shown in fig. 589, they invented a diestock with four dies, the one side of each of which was radial. The dies acted two at a time, just like turning tools, they were quite free from rubbing, and were simultaneously advanced by two wedges yoked together by a cross piece, and moved by one screw. This ingenious plan was not however regularly adopted, on account of the deficiency of the guiding power, as the screw was supported between four series of points ; but it gave rise to the mode explained in fig. 590, in which the broad guide is judiciously introduced.

It is difficult, however, to decide fairly and impartially upon the respective merits of diestocks, many of which approach very nearly to one another ; as whether the facility of cutting, or the truth of the screw, or any other point be made the standard of comparison, it is a judgment which must necessarily be given rather by opinion than by measure ; and the conditions which are aimed at in all screw-stocks, are in strictness unattainable in any, owing to the varying dimensions of the object to be produced.

From many reasons, it appears needless to strain the application of the diestock to the production of long screws, which require either a very precise total length, or a very precise equality in their several parts. The main inconvenience results from unavoidably mixing the guiding and cutting in the same part of the one instrument; an instrument which acts by producing a series of copies of the few threads in the dies, and which copies become collectively the long screw. This mode of proceeding is equally as impolitic, as setting out a line of 50 or 100 inches long, with a little rule measuring only one or two inches.

Neither can it be desirable to cut long, and consequently slender screws, by an instrument used as a double ended lever, in the application of which, the screw, supported generally at the one end in the vice, is very liable to be bent; as any small disturbing force at the end of the stock, is multiplied in the same proportion as the difference between the radii of the work and instrument. The liability to bend the screw is reduced to the minimum, in Mr. Allan's simple apparatus, (p. 582,) for cutting the screws for dividing engines and other superior works, but which mode is not adapted to ordinary screws; the machines for screwing bolts entail also little risk of bending the screw.

On the whole it appears questionable whether for short screws, which are the legitimate works of the diestock, some of the better forms of the two part dies are not as good as any; and on the other hand it appears quite certain that for those screws in which particular accuracy is of real importance, that the screw cutting engine or turning lathe is beyond comparison more proper. This valuable engine will be soon referred to, and in it the distinct processes of guiding and of cutting are completely detached, and each may independently receive the most favourable conditions; whereas in all the modifications of the screwstock they are more or less intimately commingled, and are to a certain degree antagonists.

The screw-cutting lathe has also the advantage that one good screw having been obtained as a guide, its relative degree of perfection is directly imparted to the work, and it may be employed for cutting very coarse or very fine screws, or in fact any of the various kinds referred to in the preliminary description *.

---

* Some remarks will be offered in the last section, on the proportions and forms of screws of a variety of kinds.

SECT. V.—ON SCREWS CUT BY HAND IN THE COMMON LATHE.

Great numbers of screws are required in works of wood, ivory and metal, that cannot be cut with the taps and dies, or the other apparatus hitherto considered. This arises from the nature of the materials, the weakness of the forms of the objects, and the accidental proportions of the screws, many of which are comparatively of very large diameter and inconsiderable length. These and other circumstances, conspire to prevent the use of the diestocks for objects such as the screws of telescopes and other slender tubes, those on the edges of disks, rings, boxes, and very many similar works.

Screws of this latter class are frequently cut in the lathe with the ordinary screw tool, and by dexterity of hand alone ; there is little to be said in explanation of the apparatus and tools, which then consist solely of the lathe with an ordinary mandrel incapable of traversing endways, and the screw tools or the chasing tools figs. 404 and 405, page 519, with the addition of the arm rest ; the details of the manipulation will be found in the practical section.

The screw tool held at rest would make a series of rings, because at the end of the first revolution of the object, the points A B C of the tool would fall exactly into the scratches A B C commenced respectively by them. But if in its first revolution, the tool is shifted exactly the space between two of its teeth, at the end of the revolution, the point B of the tool, drops into the groove made by the point A, and so with all the others, and a true screw is formed, or a continuous helical line, which appears in steady lateral motion during the revolution of the screw in the lathe.

It is likely the tool will fail *exactly* to drop into the groove, but if the difference be inconsiderable, a tolerably good screw is nevertheless formed ; as the tool being moved forward as equally as the hand will allow, corrects most of the error. But if the difference be great, the tool finds its way into the groove with an abrupt break in the curve ; and during the revolution of the screw, as it progresses it also appears to roll about sideways, instead of being quiescent, and is said by workmen to be " drunk," this error is frequently beyond correction.

It sometimes happens that the tool is moved too rapidly, and that the point C drops into the groove commenced by A ; in this case the coarseness of the groove is the same as that of the tool, but the inclination is double that intended, and the screw has a double thread, or two distinct helices instead of one; the tool may pass over three or four intervals and make a treble or quadruple thread, but these are the results of design and skill, rather than of accident.

On the other hand, from being moved too slowly, the point B of the tool may fail to proceed so far as the groove made by A, but fall midway between A and B ; in this case the screw has half the rise or inclination intended, and the grooves are as fine again as the tool; other accidental results may also occur which it is unnecessary to notice.

The assemblage of points in the screw tools proper for the hard woods, ivory and metals, renders the *striking* of screws in these materials comparatively certain and excellent, that is as regards those individuals who devote sufficient pains to the acquisition of the manipulation ; but the soft woods, require tools with very keen edges of 20 to 30 degrees, and for these materials the screw tool is made with only a single point, as represented in figs. 377 and 378, page 516.   With such a tool, no skill will suffice to cut a good useful screw by hand alone, as the guiding and correctional power of the many points no longer exists ; and in consequence those screws in soft wood which are cut in the lathe, require the guidance to be given mechanically in the manner explained in the following section*.

SECT. VI.—ON CUTTING SCREWS IN LATHES WITH TRAVERSING MANDRELS.

One of the oldest, most simple, and general apparatus for cutting short screws in the lathe, by means of a mechanical guidance, is the *screw*-mandrel or *traversing*-mandrel, which

---

* The twisted moulds for upholsterers' fringes, are frequently screwed by hand ; a thin gouge, or a carpenters' fluted bit of the width of the groove, is ground very obliquely from the lower side so as to leave two long edges or fangs projecting, and the tool is sharpened from within.   An oblique notch is made by hand at the end of the mould as a commencement, and the tool wedging into the groove is guided along the rest at the same angle as the notch, whilst the lathe revolves slowly, and completes the twist at one cut.   To make the second groove parallel with the first, the finger is placed beside the gouge, and within the first twist ; and so on with the others.   The process is very pleasing from its rapidity and simplicity, and is also sufficiently accurate for the end proposed.

appears to have been known, almost as soon as the iron mandrel itself was introduced.

Fig. 592 is copied from an old French mandrel mounted in a wooden frame, and with tin collars cast in two parts; the upper halves of the collars are removed to show the cylindrical necks of the mandrel, upon the shaft of which are cut several short screws. In ordinary turning, the retaining key *k*, which is shown detached in the view *k′*, prevents the mandrel from traversing, as its angular and circular ridge enters the groove in the mandrel; but although not represented, each thread on the mandrel is

Fig. 592.

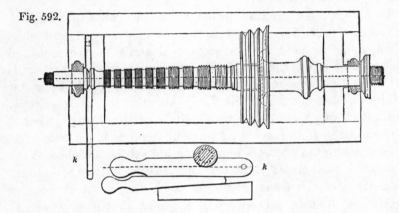

provided with a similar key, except that their circular arcs are screw-form instead of angular. In screw cutting, *k* is depressed to leave the mandrel at liberty; the mandrel is advanced slightly forward, and one of the screw-keys is elevated by its wedge until it becomes engaged with its corresponding guide-screw, and now as the mandrel revolves, it also advances or retires in the exact path of the screw selected.

The modern screw-mandrel lathe has a cast-iron frame, and hardened steel collars which are not divided; the guide screws are fitted as rings to the extreme end of the hardened steel mandrel, and they work in a plate of brass, which has six scollops, or semicircular screws upon its edge. When this mandrel is used for plain turning, its traverse is prevented by a cap which extends over the portion of the mandrel protruding through the collars*.

* For further details of the construction of the old screw-mandrel lathes, the reader is referred to Moxon, Plumier, Leupold, &c.; and to pages 36 to 42 of the

In cutting screws with either the old or modern screw-mandrel, the work is chucked, and the tool is applied, exactly in the manner of turning a plain object; but the mandrel requires an alternating motion backwards and forwards, somewhat short of the length of the guide screw, this is effected by giving a swinging motion or partial revolution to the foot wheel. The tool should retain its place with great steadiness, and it is therefore often fixed in the sliding rest, by which also it is then advanced to the axis of the work with the progress of the external screw, or by which it is also removed from the center in cutting an internal screw.

To cut a screw exceeding the length of traverse of the mandrel, the screw tool is first applied at the end of the work, and when as much has been cut as the traverse will admit, the tool is shifted the space of a few threads to the left, and a further portion is cut; and this change of the tool is repeated until the screw attains the full length required. When the tool is applied by hand, it readily assumes its true position in the threads, when it is fixed in the slide rest its adjustment requires much care.

In screwing an object which is too long to be attached to the mandrel by the chuck alone, its opposite extremity is sometimes supported by the front center or popit head; but the center point must then be pressed up by a spring, that it may *yield* to the advance of the mandrel : this method will only serve for very slight works, as the pressure of the screw-tool is apt to thrust the work out of the center. It is a much stronger and more usual plan, to make the extremity or some more convenient part of the work cylindrical, and to support that part within a stationary cylindrical bearing, or *collar plate*, which retains the position of the work notwithstanding its helical motion, and supplies the needful resistance against the tool*.

---

fourth volume. And also to pages 90 to 92 of the same, for the figures and explanation of the modern screw-mandrel lathe, with cylindrical collars of hardened steel ; the durability of which has been occasionally brought into question by those who, it must be presumed, have not personally tried them. See remarks, page 52, of Vol. IV.

* In cutting the screws upon the ends of glass smelling-bottles, and similar works incapable of being cut with steel tools, the bottle is mounted on a traversing mandrel, which is moved slowly by hand, and the cutting tool is a metal disk revolving rapidly on fixed centers, and having an angular edge fed with emery and water ; in some rare cases a diamond is used as the cutting tool.

The amateur who experiences difficulty in cutting screws flying, or with the common mandrel and hand-tool unassistedly, will find the screw-mandrel an apparatus by far the most generally convenient for those works, in wood, ivory, and metal turning, to which the screw box, and the taps and dies are inapplicable. For the screw-mandrel requires but a very small change of apparatus, and whatever may be the diameter of the work, it ensures perfect copies of the guide screws, the half dozen varieties of which, will be found to present abundant choice as to coarseness, in respect to the ordinary purposes of turning.

SECT. VII.—ON CUTTING SCREWS IN LATHES WITH TRAVERSING TOOLS.

A great number of the engines for cutting screws, and also of the other shaping and cutting engines now commonly used, are clearly to be traced to a remote date, so far as their principles are concerned.

For instance, the germs of many of these cutting machines, in which the principles are well developed, will be found in the primitive rose engine machinery with coarse wooden frames, and arms, shaper plates, cords, pulleys, and weights, described in the earliest works on the lathe, and referred to in pages 4 to 8 of Vol. I.; whilst many others are as distinctly but more carefully modelled in metal, in the tools used in clock and watch making, many of which have also been published.

The principles of these machines being generally few and simple, admit of but little change; but the structures, which are most diversified, nay almost endless, have followed the degrees of excellence of the constructive arts at the periods at which they have been severally made, combined with the inventive talent of their projectors.

In most of the screw-cutting machines a previously-formed screw is employed to give the traverse, such are *copying* machines, and will form the subject of the present section; and a few other engines serve to *originate* screws, by the direct employment of an inclined plane, or the composition of a rectilinear and a circular motion; the notice of this kind of screw machinery will be deferred until the next section.

The earliest screw-lathe known to the author, bears the date of 1569, and this curious machine, which is represented in fig. 593, is thus described by its inventor *Besson;* "*Espèce de Tour en nulle part encore veüe et qui n'est sans subtilité, pour engraver petit à petit la Vis à l'entour de toute Figure ronde et solide, voire mesmes ovale*"*.

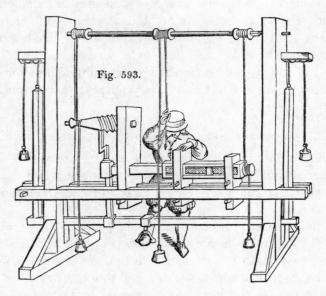

Fig. 593.

The tool is traversed alongside the work by means of a guide-screw, which is moved simultaneously with the work to be operated upon, by an arrangement of pulleys and cords too obvious to require explanation. It is however worthy of remark, that bad and imperfect as the constructive arrangement is, this early machine is capable of cutting screws of any pitch, by the use of pulleys of different diameters; and right and left hand screws at pleasure, by crossing or uncrossing the cord; and also that in this first machine the inventor was aware that a screw-cutting-lathe might be used upon elliptical, conical, and other solids.

The next illustration, fig. 594, represents a machine described as "A Lathe in which without the common art all sorts of screws and other curved lines can be made;" this was invented by

---

* The figure is copied half size from plate 9 of the work entitled "*Des Instruments Mathématiques et Méchaniques, &c., Inventées par Jaques Besson.*" First Latin and French Edit., fol. 1569. Second Edit., Lyons, 1578; also a Latin Edit., Lyons, 1582. The same copper plates are used throughout.

M. Grandjean prior to 1729 *. The constructive details of this
machine, which are also sufficiently apparent, are in some
respects superior to those in Besson's; but the two are alike
open to the imperfection due to the transmissions of motion by
cords ; and Grandjean's is additionally imperfect as the scheme
represented, will fail to produce an equable traverse of the

Fig. 594.

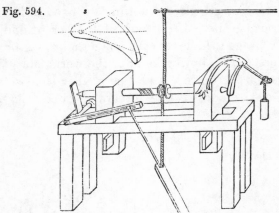

mandrel compared with its revolution, owing to the continual
change in the angular relations between the arms of the bent
lever, and the mandrel and cord respectively. Sometimes the
spiral board or templet *s*, is attached to the bent lever, to
act upon the end of the mandrel; this also is insufficient to
produce a true screw in the manner proposed.

Several of the engines for cutting screws, appear to be derived
from those used for cutting *fusees*, or the short screws of hyperbolical section, upon which the chains of clocks and watches are
wound, in order to counteract the unequal strength of the
different coils of the spiral springs. The fusee engines, which
are very numerous, have in general a guide-screw from which
the traverse of the tool is derived, and the illustration fig. 595,
selected from an old work published in 1741, is not only one of
the earliest, but also of the most exact of this kind; and it
exhibits likewise the primitive application of change wheels, for
producing screws of varied coarseness from one original.

---

* Communicated to the "*Académie Royale*," in 1729, and printed in the
"*Machines approuvées*," tome v., 1735. As a matter of arrangement, this figure
belongs to Sect. VI., but as a specimen of early mechanism, its present place seems
more appropriate.

This instrument is nearly thus described by *Thiout*. "A lathe which carries at its extremity two toothed wheels; the upper is attached to the arbor, the clamp at the end of which holds the axis of the fusee to be cut, the opposite extremity is retained by the center; the fusee and arbor constitute one piece, and are turned by the winch handle. The lower wheel is put in movement by the upper, and turns the screw which is fixed in its center; the nut can traverse the entire length of the screw, and to the nut is strongly hinged the lever that holds the graver or cutter, and which is pressed up by the hand of the workman. Several pairs of wheels are required, and the smaller the size of that upon the mandrel, the less is the interval between the threads of the fusee"*.

Fig. 595.

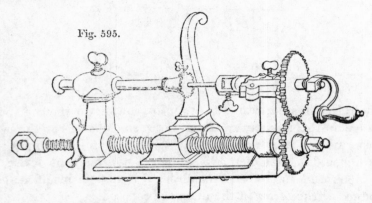

In the general construction of the fusee engine, the guide-screw and the fusee are connected together on one axis, and are moved by the same winch handle; the degree of fineness of the thread on the fusee is then determined by the intervention of a lever generally of the first order; a great variety of constructions have been made on this principle †, the mode of action will be more clearly seen in the next figure, wherein precisely the same movements are applied to the lathe for the purpose of cutting ordinary screws.

The apparatus now referred to is that invented by Mr. Healey

---

* *Thiout's Traité d'Horlogérie, Méchanique et Pratique*, &c., 4to, Paris, 1741, vol. i., page 69, plate 27. The name of the inventor is not given.

† Three are described in Thiout's Treatise : namely, in plates 25, 26, and 27, the first by *Regnaud de Chaalon*. Other examples will be found in Rees's Cyclopedia, Article Fusee, Plates Horology, 36 and 37.

of Dublin, an amateur*; it is universal, or capable within certain limits of cutting all kinds of screws, either right or left handed, and is represented in plan in fig. 596, in which C is the chuck which carries the work to be screwed, and t is the tool which lies upon $r\ r'$ the lathe-rest, that is placed at right angles to the bearer, and is always free to move in its socket s, as on a center, because the binding screw is either loosened or removed.

On the outside of the chuck C is cut a coarse guide screw, which we will suppose to be right-handed. The nut $n\ n$, which fits the screw of the chuck is extended into a long arm, and the latter communicates with the lathe-rest by the connecting rod $c\ c$. As the lathe revolves backwards and forwards the arm n, (which is retained horizontally by a guide pin g,) traverses to and fro as regards the chuck and work, and causes the lathe-rest $r\ r'$, to oscillate in its socket s. The distance $s\ t$ being half $s\ r'$, a right hand screw of half the coarseness of the guide will be cut; or the tool being nearer to, and on the other side of, the center s, as in the dotted position t', a finer and left hand screw will be cut.

Fig. 596.

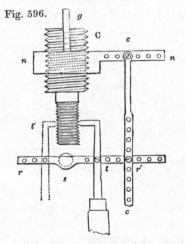

The rod $c\ c$ may be attached indifferently to any part of $n\ n$, but the smallest change of the relation of $s\ t$ to $s\ r'$, would mar the correspondence of screws cut at different periods, and therefore t and r should be united by a swivel joint capable of being fixed at any part of the lathe rest $r\ r'$, which is omitted in Mr. Healey's perspective drawing of the apparatus.

This is one of the least perfect of the modes of originating screws, it should therefore be only applied to such as are very short; as owing to the variation in the angular relation of the parts, the motion given to the tool is not strictly constant or equable; when in the midway position, the several parts should lie exactly at right angles to each other, in order, as far as possible, to avoid the error. The inequality of the screw is

---

* First described in Tilloch's Philosophical Mag. for 1804, Vol. xix., pp. 172—175.

imperceptible in the short fusee, and it would be there harmless
even if more considerable; but a perfect equality of coarseness
or of angle, is imperative in longer screws, and those to be fitted
one to the other, a condition uncalled for in the fusee, which
has only to carry a chain.

The apparatus invented by the late Mṛ. S. Varley, and represented in plan in figs. 597 and 598, although it does not present
the universality of the last, is quite correct in its action and far
more available; it is evidently a combination of the fixed mandrel, and the old screw-mandrel, fig. 592, p. 613. Four different
threads are cut on the tube which surrounds the mandrel,
and the connection between the guide screw and the work,
is by the long bar *b b,* which carries at the one end a piece *g*
filed to correspond with the thread, and at the other, a socket
in which is fixed a screw tool *t,* corresponding with the guide at
the time employed.

Figs. 597.   598.

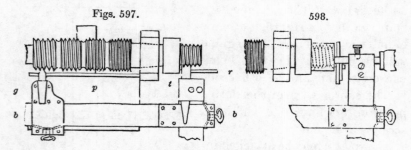

The lathe revolves with continuous motion; and the long bar
or rod being held by the two hands in the position shown, the
guide *g,* and the tool *t,* are traversed simultaneously to the left
by the screw guide; and when the tool meets the shoulder of
the work, both hands are suddenly withdrawn, and the bar is
shifted to the right for a repetition of the cut, and so on until
the completion of the screw. The guide *g,* is supported upon
the horizontal plate *p,* which is parallel with the mandrel, and
the tool *t,* lies upon the lathe rest *r.*

Beneath the tool is a screw which rubs against the lathe-rest *r,*
and serves as a stop, this makes the screw cylindrical or conical,
according as the rest is placed parallel or oblique. For the
internal screw, the tool is placed *parallel* with the bar, as in
fig. 598; and the check screw is applied on the side towards the
center, against a short bar, parallel with the axis of the lathe.

As in the screw-mandrel lathes, the screws become exact copies of the screw-guides, and to a certain extent the mechanism fulfils the office of the slide-rest; but at the same time, more trouble is required for the adjustment of the apparatus. In general the guide-rod must be supposed to act somewhat as an incumbrance to the free use of the tool, which is applied in a less favourable manner, when the screw is small compared with the exterior diameter of the work, as it must then project considerably from the bar; so that on the whole the traversing mandrel is a far more available and convenient arrangement*.

None of the machines which have been hitherto described, are proper for cutting the accurate screws, of considerable length or of great diameter, required in the ordinary works of the engineer; but these are admirably produced by the screw-cutting lathes, in which the traverse of the tool is effected by a long guide-screw, connected with the mandrel that carries the work, by a system of change wheels, after the manner employed a century back, as in fig. 595. The accuracy of the result now depends almost entirely upon the perfection of the guide-screw, and which we will suppose to possess very exactly 2, 4, 5, 6, or some whole number of threads in every inch, although we shall for the present pass by the methods employed in producing the original guide screw, which thus serves for the reproduction of those made through its agency.

The smaller and most simple application of the system of change wheels for producing screws, is shown in fig. 599. The work is attached to the mandrel of the lathe by means of a chuck to which is also affixed a toothed wheel marked M, therefore the mandrel, the wheel, and the work partake of one motion in common : the tool is carried by the slide-rest, the principal slide of which is placed parallel with the axis of the lathe as in turning a cylinder, and upon the end of the screw near the mandrel, is attached a tooth wheel S, which is made to engage in M, the wheel carried by the mandrel.

As the wheels are supposed to contain the same number of teeth, they will revolve in equal times, or make continually turn for turn ; and therefore in each revolution of the mandrel and

* The details of this apparatus will be found in the description of the same by Mr. Cornelius Varley, the nephew of the inventor, in the Trans. Soc. of Arts, vol. xliii., p. 90, 1825.

work, the tool will be shifted in a right line, a quantity equal to *one* thread of the guide-screw, and so with every coil throughout its extent of motion. Consequently, the motion of the two axes being always equal and continuous, the screw upon the work will become an exact copy of the guide-screw contained in the slide-rest, that is, as regards the interval between its several threads, its total length, and its general perfection.

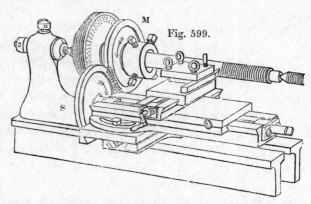

Fig. 599.

But the arrows in M and S, denote that adjoining wheels always travel in *opposite* directions; when therefore the mandrel and slide-rest are connected by only one pair of wheels, as in fig. 599, the direction of the copy screw is the reverse of that of the guide. The right-hand screw being far more generally required in mechanism, when the combination is limited to its most simple form, of two wheels only, it is requisite to make the slide-rest screw left-handed, in order that the one pair of wheels may produce right-hand threads.

But a right-hand slide-rest screw may be employed to produce at pleasure both right and left hand copies, by the introduction of either one or two wheels, between the exterior wheels M and S, fig. 559. Thus, one intermediate axis, to be called I, would produce a right-hand thread; two intermediate axes, I I, would produce a left-hand thread, and so on alternately; and this mode, in addition, allows the wheels M and S to be placed at any distance asunder that circumstances may require.

In making double thread screws the one thread is first cut, the wheels are then removed out of contact, and the mandrel is moved exactly half a turn before their replacement, the second thread is then made. In treble threads the mandrel is twice disengaged, and moved one-third of a turn each time, and so on.

When intermediate wheels are employed, it becomes necessary to build up from the bearers some description of pedestal, or from the lathe-head some kind of bracket, which may serve to carry the axes or sockets upon which the intermediate wheels revolve. These parts have received a great variety of modifications, three of which are introduced in the diagrams 600 to 602; the wheels supposed to be upon the mandrel, are situated on the dotted line M M, and those upon the slide-rest on the line S S.

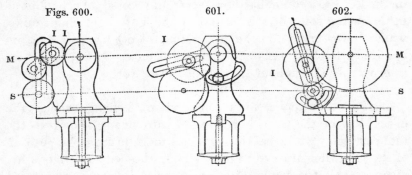

Figs. 600.   601.   602.

The rectangular bracket in fig. 600, has two straight mortises; by the one it is bolted to the bearers of the lathe, and by the other it carries a pair of wheels, whose pivots are in a short piece, which may be fixed at any height or angle in the mortise, so that one or both wheels, I I, may be used according to circumstances. In fig. 601, the intermediate wheel, or wheels, are carried by a radial arm, which circulates around the mandrel, and is fixed to the lathe head by a bolt passed through the circular mortise. In fig. 601, a similar radial arm is adjustable around the axis of the slide-rest screw, in the fixed bracket.

Sometimes the wheel supposed to be attached to the slide-rest, is carried by the pedestal or arm, fixed to the bed or headstock of the lathe; in order that a shaft or spindle may proceed from the wheel S, and be coupled to the end of the slide-rest screw, by a hollow square or other form of socket, so as to enable the rest to be placed at any part of the length of the bearer, and permit a screw to be cut upon the end of a long rod*.

---

* The shaft sometimes terminates at each end in universal joints, in order to accommodate any trifling want of parallelism in the parts, if however the shaft be placed only a few degrees oblique, the motion transmitted ceases to be uniform, or it is accelerated and retarded in every revolution, which is fatal in screw cutting.

This change in the position of the slide-rest, is also needful in cutting a screw which exceeds the length the rest can traverse, as such long screws may then be made at two or more distinct operations ; before commencing the second trip the tool is adjusted to drop very accurately into the termination of that portion of the screw cut in the first trip, which requires very great care, in order that no falsity of measurement may be discernible at the parts where the separate courses of the tool have met.   This method of proceeding, has however from necessity, been followed in producing some of the earliest of the long regulating screws, which have served for the production of others by a method much less liable to accident, namely, when the cut is made uninteruptedly throughout the extent of the work.

In the larger application of the system of change wheels, the entire bed of the lathe is converted into a long slide-rest, the tool carriage with its subsidiary slides for adjusting the position of the tool, then traverses directly upon the bed ; this mode has given rise to the name " traversing or slide-lathe," a machine which has received, and continues to receive, a variety of forms in the hands of different engineers.   It would be tedious and unnecessary to attempt the notice of their different constructions, which necessarily much resemble each other ; more especially as the principles and motives, which induce the several constructions and practices, rather than the precise details of apparatus, are here under consideration.

The arrangement for the change wheels of a screw-cutting lathe given in fig. 603, resembles the mode frequently adopted.

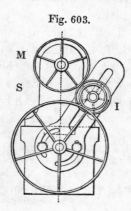

Fig. 603.

The guide-screw extends through the middle of the bed, and projects at the end ; there is a clasp nut, so that when required, the slide-rest may be detached from the screw and moved independently of the same.   The train of wheels is placed at the left extremity of the lathe ; there is a radial arm which circulates around the end of the main screw, the arm has one or two straight mortises, in which are fixed the axes of the intermediate wheels, and there are two circular mortises, by which the arm may be secured to the lathe bed, in any required position, by its two binding screws.

On comparing the relative facilities for cutting screws, either with the slide-rest furnished with a train of wheels, or with the traversing or screw-cutting lathe, the advantage will be found greatly in favour of the latter; for instance:

With the slide-rest arrangement, fig. 599, the work must be always fixed in a chuck to which the first of the change wheels can be also attached; the wheels frequently prevent the most favourable position of the slides from being adopted; and in cutting hollow screws the change wheels entirely prevent the tool carriage of the slide-rest from being placed opposite to the center, and therefore awkward tools, bent to the rectangular form, must be then used. The slide-rest also requires frequent attention to its parallelism with the axis of the lathe, or the screws cut will be conical instead of cylindrical.

With the traversing lathe, from the wheels being at the back of the mandrel, no interference can possibly arise from them, and consequently the work may be chucked indiscriminately on any of the chucks of the lathe; every position may be given to the slide carrying the tool, and therefore the most favourable, or that nearest to the work, may be always selected, and the tools need not be crooked. As the tool carriage traverses at once on the bearers of the lathe, the adjustment for parallelism is always true, and the length of traverse is greatly extended.

The system of screw-cutting just explained is very general and practical: for instance, one long and perfect guide-screw, (which we will call the *guide*,) containing 2, 4, 6, 8, 10, or any precise number of threads per inch having been obtained, it becomes very easy to make from it subsequent screws, (or *copies*,) which shall be respectively coarser and finer in any determined degree. The principal is, that whilst the copy makes one revolution, the guide must make so much of one revolution, or so many, as shall traverse the tool the space required between each thread of the copy; and this is accomplished by selecting change wheels in the proportions of these quantities of motion, or, in other words, in the proportion required to exist between the guide-screw and the copy.

In explanation, we will suppose the guide to have 6 threads

s s

per inch, and that copies of 18, 14, 12½, 8, 3, 2, 1, threads per inch are required : the two wheels must be respectively in the proportions of the fractions $\frac{6}{18}$, $\frac{6}{14}$, $\frac{6}{12\frac{1}{2}}$, $\frac{6}{8}$, $\frac{6}{3}$, $\frac{6}{2}$, $\frac{6}{1}$, the guide being constantly the numerator. The numerator also represents the wheel on the mandrel, and the denominator that on the guide-screw; any multiples of these fractions may be selected for the change wheels to be employed.

For example, any multiples of $\frac{6}{18}$, as $\frac{12}{36}$, $\frac{18}{54}$, $\frac{24}{72}$, &c., will produce a screw of 18 threads per inch, the first and finest of the group; and any multiples of $\frac{6}{1}$, as $\frac{90}{15}$, $\frac{120}{20}$, &c., will produce a screw of 1 thread per inch, which is the last and coarsest of those given.

Screws 2, 4, or 6 times as *fine*, will result from interposing a *second pair* of wheels, respectively multiples of $\frac{1}{2}$, $\frac{1}{4}$, $\frac{1}{6}$, and placed *upon one axis*.

For instance, the pair of wheels $\frac{24}{72}$, used for producing a screw of 18 threads per inch, would, by the combination A, produce a copy three times as *fine*, or a screw of 54 threads per inch.*

Combination A.			Combination B.			Combination C.		
M	Interm.	S	M	Interm.	S	M	Interm.	S
24———60			120———24			27———53		
	20———72			72———20			39———107

And the wheels $\frac{120}{20}$ used for the screw of one thread per inch, would, by the combination B, produce a copy three times as *coarse*, or of three inches rise. Whatsoever the value of the intermediate wheels, whether multiples of $\frac{3}{4}$, $\frac{7}{8}$, $\frac{9}{4}$, &c., they produce screws respectively of $\frac{3}{4}$, $\frac{7}{8}$, $\frac{9}{4}$, the pitches of those screws, which would be otherwise obtained by the two exterior wheels alone; and in this manner a great variety of screws, extending over a wide range of pitch, may be obtained from a limited number of wheels.

For instance, the apparatus Holtzapffel & Co. have recently added to the slide rest, after the manner of figs. 599 and 601, has a series of about fifteen wheels, of from 15 to 144 teeth, employed with a screw of 10 threads per inch; several hundred varieties of screws may be produced by this apparatus, the finest of which has 320 threads per inch, the coarsest measures 7⅕ inches in

---

* Fig. 601, represents the wheels referred to in combination A, and fig. 602, those in combination B.

each coil or rise; and the screws may be made right or left handed, double, triple, quadruple, or of any number of threads. The finest combinations are only useful for self-acting turning; those of medium coarseness serve for all the ordinary purposes of screws; whilst the very coarse pitches are much employed in ornamental works of the character of the Elizabethan twist: and in cutting these coarse screws, the motion is given to the slide-rest screw, and by it communicated to the mandrel.

The value of any combination of wheels may be calculated as vulgar fractions, by multiplying together all the driving wheels as numerators, and all the driven wheels as denominators, adding also the fractional value, or pitch, of the guide-screw; thus in the first example A:

$$\frac{24}{60} \times \frac{20}{72} \times \frac{1}{6} = \frac{480}{25920} \text{ or reduced to its lowest terms } \frac{1}{54}.$$

The fraction denotes that $\frac{1}{54}$th of an inch is the *pitch of the screw*, or the interval from thread to thread; also that it has 54 threads in each inch, and which is called the rate of the screw.

And in C, the numbers in which example were selected at random, the screw would be found to possess rather more than 35 threads per inch.*

$$\frac{27}{53} \times \frac{39}{107} \times \frac{1}{6} \quad \frac{1114}{39026} \text{ or reduced to its lowest terms } \frac{1}{35\frac{71}{1113}}.$$

In imitation of the method of change-wheels, the slide-rest screw is sometimes moved by an arrangement of catgut bands, resembling that represented in Besson's screw lathe, page 616.

One band proceeds from the pulley on the mandrel to a spindle overhead having two pulleys, and a second cord descends from this spindle to a pulley on the slide rest.† The method offers

---

* The fractions should be reduced to their lowest terms before calculation, to avoid the necessity for multiplying such high numbers. Thus the first example would become reduced to $\frac{1}{3} \times \frac{1}{3} \times \frac{1}{6} = \frac{1}{54}$, and would be multiplied by inspection alone, as the numerators and denominators may be taken crossways if more convenient; thus $\frac{24}{72}$ is equal to $\frac{1}{3}$, and $\frac{20}{60}$ is also equal to $\frac{1}{3}$, fractions which are smaller than $\frac{2}{5}$ and $\frac{5}{18}$, the lowest terms respectively of $\frac{24}{60}$ and $\frac{20}{72}$; the second case could not be thus treated, and the whole numbers must there be multiplied, as they will not admit of reduction. Other details will be advanced, and tables of the combinations of the change-wheels will be also given, in treating of the practice of cutting screws.

† This apparatus has been applied to cutting the expanding horn snakes. See *Manuel du Tourneur*, first edit., 1796, vol. ii., plate 21; and second edit., 1816, vol. ii., plate 16; see also page 124-5 of the first volume of this work.

facility in cutting screws of various pitches, by changing the pulleys, and also either right or left hand screws, by crossing or uncrossing one of the bands.

The plan is unexceptionable, when applied for traversing the tool slowly for the purpose of turning smooth cylinders, or surfaces; (which is virtually cutting a screw or spiral of about 100 coils in the inch;) and in the absence of better means, pulleys and bands, are sometimes used in matching screws of unknown or irregular pitches, by the tedious method of repeated trials; as on slightly reducing, with the turning tool, the diameter of either of the *driving* pulleys, the screw or the work becomes gradually *finer;* and reducing either of the *driven* pulleys makes it *coarser;* but the mode is scarcely trustworthy, and is decidedly far inferior to its descendant, or the method of change wheels.

The screw tools, or chasing tools, employed in the traversing lathes for cutting external and internal screws, resemble the fixed tools generally, except as regards their cutting edges; the following figures 604 to 606 refer to angular threads, and 607 and 608 to square threads.

Angular screws are sometimes cut with the single point, fig. 604, a form which is easily and correctly made; the general angle of the point is about 55° to 60°, and when it is only allowed to cut on one of its sides or bevels, it may be used fearlessly, as the shavings easily curl out of the way and escape. But when both sides of the single point tool are allowed to cut, it requires very much more cautious management; as in the latter case, the duplex shavings being disposed to curl over opposite ways, they pucker up as an angular film, and in fine threads they are liable to break the point of the tool, or to cause it to dig into, and tear, the work. Sometimes also, a fragment of the shaving is wedged so forcibly into the screw by the end of the tool, that it can only be extricated by a sharp chisel and hammer.

In cutting angular screws, it is very much more usual and expeditious to employ screw tools with many points, which are made in the lathe by means of a revolving cutter or hob, figs. 550 and 551, page 591. Screw tools with many points, are always required for those angular threads which are rounded at the top and bottom, and which are thence called *rounded* or *round* threads.*

Mr. Clement gives to the screw tool for rounded threads the profile of fig. 605, which construction allows the tool to be *inverted*, so that the edges may be alternately used for the purpose of equalizing the section of the thread. In making the tool 605, the hob, (which is *dotted*,) is put between centers in the traversing lathe, and those wheels are applied which would serve to cut a screw of the same pitch as the hob; the bar of steel is then fixed in the slide-rest, so that the dotted line or the axis of the tool intersects the center of the hob. The tool is afterwards hollowed on both sides with the file, to facilitate the sharpening, and it is then hardened. In using the tool, it is depressed until either edge comes down to the radius, proceeding from the (*black*) circle, which is supposed to represent the screw to be cut; the depression gives the required penetration to the upper angle, and removes the lower out of contact†.

Mr. Bodmer's patent chasing tool is represented in fig. 606; the cutter, *c*, is made as a ring of steel which is screwed internally to the diameter of the bolt, and turned externally with an undercut groove, for the small screw and nut by which it is held in an iron stock, *s*, formed of a corresponding sweep; for distinctness the cutter and screw are also shown detached. The center of curvature of the tool is placed a little below the center of the lathe, to give the angle of separation or penetration; and after the tool has been ground away in the act of being sharpened, it is raised up, until its points touch a straight edge applied on the line *a a* of the stock; this denotes the proper height of center, and also the angle to which the tool is intended to be hooked, namely 10 degrees: each ring makes four or five

---

* Mr. Clement considers the many points to act with less risk than the single point, because in the processes of hardening, first the *hob* and then the *screw tool*, they both become slightly enlarged, or a little coarser than the pitch of the screw; consequently part of the teeth cut on one side, and part on the other, but none of them on both sides of the points; which latter action gives rise to confusion by interrupting the free escape of the shavings.

† In making a hob with rounded threads, it is usual to prove whether the top and bottom of the thread are equally rounded, by driving two different pieces of lead into the hob with a hammer; the two impressions will only fit together so as to exclude the light, when the departure from the simple angle is alike at the top and bottom of the hob, and that the thread is perpendicular or does not lean. Master taps are similarly proved.

cutters, and one stock may be used for several diameters of thread.

Angular thread screws are fitted to their corresponding nuts simply by reduction in diameter; but square thread screws require attention both as to diameter and width of groove, and are consequently more troublesome. Square thread screws are in general, of twice the pitch, or double the obliquity, of angular screws of the same diameters; and, consequently, the interference of angle before explained as concerning the die-stocks, refers with a twofold effect to square threads, which are in all respects much better produced in the screw-cutting lathe.

The ordinary tool for square thread screws is represented in three views in fig. 607 : the shaft is shouldered down so as to terminate in a rectangular part which is exactly equal to the width of the groove; in general the end alone of the tool is

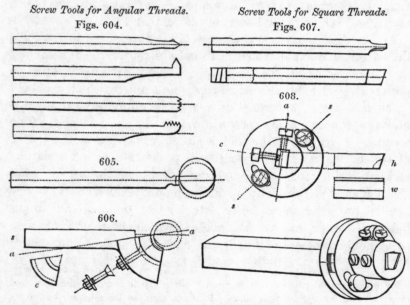

Screw Tools for Angular Threads.
Figs. 604.

Screw Tools for Square Threads.
Figs. 607.

605.

608.

606.

required to cut, and the sides are bevilled according to the angle of the screw, to avoid rubbing against the sides of the thread. Tools which cut upon the side alone, are also occasionally used for adjusting the width of the groove. In either case it requires considerable care to maintain the exact width and height of the tool; the *inclination* of which should also differ for every change of diameter.

To obviate these several inconveniences, the author several years back contrived a tool-holder, fig. 608, for carrying small blades made exactly rectangular. In height, as at h, the blades are alike, in width, w, they are exactly half the pitch of the threads, and they are ground upon the ends alone.   The parallel blades are clamped in the rectangular aperture of the tool socket by the four screws cc; and when the screws ss, which pass through the circular mortises in the sockets, are loosened, the swivel joint and graduations allow the blades to be placed at the particular angle of the thread, which is readily obtained by calculation, and is estimated for the medium depth of the thread, or midway between the extreme angles at the top and bottom.*

One blade, therefore, serves perfectly for all screws of the same pitch, both right and left handed, and of all diameters; as the tool exactly fills the groove, it works steadily, and the width of the groove and the height of center of the tool, are also strictly maintained with the least possible trouble. The depth of the groove, which is generally one-sixth more than its width, is read off with great facility by means of the adjusting screw of the slide-rest; especially if, as usual, the screw and its micrometer agree with the decimal division of the inch.

The holder, fig. 608, has been much and satisfactorily used for screws from about 20 to 2 threads per inch; but when the screw is coarse and oblique, compared with its diameter, the blade is ground away to the dotted line in h, and is sometimes bevilled on the sides almost to the upper edge, to suit the obliquity of the thread, but without altering the extreme width of the tool.

The tools for external screws of very coarse pitch, are necessarily formed in the lathe by aid of the corresponding wheels, and a revolving cutter bar resembling fig. 515, p. 569. The soft tool is fixed in the slide-rest, and is thereby carried against the revolving cutter bar, 515, which has a straight tool, either pointed or square as the case may be.   The end of the screw-tool is thus shaped as part of an eternal screw, the counterpart of that to be cut; the face of the screw tool is filed at right angles to the obliquity of the thread, and the end and sides are slightly bevilled for penetration, previously to its being hardened.

Internal square threads of small size, are usually cut with

---

* For the mode of calculating the angles of screws, see foot-note, p. 657.

taps which resemble fig. 548, p. 587, except in the form of the teeth. When internal square threads are cut in the lathe, the tool assumes the ordinary form, of a straight bar of steel with a rectangular point standing off at right angles, in most respects like the common pointed tool for inside work.

For very deep holes, and for threads of very considerable obliquity, cutter bars, such as fig. 515, p. 569, are used. The work and the temporary bearings of the bar, are all immoveably fixed for the time, and the bar advances through the bearings in virtue of its screw thread; or otherwise a plain bar, having a cutter only, and not being screwed, may be mounted between centers in the screw lathe, and the work, fixed to the slide-rest, may traverse parallel with the bar by aid of the change wheels. The cutter bar in some cases requires a ring to fill out the space between itself and the hole, to prevent vibration; and it is necessary to increase the radial distance of the cutter between each trip, by a set screw, or by slight blows of a hammer.

Very oblique inside cutters are turned to their respective forms with a fixed tool, in a manner the converse of that explained above; and some peculiarities of management are required in using them, in order to obtain the under-cut form of the internal thread,—but the consideration of which does not belong to this place.

In cutting screws in the turning lathe, the tool only cuts as it traverses in the one direction; therefore whilst the cutter is moved backwards, or in the reverse direction, for the succeeding cut, it must be withdrawn from the work. Sometimes the tool is traversed backwards by reversing the motion of the lathe; and in lathes driven by power, the back motion is frequently more rapid than the cutting motion, to expedite the process : at other times the lathe is brought to rest, the nut is opened as a hinge, so as to become disengaged from the screw, and the slide-rest is traversed backwards by hand, or by a pinion movement, and the nut is again closed on the screw, prior to the succeeding cut. This mode answers perfectly for screws of the same thread as the guide, and for those of 2, 4, 6, 8 times as coarse or as fine ; but for those of $2\frac{1}{4}$, $4\frac{1}{2}$, or any fractional times the value of the guide screw, the clasp nut cannot in general be employed advantageously.

The progressive advance of the tool between each cut, is commonly regulated by a circle of divisions or a micrometer on the slide-rest screw, which should always correspond with the decimal division of the inch. The substance of the shaving may be pretty considerable after the first entry is made, but it should dwindle away to a very small quantity, towards the conclusion of the screw. To avoid the necessity for taxing the memory with the graduation at which the tool stood when it was withdrawn for the back stroke, the author has been in the habit of employing a micrometer exactly like that on the screw, which is set to the same graduation, and serves as a remembrancer; another method is to employ an arm or stop, which fits on the axis of the screw or handle with stiff friction, but nevertheless allows the tool to be shifted the two or three divisions required for each cut.

In Mr. Roberts's screw lathe, the nut of the slide screw, instead of being a fixture, is made with two tails as a fork, which embraces an eccentric spindle; by the half rotation of which spindle, the nut, together with the adjusting screw, the slide, and the tool, are shifted, as one mass, a fixed distance to and from the center, between each cut; so as first to withdraw and then to replace the tool. Whilst the tool is running back, the screw is moved by its adjusting screw and divisions, the minute quantity to set in the tool for the succeeding cut, and the continual wear upon the adjusting screw, as well as the uncertainty of its being correctly moved to and fro by the individual, are each avoided.

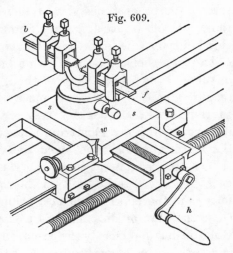

Fig. 609.

Sometimes, with the view of saving the time lost in running back, two tools are used, so that the one may cut as the tool slide traverses towards the mandrel, the other in the contrary direction. Mr. Shanks' arrangement for this purpose, as applied to the screwing of bolts in the lathe, is shown in fig. 609; f represents the front, and b the back tool, which are mounted on the one slide s s, and all three are moved as one piece by the handle h, which does not require any micrometer.

In the first adjustment, the wedge w, is thrust to the bottom of the corresponding angular notch in the slide s, and the two tools are placed in contact with the cylinder to be screwed. For the first cut, the wedge is slightly withdrawn to allow the tool f, to be advanced towards the work; and for the return stroke, the wedge is again shifted under the observation of its divisions, and the slide s s, is brought forwards, towards the workman, up to the wedge; this relieves the tool f, and projects b, which is then in adjustment for the second cut; and so on alternately. The command of the two tools is accurately given by the wedge, which is moved a small quantity by its screw and micrometer, between every alternation of the pair of tools, by the screw h.

In cutting very long screws, the same as in turning long cylindrical shafts, the object becomes so slender, that the contrivance called a backstay, is always required for supporting the work in the immediate neighbourhood of the tool. The backstay is fixed to the slide plate, or the saddle of the lathe which carries the tool, and is brought as near to the tool as possible; sometime the dies or bearings are circular, and fit around the screw; at other times they touch the same at two, three, or four parts of the circle only. Some of the numerous forms of this indispensable guide or backstay, will be hereafter shown.

In using the screw-lathe with a backstay for long screws, it is a valuable and important method, just at the conclusion, to employ a pair of dies in the place usually occupied by the tool; as they are a satisfactory test for exact diameter, and they remove trifling errors attributable to veins and irregularities of the material, which the fixed tool sometimes fails entirely to reduce to the general surface. The tool and backstay may be each considered to be built on the tops of pedestals more or less lofty, and therefore, more susceptible of separation by elasticity, than the pair of dies fixed in a small square frame. Sir John Robison has judiciously proposed, in effect, to link the backstay and turning tool together, by the employment of a small frame carrying a semicircular die of lignum-vitæ, and a fixed turning tool, adjusted by a pressure screw; the frame to be applied either in the hand alone or in the slide rest, and to be inverted, so that the shavings may fall away without clogging the cutter.

SECT. VIII.—VARIOUS MODES OF ORIGINATING AND IMPROVING SCREWS, INCLUDING THOSE OF RAMSDEN, MAUDSLAY, BARTON, ALLAN, CLEMENT, AND OTHERS.

The improvement of the screw has given rise to many valuable schemes and modes of practice, which have not been noticed in the foregoing sections, notwithstanding their collective length. These practices, indeed, could not consistently have been placed in the former pages of this chapter, because some of them must be viewed as refinements upon the general methods, the earlier notice of which would have been premature; and others exhibit various combinations of methods pursued by different eminent individuals with one common object, and are therefore too important to be passed in silence, notwithstanding their miscellaneous nature.

To render this section sufficiently complete, it appears needful to take a slight retrospective glance of the early and the modern modes of originating screws and screw apparatus; some account of the former may be found in the writings of Pappus, who lived in the fourth century.*

The progressive stages which may be supposed to have been formerly in pretty general use for originating screws, may be thus enumerated:

1. The first screw-tap may be supposed to have been made by the inclined templet, the file, and screw tool; it was imperfect in all respects, and not truly helical, but full of small irregularities.

2. The dies formed by the above were considerably nearer to perfection, as the multitude of pointed edges of 1, being passed

---

* The author has been told by a classical friend, that in the works of Pappus Alexandrinus, a Greek mathematician of the fourth century, are to be found practical directions for making screws.

The process is simply to make a templet of thin brass of the form of a right-angled triangle, the angles of which are made in accordance with the inclination of the proposed screw. This triangle is then to be wrapped round the cylinder which is to be the desired screw, and a spiral line traced along its edge. The screw is subsequently to be excavated along this line. Minute practical directions are given not only for every step of this process, but also for the division, setting out, and shaping the teeth of a worm-wheel of any required number of teeth to suit the screw. (Vide Pappi Math. Col. lib. viii., prob. xviii.)

through every groove of the die, the threads of the latter became more nearly equal in their rake or angle, and also in their distances and form.

3. The screw cut with such dies would much more resemble a true helix than 1 ; but from the irregularities in the first tap, the grooves in the die 2, would necessarily be *wide*, and their sides, instead of meeting as a *simple angle*, would be more or less filled with ridges, and 3 would become the exact counterpart of 2.

4. A pointed tool applied in the lathe, would correct the form of the thread or groove in 3, without detracting from its improved cylindrical and helical character; especially if the turning tool were gradually altered, from the slightly rounded to the acute form, in accordance with the progressive change of the screw. The latter is occasionally changed end for end, either in the die-stocks or in the lathe, to reverse the direction in which the tools meet the work, and which reversal tends to equalise the general form of the thread.

5. The corrected screw 4, when converted into a master-tap, would make dies greatly superior to 2 ; it would also serve for cutting up screw tools ; and lastly,

6. The dies 5 would be employed for making the ordinary screws and working taps ; and this completes the one series of screwing apparatus.

One original tap having been obtained, it is often made subservient to the production of others ; for example, a screw tool with several points cut over the corrected original 4, would serve for striking, in the lathe, other master-taps of the same thread but different diameters. The process is so much facilitated by the perfection of the screw tool, that a clever workman would thus, without additional correction, strike mastertaps sufficiently accurate for cutting up other dies larger or smaller than 4. Sometimes also the dies 5 are used for marking out original taps a little larger or smaller than 4.

As a temporary expedient, the screw tool may be somewhat spread at the forge fire to make a tool a little coarser, or it may be upset for one a little finer, and afterwards corrected with a file; or screw tools may be made entirely with the file, and then employed for producing, in the lathe, master-taps of corresponding degrees of coarseness and of all diameters.

These are in truth some of the progressive modes by which,

under very careful management, great numbers of good useful screwing apparatus have been produced, and which answer perfectly well for all the ordinary requirements of *"binding"* or *"attachment"* screws; or as the cement by which the parts of mechanism, and structures generally, are firmly united together, but with the power of separation and reunion at pleasure.

In this comparatively inferior class of screws, considerable latitude of *proportion* may be allowed, and whether or not their pitches or rates have any exact relationship to the inch, is a matter of indifference as regards their individual usefulness; but in superior screws, or those which may be denominated *"regulating"* and *"micrometrical"* screws, it does not alone suffice that the screw shall be good in general character, and as nearly as possible a true helix; but it must also bear some defined proportion to the standard foot or inch, or other measure. The attainment of this condition has been attempted in various ways, to some of which a brief allusion was made in the second section, and a few descriptive particulars will now be offered.

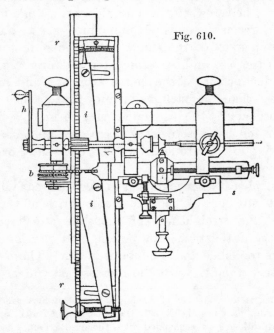

Fig. 610.

The apparatus for cutting original screws by means of a wedge or inclined plane, appears to be derived from the old fusee engine, a drawing of which is given in fig. 610; in principle it is perfect, and it is also universal within the narrow limitation of its structure *.

The handle *h*, gives rotation to the work; and at the same time, by means of the rack *r r*, and the pinion fixed on its axis, the handle traverses a slide which carries on its upper surface a bar *i*; the latter moves on a center, and may be set at any inclination by the adjusting screw and divisions; it is then fixed by its clamping screws. The slide *s*, carries the tool, and the end of this slide rests against the inclined plane *i*, through the intervention of a saddle or swing piece; the slide and tool are drawn to the left hand by the chain which is coiled round the barrel *b*, by means of a spiral spring contained within it.

Supposing the bar *i i*, to stand square or at zero, no motion would be impressed on the tool during its traverse, which we will suppose to require 10 revolutions of the pinion. But if the bar were inclined to its utmost extent, so that we may suppose the one end to project exactly one inch beyond the other, in reference to the zero line or the path of the slide, then during the 10 revolutions of the screw, the tool would traverse one inch, or the difference between the ends of the inclined bar *i*; and it would thereby cut a screw of the length of one inch, or the total inclination of the bar, and containing ten coils or threads.

But the inclination of the bar is arbitrary, and may be any quantity less than one inch, and it may lean either to the right or left; consequently the instrument may be employed in cutting all right or left hand screws, *not exceeding* 10 *turns in length*, nor measuring in their total extent above *one inch*, or the maximum inclination of the bar.

The principle of this machine may be considered faultless; but in action it will depend upon several niceties of construction, particularly the straightness of the slide and inclined bar, the equality of the rack and pinion, and the exact contact between the tool slide and the inclined plane. These difficulties augment very rapidly with the increase of dimensions; and

---

* The drawing is the half size of fig. 1, plate xvii., of Ferdinand Berthoud's *Essai sur L'Horlogerie*, Paris, 1763. M. Berthoud says, " The instrument is the most perfect with which I am acquainted ; it is the invention of M. le Lievre, and it has been reconstructed and improved by M. Gideon Duval." The templet or shaper plate determines the hyperbolical section of the fusee. Plate 37 of Rees's Cyclopedia contains an engraving of a different modification of the fusee engine, also with an inclined plane, which is ascribed to Hindley of York.

probably the machine made by Mr. Adam Reid exclusively for cutting screws, is as large as can be safely adopted : the inclined plane is 44 inches long, but the work cannot exceed $1\frac{6}{10}$ inch diam., $2\frac{1}{4}$ inch long, or ten threads in total length. The application of the inclined plane to cutting screws is therefore too contracted for the ordinary wants of the engineer, which are now admirably supplied by the screw-cutting lathes with guide screws and change wheels.

The accuracy of screws has always been closely associated with the successful performance of engines for graduating circles and right lines, and the next examples will be extracted from the published accounts of the dividing engines made by Mr. Ramsden*.

* This eminent individual received a reward from the Board of Longitude, upon the condition that he would furnish, for the benefit of the public, a full account of the methods of constructing and using his dividing machines, and which duly appeared in the following tracts :—" Description of an Engine for dividing mathematical Instruments, by Ramsden, 4to., 1777." Also, " Description of an Engine for Dividing Straight Lines, by Ramsden, 4to., 1779," from which the following particulars are extracted :—

The circular dividing engine consisted of a large wheel moved by a tangent screw ; the wheel was 45 inches diameter, and had 2160 teeth, so that six turns of the tangent screw moved the circle one degree ; the screw had a micrometer, and also a ratchet wheel of 60 teeth, therefore one tooth equalled one-tenth of a minute of a degree. The screw could be moved a quantity equal to one single tooth, or several turns and parts, by means of a cord and treadle, so that the circular works attached to the dividing wheel could be readily graduated into the required numbers, by setting the tangent screw to move the appropriate quantities ; the dividing knife or diamond point always moved on one fixed radial line, by means of a swing frame.

In ratching or cutting the wheel, says Mr. Ramsden, " the circle was divided with the greatest exactness I was capable of, first into 5 parts, and each of these into 3 ; these parts were then bisected 4 times ;" this divided the wheel into 240 divisions, each intended to contain 9 teeth. The ratching was commenced at each of the 240 divisions, by setting the screw each time to zero by its micrometer, and the cutter frame to one of the great divisions by the index ; the cutter was then pressed into the wheel by a screw, and the cutting process was interrupted at the *ninth* revolution of the screw. It was resumed at the next 240th division, (or nine degrees off,) as at first, and so on.

This process was repeated three times round the circle, after which the ratching was continued uninterruptedly around the wheel about 300 times ; this completed the teeth with satisfactory accuracy. The tangent screw was subsequently made, as explained in the text.

The *first* application of the tangent screw and ratchet to the purposes of graduation, appears to have been in the machine for cutting clock and watch wheels, by Pierre Fardoil ; see plate 23 of Thiout's *Traité d'Horlogerie*, &c. Paris, 1741. At page 55 is given a table of ratchets and settings for wheels from 102 to 800 teeth.

In Mr. Ramsden's description of his dividing engine for circles, he says: "Having measured the circumference of the dividing wheel, I found it would require a screw about one thread in a hundred coarser than the guide screw." He goes on to explain that the guide-screw moved a tool fixed in a slide carefully fitted on a triangular bar, an arrangement equivalent to a slide-rest and fixed tool; the screw to be cut was placed parallel with the slide, and the guide-screw and copy were connected by two change wheels of 198 and 200 teeth, (numbers in the proportion required between the guide and copy,) with an intermediate wheel to make the threads on the two screws in the same direction. As no account is given of the mode in which the guide-screw was itself formed, it is to be presumed it was the most correct screw that could be obtained, and was produced by some of the means described in the beginning of the present section.

Mr. Ramsden employed a more complex apparatus in originating the screw of his dividing engine for straight lines, which it was essential should contain exactly 20 threads in the inch; a condition uncalled for in the circular engine, in which the equality of the teeth of the wheel required the principal degree of attention. This second screw-cutting apparatus, which may be viewed as an offspring of the circular dividing engine, is represented in plan, in fig. 611, and may be thus briefly explained.

Fig. 611.

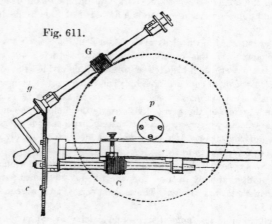

The guide-screw G is turned round by the winch, and in each revolution moves the larger tangent wheel one tooth; the tangent wheel has a small central boss or pulley p, to which is attached the one end of an elastic slip of steel, like a watch-spring; the other end of the slip is connected with the slide s, that carries the tool t, in a right line beside the screw C, which latter is the piece to be cut; and C, is connected with the guide-screw G, by a bevil pinion and wheel, g and c, as 1 to 6.

To proportion the traverse of the tool to the interval or pitch of the screw, two dots were made on the slide s, exactly five inches asunder; and in that space the screw should contain 100 coils, to be brought about by 600 turns of the handle. The guide-screw was moved that number of revolutions, and the diameter of p, was reduced by trial, until the 600 turns traversed the slide exactly from dot to dot; these points were observed at the time through a lens placed in a fixed tube, and having a fine silver wire stretched diametrically across the same as an index*.

The late Mr. Henry Maudslay, devoted an almost incredible amount of labour and expense, to the amelioration of screws and screwing apparatus; which, as regarded the works of the mill-wright and engineer, were up to that time in a very imperfect state. With the view of producing screws of exact values, he employed numerous modifications of the chain or band of steel, the inclined knife, the inclined plane, and indeed each of the known methods, which however he remodelled as additions to the

---

* See "Description of an Engine for Dividing Straight Lines," pages 13 to 16.

In the construction of his dividing engine for straight lines, Ramsden very closely followed his prior machine for circular lines, if we conceive the wheel spread out as a rectilinear slide. On the one edge of the main slide which carried the work, was cut a screw-form rack, with twenty teeth per inch, which was moved by a short fixed screw of the same pitch, by means of ratchets of 50, 48, or 32 teeth respectively; the screw could be moved a quantity equal to one single tooth, or to several turns and parts, by means of a treadle. To obtain divisions which were incompatible with the subdivision of the inch into 1000, 960 or 640 parts, the respective values of one tooth, the scale was laid on the slide at an *angle* to the direction of motion; when the swing frame was placed to traverse the *knife* at right angles to the *path* of the slide, the graduations were lengthened; when the *knife* was traversed at right angles to the *oblique* position of the scale being divided, they were shortened. This was to a small degree equivalent to having a screw of variable length. In cutting the screw-form teeth of the rectilinear dividing engine, the entire length, namely, 25·6 inches, was first divided very carefully by continual bisection into spaces of eight-tenths of an inch, by hand as usual, and the screw cutter was placed at zero at each of these divisions, pressed into the edge of the slide, and revolved sixteen times; after three repetitions at each of the principal spaces, the entire length was ratched continuously until the teeth were completed.

T T

ordinary turning-lathe with a triangular bar; a natural result, as he was then in the frequent habit of constructing that machine, and which received great improvement at his hands.

It was noticed at page 581, that of all the methods he gave the preference to the inclined knife, applied against a cylinder revolving in the lathe, by means of a slide running upon the bar of the lathe; which besides being very rapid, reduced the mechanism to its utmost simplicity. This made the process to depend almost alone on the homogeneity of the materials, and on the relation between the diameter of the cylinder and the inclination of the knife; whereas in a complex machine, every part concerned in the transmission of motion, such as each axis, wheel and slide, entails its risk of individual error, and may depreciate the accuracy of the result; and to these sources of disturbance, must be added those due to change of temperature, whether arising from the atmosphere or from friction, especially when different metals are concerned.

A rod of wood, generally of alder and about two feet long, was put between the centers, and reduced to a cylinder by a rounder or *witchet*, (fig. 343, p. 487,) attached to a slide running on the bar; the slide with the inclined knife was then applied, and the angle of the knife was gradually varied by adjusting screws, until several screws made in succession, were found to agree with some fixed measure. The experiment was then repeated with the same angle, upon cylinders of the same diameter, of tin, brass, and other comparatively soft metals, and hundreds, or it might almost be said, thousands of screws were thus made.

From amongst these screws were selected those which, on trial in the lathe, were found to be most nearly true in their angle, or to have a quiescent gliding motion; and which would also best endure a strict examination as to their pitch or intervals, both with the rule and compasses, and also when two were placed side by side, and their respective threads were compared, as the divisions on two equal scales.

The most favourable screw having been selected, it was employed as a guide-screw, in a simple apparatus which consisted of two triangular bars fixed level, parallel, and about one foot asunder, in appropriate standards with two apertures; the one bar carried the mandrel and popit heads as in the ordinary bar lathe. The slide rest embraced both bars, and was traversed thereupon by the guide screw placed about midway between the bars; the guide screw and mandrel were generally connected by three wheels, or else by two or four, when the guide and copy were required to have the reverse direction. The mandrel was not usually driven by a pulley and cord; but on the extremity of the mandrel was fixed a light wheel, with one arm serving as a winch handle for rapid motion in running back; and six or eight radial arms, (after the manner of the steering wheels of large vessels,) by which the mandrel and the screw were slowly handed round during the cut.

In a subsequent and stronger machine, the bar carrying the mandrel stood lower than the other, to admit of larger change wheels upon it, and the same driving gear was retained. And in another structure of the screw-cutting lathe, Mr. Maudslay placed the triangular bar for the lathe heads in the center, whilst a large and wide slide-plate, moving between chamfer bars attached to the framing, carried the sliding rest for the tool; in this last machine, the mandrel was driven by steam power, and the retrograde motion, had about double the velocity of that used in cutting the screw. Indeed these machines may be fairly considered to be the precursors of the present screw cutting lathes, in which the detached triangular bars or slides have been exchanged for one strong bearer with two ridges or fillets, upon which the slide plate moves for guiding the traverse of the tool.

The relations between the guide-screw and the copy were varied in all possible ways : the guide was changed end for end, or different parts of it were successively used; sometimes also two guide-screws were yoked together with three equal wheels, their nuts being connected by a bar jointed to each, and the center of this link, (whose motion thus became the *mean* of that of the guides,) was made to traverse the tool. Steel screws were also cut, and converted into original taps, from which dies were made, to be themselves used in correcting the minor errors, and render the screws in all respects as equable as possible. In fact, every scheme that he could devise, which appeared likely to benefit the result, was carefully tried, in order to perfect to the utmost, the helical character and equality of subdivision of the screw.

Mr. Maudslay succeeded by these means, after great perseverance, in making a very excellent brass screw about seven feet long, and which, compared with standard measure, was less than one-sixteenth of an inch false of its nominal length. Taking the error as the one-thousandth part of the total length of the screw, which was beyond its real quantity, to make from it a corrected screw by the system of change wheels, would have required one wheel of 1000 teeth, and another of one tooth less, or 999; but in reality the error was much less, and perhaps nearer the two-thousandth of an inch; then the wheels of 2000 and 1999 teeth would have been required; consequently the system of change wheels is scarcely applicable to the correction of very minute errors of length.

The change of the thousandth part of the total length, was therefore given to the tool as a supplementary motion, which might be added to, or subtracted from, the total traverse of the tool, in the mode explained by the diagram, fig. 612, in which all details of construction are purposely omitted. The copy C, and the guide-screw G, are supposed to be connected by equal wheels in the usual manner; the guide-screw carries the axis of the bent lever, whose arms are as 10 to 1, and which moves in a horizontal plane; the short arm carries the tool, the long arm is jointed to a saddle which slides upon a triangular bar *i i*.

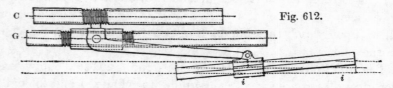

Fig. 612.

In point of fact, the tool was mounted upon the upper of two longitudinal and parallel slides, which were collectively traversed by the guide screw G. In the lower slide was fixed the axis or fulcrum of the bent lever, the short arm of which was connected by a link with the upper slide, so that the compensating motion was given to the upper slide relatively to the lower.

The triangular bar *i i*, when placed exactly parallel with the path of the tool, would produce no movement on the same, and C, and G, would be exactly alike; but if *i i*, were placed out of parallelism one inch in the whole length, the tool, during its traverse to the left by the guide-screw G, would be moved to the right by the shifting of the bent lever, one-tenth of the displacement of the bar, or one-tenth of an inch.

Therefore whilst the guide screw G, from being coarser than required, moved the principal slide the one-thousandth part of the total length in excess; the bent lever and inclined *straight* bar *i i*, pulled back the upper or compensating slide, the one-thousandth part, or the quantity in excess; making the absolute traverse of the tool exactly seven feet, or the length required for the new screw C, instead of seven feet and one-sixteenth of an inch the length of G. To have lengthened the traverse of the tool, the bar *i i*, must have been inclined the reverse way; in other words, the path of the tool, is in the diagram the *difference* of the two motions; in the reverse inclination, its path would be the *sum* of the two motions, and *i i* being a straight line, the correction would be evenly distributed at every part of the length *.

Whilst Mr. Maudslay's experiments in perfecting the screw were being carried on, his friend Mr. Barton †, paid frequent visits to his manufactory, and also pursued a similar course. Mr. Barton preferred however, the method of the chain, or flexible band, for traversing the tool the exact quantity; because the reduction of the diameter of the pulley or drum, afforded a very ready means of adjustment for total length; and all the wheels of the mechanism being individually as perfect as they could be made, a near approach to general perfection was naturally anticipated on the first trial. This mode however, is subject to the error introduced by the elasticity or elongation of the chain or band, and which is at the maximum when the greatest length of chain is uncoiled from the barrel.

These two individuals having therefore arrived, by different methods, as near to perfection as they were then respectively capable of; each made a screw of the same pitch, and 15 inches long, and the two when placed side by side were found exactly to agree throughout their length, and were considered perfect. The two screws were submitted in 1810 to the scrutiny of that celebrated mathematical instrument maker, the late Mr. Edw. Troughton, F.R.S., &c., who examined them by means of two powerful microscopes with cross wires, such as are used for reading off the graduations of astronomical instruments; applied like a pair of the most refined compasses, to measure the

---

* The apparatus was fitted to the second screw-lathe of those described, and the inclined bar was placed on temporary wooden standards.

† Subsequently Sir J. Barton, Comptroller of the Mint, &c.

equality of some 20, 50, or 100 threads, taken indiscriminately at different parts of the length of the screws *. From this severe trial it resulted, that these screws, which to the unassisted sight, and for almost every purpose of mechanism, were unexceptionable, were found to be full of all kinds of errors, being unequally coarse at different parts, and even irregular in their angles, or "drunk." This rigid scrutiny led both parties to fresh and ultimately successful efforts, but of these our limits will only allow us to notice one, apparently derived from the use of the *two* microscopes.

Mr. Barton employed *two* pairs of dies upon the one screw; the dies were fixed at various distances asunder upon one frame or bar, and the screw was passed through them. This was found to distribute the minute errors so completely, that little remained to be desired; as it is obvious that at those parts where the screw was too coarse, the outer sides of the threads were cut, and which tended to shorten the screw; and where it was too short, the inner sides were cut, which tended to lengthen the screw; in fact the two parts temporarily situated within the dies, were continually endeavouring to approximate themselves to the fixed unvarying distance, at which the dies were for the time placed †.

Mr. Maudslay did not restrict his attention to the correction of the screw for the purposes of science ‡, but he also effected a great many improvements in the system of taps and dies, by which they were made to *cut* instead of *squeeze;* as to him are due the introduction of the three cutting edges, and the division of the taps into the series of three, namely, the entering or taper tap, the middle, and the plug tap, by which shallow holes

---

* The microscope had been long used in the process of graduating instruments, but this invaluable mode of employing two microscopes in combination, was first successfully practised by Mr. Troughton.

† Mr. Barton informed the author that he employed the screw corrected in the above manner, in his engraving machine, employed for cutting with the diamond, the lines as fine as 2000 in the inch, on the steel dies referred to in the note on page 42, vol. i. ; and he said " that such was the accuracy of the mechanism, that if a line were missed, the machine could be set back for its insertion without any difference being perceptible." The author unintentionally ascribed the first application of the diamond to turning steel, to Sir John Barton, (see note, page 179, vol. i.) whereas it had been used long before by Ramsden in cutting the hardened-steel screw for his rectilinear dividing engine. See his tract, pages 14-15.

‡ The accuracy of a screw cut by Mr. Maudslay, and employed in Mr. Donkin's rectilinear dividing engine, is indisputably shown at page 654 of this volume.

or *dead* holes, in cast iron, can be safely tapped with full threads, a matter before impossible.

This engineer also made a series of taps, from six inches diameter, for attaching the pistons of steam-engines to their piston rods, to the smallest used in screw-plates for watchwork. The diameters of these taps were derived from the ordinary subdivision of the inch into eighths and sixteenths; and their threads were jointly determined by the respective strength of each screw, and the choice of defined rates, such as 3, $3\frac{1}{4}$, 4, $4\frac{1}{2}$, 6, 8, &c., threads per inch. To have employed one constant angle or proportion between the diameter and pitch, would have introduced many fractions into the rates of pitch, and an irregularity of strength in the screws themselves. The formation of these taps was rendered comparatively easy, after he had introduced the true original screw and the system of change wheels, as a common practical apparatus; many copies of these screw threads have found their way to other workshops, and have served to influence the construction of similar tools of various proportions.

Indeed, I believe it may be fairly advanced, that during the period from 1800 to 1810, Mr. Maudslay effected nearly the entire change from the old, imperfect, and accidental practice of screw-making, referred to at page 635, to the modern, exact and systematic mode now generally followed by engineers; and he pursued the subject of the screw with more or less ardour, and at an enormous expense, until his death in 1835. The results have been so important, and are so well appreciated amongst mechanical men generally, that they may be considered fully to deserve the short digression to which they have led.

In 1816, Mr. Allan was rewarded by the Society of Arts for his method of cutting micrometer screws with dies; the representation and description of the instrument will be found at page 582, where it is shown in the act of cutting an original screw with an inclined knife. Micrometer screws are cut in this apparatus much in the same manner, except that about one-third of the thread is cut with the large die, fig. 535, the inner curvature of which agrees with the curvature of the blank cylinder, and the screw is finished with the smaller die, 536, cut by an original of the same diameter as the finished screw. The piece prepared for the screw must always have two cylindrical ends to fit the semicircular bearings *b b*; this arrangement prevents the screw from being bent in the process of cutting, but which latter operation is accomplished entirely with the dies *.

About the year 1820, Mr. Clement devised and put in practice a peculiar mode for originating the guide-screw of his screw-lathe, the steps of which plan will be now described.

1. He procured from Scotland some hand-screw tools cut over a hob with concentric grooves; and to prevent the ridges or points of the screw tools, from being cut square across the end, the rest was inclined to compensate for the want of angle in the hob or cutter.

2. A brass screw was struck by hand, or chased with the tool 1.

3. The screw 2, was fixed at the back of a traversing mandrel, and clipped between two pieces of wood or dies to serve as a guide, whilst

4. A more perfect guide-screw was cut with a fixed tool, and substituted on the mandrel for 3; as Mr. Clement considered the movement derived from the opposite sides of the one screw, became the mean of the two sides, and corrected any irregularities of angle, or of drunkenness.

5. A large and a small master-tap *m*, fig. 613, were cut on the traversing mandrel with a fixed tool, the threads were about an inch long, and situated in the middle of a shaft eight or ten inches long; the small master-tap was of the same diameter as the finished screw, the large master-tap measured at the bottom of the thread the same as the blank cylinder to be screwed, as in figs. 572 and 576, page 600. The master-taps *m*, were used in cutting up the rectangular dies required in the apparatus shown in fig. 613, and now to be described.

6. On the parallel bed of a lathe, were fitted two standards or collar-heads *h h'*, intended to receive the pivots of the screw to be cut, on the extremity of which was placed a winch handle, or sometimes an intermediate socket was interposed between the

---

* Mr. A. Ross considers that the friction of Mr. Allan's apparatus is apt to retard the traverse of the screw, and therefore to cut the bottom of the thread too wide or rounding. In his practice he uses the large and small dies for a short period at the commencement and conclusion of the process, but he cuts out the principal bulk of the material, by a fixed tool inserted within a radial mortise in a semicircular *copper* die; the copper is indented more and more with the progress of the work, and serves as an efficient guide, whilst the cutting is accomplished with considerably less friction, and in a superior manner, by the cutter or turning-tool.

screw and the winch, to carry the latter to the end of the bed. The bed had also an accurate slide plate $s\ s'$, running freely upon it, the slide plate had two tails which passed beside the head h', and at the other end, a projection through which was made a transverse rectangular mortise for the dies, the one end of the

Fig. 613.

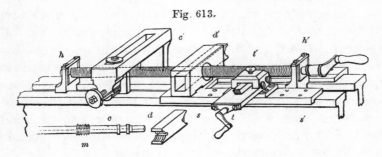

mortise is shown by the removal of the front die d, and the back die d' is seen in its proper situation; one extremity of each die was cut from the large master tap m, and the other from the small. The clamp or shackle $c\ c'$, was used to close the two dies upon the screw simultaneously; it is shown out of its true position in order that the dies and mortise may be seen, but when in use the shackle would be shifted to the right, so as to embrace the dies $d\ d'$. The plain extremity c' rested against the back die, whilst the screw c bore against the front die, through the intervention of the washer loosely attached to the clamp to save the teeth from injury; the pressure screw c had a graduated head and an index, to denote how much the dies were closed.

7. A cylinder about two feet long, prepared for the screw, was placed between the heads $h\ h'$, and the large dies, whose inner edges were of the same diameter as the cylinder, were closed upon it moderately tight, and the screw was turned round with the winch, to trace a thread from end to end; this was repeated a few times, the dies being slightly closed between each trip.

8. A screw-tool was next fixed on the slide $s\ s'$, in a chamfer slide $t\ t'$ with appropriate adjusting screws, so as to follow the dies and remove a shaving, much the same as in turning; the dies having arrived at one end of the screw, the same screw tool, or a second tool, was placed on the opposite side of the slide-plate, so as to cut during the return movement. With the progress of the screw, the screw-tool was applied at a

variety of distances from the pair of dies, as well as on opposite sides of the screw, so that the metal was cut out by the tool, and the dies were used almost alone to guide the traverse. Of course the dies were closed between each trip, and when the screw was about half cut up, the small dies were substituted for the large ones used at the commencement of the process.

9. The screw thus made, which was intended for a slide-rest, was found to be very uniform in its thread, and it was used for some time for the ordinary purposes of turning. When however it was required to be used for cutting other screws, it was found objectionable that its rate was nearly nine, whereas it was required to have eight threads per inch; it was then used in cutting a new guide-screw by means of a pair of change wheels of 50 and 56 teeth, which upon calculation were found to effect the conversion with sufficient precision.

10. From 9, the screw of 24 inches in length, one of 8 feet in length was obtained; the thread was cut one-third its depth, with the wheels, successive portions being operated upon, and the tool being carefully adjusted to the termination of the part previously cut. The general truth of the entire length was given by a repetition of the tedious mode of correction represented in the figure, with the dies and tool applied upon a bearer rather exceeding the full length of the screw*.

Although the processes 7 and 8 will produce a most uniform screw, Mr. Clement attaches little importance to the use of the dies and guide-frame alone, when *several* screws are wanted strictly of the *same length*. Of some few thus made, as nearly as possible under equal circumstances, two screws were found very nearly to agree, and a third was above a tenth of an inch longer in ten inches. This difference he thinks to have arisen in marking out the threads, from a little variation in the friction of the slide, or a difference in the first penetration of the dies.

The friction of the slide, when sufficient to cause any retard-

---

* Mr. Clement also made a very superior steel screw of about five feet in length and three inches diameter, precisely by the method 10, before he had completed the screw lathe he now commonly uses : and Mr. Whitworth followed precisely the same method in obtaining his standard screw, of about the length of 24 feet and half-inch pitch ; except that a clasp nut was used instead of the dies. It was produced from a short screw cut by Mr. Clements ; the correctional process occupied two months, and was carried with a most strict regard to avoid the unequal expansion of the screw and apparatus employed upon it.

ation, he considers to produce a constant and accumulative effect; first as it were, reducing the screw of 15 threads per inch, say to the fineness of $15\frac{1}{4}$; then acting upon that of $15\frac{1}{4}$ reducing it to $15\frac{1}{2}$, and so on; and that to such an extent, as occasionally to place the screw entirely beyond the correctional process. This cannot be the case when the thread is first marked out with the change wheels, instead of the dies.

One very important application of the screw, is to the graduation of mathematical scales, the screw is then employed to move a platform, which slides very freely, and carries the scale to be graduated; and the swing frame for the knife or diamond point is attached to some fixed part of the framing of the machine. Supposing the screw to be absolutely perfect, and to have fifty threads per inch, successive movements of fifty revolutions, would move the platform and graduate the scale exactly into true inches; but on close examination, some of the graduations will be found to exceed, and others to fall short of the true inch.

The scales assume, of course, the relative degree of accuracy of the screw employed. No test is more severe; and when these scales are examined by means of two microscopes under a magnifying power of ten or twenty times, the most minute errors become abundantly obvious, from the divisions of the scales, failing to intersect the cross wires of the instrument; the result clearly indicates, corresponding irregularities in the coarseness of the screw at the respective parts of its length. An accustomed eye can thus detect, with the microscope, differences not exceeding the one thirty-thousandth part of an inch, the twenty-five-thousandth part being comparatively of easy observation.

From Mr. Donkin's investigation of the subject, he was led to conclude that it is quite impossible to produce a screw which shall be absolutely free from error, when micrometrically proved; and in 1823, he was in consequence led to consider that as Mr. Maudslay's method of the bent lever and inclined *straight* bar, would compensate the error of total length in a nearly perfect screw, a similar mode might be applied to all the intermediate errors, by the employment of a *curve*, experimentally obtained by the method of continual bisection employed in hand dividing.

It having been explained in reference to the diagram on page 644, that the inclination given to the bar *i i*, would reduce the effective length of a screw, and the reverse inclination would increase it, Mr. Donkin considered that from the observed fact of one half of the screw, (as estimated by counting the number of threads,) being generally too coarse, and the other half too fine, the compensation would require the one half of the bar *i i*, to be inclined to the right as in the diagram, and the other half to the left, in fact thus bending the right line into an obtuse angle.

Extending this mode, upon the presumption that the quarters, eighths, or sixteenths, of the screw were also dissimilar, the bar would require many flexures instead of the one only, giving to it a more or less zig-zag character, or rather that of a gently undulating line. The undulations being proportioned *experimentally*, to effect such compensations, as should *add* to the movement of the upper platform or supplementary table, where the screw was too fine, and *subtract* from its motion, where the screw was too coarse; so as, from a screw known to be slightly irregular, to produce the divisions of a scale, or the thread of another screw, considerably nearer to equality.

He carried out this project in 1826, and he has satisfactorily proved the existence of a correctional method, which is within reach of any clever workman who will devote sufficient *patience* to the adjustment of the engine, and which latter will be now briefly explained.

Mr. Donkin's dividing machine consists first of a table or platform moving on a railway, the platform being supported by four or any greater number of wheels, that may be required for preventing flexure and for diminishing friction. The upper edges of the two rails on which the wheels turn, are made as perfectly straight as possible, the rails lie in the same horizontal plane; and they are placed at any convenient distance from each other. The table or platform is guided laterally in its course upon the rails, by four wheels, of which two are placed on each side of one of the rails; two wheels turn on fixed axles on one side of the rail, whilst the two on the other side are held tight to the rail by means of springs, thus preventing any deviation from the rectilinear course in which the platform ought to travel. To the under side of the platform is attached a claspnut, the two parts of which are so constructed, as to be applied to, or separated from the main screw, which lies below the platform, and is exactly parallel with the rails, or with the line in which the platform is made to move.

To effect the compensation, the platform or table consists

of an upper and lower plate, which are capable of a small independent motion.   The lower plate carries the fulcrum of the
bent lever, whose arms are at right angles and as fifty to one, the
lever moves in the vertical plane, so that its longer arm lies by
gravity alone on the curvilinear edge of the compensation bar; the
upper platform is pressed endlong against the shorter arm of the
bent lever, by a spring which always keeps them in close contact.

The attachment of the two platforms is peculiar; the upper,
rides upon four rollers or rather sectors, and the two plates are
connected by two slight rods placed transversely between them,
the ends of the rods are fixed over the one rail to the lower, and
over the other rail to the upper platform; the bars consequently
fulfil the office of the radius bars of a parallel rule, and suffice
by their flexure alone, for the very limited and exact motion
required in the upper table.

The compensating bar which is of the length of the screw, or 24
inches, has 48 narrow slips of metal placed like the keys of a piano-
forte, each having an appropriate adjusting and fixing screw, by
which the ends of the pieces may be placed in a continuous line,
or any of them may be placed above or below the line as required
in the following mode of compensation.   For change of total
length and adjustment for temperature, the curved bar is more
or less inclined, as in the former example, except that it is placed
edgeways or vertically; it is attached to the outside of one of
the rails, by a pivot which intersects the one end of its curvilinear
edge, and the other end is raised or depressed by a screw, which
effects the adjustment for temperature.

Conceiving the length of the guide-screw divided into 48 equal
parts, denoted by the figures 0 to 48, it would be first ascertained
by two fixed microscopes, if the halves of the screw, measured
from 0 to 24, and from 24 to 48, were absolutely equal quantities; if not, the central slip or finger would be raised or lowered
until on repeated trials the due correctional movement was applied
to the table.   The two halves would be similarly bisected and corrected in the points 12 and 36, and the quarters again bisected in
6, 18, 30, and 42; and the eighths when also bisected, would
extend the examination to the points 0, 3, 6, 9, &c., to 48.   The
easiest method is to compare the path of the slide, with the
divisions of a superior scale, fixed upon the slide or platform of
the machine.

It would now be needful to divide the whole into three parts, by the comparison of the spaces from 0 to 16, from 16 to 32, and from 32 to 48, the points 16 and 32, being adjusted until exactly equal, which is the most difficult part of the work; and then these three distances being bisected four times, every point of the 48 would have been examined, and some of them twice over. These adjustments having been repeatedly verified, during which a very frequent recurrence to the total length is imperative; the concluding step is to file off the corners of the 48 slips very carefully, so as to convert them into a line with undulations, slight it is true, but which represent fifty-fold the actual errors in the guide screw; and therefore shift the table simultaneously with its general traverse, so as to apply the exact corrections for inequality, at every point examined and found to be in error.

But the term *error* must be received in a very restricted sense, as it deserves to be noticed, that Mr. Donkin first used a screw made by Mr. Maudslay, and the maximum deflection of the curved edge of the compensation bar from a straight line, was very nearly the *eighth* of an inch, indicating the maximum *error* of the screw to have been about the 400th part of an inch; and as the curve was nearly limited to a single undulation, or a hill at one end, it may be presumed this minute error was in part attributable to a difference in the material, a source of perplexity from which no care is a sufficient protection. The dividing engine was employed as a traversing lathe in cutting a new screw, and which, although it had the advantage of the compensation, only reduced the error of the new screw to about one-third the quantity of that of the first; as shown by the new curve assumed by the compensation bar, its deflection being $\frac{1}{20}$ of an inch, when re-adjusted in the tedious and anxious method described *.

Having at length concluded the remarks on some of the most

---

* In the past year, 1842, Mr. Donkin has made a similar but enlarged dividing engine. The length of traverse of the new machine is 42 inches, the screw has 40 threads in the inch, the compensation bar is as 60 to 1, and the value of one single tooth in the counting wheel is equivalent to the 60,000th part of an inch; that of the first machine having been the 30,000th part.

It is to be hoped that Mr. Donkin will complete his labours, by publishing a detailed account of these machines, the latter of which, in particular, exhibits throughout its structure a most refined contrivance and execution, of which no adequate idea can possibly be conveyed within the limits of this slender notice, nor without exact drawings of the details, to the arrangement of which great attention has been bestowed.

refined and scientific efforts that have been employed in producing and perfectioning the screw, I shall in the next and concluding section of this already extensive chapter, proceed to the discussion of a variety of important considerations and conditions, which practically influence the proportions, forms, and general character of screws, to adapt them to multifarious purposes in the mechanical and constructive arts.

SECT. IX.—SCREW THREADS CONSIDERED IN RESPECT TO THEIR PROPORTIONS, FORMS, AND GENERAL CHARACTERS.

The proportions given to screws employed for attaching together the different parts of works, are in nearly every case arbitrary, or in other words, they are determined almost by experience alone rather than by rule, and with little or no aid from calculation, as will be shown.

In addition to the ordinary binding screws, which although arbitrary, assume proportions not far distant from a general average, many screws, either much coarser or finer than usual, are continually required for specific purposes; as are likewise other screws of some definite numbers of turns per inch, as 2, 10, 12, 20, &c., in order to effect some adjustment or movement having an immediate reference to ordinary lineal measure. But all these must be considered as still more distant, than common binding screws, from any fixed proportions, and not to be amenable to any rules beyond those of general expediency.

Neither the pitch, diameter, nor depth of thread, can be adopted as the basis from which to calculate the two other measures, on account of the different modes in which the three influence the effectiveness of the screw; nor can the proportions suitable to the ordinary $\frac{3}{4}$ inch binding screw, be doubled for the $1\frac{1}{2}$ inch screw, or halved for that of $\frac{3}{8}$ inch; as every diameter requires its individual scale to be determined in great measure by experiment, in order to produce something like a mean proportion between the dissimilar conditions, which will be separately explained in various points of view.

The reasons for the uncertainty of measure in the various fixing screws required in the constructive arts, are sufficiently manifest; as first, the force or strain to which a screw is exposed, either in the act of fixing, or in the office it has afterwards to perform, can rarely be told by calculation; and secondly, a knowledge of the strain the screw itself will safely endure without breaking in two, or without drawing out of the nut, is equally difficult of attainment; nor thirdly, can the deduction for friction be truly made from that force the screw should otherwise possess, from its angle or pitch, when viewed as a mechanical power, or as a continuous circular wedge.

The force required in the fixing of screws takes a very wide range, and is faintly indicative of the strain exerted on each. The watchmaker, in fixing his binding screws, employs with great delicacy a screw-driver the handle of which is smaller than an ordinary drawing pencil; while for screws, say of five inches diameter, a lever of six or seven feet long must be employed by the engineer, with the united exertions of as many men. But in neither case do we arrive at any available conclusion, as to the precise force exerted upon, or by each screw; nor of the greatest strain that each will safely endure.

The *absolute* measures of the strength of any individual screw being therefore nearly or quite unattainable, all that can be done to assist the judgment, is to explain the *relative* or *comparative* measures of strength in different screws, as determined by the three conditions which occur in *every screw;* whether it be right or left handed, of single or of multiplex thread, or of any section whatever; and which three conditions follow *different* laws, and *conjointly,* yet *oppositely,* determine the fitness of the screw for its particular purpose, and therefore tend to perplex the choice.

The three *relative* or *comparative* measures of strength in different screws are: first, *the mechanical power of the thread,* which is derived from its pitch; secondly, *the cohesive strength of the bolt,* which is derived from its transverse section; and thirdly, *the cohesive strength of the hold,* which is derived from the interplacement of the threads of the screw and nut.

These conditions will be first considered, principally as regards ordinary binding screws, and screw bolts and nuts, of angular threads, and which indeed constitute by far the largest number of all the screws employed; screws of angular and square threads will be then compared.

The comparative sections, figs. 614 to 617, represent screws of the same diameters, and in all of which the depth of the thread is equal to the width of the groove; figs. 615 and 617 show the ordinary proportions of ¾ inch angular and square thread screws; 614 and 616 are respectively as fine and as coarse again as 615.

Figs. 614.   615.   616.   617.

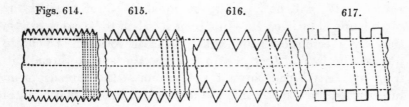

Various measures of the screws which require little further explanation are subjoined in a tabular form; and the relative degrees of strength possessed by each screw under three different points of view, are added.

MEASURES AND RELATIVE STRENGTHS OF THE SCREWS.	Fig. 614	Fig. 615	Fig. 616	Fig. 617
External diameters in hundredths of an inch .	·75	·75	·75	·75
Internal diameters in hundredths of an inch . .	·65	·55	·35	·55
Number of threads per inch, or *rates* of the screws	20·	10·	5·	5·
Depths and widths of the threads in hundredths .	·05	·10	·20	·10
Angles of the threads on the external diameters* .	1° 16′	2° 33′	5° 5′	5° 5′
Angles of the threads on the internal diameters* .	1° 28′	3° 28′	10° 47′	6° 55′
Relative mechanical powers of the threads . .	20	10	5	5
Relative cohesive strengths of the bolts . . .	4	3	1	3
Relative cohesive strengths of hold of the screws .	65	55	35	27½
Relative cohesive strengths of hold of the nuts .	75	75	75	37½

* The angles of the threads of screws are calculated trigonometrically, the circumference of the bolt being considered as the base of a right-angled triangle, and the pitch as the height of the same.

The author has adopted the following mode, which will be found to require the fewest figures; namely, to divide the pitch by the circumference, and to seek the product in the table of tangents; decimal numbers are to be used, and it is sufficiently near to consider the circumference as exactly three times the diameter.

For the external angle of fig. 616 say ·20 ÷ 2·25 = ·0888, and this quotient by Hutton's Tables gives 5 deg. 5 min.

For the internal angle of fig. 614 say ·05 ÷ 1·95 = 0·2564, and by Hutton's Tables, 1 deg. 28 min.

In this method the pitch is considered as the tangent to the angle, and the division effects the change of the two sides of the given right-angled triangle, for two others, the larger of which is 1 or unity, for the convenience of using the tables.

Square thread screws, have about twice the pitch of angular threads of similar diameters, and 617 estimated in the same manner as the angular, will stand by comparison as follows. The square thread, 617, will be found to be equal in power to 616, the pitch being alike in each. In strength of bolt to be equal to 615, their transverse areas being alike. And in strength of hold, to possess the half of that of 615, because the square thread will from necessity break through the bottom of the threads, or an interrupted line exactly like the dotted line in 616, that denotes just half the area or extent of base, of the thread of 615; which latter covers the entire surface of the contained cylinder, and not the half only.

The mechanical power of the thread, is derived from its pitch. The power, or the force of compression, is directly as the number of threads per inch, or as the *rate;* so that neglecting the friction in both cases, fig. 614 grasps with four times the power of 616, because its wedge or angle is four times as acute.

When however the angle is very great, as in the screws of fly-presses which sometimes exceed the obliquity of 45 degrees, the screw will not retain its grasp at all; neither will a wedge of 45 degrees stick fast in a cleft. Such coarse screws act by impact; they give a violent blow on the die from the momentum of the *fly,* (namely, the loaded lever, or the wheel fixed on the press-screw,) being suddenly arrested; they do not wedge fast, but on the contrary, the reaction upwards, unwinds and raises the screw for the succeeding stroke of the fly-press.

Binding screws which are disproportionately coarse, from leaning towards this condition, and also from presenting less surface-friction, are liable to become loosened if exposed to a jarring action. But when, on the contrary, the pitch is very fine, or the wedge is very acute, the surface friction against the thread of the screw is such, as occasionally to prevent their separation when the screw-bolt has remained long in the hole or nut, from the adhesion caused by the thickening of the oil, or by a slight formation of rust.

The cohesive strength of the bolt, is derived from its transverse section. The screw may be thus compared with a cylindrical rod of the same diameter as the bottom of the thread, and employed in sustaining a load; that is, neglecting torsion, which if in excess may twist the screw in two. The relative strengths are represented by the squares of the smaller diameters: in the screws of 20, 10, and 5 angular threads, the smaller diameters are 65, 55, and 35; the squares of these numbers are 4225, 3025, and 1225, which may be expressed in round numbers as 4, 3, 1; and therefore, the coarsest screw 616, has transversely only one-fourth the area, and consequently one-fourth the strength of the finest, represented in the three diagrams.

The cohesive strength of the hold, is derived from the helical ridge of the external screw, being situated within the helical groove of the internal screw.   The two helices become locked together with a degree of firmness, approaching to that by means of which the different particles of solid bodies are united into a mass; as one or both of the ridges must be in a great measure torn off in the removal of the screw, unless it be unwound or twisted out.

A slight difference in the diameter or the section of a screw and nut, is less objectionable than any variation in the coarseness or pitch; as the latter difference, even when very minute, will prevent the screw from entering the hole, unless the screw is made considerably smaller than it ought to be, and even then it will bear very imperfectly, or only on a few places of the nut.

To attempt to alter a screwed hole by the use of a tap of a different pitch, is equally fatal, as will be seen by the annexed diagram fig. 618. For instance, the upper line *a*, contains exactly 4 threads per inch, and the middle line or *b*, has $4\frac{1}{3}$ threads; they only agree at distant intervals.   The lowest line *c*, shows that which would result from forcing a tap of 4 threads such as *a*, into a hole which had been previously tapped with the $4\frac{1}{3}$ thread screw *b*, the threads would be said to cross, and would nearly

Fig. 618.

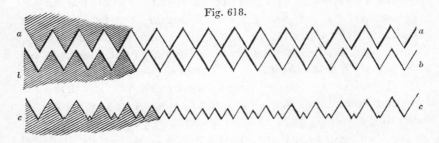

destroy each other; the same result would of course occur from employing 4 or 5 thread dies on a screw of $4\frac{1}{3}$ threads per inch.

Therefore, unless the screw tackle exactly agree in pitch with the previous thread, it is needful to remove every vestige of the former thread from the screw or hole; otherwise the result drawn at *c*, must ensue in a degree proportionate to the difference of the threads, and a large portion of the bearing surface, and consequently, of the strength and the durability of the contact, would each be lost. Some idea may thence be formed of the real and irremediable drawback frequently experienced from the dissimilarity of screwing apparatus; *nearly to agree* will not suffice, as the pitch should be identical.

The nut of a ¾-inch screw bolt is usually ¾ inch thick, as it is considered that when the threads are in good contact, and collectively equal to the diameter of the bolt, that the mutual hold of the threads exceeds the strength either of the bolt or nut; and therefore that the bolt is more likely to break in two, or the nut to burst open, rather than allow the bolt to draw out of the hole, from the thread stripping off.

When screws fit into holes tapped directly into the castings or other parts of mechanism, it is usual to allow still more threads to be in contact, even to the extent of two or more times the diameter of the screw, so as to leave the preponderance of strength greatly in favour of the hold; that the screw, which is the part more easily renewed, may be nearly certain to break in two, rather than damage the casting by tearing out the thread from the tapped hole.

Should the internal and external screws be made in the same material, that is both of wood, brass or iron, the nut or internal screw is somewhat the stronger of the two. For example, in the screw fig. 615, the base of the thread is a continuous angular ridge, which occupies the whole of the cylindrical surface represented by the dotted line. Therefore the force required to strip off the thread from the bolt, is nearly that required to punch a cylindrical hole of the same diameter and length as the bottom of the thread; for in either case the whole of the cylindrical surface has to be stripped or thrust off laterally, in a manner resembling the slow quiet action of the punching or shearing engine.

But the base of the thread in the nut, is equal to the cylindrical surface measured at the *top* of the bolt, and consequently, the materials being the same, and the length the same, considering the strength of the nut for 615 to be 75, the strength of the bolt would be only 55, or they would be respectively as the diameters of the top and bottom of the thread ; although when the bolt protrudes through the nut, the thread of the bolt derives a slight additional strength, from the threads situated *beyond* the nut, and which serve as an abutment.

It is however probable that the angular thread will not strip off at the base of the threads, either in the screw or nut, but will break through a line somewhere between the top and bottom : but these results will occur alike in all, and will not therefore materially alter the relation of strength above assumed.

Comparing 614, 615, and 616, upon the supposition that the bolts and nuts exactly fit or correspond, the strengths of the three nuts are alike, or as 75, and those of the bolts are as 65, 55, and 35, and therefore the advantage of hold lies with the bolt of finest thread ; as the finer the thread, the more nearly do the bolt and nut approach to equality of diameter and strength.

Supposing however for the purpose of explanation, that instead of the screws and nuts being carefully fitted, the screws are each one-tenth of an inch smaller than the diameters of the respective taps employed in cutting the three nuts ; 614 would draw entirely out without holding at all; the penetration and hold of 615 would be reduced to half its proper quantity ; and that of 616 to three-fourths ; and the last two screws would strip at a line more or less elevated above the base of the thread, and therefore the more easily than if the diameters exactly agreed.

The supposed error, although monstrous and excessive, shows that the finer the thread, the greater also should be the accuracy of contact of such screws; and it also shows the impolicy of employing fine threads in those situations where they will be subjected to frequent screwing and unscrewing, and also to much strain.   As although when they fit equally well, fine threads are somewhat more powerful than coarse, in hold as well as in mechanical power; the fine are also more subject to wear, and they receive from such wear, a greater and more rapid depreciation of strength, than threads of the ordinary degrees of coarseness.

In a screw of the same diameter and pitch, the ultimate strength is diminished in a twofold manner by the increase of the *depth* of the thread ; first it diminishes the transverse area of the bolt, which is therefore more disposed to break in two ; and secondly, it diminishes the individual strength of each thread, which becomes a more lofty triangle erected on the same base, and is therefore more exposed to fracture or to be stripped off.

But the durability of machinery is in nearly every case increased by the enlargement of the *bearing surfaces*, and therefore as the thread of increased depth presents more surface-bearing, the deep screw has consequently greater durability against the friction or wear, arising from the act of screwing and unscrewing. The durability of the screw becomes, in truth a fourth condition, to be borne in mind collectively with those before-named.

It frequently happens that the diameters of screwed works are so considerable, that they can neither break nor burst after the manner of bolts and nuts ; and if such large works yield to the pressures applied, the threads must be the part sacrificed. If the materials are crystalline, the thread crumbles away, but in those which are malleable and ductile, the thread, instead of stripping off as a wire, sometimes bends until the resisting side presents a perpendicular face, then overhangs, and ultimately curls over : this disposition is also shown in the abrasive wear of the screw before it yields.

Comparing the square with the angular thread in regard to friction, the square has less friction, because the angular edges of the screw and nut, mutually thrust themselves into the opposed angular grooves in the manner of the wedge. The square thread has also the advantage of presenting a more direct thrust than the angular, because in each case the resistance is at right angles to the side of the thread, and therefore in the square thread the resistance is very nearly in the line of its axis, whereas in the angular it is much more oblique.

From these reasons, the square thread is commonly selected for presses, and for regulating screws, especially those in which rapidity of pitch, combined with strength, is essential ; but as regards the ordinary attachments in machinery, the grasp of the angular thread is more powerful, from its pitch being generally about as fine again, and as before explained, angular screws and nuts are somewhat more easily fitted together.

The force exerted in bursting open a nut, depends on the angle formed by the sides of the thread, when the latter is considered as part of a cone, or as a wedge employed in splitting timber. For instance in the square thread screw, the thread forms a line at right angles to the axis, and which is dotted in the figure 619; it is not therefore a cone, but simply compresses the nut, or attempts to force the metal before it. In the deep thread fig. 620, the wedge is obtuse, and exerts much less

Figs. 619.　　　　　620.　　　　　621.

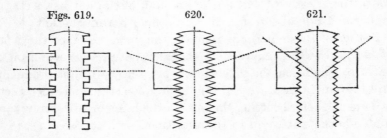

bursting effort than the acute cone represented in the shallow thread screw fig. 621; therefore the shallower the angular thread, the more acute the cone, and the greater the strain it throws upon the nut. The transverse measure of nuts, whether they are square or hexagonal, is usually about twice the diameter of the bolt, as represented in the figures, and this in general suffices to withstand the bursting effort of the bolt*.

Those nuts however which are not used for grasping, but for the regulating screws of slides and general machinery, are made much thicker, so as to occupy as much of the length of the screw as two, three, or more times its diameter; this greatly increases their surface-contact, and durability.

Should it be required to be able to compensate the nut, or to re-adapt it to the lessened size of the screw when both have been worn, the nut is made in two parts and compressed by screws, or it is made elastic so as to press upon the screw. The nuts for angular threads are divided diametrically, and re-united by two or more screws, as in fig. 622, in fact, like the semi-circular bearings of ordinary shafts; as then by filing a little of the metal away from between the two halves of the nut, they may be closed upon the angular ridges of the thread.

The nuts of square threads, by a similar treatment, would on being closed, fit accurately upon the outer or cylindrical surface of the square thread screw, but the lateral contact would not be restored; these nuts are therefore divided transversely, as shown in fig. 623, or they are made as two detached nuts placed in contact. When therefore a small quantity is removed from between them with the file, or that they are separated by one or more thicknesses of paper, the one half of the nut bears on the right hand side of the square worm, the other on the left.

Either of these methods removes the "*end play*," or the "*loss of time*," by which expression is meant that partial revolution, to and fro, which may be given to a worn screw without producing any movement or traverse in the slide upon which the screw acts. It is usual, before cutting the nuts in the lathe or with screw taps, to divide the nuts, and to re-unite them with soft solder, or it is better to hold them together with the permanent screws whilst cutting the thread.

But the screws of slides, are very apt to become most worn in the middle of their length, or at the one end, leaving the other parts nearly of their original size: it is then best to replace

Figs. 622.   623.   624.   625.

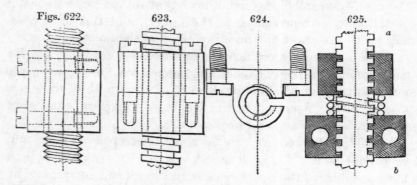

them by new screws, as the former method of adjusting the nuts cannot be used; although recourse may occasionally be had to some of the various methods of *springing*, or the elastic contrivances commonly employed in delicate mathematical and astronomical instruments. Although these should be perfectly free from shake or uncertainty of motion, they do not in general require the firm, massive, unyielding structure of engineering works and machinery.

Two kinds of the elastic nuts alone are shown; in fig. 624 the saw-cut extends throughout the length of the nut, but sometimes a portion in the middle is left uncut; the nut is usually a little *set-in*, or bent inwards with the hammer, so as to press upon the screw. In fig. 625, the two pieces *a* and *b*, bear against opposite sides of the thread, and *b* only is fixed to the slide, as in fig. 623 ; the correction is now accomplished by interposing loosely around the screw, and between the halves of the nut, a spiral spring sufficiently strong to overcome the friction of the slide upon the fittings ; the same contrivance is variously modified, sometimes two or four spiral springs are placed in cavities parallel with the screw.

The slide resists firmly any pressure from *a* to *b*, as the fixed half of the nut lies firmly against the side of the thread presented in that direction, but the pressure from *b* to *a* is sustained alone by the spiral spring ; when therefore the pressure exceeds the strength of the spring, the slide nevertheless moves endways to the extent of the misfit in the piece *b*, and which, but for the spring, would allow the slide to shake endways.   In absolute effect the contrivance is equivalent to a single nut such as *b* alone, which although possessing end play, if pulled towards *b* by a string and weight, would always keep in contact with the one side of the worm, unless the resistance were sufficient to raise the weight. The method is therefore only suited to works requiring delicacy rather than strength, and the spring if excessively strong, would constantly wear the two halves of the nut with injudicious friction and haste.

The several threads represented in figs. 626 to 638, may be considered to be departures from the angular thread fig. 626, and the square thread fig. 635, which are by far the most common.

The choice of section is collectively governed : First, by the facility of construction, in which the plain angular thread excels. Secondly, by the best resistance to strain, which is obtained in the square thread.   Thirdly, by the near equality of strength in the internal and external screw. For similar materials the space and thread should be symmetrical, as in the square thread, and in figs. 626 to 630, which screws are proper for metal works generally ; whereas in dissimilar materials, the harder of the two should have the slighter thread, as in the iron screws figs. 631 to 634, intended to be screwed into wood; the substance of the screw is supposed to be below the line, and the head to the right hand. Fourthly, by the resistance to accidental violence, either to the screws, or to the screwing tools, which is best obtained by the rejection of sharp angles or edges, as in the several rounded threads. This fourfold choice of section, like every other feature of the screw, is also mainly determined by experience alone.

Fig. 626, in which the angle is about 60 degrees, is used for most of the screws made in wood, whether in the screw-box or the turning-lathe; and also for a very large proportion of the screw bolts of ordinary mechanism. Sometimes the points of the screw tool measure nearly 90 degrees, as in the shallow thread, fig. 627, used for the thin tubes of telescopes; or at other times they only measure 45 degrees as in the very deep thread, 628, used for some mathematical and other instruments; the angles represented may be considered as nearly the extremes.

In originating accurate screws, the angular thread is always selected, because the figure of the thread is still maintained, whether the tool cut on one or on both sides of the thread, in the course of the correctional process.

Fig. 629 is the angular thread in which the ridges are more or less truncated, to increase the strength of the bolt; it may be viewed as a compound of the square and angular thread.

Fig. 630 is the angular thread in which the tops and bottoms are rounded; it is much used in engineering works, and is frequently called a round thread*.

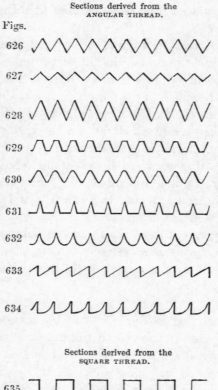

Sections derived from the
ANGULAR THREAD.

Figs.

626

627

628

629

630

631

632

633

634

Sections derived from the
SQUARE THREAD.

635

636

637

638

---

* See foot-note on p. 670.

In 631 the thread is more acute, and truncated only at the bottom of the screw, this is used for joinery-work, and greatly increases the hold upon the wood; 632 is obviously derived from 631, and is used for the same purpose.

In 633 which is also a screw for wood, the face that sustains the hold is rectangular, as in the square thread, the other is bevelled. Fig. 634 is the form of the patent wood screw, some-times called the German screw; it its hollowed to throw the advantage of bulk, in favour of the softer material, or the wood, the head of which is supposed to be on the right hand. In the last four figures, the substance of the screw is imagined to be situated below the line, and that of the wood above.

The screws which are inserted into wood are generally made taper, and not cylindrical, in order that they may cut their own nut or internal thread; some of them are pointed, so as to pene-trate without any previous hole being made : they merely thrust the fibres of wood on one side. Screws hold the most strongly in wood, when inserted horizontally as compared with the position in which the tree grew, and least strongly in the vertical position.

Fig. 635 represents the ordinary square thread screw; the space and thread are mostly of equal width, and the depth is either equal to the width, or a trifle more, say one sixth.

Fig. 366 is a departure from 635, and has been made for presses; and 637 has obviously grown out of the last from the obliteration of the angles; various proportions intermediate between 637 and 630 are used for round threads.

In some cases where the screw is required to be rapid, one single shallow groove is made of angular, square, or circular section leaving much of the original cylinder standing, as in fig. 638. For very slight purposes, a pin only is fitted to the groove, to serve as the nut; should the resistance be greater, many pins, or a comb may be employed, and this was the earliest form of nut; otherwise a screwed nut may be used with a single thread. But when the greatest resistance is required, the surface bearing of the nut is extended, by making the thread double, triple, &c. by cutting one or more intermediate grooves and a counterpart nut.

The nuts or boxes of very coarse screws for presses are now mostly cut in the lathe, although, when the screwing tools were less perfectly understood, the nuts were frequently cast. Sometimes lead, or alloys of similar fusibility, were poured in betwixt the screw and the framework of the machinery; (see note, p. 293, also 322-3, vol. 1,) but for nuts of brass and gunmetal, sand moulds were formed.   The screw was always warmed, to avoid chilling the metal; and for brass, it was sometimes heated to redness and allowed to cool, so as slightly to oxidize the surface, and lessen the disposition to a union or natural soldering of the screw and nut.   It was commonly necessary to stretch the brass by an external hammering, to counteract the shrinkage of the metal in the act of cooling, and to assist in releasing from the screw, the nut cast upon it in this manner.   The mode is by no means desirable, as the screw is exposed to being bent from the rough treatment, and to being ground by particles of sand adhering to the brass.

The tangent screws used for screw wheels, have mostly angular or truncated angular threads fig. 629, as screws absolutely square, cannot be fitted with good contact and freedom from shake between the thread and teeth; and probably the same rules by which the teeth of ordinary wheels and racks are reciprocally set out, should be also applied to the delineation of the teeth of worm-wheels, and the threads or teeth of their appropriate screws.

Tangent screws are occasionally double, triple, or quadruple, in order that 2, 3, or 4 teeth of the wheel may be moved during each revolution of the screw.   In the Piedmont silk-mills, this principle is carried to the extreme, as the screw and wheel become alike, and revolve turn for turn; the teeth supposing them to be 20, are then identical with those of a 20 thread screw, the *angular* coils of which cross the axis at the angle of 45°, that is when the shafts lie at right angles to each other; other proportions and angles may be adopted.   In reality they fulfil the office of bevel wheels, or rather of skew-bevel wheels, in which latter also, the axes, from being in different planes, may cross each other; so that the skew-bevel wheels may be in the center of long shafts, but which cannot be the case in ordinary bevel wheels, the teeth of which lie in the same plane as the axis of the wheel.   The Piedmont wheels act with a very reduced extent of bearing or contact surface, and a considerable amount of the sliding action of screws, which is disadvantageous in the teeth of wheels, although inseparable from all those with inclined teeth, and which are indeed more or less distant modifications of the screw *.

---

* When the obliquity of the teeth of worm-wheels is small, it gives a very smooth

Having treated somewhat in detail the different forms of screws, and the circumstances which adapt them to their several purposes, I have now to consider some of the inconveniences which have unavoidably arisen from the indefinite choice of proportions in ordinary screws, and also some of the means that have been proposed for their correction. The slight discussion of the more important of these topics will permit the introduction of various additional points of information on this almost inexhaustible subject, the screw.

No inconvenience is felt from the dissimilarities of screws, so long as the *same* screwing tools are always employed in effecting repairs in, or additions to, the *same* works. But when it is considered, how small a difference in either of the measures will mar the correspondence of the screw and nut; and further the very arbitrary and accidental manner, in which the proportions of screwing apparatus have been determined by a variety of individuals, to suit their particular wants, and without any attempt at uniformity of practice, (sometimes on the contrary, with an express desire to be peculiar,) it is perhaps some matter of surprise when the screws made in different establishments properly agree. Indeed their agreement can be hardly expected, unless they are derived from the same source, and that some considerable pains are taken not to depart from the respective proportions first adopted.

In a few isolated cases this inconvenience has been partially remedied by common consent and adoption, as in the so-called *air-pump thread,* which is pretty generally used by the makers of pneumatic apparatus; and to a certain degree also in some of the screws used in gas-fittings and in gun-work. But the non-existence of any common standard or scale, enhances both the delay and expense of repairs in general mechanism, and leads to the occasional necessity for making additional sizes of tools to match particular works, however extensive the supply of screw apparatus.

This perplexity is felt in a degree especially severe and costly, as regards marine and locomotive engines, which from necessity, have to be repaired in localities far distant from those in which they were made; and therefore require that the packet station,

---

action, but at the expense of friction ; but in ordinary toothed wheels, the teeth are exactly square across or in the plane of the axis, and the aim is to employ rolling contact, with the greatest possible exclusion of sliding, from amongst the teeth.

or railway depot, should contain sets of screwing tackle, corresponding with those used by every different manufacturer whose works have to be dealt with; otherwise, both the delay and expense are from necessity aggravated.

Mr. Whitworth has suggested that for steam machinery and for the purposes of engineering in general, "an uniform system of screw threads" should be adopted, and after having used some prior scales, he has proposed the following table, which may be justly considered as a mean between the different kinds of threads used by the leading engineers.

Mr. Whitworth's Table for Angular Thread Screws. *

Diameters in inches . . .	$\frac{1}{4}$	$\frac{5}{16}$	$\frac{3}{8}$	$\frac{7}{16}$	$\frac{1}{2}$	$\frac{5}{8}$	$\frac{3}{4}$	$\frac{7}{8}$	$1''$	$1\frac{1}{8}$	$1\frac{1}{4}$	$1\frac{3}{8}$	$1\frac{1}{2}$	$1\frac{5}{8}$	$1\frac{3}{4}$	$1\frac{7}{8}$	$2''$
Nos. of threads to the inch .	20	18	16	14	12	11	10	9	8	7	7	6	6	5	5	$4\frac{1}{2}$	$4\frac{1}{2}$

Diameters in inches . . .	$2\frac{1}{4}$	$2\frac{1}{2}$	$2\frac{3}{4}$	$3''$	$3\frac{1}{4}$	$3\frac{1}{2}$	$3\frac{3}{4}$	$4''$	$4\frac{1}{4}$	$4\frac{1}{2}$	$4\frac{3}{4}$	$5''$	$5\frac{1}{4}$	$5\frac{1}{2}$	$5\frac{3}{4}$	$6''$
Nos. of threads to the inch .	4	4	$3\frac{1}{2}$	$3\frac{1}{2}$	$3\frac{1}{4}$	$3\frac{1}{4}$	3	3	$2\frac{7}{8}$	$2\frac{7}{8}$	$2\frac{3}{4}$	$2\frac{3}{4}$	$2\frac{5}{8}$	$2\frac{5}{8}$	$2\frac{1}{2}$	$2\frac{1}{2}$

As regards the smaller mechanism, made principally in brass and steel, such as mathematical instruments and many others,

---

* In selecting this scale, the following judicious course was adopted :—"An extensive collection was made of screw-bolts from the principal workshops throughout England, and the average thread was carefully observed for different diameters. The $\frac{1}{4}$ inch, $\frac{1}{2}$ inch, 1 and $1\frac{1}{2}$ inch, were particularly selected, and taken as the fixed points of a scale by which the intermediate sizes were regulated, avoiding small fractional parts in the number of threads to the inch. The scale was afterwards extended to 6 inches. The pitches thus obtained for angular threads were as above :—

"Above the diameter of 1 inch the same pitch is used for two sizes, to avoid small fractional parts. The proportion between the pitch and the diameter varies throughout the entire scale.

"Thus the pitch of the $\frac{1}{4}$ inch screw is $\frac{1}{5}$th of the diameter ; that of the $\frac{1}{2}$ inch $\frac{1}{6}$th, of the 1 inch $\frac{1}{8}$th, of the 4 inches $\frac{1}{12}$th, and of the 6 inches $\frac{1}{15}$th.

"The depth of the thread in the various specimens is then alluded to. In this respect the variation was greater than in the pitch. The angle made by the sides of the thread being taken as an expression for the depth, the mean of the angle in 1 inch screws was found to be about 55°, which was also nearly the mean in screws of different diameters. Hence it was adopted throughout the scale, and a constant proportion was thus established between the depth and the pitch of the thread. In calculating the former, a deduction must be made for the quantity rounded off, amounting to $\frac{1}{3}$rd of the whole depth, i.e., $\frac{1}{6}$th from the top, and $\frac{1}{6}$th from the bottom of the thread. Making this deduction, the angle of 55° gives for the actual depth rather more than $\frac{2}{3}$ths, and less than $\frac{3}{8}$rds of the pitch."—*Quoted from the Abstract of Mr. Whitworth's Paper, given in the Proceedings of the Institution of Civil Engineers,* 1841, *p.* 157-160. *The entire paper is also printed separately.*

the screws in the above scale below half an inch diameter are admitted to be too coarse; and the acute angular threads which are not rounded, are decidedly to be preferred from their greater delicacy and durability, that is when their strengths are proportioned to the resistances to which they are exposed. In these respects the following table may be considered preferable.

*Table for Small Screws of Fine Angular Threads.**

Diameters in vulgar fractions of the inch	$\frac{1}{2}$	$\frac{15}{32}$	$\frac{7}{16}$	$\frac{13}{32}$	$\frac{3}{8}$	$\frac{11}{32}$	$\frac{5}{16}$	$\frac{9}{32}$	$\frac{1}{4}$	$\frac{7}{32}$	$\frac{1}{8}$
Diameters in hundths. of the inch nearly	·50	·47	·44	·41	·37	·34	·31	·28	·25	·22	·20
Number of threads to the inch . .	16	18	18	20	20	24	24	28	28	32	36
Diameters in hundredths of the inch . .	·18	·16	·14	·12	·10	·09	·08	·07	·06	·05	·04
Number of threads to the inch . .	36	40	40	48	48	56	56	64	72	80	100

* This table was arranged by Mr. Chidson, of Liverpool, who made, first, a set of coarse angular thread taps from ¼ to 1 inch, agreeably to the terms of Mr. Whitworth's table, giving to the screw tool the angle of 55 degrees, and also a set of square thread taps, of the same diameters, and, as usual, of twice the pitch. This led Mr. Chidson to set out and construct a series of finer and deeper threads, from ¼ inch to 14 hundredths diameter, agreeably to the arrangement in the second table, and with screw tools of the angle of 45 degrees.

I have great pleasure in stating my individual opinion of the suitability of the table to its intended purpose, and on comparing the screws with those of similar diameters used by Holtzapffel and Co., I found about one third to be nearly identical in pitch, one third to be slightly coarser, and the others slightly finer. As regards the workmanship of these taps, made by Mr. Chidson for his own use, and principally with his own hands, by means of the change wheels and single point tools, it gives me great pleasure to report most favourably.

The tables above given, and which have been *selected* and not *calculated*, will serve to explain the inapplicability of the mode of calculation proposed in various popular works; namely, for angular thread screws, to divide the diameter by 8 for the pitch, when, it is said, such screws will all possess the angle of 3½ degrees nearly; and for square threads to divide by 4, thus giving an angle of 7 degrees nearly; therefore

Angular thread screws of	8	6	4	2	1	½	¼	inches diameter
would have pitches of	1	¾	½	¼	⅛	$\frac{1}{16}$	$\frac{1}{32}$	inches rise
or rates of	1	1⅓	2	4	8	16	32	threads per inch
which differ greatly from		2½	3	4½	8	12	20	Whitworth's observational numbers.

By the use of the constant divisor 8, the one-inch screw agrees with Whitworth's table, the extremes are respectively too coarse and too fine; as instead of 8 being employed, the actual divisors vary from about 5 to 16, and therefore a theoretical mode would probably require a logarithmic scheme. But were this followed out with care, the adjustment of the fractional threads so obtained, for those of whole numbers, would completely invalidate the precision of the rule; and the result would not be in any respect better than when adjusted experimentally, as at present.

There is little doubt that if we could entirely recommence the labours of the mechanist, or if we could sweep away all the screwing tools now in use, and also all the existing engines, machines, tools, instruments, and other works, which have been in part made through their agency, these proposed scales, or others not greatly differing from them, (as the choice is in great measure arbitrary,) would be found of great general advantage ; the former for the larger, the latter for the smaller works. But until all these myriads of objects are laid on one side, or that repairs are no longer wanted in them, the old tools must from absolute necessity be retained, in addition to those proposed in these or any other schemes. It would be of course highly judicious in *new* manufacturing establishments to adopt such conventional scales, as they would, to that extent, promote this desirable but almost impracticable end, namely, that of unity of system ; but which, although highly fascinating and apparently tenable, is surrounded by so many interferences, that it may perhaps be considered both as needless and hopeless to attempt to carry it out to the full, or to make the system absolutely universal : and some of the circumstances which affect the proposition will be now briefly given.

First, *agreement with* STANDARD MEASURE, *although convenient, is not indispensable.* It may be truly observed, that as regards the general usefulness of a screw such as 615, which was supposed to measure ¾ inch diameter, and to have 10 threads per inch, it is nearly immaterial whether the diameter be three or four hundredths of an inch larger or smaller than ¾ of an inch; or whether it have 9, $9\frac{1}{16}$, $9\frac{3}{4}$, $10\frac{1}{2}$, or 11, threads per inch, or any fractional number between these ; or whether the thread be a trifle more or less acute, or that it be slightly truncated or rounded; so long as the threads in the screw and nut are but truly helical and alike, in order that the threads mutually bear upon each other at every part; that is, as regards the simple purpose of the binding screw or bolt, namely, the holding of separate parts in firm contact. And as the same may be said of every screw, namely, that a small variation in diameter or pitch is commonly immaterial, it follows, that the good office of a screw does not depend on its having any assigned relation to the standard measure of this or any other country.

Secondly, *The change of system would cause an inconvenient increase in the number of screwing tools used.*—Great numbers of excellent and useful screws, of accidental measures, have been made by various mechanicians; and the author hopes to be excused for citing the example with which he is most familiar.

Between the years 1794—1800, the author's father made a few varieties of taps, dies, hobs, and screw tools, after the modes explained at pages 635 and 636; these varieties of pitch were ultimately extended to twelve kinds, of each of which was formed a deep and shallow hob, or screw tool-cutter. These, when measured many years afterwards, were found nearly to possess in each inch of their length, the threads and decimal parts that are expressed in the following table.

Approximate Values of I. I. Holtzapffell's Original Screw Threads.

Number . .	1	2	3	4	5	6	7	8	9	10	11	12
Threads in 1 inch	6·58	8·25	9·45	13·09	16·5	19·89	22·12	25·71	28·88	36·10	39·83	55·11

The angle of the deep threads is about 50 degrees; of the shallow 60 degrees.

This irregularity of pitch would not have occurred had the screw-lathe with change-wheels been then in use; but such was not the case. For a long series of years I. I. Holtzapffel, (in conjunction with his partner, I. G. Deyerlein, from 1804 to 1827,) made, as occasion required, a large or a small screw, a coarse or fine, a shallow or deep thread, and so forth. By which accumulative mode, their series of working taps and dies, together with screw tools, gages, chucks, carriers, and a variety of subordinate apparatus, became extended to not less than one hundred varieties of all kinds.

About one-third of these sizes have been constantly used, up to the present time, both by H. & Co., and by other persons to whom copies of these screw tackles have been supplied, and consequently many thousands of screws of these kinds have been made : this implies the continual necessity for repairs and alterations in old works, which can only be accomplished by retaining the original sizes.

Since the period at which H. & Co. made their screw lathe, they have employed the aliquot threads for all screws above half an inch; indeed, most of these have also been cut in the screw lathe. To have introduced the same method in the small binding screws which are not made in the screw lathe, but with the diestocks and chasing tools, would have doubled the number of

X X

their working-screw tackle, and the attendant apparatus; with the risk of confusion from the increased number, but without commensurate advantage as regards the purposes to which they are applied.

Doubtless the same reasons have operated in numerous other factories, as the long existence of good useful tools has often lessened, if not annulled, the advantage to be derived from a change which refers more immediately to engineering works; and in which a partial remedy is supplied, as steam-engines, &c. are frequently accompanied with spare bolts and nuts, and also with corresponding screw apparatus, to be employed in repairs; the additional cost of such parts being insignificant, compared with the value of the machinery itself.

Thirdly : *Unless the standard sizes of screws become inconveniently numerous, many useful kinds must be omitted, or treated as exceptions.* For instance, in ordinary binding screws, more particularly in the smaller sizes, two if not three degrees of coarseness should exist for every diameter, and which might be denominated the coarse, medium, and fine series ; and again, particular circumstances require that threads should be of shallow or of deep angular sections, or that the threads should be rounded, square, or of some other kinds; in this way alone, a fitness for all conditions would inconveniently augment the number of the standards.

In many cases besides, screws of *several* diameters are made of the *one* pitch. In order, for example, that the hole when worn may be tapped afresh, and fitted with screws of the same pitch or thread, but a trifle larger*; or that a partially worn screw may be corrected with the dies or in the lathe, and fitted with a smaller nut of the same pitch. A succession of taps of the same pitch also readily permits a larger screw to be employed, when that of smaller diameter has been found to break, either from an error of judgment in the first construction of the machine, or from its being accidentally submitted to a strain greater than it was intended ever to bear †.

---

* This is done in some of the patent screws for joinery work, so that when the thread in the wood is deteriorated from the frequent removal of the screw, another of the same pitch, but larger diameter, may be substituted.

† Mr. Clement has screw taps of $\frac{3}{4}$, $\frac{7}{8}$, 1, $1\frac{1}{8}$, $1\frac{1}{4}$, $1\frac{3}{8}$, $1\frac{1}{2}$, &c., inch diameter, and all of seven threads per inch. Holtzapffel and Co. have taps, &c., for screws of ten threads per inch of fifteen different kinds, which are used for slides and adjustments ; besides less extensive repetitions of other threads.

It is also in some cases requisite to have right and left hand screws of the same pitch, that, amongst other purposes, they may effect simultaneous yet opposite adjustments in machinery, as in some universal chucks : and also some few screws, the threads of which are double, triple, quadruple, and so forth, for giving to screws of small diameters considerable rapidity of pitch or traverse, or a fixed ratio to other screws associated with them, in the same piece of mechanism.

Fourthly : *Friction prevents the strict maintenance of standard gages for screws.* The universality of system, to be perfect, should admit that a bolt made this year in London, should agree with a nut made ten or fifty years hence in Manchester, which is not called for, nor perhaps possible, if an absolute fit be required : in reference to this we must commence by a small digression.

In comparing the Exchequer Standard Yard Measure with the copies made from it, friction in no way interferes, as the two measures are successively observed through two fixed microscopes, as before adverted to. But we cannot thus measure a cylinder, as either callipers, or a counterpart cylinder *placed in contact,* must be employed as the test ; and each time of trial the cylinder is absolutely, although very slightly worn, by the traverse of the surfaces against each other ; the form of the cylindrical gage being simple, to increase its durability, it is worked to the figure after having been hardened.

In measuring a screw, the callipers are insufficient, and the one screw must be screwed into the other : from this trial much more motion, friction, and abrasion arise. Further, the screw gage cannot, from its complex form, be readily figured after the material has been hardened; and if hardened subsequently to the helical form having been given, the measure becomes, in some degree, altered, from the action of the fire and water, which is a fatal objection.

Under ordinary and proper management, the production of a number of similar pieces may be obtained with sufficient exactitude, by giving to the *tool* some constant condition. For example, a hundred nuts tapped with the same tap, will be very nearly alike in their thread ; and a hundred screws passed through the hole of a screw-plate, will similarly agree in size, because of the nearly constant dimensions of the tools, for a moderate period.

In practice, the same relative constancy is given to the dies of

die-stocks and bolt-screwing engines, and partly so to the tools
of the screw-cutting lathe.   Sometimes the pressure or adjusting screw has graduations or a micrometer; and numerous
contrivances of eccentrics, cams, and stops, are employed to effect
the purpose of bringing the die or turning-tool to one constant
position, for each succeeding screw; these matters are too varied
and general to require more minute notice. Part of such modes
may serve sufficiently well for ten, or a hundred screws, provided
that no accident occur to the tool; but if it were attempted to
extend this mode to a thousand, or a hundred thousand pieces,
the same tool could not, even without accident, endure the trial:
it would have become not only unfit for cutting, but also so far
worn away as to leave the last of the works materially larger
than the first.

    In respect to screws, the instrument, the size of which claims
the most importance, is perhaps the plug-tap, or that which
removes the last portion of the material, and therefore determines the diameter of the internal thread; but as the tap is
continually, although slowly, wearing smaller, the first and last
nut made with it unavoidably differ a little in size. It is on
account of the wearing of the tap, amongst other circumstances,
that when screws and nuts are made in large numbers, and are
required to be capable of being interchanged, it becomes needful
to make a small allowance for error, or to make the screws a
trifle smaller than the nuts.

    In order to retain the sizes of the taps used by Holtzapffel & Co.

they some years ago made a set of original taps
exactly of the size of the proposed screws, and to
be called A; these, when two or three times
used, to rub off the burrs, were employed for
cutting regulating dies B, of the form of fig. 639,
with two shoulders, so that the dies could be
absolutely closed, and yet leave a space for the
shavings or cuttings. In making all their plug-
taps, they are first prepared with the ordinary
shop tools, until the taps are so nearly com-

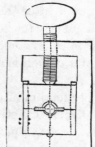

pleted, that, grasped between the regulating dies B, the latter
close within the fortieth or fiftieth of an inch, therefore leaving
the dies B next to nothing to perform in the way of cutting,
but only the office of regulating the diameter of the working

plug-taps. Should the dies B meet with any accident, the taps A, which have to this stage been only used for one pair of regulating dies, exist for making repetitions of B. This method has been found to fulfil its intended purpose very effectually for several years, but at the same time it is not proposed to apply this or any other system universally.

In conclusion, it may be said that by far the most important argument in favour of the adoption of screws of aliquot pitches applies to steam machinery and similar large works, and that, principally, because it brings all such screws within the province of the screw-lathe with change-wheels, which has become, in engineering establishments and some others, a very general tool. This valuable tool alone renders each engineer in a great measure independent of his neighbour, as screws of 2, $2\frac{1}{4}$, $2\frac{1}{2}$, 3, 10, or 20 threads in the inch, are readily measured with the common rule, and copied with the screw-wheels, and a single-pointed tool, or an ordinary comb or chasing tool with many points.

And therefore, with the modern facility of work, were engineers severally to make their screw tackle from only the *written* measures of any conventional table, they would be at once abundantly within reach of the adjustment of the tools, and that without any standard gages; the strict introduction of which would almost demand that all the tools made in uniformity with them should emanate from one center, or be submitted to some office for inspection and sanction,—and this would be indeed to buy the *occasional* advantage at too dear a rate.

It must, however, be unhesitatingly granted, that the argument applies but little, if at all, to a variety of screws which from their smaller size are not made in the screw-lathe, but with die-stocks and the hand-chasing tools only; and which are employed in branches of art that may be considered as almost isolated from one another, and therefore not to require uniformity.

For instance, the makers of astronomical, mathematical, and philosophical instruments, of clocks and watches, of guns, of locks and ironmongery, of lamps and gas apparatus, and a multitude of other works, possess, in each case, an amount of skill which applies specifically to these several occupations; so that unless the works made by each are returned to the absolute makers for reparation, they are at any rate sent to an individual engaged in the same line of business.

Under these circumstances, it is obvious that the gunmakers, watchmakers, and others, would derive little or no advantage from one system of threads prevailing throughout all their trades; in many of which, as before noticed, partial systems respectively adapted to them already exist. The means employed by the generality of artizans in matching strange threads, are, in addition, entirely independent of the screw lathe, and apply equally well to all threads, whether of aliquot measures or not; as it is usual to convert one of the given screws, if it be of steel, into a tap, or otherwise to file a screw tool to the same pitch by hand, wherewith to strike the thread of the screw or tap; and when several screws are wanted, a pair of dies is expressly made.

But at the same time that, from these manifold considerations, it appears to be quite unnecessary to interfere with so many existing arrangements and interests, it must be freely admitted that advantage would ultimately accrue from making *all new screws of aliquot measures;* and which, by gradually superseding the old irregular threads, would tend eventually, although slowly, to introduce a more defined and systematic arrangement in screw tackle, and also to improve their general character.

The author has now concluded the various remarks he proposes to offer on the formation of the screw for the general purposes of mechanism; on the modes pursued by various celebrated mechanicians for its improvement; and on various practical considerations which influence the choice of screws: but he is desirous briefly to advert to some few peculiar, interesting and practical methods of producing this important element of construction.

The threads of wrought-iron screws, have been forged whilst red hot, between top and bottom swage tools, having helical surfaces like those of screw dies; screws have been twisted whilst red hot, out of rectangular bars, by means of the tail vice and hook wrench; as in making screw augers. Screws intended for ordinary vices, have been compressed whilst cold, somewhat as with die-stocks; the lever is in this case very long, and the die is a square block of hardened steel, with an internal square thread screw, left smooth or without notches. The thread it partly indented and partly squeezed up, the diameter of the iron cylinder being less than that of the finished screw : this action severely tests the iron *.

A patent was taken out in 1839 by Mr. Wilks, for making both the boxes and screws of tail vices and presses in malleable cast iron.   The peculiarities in the moulding processes are that the core for the hollow worm, or box, is made in a brass core box, divided longitudinally into three parts, which are filled separately, and closed together with a stick of wood in the center, to stiffen the core and serve for the core print.   The core box is then connected by rings, like the hoops of a cask : this completes the core, which is removed, dried, and inserted in a mould made from a model of the exterior of the box, constructed as usual.

In moulding the solid screw, the moulding-flask is a tube with a cap having an internal thread, exactly like that of the screw ; the tube is filled with sand, and a plain wooden rod, nearly equal in diameter to the axis of the screw, is thrust in the sand, to form a cavity.   The screwed cap is then attached to the flask, and a brass screw, exactly like that to be cast, is guided into the sand by means of the screw-cap, and taps a thread in the sand mould very accurately.   The screw-cap is then removed, and the second part of the flask, in which the head of the vice-screw has been moulded, is fitted on, and the screw is poured.

After having been cast, the screws and boxes are rendered malleable in the usual way, except that they are placed vertically; in general the box is slightly corrected with a screw-tap.

Large quantities of screws have been produced by Mr. Warren's patent process for manufacturing screws of malleable cast-iron for joinery work : a most ingenious plan is employed therein for winding the models into and out of the *solid* sand-mould, which is thereby made beautifully smooth and accurate. After the last description the general method will be readily understood, if it be considered that the first side of an ordinary flask is rammed full of sand, on an iron plate having conical projections like the heads of screws, in regular lines half an inch asunder, and ribs to form the channels by which the metal is to be admitted.   The flask when filled is placed in a machine, beneath a plate of metal

---

* Applied by the Wrights' Vice-makers of Birmingham. See Technological Repository, vol. vi., p. 289. For the mode of soldering the thread in the box or the hollow screw of the vice, see the same paper, and also vol. i., p. 443, of this work.

with screwed holes, also half an inch asunder, and each fitted with a pattern screw terminating above in a crank, like a winch handle, say of $\frac{1}{4}$ inch radius.

Any of these screws on being turned by its crank with the fingers, would pierce the sand as in Wilks's process; but by employing a *crank-plate* pierced with a like number of holes, to receive the pins of all the cranks, the whole of the screw models are twisted in at once, and removed with the same facility.

The notches of the screws are cut by a circular saw; if large they may be moulded. The cast-iron screws are subsequently rendered malleable, by the decarbonizing process described in the former volume, pages 259-260 *.

Mr. Perkins's patent cast-iron water-pipes with screw joints, may be considered as another example. The patent pipes are connected with right and left hand screws and loose sockets, which draw the ends of the pipes into contact, or rather against a thick greased pasteboard washer interposed between them. The pipes are made entirely by foundry-work, and from patterns and core-boxes divided in halves, in the ordinary manner. Mr. Perkins says that although the patent pipes possess several advantages over ordinary cast-iron pipes with the *spigot and faucet* joint, they are produced at the same price, and save much ultimate expense in fixing †.

In Mr. Scott's subsequent patent for joining cast-iron and other pipes for various fluids, the method commonly known as the "union-joint" is employed, and which offers additional facility in the removal of one pipe from the midst of a series. Each pipe has at the one end a projecting external screw, and at the other a projecting fillet or flange; the socket is cast loosely around the pipe, but is prevented from being removed or lost by the projections at each end of the same. The inside screw of the socket cast upon the first pipe *a*, screws upon the external screw of the next pipe *b*, until the socket comes in contact with the fillet on *a*, and thus draws *a* and *b* into close contact with the washer that is placed between them. One cast-iron pipe and its appro-

---

* Date of Mr. Warren's patent for an improved machine for making screws, 4th August 1841; described in Rep. of Patent Inv., for March 1843, also in the Glasgow Mechanics' and Engineers' Mag., same date. The machine was constructed by Mr. Ingram of Birmingham, and is successfully worked by him.

† Date of patent, 21st Sept. 1841, described in Rep. of Patent Inv. Oct. 1841.

priate socket are moulded at one operation, which is curiously accomplished by the use of two sand cores, the inner of which is of the length of the pipe, and solid as usual; the outer core is made as a loose ring around the inner. The union-joint is differently produced by Mr. Scott in wrought-iron and soft metal pipes *.

A peculiar method of making screw joints is employed in Mr. Rand's patent collapsible tubes for preserving paints, provisions, &c. The tin, whilst at the ordinary atmospheric temperature, is forced, almost as a cement, into the screwed recesses of brass or iron moulds; and the threads are thus made to assume the helical form, with great rapidity, uniformity, and perfection †.

Indeed it is difficult, nay impossible, to find the limit of the methods employed in producing, or those of subsequently employing this interesting object, the screw ; which not only enters in endless variety into appliances and structures in metal, wood, and other materials, but is likewise rendered available in most different yet important modes, as in the screw-piles for sandy foundations, screws for raising water, for blowing furnaces, ventilating apartments, and propelling ships.

Should it appear that the formation of the screw has been treated in greater detail than the other subjects with which it is associated, either as regards the modes of proceeding or the mechanism employed ; the author would observe that it appeared to him that by this mode alone he could introduce, in something like order, a variety of interesting particulars, which although they have occupied very .many pages, are but as a fragment of what might be said on a subject which has engrossed so much attention.

---

* Date of patent, 6th July, 1842. See Mechanics' Magazine, 1843, page 104.

† Rand's second patent for making collapsible vessels, 29th Sept. 1842. Under the first patent the tin was drawn into tube, (see vol. i., p. 431,) and the convex and screwed ends were cast and soldered in ; by the improved method the entire vessel is made from a small thick perforated disk of tin by one blow of a fly-press. The lower part of the mould has a shallow cylindrical cup, concave and tapped at the base ; the upper part of the mould is a cylinder as much smaller than the cup as the intended thickness of the metal, which on the blow being given is compressed into the screw, and ascends four or five inches up the cylinder or ram. For large sizes a hydrostatic press is employed.

CHAPTER XXVII

SAWS.

SECTION I.—DIVISION OF THE SUBJECT—FORMS OF SAW TEETH.

THE saw is the instrument which is almost exclusively employed for converting wood, ivory, and various other substances, from their original forms to those shapes required in the arts ; and in general, the thin serrated blade proceeds along the superficies of the required object, whether they be plane, circular, or irregular, and effects its office with considerable speed and accuracy, and comparatively insignificant waste. Unless a tree is felled with the axe, the saw is employed, first, in the forest in separating the tree from its roots, and cutting it into lengths convenient for transport; the saw is next used at the saw-pit in converting the timber into plank and scantling of various dimensions ; and the saw is subsequently employed in the workshop, by the joiner, cabinet-maker, and numerous other artizans, in reducing the plank or board into smaller pieces, ready for the application of the plane, the file, and other finishing tools. In some elaborate and highly ornamental arts, the saw as will be shown is nearly the only instrument used.

Many of the machines now employed in sawing are, as it will be seen, derived from similar processes before executed, and in many cases less perfectly so, by hand labour. The saw is but little used for similar preparatory works in metal, the figuration of which is for the most part, accomplished by the furnace, the hammer, or rollers; matters that have been described in the first volume.

It is proposed to consider saws in two groups, namely, rectilinear saws, and circular saws : the precedence will be given to the more simple kinds, or those rectilinear saws used by hand, and generally without additional mechanism ; conditions which do not apply to the circular saw, which is always combined with some portion of machinery. And for the perspicuity of the whole subject, it has been thought best to place the general remarks on the forms of teeth of saws, at the beginning of the chapter ;

from which arrangement many advantages appear to arise, notwithstanding that it implies the necessity for adverting to various saws, before their specific or particular descriptions have been given, and which objection will be in part removed by the previous inspection of the table on page 699.

The blade of the rectilinear saw is usually a thin plate of sheet steel, which in the first instance is rolled of equal thickness throughout: the teeth are then punched along its edge, previously to the blade being hardened and tempered, after which it is smithed or hammered, so as to make the saw quite flat. The blade is then ground upon a grindstone of considerable diameter, and principally crossways, so as to reduce the thickness of the metal from the teeth towards the back. When, by means of the hammer, the blade has been rendered of uniform tension or elasticity, the teeth are sharpened with a file, and slightly bent, to the right and left alternately, in order that they may cut a groove so much wider than the general thickness, as to allow the blade to pass freely through the groove made by itself. The bending, or lateral dispersion of the teeth, is called the set of the saw *.

The circular saw follows the same conditions as the rectilinear saw, if we conceive the right line to be exchanged for the circle; with the exception that the blade is, for the most part, of uniform thickness throughout, unless, as in the circular veneer saws, it is thinned away on the edge, as will be explained.

It is to be observed that the word *pitch*, when employed by the saw-maker, almost always designates the *inclination* of the *face of the tooth*, up which the shaving ascends; and not the interval from tooth to tooth, as in wheels and screws.

In the following diagrams of teeth, which, for comparison, are drawn of equal coarseness or size, some kinds are usually small, and seldom so distant as ½ an inch asunder : these are described as having 2, 3, 4, 5, to 20 *points to the inch;* and such of the other teeth represented as are used by hand, are commonly from about ½ to 1¼ inch asunder, and are said to be of ½ or 1¼ inch *space*, although some of the circular saws are as coarse as 2 to 3 inches and upwards from tooth to tooth.

---

* For the mode of hardening and tempering saws, the reader is referred to vol. i., p. 249—250, of this work ; and for the principles upon which they are flattened and rendered of uniform elasticity, to the same volume, pp. 414—422.

The usual range of size or space for each kind of tooth, is accordingly expressed beside the diagrams; as are also the angles of the faces, and of the tops of the teeth, measured from the line running through the point of the teeth, or the edge of the saw.

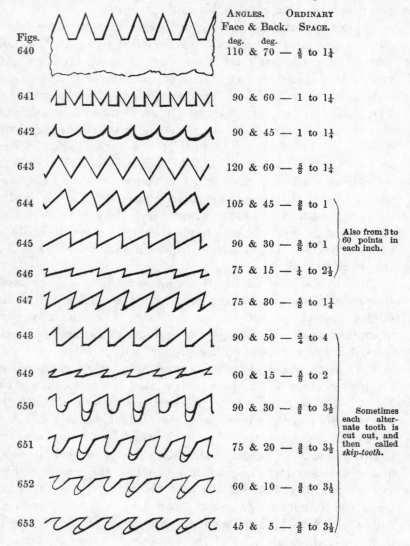

Figs.	ANGLES. Face & Back.	ORDINARY SPACE.	
	deg. deg.		
640	110 & 70	— $\frac{5}{8}$ to $1\frac{1}{4}$	
641	90 & 60	— 1 to $1\frac{1}{4}$	
642	90 & 45	— 1 to $1\frac{1}{4}$	
643	120 & 60	— $\frac{5}{8}$ to $1\frac{1}{4}$	
644	105 & 45	— $\frac{3}{8}$ to 1	
645	90 & 30	— $\frac{3}{8}$ to 1	Also from 3 to 60 points in each inch.
646	75 & 15	— $\frac{1}{4}$ to $2\frac{1}{2}$	
647	75 & 30	— $\frac{5}{8}$ to $1\frac{1}{4}$	
648	90 & 50	— $\frac{3}{4}$ to 4	
649	60 & 15	— $\frac{5}{8}$ to 2	
650	90 & 30	— $\frac{3}{8}$ to $3\frac{1}{2}$	Sometimes each alternate tooth is cut out, and then called *skip-tooth*.
651	75 & 20	— $\frac{3}{8}$ to $3\frac{1}{2}$	
652	60 & 10	— $\frac{3}{8}$ to $3\frac{1}{2}$	
653	45 & 5	— $\frac{3}{8}$ to $3\frac{1}{2}$	

The angle of the point itself will be found by subtracting the angle of the back from that of the face of the tooth, or the less from the greater of the first two numbers.

The four varieties of teeth at the commencement of the annexed group, from presenting the same angles in either direction also cut in both directions; in fact, the face and back may be considered to change places in each alternate cut. These teeth are used for such cross-cutting saws as have a handle at each end, and are worked by two or more men; as in cutting down trees, and dividing them when they have been felled; and similar saws are used for the soft building stones when they are first raised from the quarry. Fig. 640 is called the *peg-tooth,* or the *fleam-tooth,* and is much used in North America and elsewhere; fig. 641, the *M-tooth,* which is so named from its resemblance to the letter, is now but very rarely employed; fig. 642, the *half-moon-tooth,* is used in South America for cross-cutting; and fig. 643 is that commonly described as the *cross-cutting-tooth,* although in England the peg-tooth or 640, the *hand-saw-tooth* or 645, and the *gullet-tooth* 650, are also used for cross-cutting timber, more especially the last form when sharpened more acutely than usual, and used to cut in one direction only.

Referring to the preliminary remarks on cutting tools, pages 457 to 463 of the present volume, it will be seen that saws were considered to belong to the group of scraping tools, and that *e* and *f,* fig. 316, were viewed as the generic forms of the teeth, the angle of which is commonly 60 degrees, from the circumstance of the simple angular teeth being mostly produced by angular notches, filed with two of the sides of an equilateral triangular file; and therefore the points assume the same angle as the spaces, or 60 degrees.

But the angle of 60 degrees is variously placed; for instance, the teeth in fig. 643 are said to be *upright,* or to have no pitch; and the teeth in fig. 646 to be *flat,* or to have considerable pitch: these may be considered as the extremes of this kind of tooth, between which every *inclination* or *pitch* is more or less used; but, for the sake of definition, four varieties have been assumed, the straight lines of which are 15 degrees asunder.

Fig. 643, as already explained, is the ordinary tooth for cross-cutting, and which, from presenting equal angles on each side, is said to be of *upright pitch.* The tooth that is, however, more generally used for small cross-cutting saws is fig. 644, which is inclined about 15 degrees from the last. This form of tooth, called *slight pitch,* is used for the cross-cutting saws for

firewood; those for joiners' use; and also for those employed
in cutting up ivory; in which latter case the blade is stretched
in an iron frame.

Fig. 645 is the tooth in most general use: it is known as
ordinary pitch or the *hand-saw-tooth*. The face is perpendicular,
and the back inclines at an angle of 30° from the edge of the
saw, or the line of work. Most of the saws used by cabinet-
makers and joiners are thus toothed, or rather at an inclination
intermediate between figs. 644 and 645.

The tooth, fig. 645, is likewise generally employed for saws
used for metal; for circular saws used for fine work, including
veneer-saws, and for many of the circular saws for cross-cutting.

In fig. 646 the face of the tooth is "*set forward*," or stretches
beyond the perpendicular, at an inclination of 15 degrees: this
kind is employed in mill-saws used abroad for soft woods, and
they are the most inclined of those teeth formed by the two
faces of the triangular file at the one process.

Nearly the same tooth as fig. 646 is also used for circular saws
and cutters for metal. The object is then to assimilate the points
to those suitable to tools for turning the metals; therefore, the
angle of separation betwixt the end of the tooth and the plane
to be wrought, is made small. The hook form of the point is
incidental to the employment of the triangular file, and is also
proper for the material to be cut.

Fig. 647 is a form of tooth that is set forward like 646, but
the point is more acute than the last five, or it is about 45
degrees instead of 60. It is used for some circular saws,
and occasionally also for pit-saws and cross-cut saws; and is
frequently employed for cutting soft Bath stone.

Sometimes the acute angular notch is not continued to an
internal angle; a method adopted in some mill saws, both those
of ordinary or perpendicular pitch, fig. 648, and those of greater
pitch or inclination, fig. 649; the former being more common
for rectilinear, the latter for circular saws. Various intermediate
forms are met with.

The three kinds of teeth, figs. 647, 648, and 649, from being
more acute than 60 degrees, cannot be sharpened with the
ordinary three-square or equilateral file, as it will not reach to
the bottoms of the teeth. The mill-saw file is then used, namely,
a thin flat file with square or round edges, as the definition

of the internal angle is not needful, although given by the punch in the formation of the tooth. The angular mill-saw teeth are employed, partly because they are more easily sharpened than the gullet teeth, which conclude the series of diagrams.

The teeth, figs. 650 to fig. 653, are called *gullet teeth*, on account of the large hollow or gullet that is cut away in front of each tooth, in continuation of the face; and they are also known as *briar teeth*. The tooth is in general cut by one punch filling the entire space; but two punches, an angular and a gulleting punch, have been occasionally used.

The gullet is adopted to allow the tooth to be sharpened with a round or half-round file, by which the face of the tooth becomes concave when viewed edgeways, and acquires a thin and nearly knife-like edge, as will be explained. The increased curvilinear space allows more room for the sawdust, and is less disposed to retain it than the angular notch.

For the facility of explanation, the faces of the teeth differ fifteen degrees in pitch, and the tops of the teeth are variously inclined to the edge of the saw, as tabulated. The medium kinds, figs. 651 and 652, are perhaps more common, although the saw-maker forms the teeth originally more acute, for the facility of first sharpening; and the sawyer sometimes neglects to file the gullets in the same proportion as the tops, by which the advantage attending the gullets is in a measure lost. Each alternate tooth appears to be deeper than the others; but this only arises from the peculiar mode of sharpening the gullet with a round or half-round file, which makes a broad chamfer, the edge of which is elliptical.

For the general purposes of pit saws, and also for straight and circular mill-saws, the medium teeth, 651 and 652, are suitable; but for hard woods, as mahogany, rosewood, and others, and also for cross-cutting, the form should lean towards fig. 650; and for soft woods and ripping with the grain, towards the more inclined tooth, fig. 653. The whole of the forms of teeth may be materially diverted from those originally given by the saw-maker, in the important process of sharpening, and which will be now described, as the most proper way of concluding the remarks respecting the angles or bevils given to the edges of the teeth, independently of their simple profiles.

The processes denominated *sharpening* and *setting* a saw, consist, as the names imply, of two distinct operations: the first being that of filing the teeth until their extremities are sharp; the second, that of bending the teeth in an equal manner, and alternately to the right and left, so that when the eye is directed along the edge, the teeth of rectilinear saws may appear exactly in two lines, forming collectively an edge somewhat exceeding the thickness of the blade itself.

Circular saws require exactly similar treatment, if we consider the tangent of the circle to be substituted for the right line; and therefore the sharpening of straight saws will be first described, and those peculiarities alone which attach to the sharpening of circular saws will be then separately noticed.

Setting the teeth, which in practice is always subsequent to the sharpening, will be also placed subsequently in the section; the commencement of which will be devoted to the modes of holding the saw in the operation of sharpening, and the description of the files used.

In sharpening the saw it is mostly fixed perpendicularly, and with its teeth upwards, various modes being adopted according to circumstances. The tail-vice used by the saw-maker in sharpening the saw, measures from nine to twelve inches wide in the chops, and also nine to twelve inches high, or above the screw; proportions exceeding those of tail vices used by mechanicians generally. Slips of wood, or clamps of sheet lead bent to the figure of the jaws of the vice, are interposed between the saw and the vice, so that the elasticity of the wood, or the inelasticity of the lead, may give a firm hold, and prevent the disagreeable screeching noise that accompanies the action of the file when the saw is insecurely held; and the greater the noise the less the amount of work that is done.

The joiner employs a wooden vice resembling that of the saw-maker as to proportions, but it is fixed in the screw chops of his work bench.

In sharpening pit-saws, the sawyer seldom finds it necessary to remove the handles or frames. The long or whip-saw, and others not having frames, are supported in the *sawing horse*, a trestle about five feet long and two feet high, with four or five uprights or wooden pegs, sawn half-way through to receive the back edge of the blade; the horse raises the edge of the saw about three feet above the ground.

A more convenient mode is to have a *jointed horse*, fig. 654, the two halves of which open somewhat like the jaws of a pair of pliers; when the saw has been inserted, the legs of the horse are distended by the stretchers at the ends, and fix the blade.

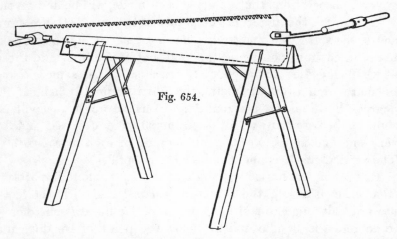

Fig. 654.

The files used in sharpening saws are triangular, round, half-round, and mill saw-files.   The equilateral triangular files, commonly designated as *three-square files,* vary from about three to nine inches long: for small saws they are generally taper; for large, sometimes nearly parallel, when they are called *blunts,* a term applied to other nearly parallel files.   The triangular file is exclusively used for the teeth of figs. 643 to 646, and more or less for all the rectilinear teeth.   For small teeth, the double-cut Lancashire files are the most used, on account of the keenness of their edges, and the common size is $4\frac{1}{2}$ inches long.   The generality of other saw-files are single or float-cut, that kind of file tooth being considered to ' *cut sweeter,*' and do more work.

Round files from 5 to 8 inches long, are used in saw mills for the gullets of the teeth, figs. 650 to 653, and flat files for the tops; but the pit-sawyer and some others always employ half-round files, as the one instrument may be then applied to both purposes: these files are always blunt or parallel.

Mill saw-files are in general thin, flat and parallel, from 6 to 14 inches long, float-cut on the sides, and with smooth, square edges. Sometimes, however, they have round and cutting edges, and are of taper figure.

The five ordinary modes of sharpening saws will be explained and illustrated by enlarged diagrams in three views, which denote the ways in which the teeth are bevelled and set; but a few general observations that apply to each mode, will be first given.

In general, the angles of the points of the saw-teeth are more acute, the softer the material to be sawn, agreeably to common usage in cutting tools; and the angles of the points, and those at which the files are applied, are necessarily the same. Thus in sharpening saws for metal, the file is generally held at 90 degrees both in the horizontal and vertical angle, as will be shown; for very hard woods at from 90 to 80 degrees, and for very soft woods at from 70 to 60 degrees, or even more acutely. The vertical angle is about half the horizontal.

In general the horizontal angle of the file is alone important, (that is, considering the saw-blade vertical and with the teeth upward,) although to assist the action of the file it is customary to depress the handle a little below the point of the file, and only to file on those teeth which are bent *from* the operator. When the tooth that is bent *towards* the individual is filed, it vibrates with much noise, and is disposed to strip off the teeth from the file, instead of being itself reduced.

To insure the action of each tooth, the edge of the saw should be quite straight; it is therefore occasionally *topped*, by laying the file divested of its handle, lengthways upon the teeth, and passing it along once or twice, to reduce those few points which may be above the general level. The file is pressed hard at the two ends of the saw, where the blade is less worn, and is applied lightly in passing the middle; the file should be held perfectly square, to reduce the edges alike. The new point of each tooth is then made to fall as nearly as possible upon the center of the little facet, thus exposed by the process of topping or ranging the teeth; and the faces or fronts of the teeth are always filed before the tops of the same.

When the file is perfectly square to the saw plate, every tooth is sharpened exactly alike, and in direct succession, that is, in the order 1, 2, 3, 4. Whenever the file is inclined, the teeth 1, 3,

5, 7, 9, are sharpened, say to the right, and the teeth 2, 4, 6, 8, to the left, after which they are set in the same order; so as collectively to form a double line of points, somewhat resembling the tail of a bird, when the section is coarsely magnified and exaggerated as in the several diagrams to be given. The teeth are the more set, the softer or the wetter the wood.

The first diagram on sharpening saws, fig. 655, represents in plan and two elevations the saw-teeth that are the most easily sharpened, namely, those of the frame-saw for metal, commonly used by the smith: the teeth of this saw are not set or bent in the ordinary manner, owing to the thickness and hardness of the blade, and the small size of the teeth.

Fig. 655.

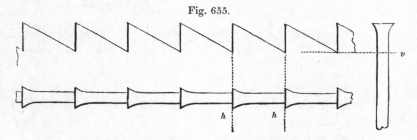

The smith's-saw blade, when dull, is placed edgeways upon the jaws of the vice, and the teeth, which are placed upwards, are slightly hammered; this upsets or thickens them in a minute degree, and the hammer face reduces to a general level those teeth which stand highest. They are then filed with a triangular file held perfectly square, or at ninety degrees to the blade, both in the horizontal direction *h*, and the vertical *v*, until each little facet just disappears so as to leave the teeth as nearly as possible in a line, that each may fulfil its share of the work.

The most minute kind of saws, those which are made of broken watch-springs, have teeth that are also sharpened nearly as in the diagram, fig. 655, but without the teeth being either upset or bent; as in very small saws the trifling burr, or rough wiry edge thrown up by the file, is a sufficient addition to the thickness of the blade, and is the only *set* they receive.

Three modes of spacing out the teeth of fine saws will be now described, and which modes, although not employed by the saw-maker, may assist the amateur who is less accustomed to the use of the file.

Fine saw teeth are sometimes indented with a double chisel, fig. 656, the one edge of which is inserted each time in the notch previously made, and the other edge makes the following indentation; the intervals thus become exactly alike, and the teeth are completed with the file.   For still more delicate saws recourse may be had to a little piece of steel bent at the end as a minute rectangular hook, which is magnified in fig. 657 ; the hook or filing guide, being inserted into each tooth as it is successively formed, regulates the distance of the file for the next tooth, as the file is allowed to bear slightly against the blunt and hardened end of the hook.

Figs. 656.   657.   658.

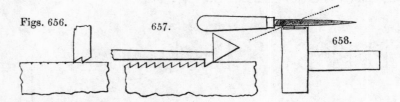

The third mode is used for piercing and inlaying saws, these measure about one one-thirtieth of an inch wide, one one-hundredth thick, and have about twenty points to the inch for wood, thirty for ivory, forty for ebony and pearl, and sixty for metals. They are made from pieces of watch-spring, which are straightened by rubbing them the reverse way of their curvature through a greasy rag, after which they are cut into strips with shears. When the saw is either being *made*, or sharpened, it is kept distended in its frame, and is laid in a shallow groove or kerf in a plate of brass embedded in the wood block, fig. 658, which is clamped to the table.   First, the back of the blade is filed smooth and round; the edge is then smoothed; after which the teeth are set out, beginning near the handle of the frame.

The spaces between the teeth are determined, in this case, by the facility with which the hand appreciates any angular position to which it is accustomed.   Thus in the act of filing the teeth, —the file is always used, say at an horizontal angle of twenty degrees with the blade—the file is sent once through the first tooth, and allowed to rest for an instant without being drawn backwards; the file still resting in the first notch of the blade, as shown in elevation, is then placed two to five degrees nearer square in the horizontal angle, or at fifteen degrees with the

blade, instead of twenty. It is then supported for an instant on
the *edge* of the wood block, and raised out of the notch; the
file, whilst supported on the block, as in the dotted line, is
replaced on the saw at twenty degrees, its first position. By
the two lateral movements it is shifted a trifle to the right, and
a second notch is made at the spot thus determined. The
routine is continued, and after each traverse of the file the
stepping process is repeated, during which the file rests alternately on the saw blade, and on the edge of the block, by which
curious yet simple mode the spaces of the teeth are given with
great rapidity and exactness.

In this first range each notch has only received one stroke of
the file; but three or four ranges, commenced from the other
end of the blade, are required to bring the teeth up sharp.

The second diagram, fig. 659, illustrates the peg-tooth; but it
may also be considered to apply to 641, the M-tooth, and, in part,
to the mill-saw-tooth, 648.   The points of the cross-cutting
saws for soft woods are required to be acute or keen, that they
may act as knives in dividing the fibres transversely.

Fig. 659.

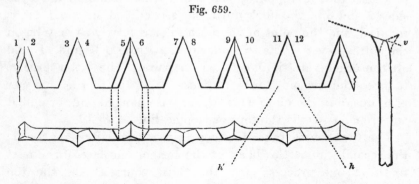

The sides 1, 5, 9, that is, the left of each alternate tooth, are
first filed with the horizontal angle denoted by *h*, and then the
opposite sides of the same teeth, or 2, 6, 10, with the reverse
inclination, or *h'*. The other teeth are then treated just in the
same manner, from the other side of the blade; that is, first the
sides 12, 8, 4, and then 11, 7, 3, are successively filed, the work
being thus completed in four *ranges*. The first and second
ranges are accomplished, a few inches at a time, throughout the
entire length of the saw; after which, the third and fourth are
completed in the same interrupted order.

The third diagram, fig. 660, may be considered to refer generally to all teeth the angles of which are 60 degrees, (or the same as that of the triangular file,) and that are used for wood. The most common example is the ordinary hand-saw tooth; but teeth of upright pitch, such as the cross-cut saw, fig. 643, or of considerable pitch, as in 646, are treated much in the same manner.

Fig. 660.

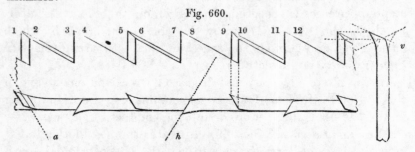

The teeth having been topped, the *faces* 1, 5, 9, are first filed back, until they respectively agree with a dotted line *a,* supposed to be drawn through the center of each little facet produced in the topping; the file is then made to take the sides 2 and 3 of the nook until the second half of the facet is reduced, and the point of the tooth falls as nearly as may be on the dotted line *a.* The two sides 6 and 7, those 10 and 11, and all the others, are similarly filed in pairs. The latter process reduces the second series of faces 3, 7, 11, to their proper positions, and therefore when the saw is changed end for end, it only remains to file the tops or sloping lines 4, 8, 12.

The first course takes the face only of each alternate tooth ; the second course the back of the former and face of the next tooth at one process ; and the third course takes the top only of the second series, and completes the work. This order of proceeding is employed, that the *faces* of the teeth may be in each case completed before the *tops* or *backs.*

The fourth diagram, fig. 661, which follows next in order, exhibits also in three elevations a somewhat peculiar form of tooth, namely, that of the pruning-saw for green wood. The blade is much thicker on the edge than the back, so that the teeth are not set at all. The teeth are made with a triangular file, applied very obliquely as to horizontal angle, as at *h,* sometimes exceeding 45 degrees, but without vertical inclination as at *v*; and the faces of the teeth are nearly upright, as in the hand-saw.

Fig. 661.

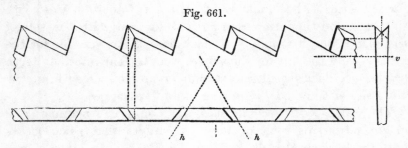

Looking at the pruning-saw in profile, it appears to have large and small teeth alternately; this only arises from the excessive bevil employed; the large sides of the teeth are very keen, and each vertical edge is acute like a knife, and sharply pointed; in consequence of which it cuts the living wood with a much cleaner surface, and less injury to the plant, than the common hand-saw tooth.

The fifth diagram, fig. 662, explains the method employed in sharpening gullet or briar-teeth; in these, as before explained, there are large curvilinear hollows, in the formation of which the faces of the teeth also become hollowed so as to make the projecting angles acute.

Fig. 662.

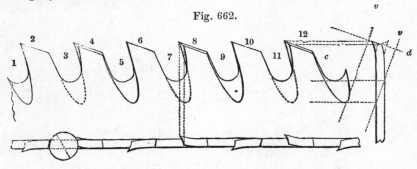

The gullets, 3, 7, 11, are first filed, and from the file crossing the tooth very obliquely, as at *v v* in the section, the point of the tooth extends around the file, and gives the curvature represented in the plan.   The file should not be so large as the gullet; it is therefore requisite that the file be applied in two positions, first upon the face of the one tooth, and then on the back of the preceding tooth.   The tops of the teeth, 4, 8, 12, are next sharpened with the flat side of the file, the position of which is of course determined by the angles c and d; the former varies with the material from about 5 to 40 degrees with the edge, and the latter from 80 to 60 degrees with the side of the blade; the first angles in each case being suitable for the hardest, and the last for the softest woods. The alternate teeth having been sharpened, the remainder are completed from the other side of the blade, requiring in all four ranges.

The gullet-tooth accomplishes, in a different manner, and in one possessing some peculiar advantages, that which occurs from the horizontal inclination of the file in most other cases ; and although the position may seem difficult, it will be found very manageable, as the hollow forms a convenient bed for the file. See Appendix, Note B L, page 1011.

The saw having been sharpened, it is afterwards *set*, or, as before explained, the teeth are bent. The best mode is that which is almost always adopted by the saw-maker, who fixes in the tail-vice a small anvil or stake with a rounded edge, such as fig. 663. The saw is held with its teeth along the center of the ridge, and the teeth are bent upon, or rather around the curve of the stake, with two or three light blows of a small hammer also shown, the face of which is at right angles to the handle, and narrow enough to strike one tooth only.

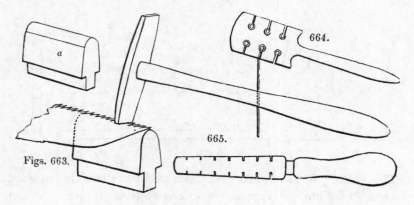

Figs. 663.

The set, or lateral curve, given to each alternate tooth, is in great measure determined by the curve of the stake, the edge of which, for fine saws, has a ridge like a pointed gothic window. Half the teeth having been bent, the saw is changed end for end, and the intermediate teeth are similarly treated.

Those who are less used to the treatment of the saw, employ the *saw-set* for bending the teeth: it consists of a narrow blade of steel, with notches of various widths for different saws; fig. 664 is for large, and fig. 665 for small saws. In using the saw-set, the saw is allowed to remain in the clamps after having been filed, and the alternate teeth are inserted a little way in that notch which fits the blade the most exactly; and they are bent over by applying a small force to the handle, which is either raised up or depressed equally for each tooth.

In some few cases saw-set pliers, fig. 666, are used. Two adjustments are required, respectively to determine the quantity of the tooth which shall be bent, and the angle that shall be given to it. The quantity is adjusted by shifting the stop *b*, which is held by the thumb-screw *c*, that passes through a mortise in *b*; the angle of the part bent is adjusted by the screw *d*. The tooth is first grasped between the jaws of the pliers, which are then rotated until the screw *d* touches the blade.

Fig. 666.

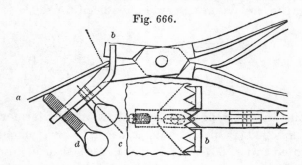

In which way soever the saw is set, it requires to be accomplished with great uniformity, so that the two series of points may form two exact lines. It is proper to change ends with the blade in order that each side may have, as nearly as possible, the same treatment; as unless the two sides of the saw are very nearly in the same condition, or set alike, the saw is apt to run, or cut a crooked instead of a straight path; it cuts most rapidly on the side that is most set, and consequently glances off in a curve from its too rapid encroachment.

The only changes in treating the circular saw, arise from the difference between the right line and the curve; that is, the files are applied in the same relation to the *tangent* of the circle, that

they are to the rectilinear edge of the straight saw. When
the teeth of circular saws are topped, a small lump of grindstone
is held upon the saw-bench and against the revolving saw, and
moved continually sideways; the highest teeth are soon rubbed
down, indeed almost in a moment, as only a very small quantity
is thus removed from them; sometimes a file is used instead of
the stone.

In sharpening circular saws with angular teeth, and the tops
of gullet-teeth, they are clamped between two upright boards,
connected by a screw passing through the center of the saw.
For saws of small diameter the three are nipped in the vice;
but for large saws, the boards are shaped like the letter T,
and are screwed against an upright post or the side of the
bench, by a screw bolt and nut.

In gulleting circular saws, the two boards grasping the saw
are often fixed at an angle of about 30 degrees, by which the
file is brought to the horizontal position, and the saw is turned
over when the gullets on one side have been finished.

Fig. 667.

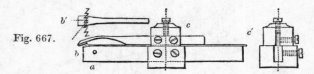

In setting the teeth of the circular saw, all the former modes
may be employed; and also one other little instrument which
is represented in fig. 667. It consists of a bed or anvil of steel,
which is held in the vice at *a*; it has an axis *c*, placed at such
a distance from the sloping plane on *a*, as suits the radius of
the saw; and the end *b* of the upper piece, which is somewhat
elastic, is filed to a corresponding angle, and is besides pointed
so that the blow of the hammer may only bend or set one tooth
at a time, as shown by the dotted lines in the inverted plan *b'*.
The axis, shown detached and in the other view at *c'*, is a turned
block of brass having a shoulder to fit the hole in the saw, two
diametrical mortises for the pieces of steel *a* and *b*, and also five
binding screws to retain the several parts in position.

SECT. III.—RECTILINEAR SAWS USED BY HAND.

Rectilinear saws used by hand, are divisible into three groups,
as arranged and tabulated on the next page.

TABLE OF THE DIMENSIONS OF RECTILINEAR SAWS.

The first column refers to the pages where the saws and their uses are described.

The last column refers to the Birmingham iron wire and sheet iron gage: the comparison of which with ordinary linear measure is given in the table on page 1013 of the Appendix.

(1). Taper Saws, mostly without Frames.

Page.	*With a handle at each end.*	Length of Blade.	Width at wide end.	Width at narrow end	Form of Tooth.	Space of Tooth.	Gage of Metal.
700	Cross-cut saw	4 to 10 ft.	6 to 12 in.	3 to 7 in.	640 to 643 and 650.	$\frac{3}{4}$ to 1 in.	12 to 15
701	Long, pit, or whip saw	6 - 8 -	9 - 12 -	$3\frac{1}{2}$ - 5 -	650 & 651	$\frac{5}{8}$ - 1 -	12 - 16
703	Pit frame saw	4 - 6 -	7 - 11 -	3 - $4\frac{1}{2}$ -	- -	$\frac{1}{2}$ - $\frac{3}{4}$ -	15 - 18
707	*Felloe, or pit turning saw	4 - 6 -	3 - 4 -	2 - 3 -	- -	$\frac{1}{2}$ - $\frac{5}{8}$ -	13 - 15

Page.	*With a handle at one end.*	Length of Blade.	Width at wide end.	Width at narrow end	Form of Tooth.	Points per inch.	Gage of metal.
708	Rip saw	28 to 30 in.	7 to 9 in.	3 to 4 in.	644 & 645	$3\frac{1}{2}$	18
—	Half rip saw	26 - 28 -	6 - 8 -	3 - $3\frac{1}{2}$ -	- -	4	18 to 19
—	Hand saw	22 - 26 -	5 - $7\frac{1}{2}$ -	$2\frac{1}{2}$ - 3 -	- -	5	18 - 19
—	Broken space or fine hand	22 - 26 -	5 - $7\frac{1}{2}$ -	$2\frac{1}{2}$ - 3 -	- -	6	18 - 19
—	Panel saw	20 - 24 -	$4\frac{1}{2}$ - $7\frac{1}{2}$ -	2 - $2\frac{1}{2}$ -	- -	7	19 -
—	Fine panel saw	20 - 24 -	4 - 6 -	2 - $2\frac{1}{2}$ -	- -	8	19 - 20
—	Chest saw, (for tool chests)	10 - 20 -	$2\frac{1}{2}$ - $3\frac{1}{2}$ -	$1\frac{1}{4}$ - 2 -	- -	6 to 8	18 - 21
711	*Table saw	18 - 26 -	$1\frac{3}{4}$ - $2\frac{1}{4}$ -	1 - $1\frac{1}{2}$ -	- -	7 - 8	16 - 19
—	*Compass, or lock saw	8 - 18 -	1 - $1\frac{1}{2}$ -	$\frac{1}{2}$ - $\frac{3}{4}$ -	- -	8 - 9	18 - 19
712	*Keyhole, or fret saw	6 - 12 -	$\frac{1}{2}$ - $\frac{3}{4}$ -	$\frac{1}{8}$ - $\frac{1}{4}$ -	- -	9 - 10	19 - 20
—	Pruning saw	10 - 24 -	2 - $3\frac{1}{2}$ -	$\frac{1}{2}$ - $1\frac{1}{4}$ -	644 661	4 - 7	13 - 16

(2). Parallel Saws with Backs.

Page.	*With a handle at one end.*	Length of Blade.	Width of Blade.		Form of Tooth.	Points per inch.	Gage of Metal.
713	Tenon saw	16 to 20 in.	$3\frac{1}{4}$ to 4 in.		644 & 645	10	21
—	Sash	14 - 16 -	$2\frac{1}{2}$ - $3\frac{1}{4}$ -		- -	11	22
—	Carcase	10 - 14 -	2 - $2\frac{1}{2}$ -		- -	12	23
—	Dovetail	6 - 10 -	$1\frac{1}{2}$ - 2 -		- -	14 to 18	24
722	Smith's screw head saw	3 - 8 -	$\frac{1}{2}$ - 1 -		- -	12 - 16	15 to 22
723	Comb-cutter's saw	5 - 8 -	$1\frac{1}{2}$ - $2\frac{1}{2}$ -		- -	10 - 20	18 - 25

(3). Parallel Saws used in Frames.

Page.	*Stretched lengthways.*	Length of Blade.	Width of Blade.		Form of Tooth.	Points per inch.	Gage of Metal.
725	Mill saw	4 to 8 ft.	4 to 5 in.		648 & 651	$\frac{5}{8}$ to 1 in.	10 to 14
—	Mill saw webb	4 - 6 -	3 - 4 -		- -	$\frac{5}{8}$ - 1 -	17 - 20
—	Veneer saw	4 - 5 -	4 - 5 -		645	2 - 4 -	19 - 21
—	Chair-maker's saw	20 in. 30 in.	$1\frac{1}{2}$ - $2\frac{1}{2}$ -		—	3 - 4 -	19 - 22
726	Wood-cutter's saw	24 - 36 -	2 - $3\frac{1}{2}$ -		644	3 - 4 -	19 - 22
—	Continental frame saw	15 - 36 -	1 - 3 -		645	4 - 12 -	19 - 24
728	*Turning, or sweep saw	6 - 22 -	$\frac{1}{10}$ - $\frac{5}{8}$		—	10 - 20 -	19 - 24
—	Ivory saw	15 - 30 -	$1\frac{1}{2}$ - 3 -		644	4 - 6 -	22 - 24
729	Smith's frame saw	3 - 12 -	$\frac{1}{4}$ - $\frac{7}{8}$ -		646	10 - 14 -	20 - 26
730	*Piercing saw	3 - 5 -	$\frac{1}{30}$ - $\frac{1}{40}$ -		645	40 - 60 -	$\frac{1}{100}$ in.
732	*Inlaying or buhl saw	3 - 5 -	$\frac{1}{25}$ - $\frac{1}{30}$ -		—	15 - 40 -	$\frac{1}{70}$ to $\frac{1}{100}$

* *Those Saws marked with an Asterisk are used for Circular and Curvilinear Works.*

The first kind of saw is usually taper; and if long, it has a handle at each end as in the *pit saw;* but if short, or not exceeding about thirty inches in length, it has only a handle at the wide end, as in the common *hand-saw.*

The second kind of saw is stiffened by a rib placed on the back of the saw, and parallel with the teeth; the rib or back is generally a cleft bar of iron or brass; as in the *tenon-saw, dove-tail-saw,* and others.

The third kind of saw is provided with an external skeleton, by which the saw-blade is strained in the direction of its length, like the string of a bow; as in the *turning* or *sweep-saw* for wood, and the *bow-saw* or *frame-saw* for ivory.

These three classes of saws differ much in proportions and details, as will be seen by the inspection of the foregoing table, and the subsequent remarks. The longest saws are placed at the beginning of each group, and the names mostly denote the ordinary purposes of the respective instruments.

Immediately subsequent to the description of the several saws, some account will be given of the general purposes of each instrument, and of its manipulation. The numbers prefixed to the table, refer to these respective remarks, which are expressed somewhat in detail, owing to the importance of the instruments themselves, and the circumstance that many of the topics will not be resumed. Whereas the turning, boring, and screw-cutting tools, the subject matters of the previous chapters, will be more or less returned to, in speaking of the practice of turning.

The saw which claims priority of notice, is that used in felling timber, when the axe is not employed for the purpose.

The *felling-saw* mostly used of late years in this country, is a taper blade about five feet long, with ordinary gullet teeth, closely resembling the common pit-saw, except that the teeth are sharpened more acutely.

The handle of the wide end, fig. 668, is fixed by an iron bolt and wedge; that at the narrow end, fig. 669, is calculated for two men, and is made of wood, except a plate of iron at the bottom attached by rivets or screws to the wood, so as to make a crevice for the saw, which is fixed therein by a wooden wedge on the upper surface of the blade.

When the saw has entered a moderate distance, wedges are

driven in to prevent the weight of the tree from closing the saw-kerf and fixing the blade; and it is needful the handles should be removeable, that one or other may be taken off, to allow the saw to be withdrawn lengthways, which could not be done, were the handles riveted on.

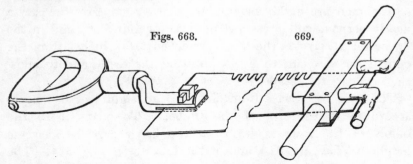

Figs. 668.   669.

In *cross-cutting* saws, the straight handles are sometimes attached as in fig. 670, by a piece of sheet-iron serving as a ferrule, and extending in two flaps which embrace the saw, and are riveted to it.

Figs. 671 and 672 represent two other kinds: the former is attached by a bolt and key, and the spike is riveted through the wooden handle. In the latter the handle is perforated for the reception of a slender rod of iron, slit open as a loop to receive the saw-blade, and which is drawn tight by means of the nut and washer above the handle.

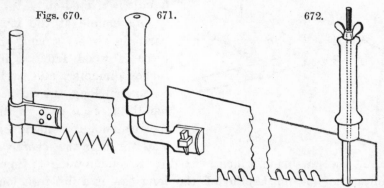

Figs. 670.   671.   672.

Some of the cross-cutting saws used in the colonies for very large logs, are made as long as twelve, fourteen, and sixteen feet, nine to eleven inches wide in the center, and six or seven inches at the ends. The peg-tooth is commonly used for them. The *long* saw, *pit* saw, or *whip* saw, which follows in the table,

is also the next saw that is commonly applied to the piece of
timber, which is then placed over the saw-pit, in order that
the saw may be used in the vertical position by two men, called
respectively the *top-man* and the *pit-man*, the former of whom
stands upon the piece of timber about to be sawn.   The positions
of the men are highly favourable, as they can give the saw a
nearly perpendicular traverse of three or four feet; and in the
up or return stroke, the saw is removed a few inches from the
end of the saw cut, to avoid blunting the teeth, and to allow
the sawdust free escape.

The long saw varies from about six to eight feet in length,
according to the size of the timber.   To adapt it to the
hands of the sawyers, it has at the upper part a transverse
handle or *tiller*, fig. 673, and at the lower a *box*, fig. 674.   The

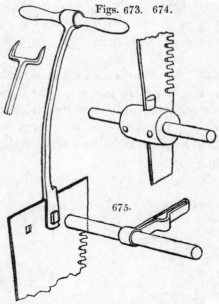

Figs. 673. 674.

675.

tiller consists of a bar of iron,
divided at the lower part to
receive the blade, to which it
is fixed by a square bolt passing through the two, and
fastened by a wedge; and at
the upper end, the tiller is
sometimes formed as an eye
for a wooden stick, or else it
is made as a fork, and the
handle is riveted on.

The handle at the lower
part, fig. 674, is simply a
piece of wood four or five
inches diameter, and twelve
to sixteen long, turned as a
handle at each end; a diametrical notch is made half
way through the center to
admit the saw blade, which is fixed by a wooden wedge.   Sometimes the bottom handle of the long saw is a flat iron loop,
as in fig. 675, with a space for the fixing wedge, and an eye
for the wooden handle.   Occasionally a screw box is used, or
one like fig. 674, but with the one handle screwed in, so that its
point may bear upon the saw, in place of the wedge.   In all
cases it is desirable the lower handle should be capable of being
easily removed.

The *pit frame-saw*, fig. 676, is commonly used for deals, and for such pieces of the foreign hard woods as are small enough to pass between its frame, which is about two feet wide.

The frame-saw blade has two holes above or at the wider end, and one below, and is attached to the wooden frame by two iron *buckles* or loops, which are split about half way round. The upper buckle fits squarely and firmly to the top head, and receives, above its lower side, two pins passing through the holes in the saw. The lower buckle is similarly cleft, and receives one pin only; this buckle is drawn tight by a pair of equal or folding wedges, beneath the bottom transverse piece.

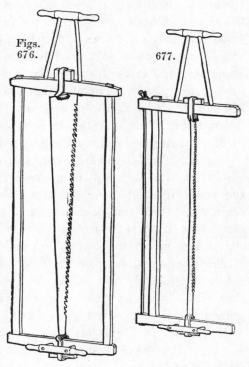

Figs.
676.

677.

The blade is usually five or six feet long, and thinner than that of the whip saw, which latter, although it may be used for the widest timbers, is more wasteful. In some few cases, where the double frame, fig. 676, is inapplicable, as in removing a plank from outside a very large log, the single frame, 677, is used; but this latter is generally narrow, and employed alone for small curvilinear works.

It is now proposed to give some few particulars of the sawpit, and the modes employed by the sawyers in marking out the timber preparatory to sawing.

The sawpit varies from about twenty to fifty feet in length, four to six feet in width, and five to six feet in depth; it has two stout timbers running the whole length, called *side strakes*, and transverse pieces at each end, called *head sills*, upon which the one end of the timber rests, whilst the other end is supported on a *transome,* or a joist lying transversely upon the strakes : a second transome, is used in case of the first breaking; this is called a *trap transome.*

Sometimes holdfasts, or L-formed iron brackets, are added to the head-sills, by which thick pieces of plank are fixed horizontally; screw chops are also used for fixing short pieces of hard-wood vertically or edgeways, for slitting them.

In cutting deals into thin boards, three deals, which from being as many as the frame of the saw will include, are called a pit-full, are placed vertically against the stake, and are securely attached to it by a rope passed once round the deals and the lower end of the stake, and strained by a binding-stick.

Foreign timbers and hard woods are mostly squared with the axe or adze, for the convenience of transport and close stowage on shipboard, and such square pieces are readily marked out with the chalk line into the scantling, or the planks and boards required.   More skill is called for in setting out the lines upon our native timbers, which are mostly converted into plank, or the various pieces, without being previously chopped square.

The *converter* determines in which direction the tree can be cut most profitably into plank, and the section chosen is usually that, which when opened, shows the greatest curvature or irregularity; this section is supposed to be shown longitudinally by *a, b, c, d,* fig. 678, and, on a larger scale and transversely, by *e′ e,* fig. 679 ; the central points *a* and *b,* and the line *b c,* being given by the converter, who also gives instructions as to the thicknesses desired in the planks. The sawyer's first object is accurately to mark the margins of the irregular central plane, *a b c d,* so truly, that when the lines are followed with the saw, the surface shall be true and thoroughly *out of winding* or twist.

The sawyer gets the timber on the sawpit, with the hollow side upwards : that being always first marked : it is plumbed upright, or, so that the plumb-line, suspended by the hand at *z,* exactly intersects the line *b c,* which has been marked on the end. The butt is then secured from rotating, by dogs or staples, *s s,* fig. 679, driven both into the end of the timber and into the vertical face of the head-sill; for which purpose the two ends of the dogs are bent at right angles, both to each other and to the intermediate part of the dog, the extremities of which are pointed with steel, made chisel-form, and hardened.

A chalk-line is now stretched in the dotted line from *a* to *b*, and pulled vertically upwards, exactly in the plane in which it is desired to act; the string is then let go, as in discharging an arrow, and, striking the timber, it leaves thereupon a portion of the white or black chalk with which the line was rubbed.

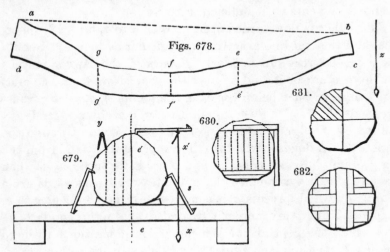

Figs. 678.

Should the curvature of the timber be such that, as in the example, the chalk-line would scarcely reach the hollow, it is strained on the dotted line *a*, *b*, and left there; the plumb-line is held in the hand at *z*, and an assistant holds a piece of chalk on the top of the timber at the point *e*. The principal then observes, in the same glance, that the plumb-line *z*, intersects the string *a b*, the line *b c*, and also the point of the chalk, showing them all to be in the plane of vision; a mark is then made at *e*. Marks are similarly made at *f* and *g*, or as many places as may be required; and, lastly, the points *a g*, *g f*, *f e*, and *e b*, are connected by short lines struck with the chalk-line around the curve.

The required thickness of the planks is then taken in the compasses, with a little excess for the waste of the saw, and two, three or more planks are pricked off on each side the center *e′ e*, fig. 679; until, from the circular section of the timber, its surface becomes so inclined, that the compasses would measure a slanting instead of a horizontal distance, and which would diminish the thickness assigned to the boards.

The sawyer then holds the compasses as at *y*, and fixing his eye on the part of the wood perpendicularly beneath the off leg of

the compasses, he removes the instrument and pricks a mark
therewith; after which the compasses are replaced as at *y*, to see
that the mark is correct.   This is repeated at different points in
the length, and the chalk-line is stretched from point to point
thus set out with the compasses, and marks the edges of the
intended saw-cuts with sufficient certainty.

The timber is now turned over, or with *c* to *d*, fig. 678, uppermost and the end line exactly perpendicular as before.   Should
the piece be very crooked or *high-backed*, the sawyer may be
unable to see over it, and observe the central marks at the ends
of the timber; such being the case, the points *e*, *f*, *g*, are transferred to *e'*, *f'*, *g'*, on the top of the timber, by the mode explained by the figure 679, supposed to be a section through the
plane *e e'*.   A dog is driven into the timber near *e'*, and from the
dog a plumb-line, *x' x*, is suspended; the distance *e x*, is then
measured with a common rule, and measured backwards from
x' to *e'*, by which process *e'* becomes exactly perpendicular to *e*;
the points *f* and *g* are similarly treated to obtain the points *f' g'*;
after which the central line is made at four operations, through
c, e', f', g', d; the plank lines are set out with the compasses as
before explained.

Large timber is usually cut into plank as in fig. 679; the
planks are sometimes *flatted* or their irregular edges are sawn
off and for the most part wasted; but this is not generally done
until the wood is seasoned and brought into use.

When many planks are wanted of the same width, it is
a more economical mode, first to leave a central parallel balk,
as in fig. 680, by removing one or two boards from each
side, and then to flat the balk, or reduce it into planks.   The
central line is in this case transferred from the lower to the
upper side, by aid of the square and rule, instead of by the
plumb-line.

According to Hassenfratz, the setting out shown in fig. 681 is
employed in large wainscot oak, in order to obtain the greatest
display of the medullary rays which constitute the principal
figure in this wood; and the same author strongly advocates
the method proposed by Moreau, and represented in fig. 682,
in which he says one-sixth more timber is obtained than by any
other mode, and also that the pieces are less liable to split and
warp; but on examination there does not appear to be any

inducement to incur the increased trouble in marking and sawing the timber on this method*.

When the timber has been properly marked out, the sawyers take their respective places, upon the timber and in the pit: the saw is sloped a little from the perpendicular; that is, supposing the piece about eighteen inches through or deep, the saw, when it touches the top angle, is held off about two inches from the bottom. A few short trips are then very carefully made, as much depends on the saw entering well; and should it fail to hit the line, the blade is sloped to the right or left at about the angle of 45 degrees, to run the cut sideways and correct the incision in its earliest stage. It is usual to take all the cuts as in figs. 679 and 680, to the depth of three or four feet, and then the whole of them a further distance, and so on.

When the saw has penetrated three or four feet, a wooden *heading wedge* is driven into the cut, to separate the timber, for the relief of the saw; and when, from the length of the cut, the timber is sufficiently yielding, the *hanging wedge* is used, which is a stick of timber about twelve to twenty inches long and an inch square, with a projection to prevent the wedge from falling through. The wedges lessen the friction upon the saw; but if too greedily applied they split the wood, and tear up the loose parts sometimes observed in planks.

In sawing straight boards, it is advantageous that the saw should be moderately wide, as it the better serves to direct the rectilinear path of the instrument; but for curvilinear works, as the felloes of carriage wheels, the sawyer employs a much narrower saw, to enable him to follow the curve. The blade of one kind of felloe-saw is about five feet long, and it tapers from nearly four inches at the wide, to two inches at the narrow end; it is used with a tiller and box, exactly the same as the ordinary long saw, and also without a frame.

The more general felloe-saw, or *pit turning-saw*, has a blade about $1\frac{1}{4}$ inch wide, and is stretched in a frame exactly like those represented in figs. 676 and 677. The turning-saw with two side-rails is the best where it can be applied; sometimes the

---

* *Traité de l'Art du Charpentier, par* J. H. Hassenfratz. 4to. Paris, 1804. Plate 12.

frame is obliged to be made single, and with a wire and screw nuts, by which the saw is strained as in fig. 677, page 703.

In cutting out very small sweeps, as in the small wheels or trucks for wooden gun-carriages, no frame whatever can be used, and slender blades about five or six feet long, five eighths of an inch wide, with a handle at each end, were employed for this purpose during the late war. In using the various pit-turning saws, the thick plank having been sawn out in the ordinary manner, the work is marked off on one side from a pattern or templet, and then held down, upon the head-sill of the saw-pit and one transome, by means of the holdfast before noticed.

The *rip-saw, half-rip, hand-saw, broken-space, panel-saw,* and *fine-panel,* which, in respect to appearance, are almost alike, may be considered to be represented by fig. 683; their differences of size will be gathered from the dimensions in the table; the chest-saws are merely diminutives of the above, and such as are used for small chests of tools, whence their name.

Fig. 683.

This kind of saw is made taper, in order that the blade may possess a nearly equal degree of stiffness throughout, notwith-standing that it is held at the one end, and receives at that end, as a thrust, the whole of the power applied to the instrument; the greater width also facilitates the attachment of the handle. Were the blade as wide at the point, as at the handle or heel, it would add useless weight, and instead of being a source of strength, it would in reality enfeeble the saw, which from the increased weight at the far end, would be more flexible near the handle than at the point.

It will be seen that the saws in this group are progressively smaller and finer. The *rip*-saw has the coarsest teeth, and which are of slight pitch, or midway between the upright or cross-cutting teeth, fig. 643, and those of ordinary pitch, fig. 645; the *half-rip* is similar, but a little finer; these two are used in carpentry for ripping or cutting fir-timber rapidly *with* the grain.

The hand and fine-hand saws are somewhat finer in the teeth, which are of ordinary pitch, or the face of the tooth is perpendicular; the hand-saws are much used by the joiner for ordinary purposes, and also by the cabinet maker, for cutting mahogany and other hardwoods with the grain.

The panel and fine-panel are still finer saws of the same kind, which probably derived their name from having been made for cutting out panels, when oak and other wainscotting were more common in our houses than plastered walls; and they may be considered as intermediate between the hand-saw, by which most of the work is done, and the tenon or back-saw hereafter to be described.

The same workman does not require each of the six saws, but commonly selects the two or three most suited to his particular class of work; they are principally used for still further preparing the woods to their several purposes, after they have been cut at the sawpit into planks and boards. The outlines of the works are marked out upon the surface of the plank by aid of the rule, compasses and chalk line, or the straight edge and square, with much greater facility than setting out the round timber into planks, which has been already explained. The board having been marked, is rested upon a sawing stool or trestle, the height of which is about 20 inches; if the work be long two stools are employed. The workman commonly places his right knee upon the board to fix it, and applies the saw on the portion that overhangs the end of the stool.

The saw is grasped in the right hand, and the left is applied to the board, in order that the end of the thumb may be placed just above the teeth and against the smooth blade of the saw, to guide it to the line; the saw is then drawn backwards a few inches, with light pressure, to make a slight notch, a short gentle down-stroke is then made almost without pressure. In the first few strokes, the length and vigour of the stroke of the saw are gradually increased, until the blade has made a cut of two to four inches in depth; after which the entire force of the right arm is employed, the saw is used from point to heel, and in extreme cases, the whole force of both arms is used to urge the saw forward. The blade is occasionally greased to lessen the friction, the end of a tallow candle being mostly used, or else hog's lard smeared on a piece of thick leather.

In most instances little or no pressure is directed edgeways, or on the teeth; and when the effort thus applied is excessive, the saw sticks so forcibly in the wood, that it refuses to yield to the thrust otherwise than by assuming a bow or curved form, which is apt permanently to distort the saw from the right line. The fingers should never be allowed to extend beyond the handle, or they may be pinched between it and the work.

In order to acquire the habit of sawing well, or in fact, of performing well most mechanical operations, it is desirable to become habituated to certain defined positions. Thus in sawing, it is better the work should, as often as practicable, be placed either exactly horizontal or vertical; the positions of the tools and the movements of the person will also be then constantly either horizontal or vertical, instead of arbritary and inclined.

In sawing, the top of the sawing-stool should be horizontal, the edge of the saw should be exactly perpendicular, when seen edgeways, and nearly so when seen sideways; the eye must watch narrowly the path of the saw, to check its *first* disposition to depart from the line set out for it. If however, the eye be directed either so far from the right or left side of the blade as to form a material angle with the line of the cut, the hand is liable almost unconsciously to lean from the eye, and thence to incline the saw sideways. It is therefore best to look so far only on the right and left of the blade alternately, as to be just able to see the line, and thence to detect the smallest deviation of the instrument at the very commencement of its departure. And then, by twisting the blade as far as the saw-kerf will allow, the back being somewhat thinner than the edge, the true line may be again returned to; indeed, by want of caution, the saw may be made to cross the line and err in the opposite direction. It is however, best to make it a habit to watch the blade so closely as scarcely to require any application of the correctional or *steering* process at all. The saw, if most set on the left side, or having teeth standing higher on the left side, cuts more freely on that side, and has a tendency to run or arcuate towards the left; and under the reverse circumstances the saw is disposed to run to the right.

Thick works are almost always marked on both sides the plank, and the piece is turned over at short intervals, so that a portion of the work is performed from each side; the saw-cut will then assume a series of slight bends, to the right and left alternately, and will depart less from the true line, than if these disturbances had effect from the one side only, and thus produced an accumulating error, or a line swerving in one direction alone, or as a sweep of a large circle. The practice of changing sides with the work will, under most circumstances, be found to lessen the errors incidental to the process, and the practice is therefore especially desirable for beginners.

The work is not always placed on the sawing-stool, as in some cases it is laid on the bench, and fastened down upon the same with the holdfast or hand screws, and with the intended cut situated beyond the edge of the bench; the workman then stands erect, and uses the saw with both hands, placing the back of the saw towards his person, and sawing from it; this with many is a favourite position. In some cases, especially in small and thick works, the wood is fixed perpendicularly in the screw-chops of the bench, and the saw is applied horizontally. These modes are both good, inasmuch as they relieve the individual from the necessity for holding the work with the knee, and he is less restrained in the action of the limbs.

In using the hand-saw for preparing hardwood for turning, the log is either laid on the common X-form sawing horse or else it is fixed in the jaws of the tail-vice, which latter mode is generally more convenient. In speaking of sharpening the saw, it was shown that the points of saw-teeth, proper for hardwoods, are somewhat less acute than those for deal and ordinary timber.

The remarks on the hand-saws have been given in greater detail than those which follow, because it is considered these instructions will assist in the manipulation of all the other saws used by hand.

Figs. 684 and 685 represent the narrow taper saws used for cutting curves and sweeps, especially those required in wide boards. Compared with the generality of saws, these are made thicker on the edge, and are ground thinner on the back, to allow them more freedom in twisting round curves, the smallest of which require the narrowest blades.

The *table-saw*, and the *compass* or *lock-saw*, fig. 684, which only differ in size, resemble the hand-saws in their general structure and in the forms of their teeth, except that the blades are smaller and narrower, to allow them to lie as a tangent to the curve.

The *key-hole* or *fret* saw-blade, 685, which is drawn to the same scale as the last, is held in a saw-pad, or a handle having a stout ferule with a mortise and screws, so that the blade may be strongly grasped; and as the handle is perforated throughout its length, either the whole or part only of the blade may be allowed to project. The key-hole saws are sometimes fixed in a handle like that for a file, which is less proper.

Fig. 684.

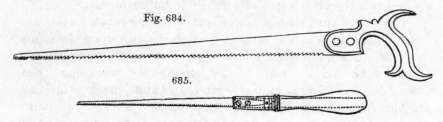

685.

The table, compass, and key-hole saws, all require care in their use, for if much pressure is thrown on the teeth, they stick fast in the material, and a violent thrust is liable to bend and permanently injure, or indeed, to break the saws; and besides, their paths are the less easily guided, the more vigorously they are used. It would be desirable, if in the narrow taper saws with only one handle, we more frequently copied the Indian, who prefers to reverse the position of the teeth, so that the blade may cut when *pulled* towards him, instead of in the *thrust;* this employs the instrument in its strongest instead of its weakest direction, and avoids the chance of injury. The inversion of the teeth, which in India is almost universal, is with us, nearly limited to some few of the key-hole and pruning saws.

Pruning-saws are often made exactly like the table and compass-saws, fig. 684, recently described, but with teeth which are coarser, thicker, and keener than those for dry wood. The forms of teeth figs. 644, and 645, namely the hand-saw tooth, and slight pitch, are used, and also the double teeth, fig. 661, which are rarely employed but for living timber. An excellent modification of the pruning-saw is to mount the blade at the end of a light pole 4 to 6 feet long, so that the edge of the blade may form an angle of about 150 degrees with the handle. This saw may be applied to branches eight or ten feet from the ground; the inclination of the blade just suffices for the onward pressure, and the teeth being inverted, the saw cuts in the pull instead of in the thrust, which is both more commodious to the individual, and free from the risk of accident to the blade.

Fig. 686.

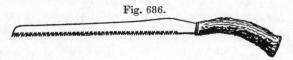

Many pruning-saws are made with blades nearly parallel in width, but as thick again on the edge as on the back, and with double teeth, fig. 661.   The larger pruning-saws of this kind, fig. 686, are mounted as carving-knives, or with straight handles of buck-horn; such blades measure from 8 to 10 inches long, and $\frac{5}{8}$ to $\frac{3}{4}$ inch wide; the smaller kind are made as clasp or pocket-knives, and are of about half the dimensions given.

The next group of saws enumerated in the table, are *Parallel Saws with Backs;* those most commonly known are in some measure particularised by their names, as *tenon-saws, sash-saws, carcase-saws,* and *dovetail-saws;* they only differ in size, as already shown, and they are represented by fig. 687.

Fig. 687.

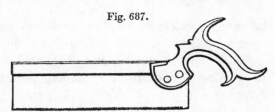

The blades of the back-saws are thin, and require to be very carefully hammered; the handle of the saw is affixed to the blade itself by the screws.   The back is either a piece of stout sheet-iron or brass folded together, first as an angle between top and bottom tools, and then closed with the hammer upon a parallel plate thicker than the saw.   When the inside of the groove has been filed to remove the irregularities, the two edges of the back are grasped in the tail vice, and the ridge is hammered to make the edges spring together almost as a pair of forceps. The back is held upon the blade by this elasticity or grasp alone, and the blade only penetrates about half-way down the groove.

The general condition of the blade depends in great measure

upon that of the back, which should not be exposed to rough
usage; as a blow on the middle of the back tends to throw the
blade more in at that part, and make it crooked on the edge, a
fault that may be in general corrected by tapping slightly upon
the back near the ends, in order to drive the blade as much
inwards at those parts as in the center, and balance the first
error.   When the blade itself is buckled, which is less liable to
occur than with hand-saws, from the more careful manner in
which the back-saws are used, the saw must be taken to pieces
and the blade corrected on the anvil as in other cases.

The back-saws, which are much employed for accurate works,
are often assisted or guided by *sawing-blocks*, in which one or
more saw-kerfs, that have been very carefully made, serve to
guide the blades; consequently this method saves a part of
the trouble in marking out the lines to be cut, and also of the
risk of making incorrect incisions.   The sawing block, fig. 688,

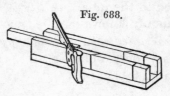

Fig. 688.

which is of the ordinary form, is
a trough made parallel both inside
and out, and having three saw-kerfs,
which are all exactly vertical.   The
one kerf is at right angles to the side
of the block, and serves for cutting
off pieces, the ends of which are required to be perfectly square;
the two other saw-kerfs are at angles of 45°, and slope opposite
ways: these serve for cutting mitres, or the bevilled joints always
employed for uniting mouldings at right angles to each other,
as in picture-frames and panels.   The work is simply held close
to the further side of the box, and with the line of division
opposite the saw-kerf, the saw is then allowed to pursue the
direction given by the saw-kerf; and when many pieces of
similar length are wanted, stops are added to the block.   The
joiner frequently uses the shooting boards represented on page
502, for sawing as well as planing, especially when the work is
to be planed immediately after on the same shooting board; the
saw is then applied parallel with, but slightly in advance of, the
face against which the sole of the plane rubs.

Before concluding the remarks on saws with backs, fig. 687,
it appears desirable to offer some particulars on the modes of
constructing *tenons* and *dovetails*, from which most useful and
general modes of uniting materials, two of these saws have
derived their names.

In a rectangular frame, represented partly finished in fig. 689, the *tenons* are commonly made on the shorter pieces, called the *rails*, and the mortises on the longer or the *styles*, which are always left somewhat longer than ultimately required, to prevent them from breaking out, either in making the mortises or in wedging up the frame. In carpentry, the panel is fitted in a groove, as at *a*, and is inserted or *planted* before the frame is glued up; but in cabinet-work the panel is fitted in a rebate, as at *b*, and is fixed by slips of wood after the frame is finished.

Figs. 689.   690.

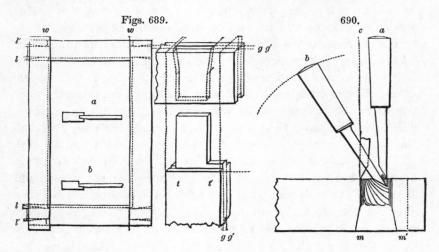

When the styles and rails have been planed up to their widths and thicknesses, (see pp. 498 to 503,) the internal length of the frame is marked on the styles at *l l*, and the width on the rails at *w w*; these lines are scribed on the four sides of each piece, with the square and scriber. The additional lines *l' l'*, indicating the ultimate length of the style, are also marked.

The width of the enlarged tenon *t t'*, is from one-half to two-thirds that of the entire rail; the inner haunch *t*, is required to be lower than the groove or rebate, and the outer haunch *t'*, is generally about three times as wide as the inner, to leave room for the wedges, and the end wood of the style exterior to them. The thickness of the tenon is commonly about one-third that of the style, but from the mode of work, its actual thickness, if not exceeding about ¾-inch, becomes exactly the same as the width of the mortise-chisel employed.

The appropriate chisel having been selected, the gage-lines

g g, corresponding with its width, are gaged on each edge of the styles and rails. Frequently the mortise-chisel is slightly stuck into the work to imprint its own width, by which to adjust the gages ; and every piece is gaged from the face side, so that when the whole are put together they may be flush with one another.

The several styles to be mortised, if small, as in cabinet work, are placed side by side with their inner edges upwards, and are fixed upon the bench with the holdfast ; the mortises are then commenced near the outer end, *m'*, 690. The styles, if large as in carpentry, are placed upon the stout mortising stool ; the workman sits upon them, and begins near the inner end *m*.

The mortises are made half-way through from the inner side of the rails, and are completed from the outer ; and the operation is by no means difficult, provided the mortise-chisel, which although narrow is very thick and strong, is kept exactly perpendicular to the side of the wood, and truly to the gage-lines. The chisel is mostly held with its face towards the operator, and the first cut is perpendicular and about one-sixth from the end of the mortise, as at *a*, fig. 690 ; the chisel is driven with two or three blows of a mallet of proportionate size ; the second cut is inclined, as at *b*, and between each of the inclined blows, the chisel is moved to loosen the chips. By the two cuts a triangular portion of wood or a *core* is loosened, and which is prized up by thrusting the chisel backwards through the dotted arc, the bevil or bulge of the chisel then resting upon the angle of the wood as a fulcrum.

The neighbouring lines in fig. 690 show the successive cuts employed in making the mortise ; some workmen prefer taking the cuts *a* and *b* alternately, always prizing up the chips by thrusting the chisel from them, after each cut *b* ; others prefer taking most of the cut *a*, at an earlier stage of the work. When the triangular incision reaches half-way through the wood, it is extended in length either by sloping cuts with the chisel, as at *b*, or with perpendicular cuts, as at *c*.

At the completion of the inner half of the mortise, the face of the chisel must be applied exactly perpendicular at each end, as *a* and *c*, and in releasing the shavings, the handle is moved towards the center of the mortise, using the cutting edge as the fulcrum, and not the angle of the wood, which would be thereby bruised. The style is now turned over, and the remaining half of the mortise is completed; but the outer ends are bevilled for the reception of the wedges, as marked in the diagram. The mortise is mostly left from the mortise-chisel, although when the two incisions do not exactly meet, it is needful to pare down the inequalities with an ordinary chisel.

The cutting of the tenon is less difficult of explanation than the mortise. The shoulders, or the transverse cuts of the tenon, are generally made with the dovetail or carcase-saw, whilst the rail lies on the bench against the sawing stop, or a peg near the corner of the bench; the rail may be held with the holdfast if preferred. The side or longitudinal cuts are usually made with the tenon or sash-saw, the rail being then fixed perpendicularly in the bench screws.

These cuts, which remove two thin rectangular pieces called *cheeks*, should be made with great accuracy, and so as just to avoid encroaching on the gage lines; as the tenon is left from the saw, or at most the angle is cleared out with the corner of a chisel applied almost as a knife.

The haunches are marked by laying the end of the rail, in contact with the gage lines on the inner side of the style, and marking the tenon from its corresponding mortise.

Tenons and mortises do not in all cases extend through the wood, and as they cannot be then wedged up, they have to depend exclusively on good fitting or surface contact, and the glue; in many cases also, screw bolts, straps, and wooden pins are used to draw the tenon into the mortise in various ways, subjects that are too varied to be here particularized.

In mortises that are wider or deeper than usual, it is a common practice to remove a portion of the wood with center-bits, or nose-bits, and to complete the mortises with firmer chisels.

Dovetailed joints are employed for uniting the *ends* of boards at right angles to each other, as in boxes, drawers, and numerous other works. The dovetails are made of several forms; thus, fig. 691 is a kind of factitious dovetail, in which the boards are first mitred, or their edges are planed at the angle of 45 degrees, and slightly attached by glue or otherwise; a few cuts leaning alternately a few degrees upwards and downwards are then made with a back-saw upon the angles, pieces of veneer are afterwards glued and drawn into the notches. This method is principally employed in toys and very common works, which are then said to be *mitred and keyed*; the hold is much stronger than might be expected.

Figs. 691.   692.   693.

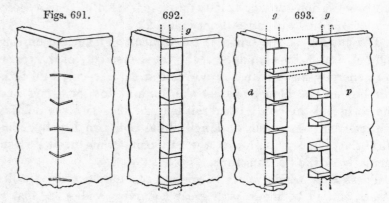

Fig. 692 represents the ordinary dovetail joint; *p*, fig. 693, the pins, and *d*, fig. 693, the dovetails of which the same is composed. In some cases the pins and dovetails are nearly alike in size, and this makes the strongest attachment; but in joinery and cabinet work, the dovetails are made on the front or more exposed part of the work, and the pins are cut of only one-fourth or less the size of the dovetails, in order that but little of the end wood may be seen. Usually, the pins are the first made; and as in making ordinary dovetails as well as tenons, the surfaces are left from the saw, this instrument must be well applied to produce the close joints met with in works of the best quality.

In setting out dovetailed works, the sides and ends of the box are first marked across on both sides, with the gage or square at *g g*, which lines indicate both the inside measures of the box and the bottoms of the pins and dovetails; the portions beyond the lines are left a trifle longer than ultimately required. Very little care is taken in setting out the pins; indeed, their distances are usually marked with a pencil, without the rule or compasses, and the two external pins are always left nearly as strong again as the others.

One of the fronts, fig. 694, is fixed upright in the bench screws, and the pins are sawn as shown at *a a*. These saw cuts are made exactly perpendicular, and terminate upon the gage lines; but horizontally they are sloped opposite ways, so that every pin is about as wide again on the inner as on the outer side of the front of the box. The wood between the dovetail pins is generally cut out with the bow or turning saw, leaving the space as at *b*, fig. 694; and the spaces are then pared out with the firmer chisel from opposite sides, as at *c*, the chisel being placed exactly on the gage lines, but slightly overhanging, so that the insides are cut hollow rather than square, to insure the exact contact at the inner and outer edges of the dovetails.

When the wood between the pins is removed entirely with the chisel, this instrument is driven with the mallet perpendicularly into the wood just in *advance* of the gage line, and sloping cuts are then made to form a notch half-way through the wood as at *f*; and when the space has been thus cleared, a more careful vertical cut is made exactly upon the gage line itself, as in the former case.

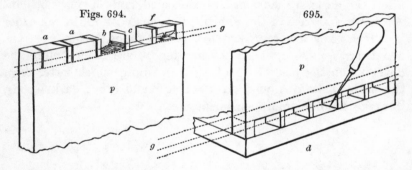

Figs. 694.   695.

The dovetails are next *marked from the pins,* and thus become their exact counterparts. In marking the dovetails, the end piece *d*, fig. 695, is laid upon the bench, and the pins in *p* are placed exactly vertical, and in their intended positions; and lastly, the scriber is passed along the two sloping sides of every pin. The gage lines are followed with the dovetail saw, the waste of the tool being taken from the hollows, so as to leave the gage lines almost standing: the hollows between the dovetails are now removed with the chisel unless the work is very large, when, as in cutting away the wood between the dovetails, the frame saw may be previously employed.

As the gage lines are almost left in sight, the pins and dovetails are mutually a trifle too large, so that in driving them together, they somewhat compress each other, and produce that close accurate contact to be observed in good works; and which gives rise to so much surface-friction, that the glue might in some cases be nearly dispensed with between the joint; but if the pins are left too large, they split the wood.

Whilst the chisel is being employed in dovetailing, it is usual to lay the several pieces of wood upon the bench, with their ends slightly extending beyond each other, like a flight of steps, an arrangement that admits of every edge being readily seen and operated upon; the pieces are fixed in this position by the hold-fast, and when they have been cut half-way through, they are turned over and finished from the other side.

Figs. 696 to 701 represent in plan, and in one group, the several ways of dovetailing the edges of boxes and similar works: fig. 696 is the mitre and key joint, and fig. 697 the common dovetail joint already spoken of, in which the pins and dovetails are both seen from the outside of the box. In the four other kinds the parts are more or less concealed, and they may be considered to increase in the difficulty of construction, in the order in which they are represented. It is supposed that the pins which are on the upper pieces marked *p*, are made before the dovetails on the pieces *d*, and before scribing which latter from the pins, chalk is rubbed on mahogany and other dark woods, to make the lines more conspicuous.

Figs. 696. 697. 698. 699. 700. 701.

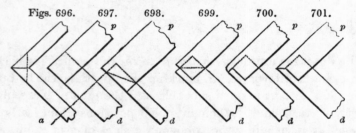

Fig. 698 is the *half-lap dovetail*, which is much used for the front of drawers. The pins in *p*, or the front of the drawer, are first marked, and the wood is also gaged at the end to denote how far the pins shall extend inwards: the saw can only be used obliquely, as shown by the dotted line, and the pins are finished with the chisel applied on the lines *a* and *d*. When, however, the drawer front is to be veneered, the pins are often sawn quite through on the line *d*, as the pins may be thus more easily cut, and the veneer conceals the saw kerfs in the drawer front. The dovetails on the sides of the drawer, or *d*, are afterwards marked and cut as in the first example, fig. 697, but of their exact lengths.

In fig. 699, sometimes called the *secret dovetail*, the pins and dovetails are both concealed, as neither of them extend through the work ; the saw can be only used at the angle of 45 degrees, either for the pins or dovetails, and most of the work is done with the chisel. The angle is filled in with a corner line.

The *lap dovetail*, fig. 700, is often used for writing-desks, and similar works with rounded edges, and not having corner lines : the front of the desk, or *p*, is first rebated out to leave the lap, the pins are then made in this piece, and the dovetails are afterwards scribed on *d*, and made as in the last case; only a small portion of the end wood is then seen at the ends of the desk, and this is in great measure removed from observation when the angle is rounded.

The mitre dovetail, fig. 701, requires each piece to be rebated out square, as in *p*, fig. 700 ; and after the pins and dovetails have been respectively made, the square rebates are converted into a mitre joint with a rebate plane. When finished, neither the pins, nor the modes of their concealment, are distinguishable, and the work appears to have a plain mitre joint.

When the lid of a box has a dovetailed rim, or that the box and lid only differ in respect to depth, the box is technically said to have a *tea-chest top*, and four pieces of wood, sufficiently deep to make both the box and its cover, are then dovetailed together in either of the ways before mentioned. When the top and bottom of the box are also added, the six pieces present the appearance of a rectangular block, and which is known as a *carcase*, a term also applied to other entire framings. The saw used in cutting open the carcase, or in separating the top of the box from the bottom, is thence called a carcase saw.

This mode of work, besides saving much of the labour of dovetailing, ensures the exact agreement in size, and the general correspondence of the two parts; which it would be more difficult to obtain if they were separately made, especially in sloping works, such as portable writing-desks and others of similar character.

In every case where the box and the lid are made together, the line of division is gaged on the four sides exteriorly, and one of the dovetail pins is placed upon that line; but it is made fully as wide again as the others, to admit of division, and yet be of the ordinary size.   If the joint-pin were made as usual, or left square, the carcase, on being cut open, would exhibit the rectangular lines of the pin and dovetail; to avoid which the joint-pin and dovetail should be pared away to the mitre, and then the cover and the box will also exhibit a mitre joint.

The top and bottom are fitted in various ways: sometimes they are glued on the square edges of the sides, but generally the sides and the top are both rebated, just as represented in fig. 700, on the supposition that p is the top, and d the side of the box; or they are rebated and mitred as in fig. 701.

A box made as above described, with mitred dovetails, with mitred joint-pins, and with the top and bottom rebated and mitred, would not show any joint, either within or without the box, except those constituting the margins of the twelve super-ficies of the work: in fact, the joints would alone occur at the several angles, and escape observation, as will be apparent from the inspection of figure 701.

Such a box, if neatly made, would be a finished specimen of work, but so much care is seldom taken, and it is more usual to employ corner lines and lippings to conceal the joints, or else to cover the box with veneers, and all of which are sometimes mitred.   In these cases the interior frame or the carcase of the box is of common mahogany, and dovetailed in the manner of fig. 697; or in very inferior works, the fabric is of deal attached by glue and brads, the principal reliance being then placed on the veneer for uniting the parts and concealing the defects.

Having concluded this long but important digression, respect-ing the formation of tenons and dovetails, the consideration will be now resumed of the saws enumerated in the table on page 699.

The *smith's screw head-saw*, fig. 702, which, in the table, follows the back saws last noticed, differs from them in propor-tions, and also in the handle, which resembles that of a file; the blade is generally also thicker and harder, to accommodate it to its work.   Some of the screw head-saws are made considerably smaller than those noticed in the table, the blade being a piece of watch-spring fixed in a brass back; but these little tools are generally made by the watch-maker, or other artizan requiring them.

In all screws that are made in the turning lathe, it is desirable, in separating them from the neighbouring metal, to use the turning tool, and to nick them in rather small behind the head. The little neck that is left, is broken through, just

Fig. 702.

flattened with a file, and then slightly notched with a triangular file, as an entry for the screw-head saw; by these means the risk of notching the head otherwise than truly diametrical is avoided.

The *comb-cutter's double saw* shown in profile in fig. 704, and in section on a larger scale in fig. 703, is called a *"stadda,"* and has two blades so contrived as to give, with great facility and exactness, the intervals between the teeth of combs, from the coarsest, to those having from 40 to 45 teeth in the inch.

The blades of the saw, or its *plates*, are made of thick steel, and are ground away on the edge as thin as the notches in the comb, either in the manner of *a* or *b*, and they have about 10 to 20 points in the inch, of slight pitch, fig. 644. The plates are fixed in the two grooves in the wooden handle or *stock*, by means of the *stuffing*, either two long wooden wedges, or folds of brown paper; the plates would rest in contact but for the introduction of the thin slip or tongue of metal *l*, called a *languid*, which is of the thickness of the teeth required in the comb, the one blade is in advance of the other from $\frac{1}{16}$th to

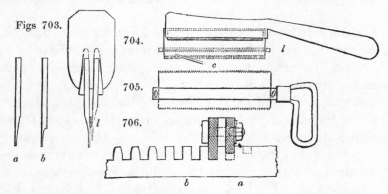

Figs 703.

704.

705.

706.

$\frac{1}{4}$th of an inch. At the first process a notch nearly of the full depth is made in the comb *c*, and a second notch is commenced;

at the next process the notch in advance is deepened, and a third commenced, and so on consecutively.

The *gage*-saw, or *gage-vid*, is used to make the teeth square and of one depth. This saw is frequently made with a loose back, like that of ordinary back-saws, but much wider, so that for teeth ½ ⅝ ¾ inch long, it may shield all the blade except ½ ⅝ ¾ inch of its width respectively, and the saw is applied until the back prevents its further progress. Sometimes the blade has teeth on both edges, and is fixed between two parallel slips of steel connected beyond the ends of the saw blade by two small thumb-screws, as in fig. 705; the less common instrument is represented, because it is useful for other purposes.

Double saws, fig. 706, analogous to those of the comb-maker, have been also frequently applied to cutting metal racks, similar to those used in air-pumps. The blades, which in 706 are shaded, are as thick as the widths of the spaces, and are separated by a parallel slip of metal, represented white, exactly equal to the thickness of the teeth; the separating slip also serves, as the stop to make the teeth of one depth from the surface; the three parts are strongly united by two or more screws, or bolts and nuts. The *rack saw* if carefully made, fulfils its work with considerable accuracy; the dotted lines at *a*, denote the succeeding step, those at *b*, the square notches when completed, and *c*, the teeth when rounded, which is done afterwards with a file. In modern practice, however, the teeth of wheels and racks are usually cut and rounded at the one process, which is performed in appropriate machines.

The third division of the table on page 699, refers to parallel saws used in frames, of which the measures are tabulated.

The saw-frames of these and other kinds, keep the blades straight, give them tension, and enable the force to be applied virtually as in the Indian saws, or by pulling the blades, thereby avoiding the risk of buckling them. From these several reasons the blades of frame-saws may be made very thin, consequently they act with less labour and waste, and may in general be used more vigorously than those saws having only a thrusting handle at the one end. The blades are sometimes left a trifle thicker where the pins are to be inserted, and these parts are softened by being pinched between red-hot tongs, prior to drilling the pin-holes by which they are attached to their frames.

The *mill-saw,* and *mill-saw web,* at the beginning of this group, are used in vertical saw machines, which will be described in the fourth section of this chapter. It will suffice here to observe, that the first, or mill-saws, which are the larger and stouter, are employed for sawing round timber into thick planks; and the mill-saw webs, for cutting deals into thin boards.

The *veneer saw* formerly in use at the saw-pit was, excepting the blade, a copy of the pit-frame saw, fig. 676, p. 703, and skilful sawyers would therewith cut about six veneers from the solid inch of wood. Smaller veneer saws more nearly resembling that shown in fig. 708 were also used by cabinet-makers, who would cut seven or eight veneers in each inch from smaller pieces of wood, fixed upright in the chops of the bench, two individuals being mostly required. The hand veneer saws, are now scarcely used in England.

The *chairmaker's saw* is in general a diminutive of the ordinary pit saw, and has a central blade strained by buckles and wedges. The work is fixed horizontally upon the bench by the hold-fast, the saw is grasped by the side rails with both hands, and with the teeth from the operator, who stands in the erect posture. He can thus saw with great rapidity and accuracy all straight and slightly curved pieces, not exceeding in width half the span of the frame, which is sometimes nearly as wide as the length of the blade. The wheelwright employs precisely the same saw for ˙cutting the felloes of wheels; the timber, wide enough for two felloes, is then fixed in the ordinary tail-vice.

The three following figures represent different kinds of frame saws, in which the blades are neither strained by buckles and wedges, nor placed centrally, as in those hitherto considered.

There is a central rod or stretcher, to which are mortised two end pieces that have a slight power of rotation on the stretcher; the end pieces are at the one extremity variously adapted to receive the saw, and at the other they have two hollows for a coil of string, in the midst of which is inserted a short lever. On turning round this lever the coil of string becomes twisted and shortened; it therefore draws together those ends of the cross pieces to which it is attached, whilst the opposite ends from separating, strain the saw in a manner the most simple, yet effective. The tension of the blade is retained by allowing the lever to rest in contact with the stretcher, as represented, but when the saw is not in use, the string is uncoiled one turn to relieve the tension of the blade and frame, one or other of which may be broken by an excessive twist of the string.

In the *wood-cutter's saw*, fig. 707, the end pieces are much curved, and one of them extends beyond the blade, which is

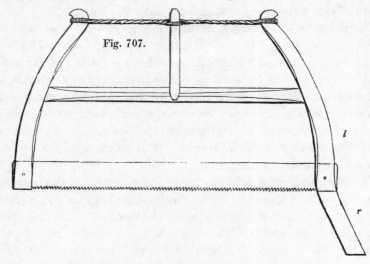

Fig. 707.

embedded in two saw-kerfs, and held by a wire at each end; the blade is therefore always parallel with the frame of the saw, which is mostly used vertically.   The end piece alone is grasped at *r* and *l*, by the right and left hands respectively; the wood is laid in an **X** form sawing-horse, and is sometimes held by a chain and lever, or less frequently in a strong pair of screw-chops.

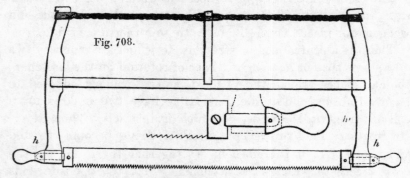

Fig. 708.

The *Continental frame-saw* used abroad for the general purposes of carpentry and cabinet-making, is shown in fig. 708; in the largest of these the blades are about three feet long, one and a half to three inches wide, and very thin; and others as small as half those sizes are also used. The wooden handles, *h h*, shown also detached and of twice the size at *h'*, have cylindrical stems, which pass through the end pieces; they are cut through longitudinally for admitting the sheet iron **T** form clamps, which are each held by a rivet passing through the handle outside the frame; the blade is fastened between each pair of clamps by a pin or screw.

The handles being cylindrical, the saw can be placed at all angles with regard to the frame, and may therefore be employed for cutting off pieces of indefinite length, provided they do not exceed the width from the blade to the stretcher, which latter is forked at the extremities to embrace the cross pieces, and this allows it to be shifted nearer to the string when required for wide pieces. Before using the saw it should be observed to place the blade exactly in a plane, or *out of winding*.

Most of the works performed in England with the hand-saw, the tenon, dovetail, and similar saws, are abroad accomplished with frame-saws of various sizes; the pieces are mostly fixed, either to or upon the bench, and the contrivance for holding long works, shown in fig. 709, is also general on the Continent.

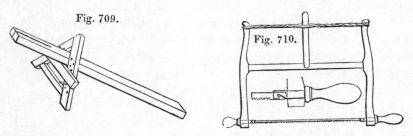

Fig. 709.

Fig. 710.

The work to be sawn is passed through the triangular opening in a wooden frame, nearly in the form of the letter **A**; when the frame and work lie at an obtuse angle, they constitute a three-legged stool. The upper edges of the board become wedged fast in the angular sides of the triangle, and the lower side of the board rests on the cross piece of the supposed letter, which may be placed at various heights, according to the size of the work, as it rests on two moveable pegs. In sawing small works, the man rests his knee on the work near the top of the frame, and the board is changed end for end when sawn through half its length. Triangular frames, with various modifications, are

also commonly used abroad instead of the saw-pit; but our own
occasional method, namely, a pair of trestles about six feet
high, is much better, as each of the sawyers is then far more
favourably situated than when the timber is placed aslant.*

The *turning-saw,* or *sweep-saw,* fig. 710, which is also called the
frame-saw, or *bow-saw,* resembles fig. 708, except in its smaller
size and greater proportionate width of frame; this will be
apparent, as the figures are drawn to the same scale.

Its handles have always cylindrical wires that pass through
the end rails; the wires are sawn diametrically to admit the
saw blade, and are drilled transversely for the pins; frequently
the one handle has an undercut notch, as represented on a larger
scale, so that the saw may be removed sideways from the one
handle, and allowed to move as on a joint upon the other, a provision that is often turned to a useful account.

In using the bow-saw the work is mostly fixed vertically, and
therefore the blade is used horizontally; but the frame is
placed at all angles, to avoid the margin of the work, and it is
frequently necessary to twist the handles or pins during the cut,
to modify the position of the frame. It often happens that the
cut has to be commenced from a hole or aperture, in which case
the tension of the blade is relieved by a turn of the stretcher,
and the saw is disconnected at one end for its introduction. The
disunion of the blade is also convenient for withdrawing it sideways, without the tedious necessity for retracing the tortuous
course by which it may have entered the work.

It still remains to notice those saws, the frames of which
may be considered to be slightly flexible, and to form the three
sides of a rectangle. The *ivory-saw,* which has been already
figured and described at pages 146 and 147 of the first volume,
is the largest of this kind, and the full particulars have been
there given, of its use in the preparation of ivory. Sometimes
the frames of saws for ivory are made of iron, and without the
adjusting screw clamp; the frame is then sprung inwards by
means of a long hook whilst the saw is inserted.

---

* These and relative matters are fully described and figured by A. R. Emy, in
his *Traité de l' Art de la Charpenterie.* Paris, 1837. Plates 2 to 11.

The *smith's frame-saw*, fig. 711, is nearly a copy of the saw last referred to, and it almost always possesses a screw and nut for stretching the blade.

The mode of using the saws, for metal, is the reverse of that in saws for wood; as for metal, the motion should be slow, and the pressure somewhat considerable, and the necessity for each of these conditions increases with the hardness of the material. The saw is almost invariably moistened with oil or tallow-grease, and in the back strokes the pressure on the blade is discontinued, but the saw is not raised from the bottom of the notch; in this respect the action resembles that of the file.

The smith's frame-saw is the common instrument used in metal works for the removal of pieces that are in excess, and in many cases instead of the whole substance being cut through, a notch is made on two sides of the work, and the center part is broken. This saw is also used for making notches and grooves, much the same as in cabinet-work; but except in small works, preference is given to the figuration of materials by casting, forging, and other modes already described.

Fig 711.

713.

712.

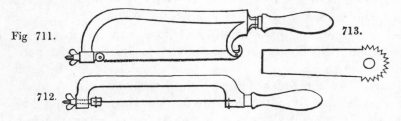

The *side frame-saw*, fig. 712, although far less common, is greatly preferred by some workmen; thus, in making the joints of drawing instruments, much depends on the correct use of the frame-saw, by which the notches are made for the reception of the steel plates used in the joints, and fig. 712, in which the blade is more immediately under observation, is preferred to fig. 711. For routing out the concave part, a saw like fig. 713 is used, and inserted a little way into the joint, until the holes in the joint and tool are sufficiently opposite to admit the end of a taper pin; the *joint-saw* or router is then moved to and fro, and as the concavity is cut away, the pin is set forward until its cylindrical part causes the two holes to be exactly opposite, and then the work is completed.

Piercing-saw blades commonly measure from 3 to 5 inches long, and they are fixed in very light frames, such as fig. 714, which are from about 2 to 4 inches deep from the saw to the back; in some instances piercing-saws exceed the depth of 8 inches, as in *m*, fig. 716. The blades are fixed between small screw clamps, the inner sides of which are mostly cut like files. Sometimes, as in fig. 715, the clamp near the handle is extended as a wire through the handle, and is tightened by a nut at the extremity, somewhat as in a violin-bow; but in general the slide is considered sufficient and preferable, as when it is loosened the tension of the saw can be appreciated with the fingers, and retained with the thumb-screw.

Fig. 714   715.

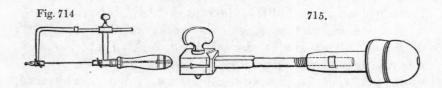

Some kinds of silversmith's works are pierced with this instrument, and embellished with the graver. When the design is original, the engraving is usually first done, and the interstices are cut out with the saw. But for the convenience of repetition, recourse is had to brass pattern plates, pierced and engraved like the finished work; the brass pattern is laid on the work, and all its interstices are marked through with a fine scriber. In copying designs from any article of silver, the new piece is laid upon the original, the interstices of which are smoked through with a lamp: and in curvilinear works that cannot be pierced while straight, the pattern is dabbed with printing-ink, a paper is laid thereon, and rubbed on its upper surface with a burnisher; the paper thus printed is then pasted upon the object to be pierced. The under side of the original is printed from, to make the copy direct and not reversed.

The outline having been obtained by one of the above modes, a hole is made with the breast-drill in every piercing, and where practicable, the holes form the circular terminations of the apertures. The several curves are then followed with the saw, which is used vertically and with the handle downwards, whilst the plate is held horizontally upon the pin of the jeweller's bench with the fingers, in order that both the work and the saw may be freely twisted about in sawing out the several parts.

The silver-piercer sits at the silversmith's and jeweller's ordinary work-bench, formed like a round table, with four or six semicircular scollops about 18 inches diameter around it; the pins, or small filing boards, are about 3 inches square, and project inwards into the bottoms of the bays or scollops, each of which has a *skin* or a leather bag nailed around its edge, that serves to collect the filings removed from the work.

This form of work-table is adopted, in order that a central lamp may serve for the four or six workmen, each of whom has a glass globe 6 to 8 inches diameter, filled with water, to act as a condensing lens, and direct a strong light to the spot occupied by his work. Spirits of wine are added to the water, to prevent it from freezing and bursting the globe. The benches are frequently made semicircular and placed against a window, as the circular bench requires a sky-light.

The amateur can employ in piercing, a small square filing-board with a fillet beneath, by which it is fixed horizontally in the ordinary vice. Should he prefer fixing the work, it may be still held horizontally, provided he employs a hand-vice, and pinches it by the half of its joint in the tail-vice, so as to place its jaws horizontally. In passing round the small curves, the strokes of the saw must be short, quick, and feeble; in the larger curves, the full length of the blade may be more vigorously used.

Some of the very minute pierced works are drilled and then finished with small files, as in the plates formely used for covering the balances of watches, but in general, the file is not used. The piercing saw is also employed for cutting out small escutcheons and other pieces for inlaying.

From the pierced works, appear to have been derived those inlaid works, consisting of curved and flowing lines, which are produced by a method that may be called *counterpart sawing*, and in which two plates of differently coloured materials, whether wood, metal, ivory, tortoise, or pearl shell, are temporarily fixed together, and then cut through at the same time with a fine hair-like saw. By this process the removed pieces so exactly correspond in form with the respective perforations, that when the two colours are separated and interchanged, the one material forms the ground, the other the inlay or pattern, and *vice versá :* and the pieces fit so nearly together, that the route of the saw is only visible as a fine line on close inspection.

These works receive the general name of inlaid or marquetry works ; and also the specific names of buhl works and reisner works, from their respective inventors.*

The saws used in piercing and inlaying scarcely differ but in size : thus, the black line *m*, in fig. 716, is drawn from a large piercing saw of metal, and the dotted line *w*, from an ordinary buhl saw of wood : the former measures eight inches from the blade to the frame, the latter twelve or sometimes twenty inches, to avoid the angles of large works. The wooden frames are made of three pieces of wood, halved and glued together to constitute the three sides of a rectangle, after which two pieces are glued upon each side, each at the angle of 45 degrees across the corners : the whole, when thoroughly dry, is cut round to the form represented. The screws for giving tension to the blade, although commonly added, are seldom used, as the frame is only sprung together at the moment of fixing the saw, and by its reaction stiffens the blade.

The buhl cutter sits astride a horse, or a long narrow stool, fig. 717, having near the one extremity two vertical jaws lined with brass at the top ; the one jaw is fixed, the other is notched

---

* The term marquetry seems to be employed to designate all kinds of inlaid work, known in France as *marqueterie en bois*, and *marqueterie en métal*. It includes not only the works of counterpart sawing, in which flowers, animals, landscapes, and other objects are represented in their proper tints, by inlaying, and without the aid of the artist's pencil ; but it also includes those geometrical patterns composed of angular pieces, laid down in succession more after the manner of ordinary veneering ; and amongst which, the specimens of *parquetage*, or inlaid floors, appear to claim a place.

Boule work, and reisner work, are considered by the virtuosi to apply exclusively to the works of two celebrated *ébénistes* of those names, both settled in France ; the former, an Italian, in the reign of Louis XIV., the latter, a German, in the time of Louis XIV. to XV. Their cabinet works were as much celebrated for their graceful forms or outlines, as for their embellishment with inlaying.

Boule, mostly employed dark-coloured tortoise-shell inlaid with brass, in flowing patterns, occasionally ornamented with the graver. Reisner, used principally as the ground tulip-wood (called in France *bois de rose*,) inlaid with flowers in dark woods, grouped in a much less crowded manner than in ordinary marquetry. Reisner occasionally combined therewith bands and margins, in which the woods were contrasted as to the *direction* of the grain, as well as colour.

The terms *buhl* or *bool* work appear to be corrupted from boule, and now refer to any two materials of contrasted colours inlaid with the saw, and which, in France, would be called by the general name of *marqueterie*.

below, and springs open when left to itself, but is closed by a strut which is loosely attached to the stool by a tenon and mortise, and rests in a groove in the moveable jaw. When the strut is pulled downwards, by a string leading to the treadle, it closes the flexible jaw of the vice. In the plan the jaws are inclined some twenty degrees, so as to be at right angles to the path of the workman's right hand.

Figs 716.   717.

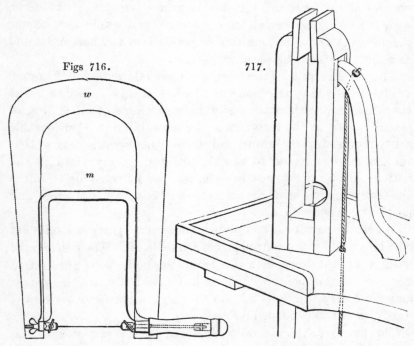

In the following descriptions of counterpart sawing, the several methods will be noticed in that order which appears to offer the most facility of explanation, regardless of other considerations.

In buhl work the patterns generally consist of continuous lines, of which the honeysuckle ornament may be taken as a familiar example. To make this, two pieces of veneer of equal size, say of ebony and holly, are scraped evenly on both sides with the toothing-plane, and glued together with a piece of paper between, for the convenience of their after separation.* Another piece of paper is glued outside the one or other veneer, and on which the

---

* Veneers, like other thin plates, are pinched by one corner with a screw clamp to the table or bench ; the tools are applied from the fixed end, in order that they may pull the material and keep it straight instead of forcing it up in a wave.

design is sketched; a minute hole is then made with a sharp-pointed awl or scriber, for the introduction of the saw, that spot being selected in which the puncture will escape observation.

The buhl cutter being seated on the horse, the saw is inserted in the hole in the veneers, and then fixed in its frame; the work, held in the left hand, is placed in the vice, which is under control of the foot, and the saw is grasped in the right hand, with the fore-finger extended to support and guide the frame; the medium and usual position of which is nearly horizontal and at right angles to the path of the saw.

The several lines of the work are now followed by short quick strokes of the saw, the blade of which is always horizontal; but the frame and work are rapidly twisted about at all angles, to place the saw in the direction of the several lines. Considerable art is required in designing and sawing these ornaments, so that the saw may continue to ramble uninterruptedly through the pattern, whilst the position of the work is as constantly shifted about in the vice, with that which appears to be a strange and perplexing restlessness.

When the sawing is completed, the several parts are laid flat on a table, and any removed pieces are replaced. The entire work is then pressed down with the hand, the holly is stripped off in one layer with a painter's palette-knife, which splits the paper, and the layer of holly is laid on the table with the paper downwards, or without being inverted.

The honeysuckle is now pushed out of the ebony with the end of the scriber, and any minute pieces are picked out with the moistened finger, these are all laid aside: the cavity thus produced in the ebony is now entirely filled up with the honeysuckle of holly, and a piece of paper smeared with thick glue, is rubbed on the two to retain them in contact. They are immediately turned over, and the toothings or fine dust of the ebony are rubbed in to fill up the interstices; a little thick glue is then applied, and rubbed in, first with the finger, and then with the pane of the hammer, after which the work is laid aside to dry.

When thoroughly dry, it only remains to scrape the bottom with the toothing-plane or, when the work is small, with its iron alone, and then the buhl is ready to be glued on the box or furniture in the manner of an ordinary veneer, as already explained ; when the work is again dry, it is scraped and polished.   Exactly the same routine is pursued in combining the holly ground and the ebony honeysuckle, and these constitute the *counter* or *counterpart buhl*, in which the pattern is the same but the colours are reversed.

It is obvious that precisely the same general method would be pursued to make four satin-wood honeysuckles at the respective angles of a rosewood box ; the veneers for which would be then selected of the full size, and glued together with paper interposed.   To ensure the exact similitude of the several honeysuckles, one of them having been cut out would be printed from, by sticking it slightly to the table, dabbing it with printing-ink, and then taking impressions, to be glued on the other angles of the box at their exact places.   The counter would have, in this case, a satin-wood ground, with the honeysuckles in rosewood.

To advance another stage, three thicknesses of wood may be glued together, as rosewood, mahogany, and satin-wood, and a center ornament added to the group of four honeysuckles.   The three thicknesses, when cut through, split asunder, and re-combined, would produce three pieces of buhl work, the grounds of which would be of rosewood, mahogany, and satin-wood, with the honeysuckle and center of the two other colours respectively. Such are technically known as *works in three woods*, and constitute the general limit of the thicknesses, but the patterns consist of many more parts than here supposed.

In a series of three woods in the possession of the author, or three veneers, cut and interchanged, as above explained, the three tablets each present forty-eight different pieces, and by the introduction of a broad arabesque band, the ground consists of a central panel of one colour, and a margin of another.   It is the general aim so to arrange the design as to have about an equal quantity of each colour, to make every combination effective, or without the predominance of any one colour.

Before glueing such works together, it is sometimes required to take off a printed impression for future use ; in such cases one thickness is entirely stripped off, and those pieces of this thickness which best display the character of the pattern, are slightly glued on their corresponding places on the two thicknesses, and project therefrom in the manner of type ; so that they alone receive the printing-ink, and return it to the paper pressed upon them with the hand, or with a tool handle used as a burnisher.

Brass borders, technically known as *vandykes*, are worked in narrow slips, and in other respects as above, except that unless a small hole is drilled through the brass and wood for the saw, it is allowed to cut its own path from the outside edge of the materials, and which is more usual. The true buhl, or the wood ground with brass scrolls, is laid down in four or more pieces around one box or panel; and the counter, or the brass ground with wood scrolls, upon another.

When the material is small and costly, as pearl shell, it becomes necessary to use two or several pieces, accurately placed edge to edge, to cover the entire surface to be ornamented; and the joints are placed where least observable in the pattern. The paper knife, from part of which fig. 718 was drawn, required eight pieces of pearl shell; in using this material, a hole is made in the wood close against the pearl, and the saw is sent in from the edge of the same. The counter, when glued on another veneer, is not inlaid of the irregular angular form of the rough pieces of pearl, but it is cut around the general margin of the pattern, as at the one part of fig. 719, which represents the counter to fig. 718.

Fig. 718. the buhl or true bnhl.

Fig. 719, the counter or counterpart buhl.

Inlaid by ordinary cutting.   Inlaid by internal cutting.

Sometimes, to give additional elaboration and minuteness, the saw is made to follow all the device of the counter, and leave a narrow line of pearl both within and without: this is called internal cutting, and is represented in figure 719; but in general, the counter fails to present the same good effect as that of the true buhl, in which the drawing of the ornament is more effectually preserved ; and in the internal cutting the pattern presents a thready or liny appearance.

Before concluding this part of the subject, it deserves to be noticed that in the more minute buhl works, the parts are not cut exactly square, but slightly bevilled, so that the pearl may be left a trifle larger than the interstices in the wood, to compensate for the saw kerf, and make the fitting close as regards the true buhl. But this bevilling is prejudicial to the counter, as the line of junction in it becomes wider than usual ; this defect is however considered to be less observable in the counter, and which is also the less valuable piece. The *stringings*, or the straight and circular lines combined with pearl buhl work, are mostly of white metal, such as tin or pewter, and are inlaid with the routing gage.*

In buhl works no part of the material is wasted, and the whole of the work is cut at once. The circumstances are entirely different with the marquetry works now to be described, of which a slight specimen is represented in fig. 720,

Fig. 720.

The ground Black Ebony. The green leaves, are of Holly stained green, notched, and engraved.

Holly-stained. Blue.   White. Holly.   Yellow. Zante.   White. Holly.   Red. Brazil Wood.   White. Holly-scorched.   White. Ivory.

---

* Buhl works of brass and wood, are sometimes made by *stamping* instead of *sawing*. As however the action of stamps and punches will be considered in a subsequent chapter, it need only be here observed, that the brass inlay, whether a honeysuckle or other ornament, is stamped out of sheet brass, and the wood veneer is stamped with the same tools ; the brass honeysuckle is then inserted into the cavity in the wood as before. This method produces, so far as the nature of the materials will allow, an absolute identity of form, but it must be obvious the mode is not applicable to small patterns, as the punches then inflict too much injury on the wood ; neither does the stamping admit of the unbounded choice of design attainable with the saw, as the punches are necessarily expensive and limited to their particular forms.

3 B

wherein the ground is ebony, and the flowers or other ornaments are made of coloured woods, as denoted by the annexed names. The dyewoods are used so far as they are available, and the greens, blues, and some other tints, are of holly stained to those colours. Each different leaf or coloured piece is produced one at a time, and mostly requires two cuttings, which may be accomplished in three several ways.

In the first mode, an engraving of the design is carefully pasted on the ground or counter, and cut out entirely; after which the several leaves are sawn out from different veneers, by aid of another impression of the engraving cut into pieces, and the leaves are inserted in their respective places; this mode requires extreme exactness, but admits of complete success.

In the second mode, the design is also pasted on the counter, which is then left entire: the leaves are cut out from woods of appropriate colours, and are then glued on the respective parts of the paper pattern on the counter. The projecting leaves are cut in, either singly or in groups, with the saw, which is just allowed to graze their external margins. The leaves are then all parted from the ground, and inserted in their respective apertures in the counter. By this, or the counterpart method, the fitting becomes more easy, and the cuts may be slightly bevilled, to improve the closeness of the joints.

In the third mode, the separate leaves to constitute the inlay, are cut out from the different coloured veneers, and glued in their appropriate positions on a sheet of paper. A sheet of white paper is also glued or pasted on the veneer to be used for the counter or ground; and further, a sheet of the blackened or camp paper, such as that used in the manifold writers, is also required.

The three are assembled together—at the bottom, the veneer with the paper upwards, then the camp paper, and at the top the leaves, the backs of which are then struck at every part, with several blows of a light mallet, so as to print their own impressions on the white paper. The printed apertures are then cut in the counter one at a time, so that the outer edge of the saw-kerf falls exactly on the margin of every aperture.

In this, or the third mode, the fitting of the parts may be made unexceptionably good, as the operation is not prejudiced by the unequal stretching of the paper, which is liable to occur when two copies of the engraved design are employed, as in the first and second modes.*

The ribs and markings of the leaves in marquetry work, are made by cuts of the saw, or scratches of the graver, which become filled with the fine wood dust and glue.

Occasional assistance is derived from the judicious disposition of the grain of the wood ; and the shading of the leaves, to give them roundness, is obtained by scorching their edges by holding them near a heated iron before they are laid down.   In this manner white roses and other flowers with many leaves are most successfully imitated in holly ; the several leaves being cut out, scorched on the edge, and grouped together to form the flower, before incision.   Ivory is used for very white flowers ; and ivory, either white or stained, and also pearl shell, and other materials, are used for insects, and parts requiring additional brilliancy of effect.

SECT. IV.—RECTILINEAR, OR RECIPROCATING, SAW MACHINES.

Rectilinear sawing machines are for the most part derived from saws used by hand for similar purposes ; and under these circumstances, it appears desirable that the machines to be noticed, should so far as practicable, be introduced in the order adopted in the last section ; namely, machines derived from the felling, cross-cutting, and pit saws, and those from the frame, bow, and buhl saws.

Few sawing machines have been made for felling timber, because the labour of removing the machines from tree to tree, in general outweighs any mechanical advantage to be derived from their use.   In the most simple machine of this kind, the saw is formed as the arc of a circle, attached to a wooden sector moving on its center, and worked with reciprocating motion by a horizontal lever.†

---

* As a more expeditious mode of transferring the pattern than with the mallet, the three parts above described, have been squeezed in a flat screw press, this fails to bring up the impression, from the unequal thicknesses of the veneers ; the hydrostatic press does not produce the required effect, and is liable to crush the wood from its enormous force ; but the rolling press, such as that for copper-plate printing, was tried by Holtzapffel and Co., and found to succeed in all respects in transferring the pattern.

† Another construction for a felling and cross-cutting saw, which is mor elaborate, is described in the Mechanics' Mag. Vol. ii. p. 49-50 ; and at vol. iii. p. 1 of the same Journal, is a proposition for a pit-saw, which as well as the above, it

In cross-cutting saw machines erected in the **Portsmouth Dock-yard** and **Woolwich Arsenal**, the timber is laid as through a doorway, the posts of which are double, so as to form two narrow grooves for the guidance of the saw; this resembles the ordinary cross-cut saw, except that it has two guide-boards riveted to it, in continuation of its length, and the boards work freely through the grooves in the posts. The saw is actuated by a vertical lever, or inverted pendulum, moved by the steam engine, and the work-man bears down the opposite end of the saw with any required degree of force; the saw is guided in its first entry by a board with a saw-kerf, which then rests upon the timber, and when not in use, the saw is turned up on its joint, leaving the doorway free for the reception of other timber.*

A cross-cutting saw machine of a more exact kind is erected at the City Saw Mills: the saw blade is strained in a rectangular frame, which both reciprocates and descends in a vertical plane. The machine has a large double cross; the two horizontal arms have grooves that receive the rails of the saw frame, and which is reciprocated by a crank and connecting rod; the vertical arms of the cross fit in a groove formed by double vertical beams.

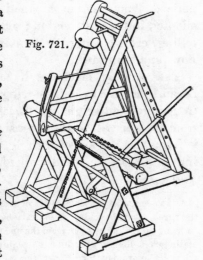

Fig. 721.

The cross and saw frame are almost counterpoised, so that a moderate pressure alone, and not their whole weight, falls on the saw teeth, and the timber is clamped on a railway or slide, which is at right angles to the plane of the saw's motion.

A cross-cutting saw machine worked by hand, that is much used on the Continent and in America, for cutting firewood, is represented in fig. 721. The wood is laid in an **X** form sawing horse, and fixed by a chain and wooden lever, which latter is brought

is proposed to work by means of the oft-repeated scheme, of a heavy pendulum put in motion by manual power.

* See Rees's Cyclopædia, Art. Machinery for Manufacturing Ships' Blocks, Vol. xxii.; also Encycl. Metrop. Part Manufactures, Art. 532.

under a peg. The frame saw is suspended by its lower angle in the cleft of a lever that swings as a pendulum when the saw frame is moved. The lever supports and guides the saw frame, the action of which is assisted by the momentum of an adjustable weight, built out at right angles to the suspending lever. The saw always rests on the timber, and cuts both ways; and being guided in its required position, a person but little experienced in the use of the ordinary frame saw, can exert his whole strength in the act of cutting, and accomplish the work expeditiously, especially as the saw is longer than that shown on page 726, and employed in the ordinary manner for the same purpose.

Upright or reciprocating saw machines, are largely employed to perform that kind of sawing which is usually done at the saw-pit ; the larger upright or frame saws are used for cutting large round or square timber into thick planks and scantling, the smaller for cutting deals into boards. The earlier of these machines appear to have been those for round timber : they were mostly built of wood and driven by water power, these have been repeatedly described.*

The vertical saw mills now used in England are made almost entirely in iron, and driven by steam power, and as the several constructions differ but little either in respect to principle or

---

* The reader interested in the practical details of the earlier saw mills, is directed to Gregory's Mechanics, 1807, vol. ii , p. 324 ; and, in addition to the authorities there quoted, he will find useful matter on the subject in Hassenfratz's *Traité de l'Art du Charpentier,* Paris, 1804, in Evan's Young Millwright, and Miller's Guide, Philadelphia, 1821, and more particularly, in the reprint of Belidor's work, *Architecture Hydraulique, avec Notes, par M. Navier,* Paris, 1819.

In Besson's *Instrumentarum,* published in 1578, at Plates 13 and 14, are two very curious and graphic drawings of saw machines driven by manual power ; the one by a crank and winch handle ; the other by a pendulum pulled as a church bell, and acting through the medium of a right and left-handed screw, and a system of diagonal links, as in the so-called " lazytongs." One of the saws has curvilinear teeth, of which 1, 3, 5, 7, cut during the descent, and 2, 4, 6, 8, during the ascent of the blade.

In the saw invented by Lieutenant J. W. Hood, for cutting through ice, the blade is suspended from the end of a lever, like that of an ordinary hand-pump, and has a heavy weight beneath the ice. The axis of the lever is in a wooden frame, or sledge, the progression of which is caused by the end of a rod or paul, that sticks into the ice; the rod being jointed to the lever a little in advance of its pivot, thrusts the frame and saw some three or four inches forward during the act of cutting. This ice saw is worked by two to four men, whereas the previous methods used in the Greenland fisheries, with a triangle and pulley blocks, required from twenty to thirty men.—Trans. Soc. of Arts, 1827, vol. xlv., p. 96.

general arrangement, the modern frame saw for deals, fig. *722*, will be principally spoken of. In this drawing the whole of the mechanism has been brought into view, by supposing the floor to have been removed, and some unimportant alterations to have been made; in reality the pedestals F F rest *upon* the floor, and the machine occupies considerable length.

The stationary frame work in fig. 722, consists of two standards or vertical beams, in front of which are fixed two accurate square

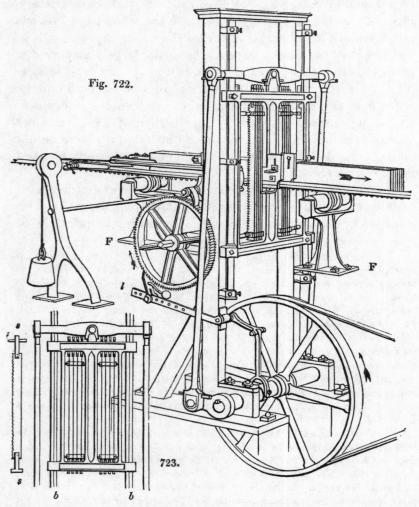

Fig. 722.

723.

bars, by means of six loops. The sliding saw frame shown geometrically in fig. 723, has four vertical and two horizontal bars and is cast in one piece, or as a rectangular frame, which is attached to the stationary square bars *b b*, by appropriate bearings at the four angles.   One central crank is in general used, but for greater distinctness, the drawing is made from a machine having two exterior cranks, although one only is represented; the crank rods are not attached directly to the saw-frame, but to a floating lever, which is jointed at its center to the saw-frame; so that even supposing the two cranks to be a little dissimilar in length or angular position, they nevertheless move the platform equally, without straining or racking it.

When only one crank placed beneath the floor is employed, it is needful, both to avoid excessive height in the machine, and the disadvantage attending the action of a short connecting rod, that the latter should pass freely through an oval loop in the lower cross rail of the saw-frame, and be united to the upper rail ; sometimes the crank shaft is fixed to the ceiling of the building, but this construction is the least in estimation.   The crank shaft, in addition to the driving pulley, has always a heavy fly-wheel to equalise the action of the machine, but which is not shown in the drawing.

Two deals are usually sawn at once; the parts now to be described, are therefore in duplicate, although in the figure, one deal is supposed to be removed for the purpose of showing the mechanism more distinctly.   Generally each deal has to be cut into three boards, and two saws are then employed on each side of the frame ; but sometimes as many as eleven thin saws or webs are used, then producing twelve thin boards or *leaves* from each deal.   The saws, of which one is shown at *s s*, have buckles riveted to them, and these pass through mortises in the top and bottom rails of the sliding frame; the buckles at the bottom are solid and shaped like an inverted T, those at the top have mortises and thin steel wedges; the T pieces and wedges bear on the outsides of the frame.

The distances between the blades are adjusted by interposing pieces of wood, and pressing the whole together by the side screws, after which the saws are separately tightened by the steel wedges ; these details are sufficiently manifest in the geometrical view, fig. 723.   It is to be further observed that the edges of the saws are not quite perpendicular, but have a little *lead*, or their upper ends overhang the lower about $\frac{1}{4}$ or $\frac{3}{8}$ inch, to extend the cut throughout the descent of the blade, and to carry the saws a little distance *from* the cuts, in the ascending or back stroke.

The two deals lie on a series of rollers built on pedestals, of which two only are shown at F F; the rollers also support a long rack, which, at the left of the figure, has *dogs* or nippers, that grasp the end of the deal by means of a side screw. The weight to the left of the figure, pulls the longer end of a horizontal lever, the shorter end of which, (not seen,) has a roller that presses the part of the deal contiguous to the saw, against a *fixed* vertical plate or *fence*, so that the cuts become exactly parallel with the side of the deal, whether it be straight or crooked.

The deal is advanced by means of the rack and pinion, which are actuated by a ratchet movement as follows : an eccentric on the main shaft alternates the shorter end of the lever l, and to the longer end of the same is fixed the ratchet or paul, which according to its distance from the center, slips over two or three teeth in its descent, and in rising thrusts the ratchet-wheel round the same distance, and by its connexion with the pinion for the rack, advances the rack and wood a proportionate quantity. The retaining pauls or detents on the top of the wheel prevent its retrogression; when they are turned back, the wood ceases to advance, and the slide may be run quickly back by a winch.

The plank frame by the late Mr. Benjamin Hick, of Bolton, (of which a model is deposited in the Museum of the Inst. Civil Engineers) has no long rack. Each deal is grasped between two grooved feeding rollers; the one fixed to the framing of the machine, the other pressed up by a loaded lever, and moved a small step at a time, by a ratchet as usual.

The single saw-frames above described make about 100 to 120 strokes, of 18 or 20 inches long, in the minute, and cut two 12-foot deals in from five to ten minutes; the saws require to be sharpened about every tenth *round*, or journey, for hard deals, and every twentieth for pine. Similar frame saws are made double, so as to operate on four deals at a time; the crank is then double, and so contrived that the saws in one frame descend, whilst those of the other ascend. By this arrangement the vibrations of the machine are somewhat lessened, so that the velocity may be increased to about 160 or 200 strokes in the minute; but the time occupied in fixing and adjusting is also greater, so that but little if any real advantage is obtained.

Sawing machines for round timber, are larger, stronger and somewhat different from the deal frames. The timber-slide moves on fillets or **V. V.**'s, which are fixed to the floor, and passes between the standards of the saw frame ; the timber slide has strong vertical end plates, through mortises in which, stout iron spikes or dogs are driven like nails, into the ends of the required planks. The dogs are then secured by side screws or wedges in the dog plates, from which they project sufficiently, to allow the saw blades to stand between the end of the timber and the dog plate, at the commencement of the sawing.

The sliding frames carrying the saws for timber frames are longer than for deal frames, and those in the Government saw mills at Woolwich, rest in contact with rectangular fillets on the standards, against which they are pressed by powerful springs, so that the square bars $b\,b$, fig. 723, are dispensed with. In these same machines the blades are strained one at a time by a loaded lever, like a Roman steelyard, which gives to each the tension of about one ton, and whilst under this tension, the wedges are driven just home, but without violence; each blade becomes therefore tense alike. Various contrivances are added to vertical saw machines driven by power, so that, when the saws have arrived at the end of the timber, the motion of the wood or that of the entire machine may be arrested automatically.

Rectilinear sawing machines are not much used for those kinds of work that are performed with the ordinary hand saws, back saws, and frame saws, used in carpentry ; but two useful *scies mécaniques* suited to works of this scale are described in the Manuel du Tourneur and fig. 724, is reduced from one of these.

The saw frame has a central wooden rod, and a blade on each edge, which are stretched by clamps, screws and nuts, much as usual. The saw is guided perpendicularly by fixed wires; these pass through holes in the cross heads of the saw frame, which are sometimes fitted with rollers to relieve the friction. The saw frame is suspended from a bow spring attached to the column erected on the bench ; and the lower end communicates by a double-ended hook, with a light treadle. The spring, when left to itself, raises the saw frame and treadle some 8 or 10 inches, and the pressure of the foot gives the cutting motion.

For straight pieces a wide saw is used, and the work is guided against a square fence, which overlaps the front edge of the bench, and is fixed by a binding screw passing through a mortise. For bevilled pieces a chamfered bar c, is fixed to the right hand side of the bench, and carries a square sliding block, surmounted by an angular fence, with graduations and a clamping screw; the work is laid against the angular fence, and moved upon the chamfer slide past the saw.   For circular works a narrow blade is employed, and the popit head or center point connected with the stationary frame work, serves as the axis of motion for the piece of wood to be cut.

Fig. 724.

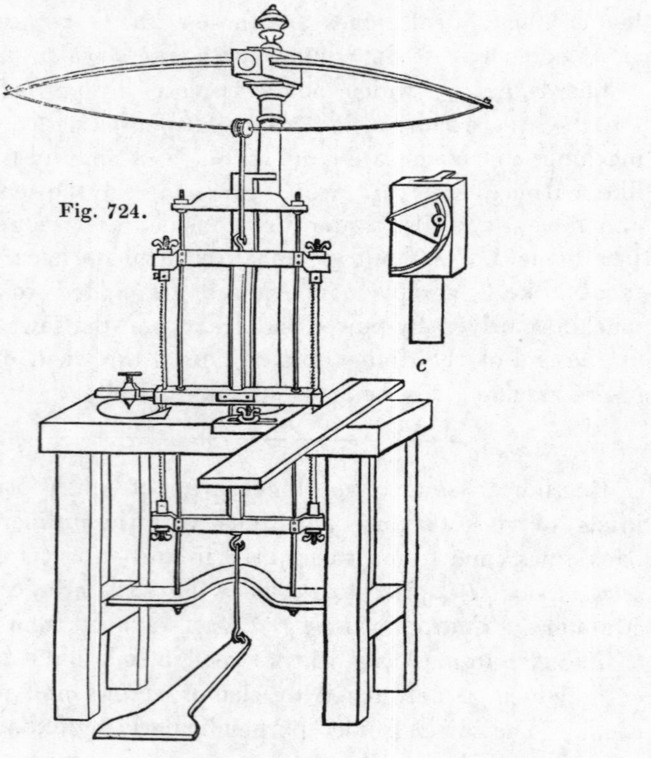

In order to leave the bench unobstructed, so that large pieces may be sawn, the guide rods upon which the saw frame works are discontinuous; the lower parts terminate beneath the bench, the upper are fixed to cross pieces, connected with a dovetail bar, itself attached in front of the column, so that the group of pieces carrying the upper wires may be fixed at a greater elevation to admit of thicker work. The back edges of the blades run in saw-kerfs in the lower rail of the guide frame.*

Three small reciprocating saw machines, fitted up as adjuncts to the lathe, will now be described; their constructions are entirely different, and they were planned by their respective inventors quite independently of each other. The one first described was especially contrived for buhl cutting; this appears however, to be far the least valuable application of these machines, as they may be much more efficiently used for various works similar to those done by the slender bow or sweep saw. The extreme delicacy of buhl work, is incompatible alike with the encumbrance arising from the mechanism, and the friction of the work upon the supporting platform.

In Mr. Mac Duff's buhl cutting machine, the saw is stretched in a frame about 4 to 6 inches high and 10 to 14 inches wide; the frame reciprocates vertically upon small fixed wires, by the modification of the crank shown in fig. 725. The pulley e, beneath the lathe bearers b, receives continuous motion from the foot-wheel, the lower end of a cord c, is fixed to a pin about an inch from the center of e, passed around the fixed pulley p, then between the bearers to the saw frame, which is raised by a spiral spring; by this arrangement, the parallelism of the cord is obtained. The work is supported upon a table or platform, midway between the path of the saw frame.†

Fig. 725.

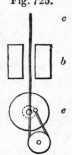

---

* A machine on a somewhat larger scale was erected by Mr. Brunel, at the Woolwich dockyard, and worked by the peculiar but expensive parallel movement of the interior epicycloid. There is a *fixed* wheel, say of 16 inches diameter, with internal teeth, and a corresponding pinion of 8 inches diameter, carried round by, and revolving upon, the end of a crank of 4 inches radius; the pinion carries a stud by which it is connected with the saw frame. The velocities of the crank and pinion are as 2 to 1, and in the *same* direction; the stud, if attached to the *center* of the pinion, would move in a circle of 8 inches; but when attached to the edge or *pitch line* of the pinion, it reciprocates in a right line, 16 inches long; the stud, if placed in any intermediate position, would travel in an ellipsis.

A reciprocating saw machine for sawing, boring, and manufacturing bevilled and curvilinear works in wood, was patenteed in 1833, by Mr. Samuel Hamilton, and is briefly noticed in the foot note following the application of the circular saw to curvilinear works.

† Mac Duff's buhl saw received the prize of 10*l.* awarded by Dr. Fellowes: and is fully described in the Mech. Mag. 1830, vol. xiii. p. 129; at page 285 of the same volume Mr. Mac Duff has described a larger and more simple mac ine of the same kind.

In the two following machines the saw is unprovided with the frame, by which, under ordinary circumstances, it is stretched and guided, these functions being fulfilled by the motive parts of the respective apparatus.

Mr. Lund's vertical saw machine, which is represented from the back in fig. 726, consists of a bench with foot wheel and treadle, surmounted by a rectangular frame, the lower rail of which is rebated to fit the bearers; the center rail is extended into a platform about three feet square, which, for the sake of portability, consists of two wide flaps with hinges and brackets, somewhat as in an ordinary pembroke table. To the extremities of the upper rail are fixed two long and narrow springs, made of hammered steel, that spring downwards when left to themselves. The ends of the saw are grasped in screw clamps, formed at the ends of square wires, working rather freely in the two outer rails, within holes fitted with metal. The lower saw clamp is connected by a cat-gut with an eccentric and guide pulley, as in Mac Duff's, but the eccentric shown detached in fig. 727 has more range, the traverse being sometimes 4 or 5 inches.

The upper saw clamp is connected with the straight springs by means of a catgut line, reeved in the manner shown more at large in fig. 728, (one of the side frames being removed,) the catgut proceeds from the springs, *over* the two fixed pulleys, and under the pulley on the top wire or clamp; this arrangement equalises the action of the springs, and gives a parallel motion to the blade, the back edge of which lies towards the operator, and works in a notch on the edge of a hardened steel disk, inlaid in the platform. One end of the catgut has a small circular button, which is passed through a round hole in the spring, and then sideways into a notch, so as to be readily detached for the removal of the saw.

Mr. Lund's machine is simple and effective for inlaid and fret works, and a variety of thin curvilinear pieces, which occur in cabinet work and pattern making. For cutting parallel and bevilled pieces, appropriate guides are added to the platform, similar to those elsewhere described. For circles, a brad-awl is passed through the center of the work into the platform, or rather into a subsidiary and common platform then added. And to shorten the length of stroke during the working of the machine, as required in sawing around small curves and rounded angles, a sliding bolt beneath the platform, is thrust across the path of the saw, so that the ascent of the saw to the full height is then prevented by the temporary increase of thickness in

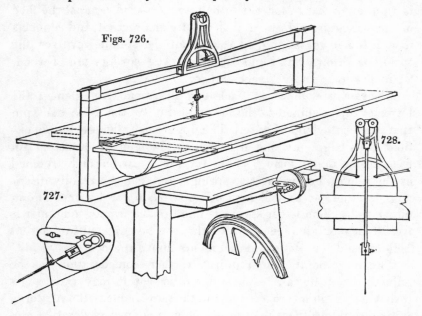

Figs. 726.

728.

727.

the platform, as the saw clamp strikes against the sliding-bolt or slide.*

Fig. 729 is copied from Professor Willis's sketch of a vertical saw for curvilinear works, constructed by himself in 1837. The frame of the machine is elevated above its true position to show the details, and is clamped on the bed of a lathe or

---

* Mr. Lund makes an ingenious use of this machine for inlaying the instruments in dressing cases lined with velvet. The bottom of the trays are glued up in three thicknesses, the grain of the inner piece being crossways, of the outer lengthways, a piece of white paper is added to receive the outlines of the instruments, the spaces for which are then cut in the saw machine, with a saw thinned away at the back, and very much set to cut a wide path.

The inner pieces having been removed, are split through the joint and glued flat down on a piece of velvet; each inner piece is then cut round with a penknife, leaving the face alone covered. The principal piece, or skeleton, is then glued and laid on another piece of velvet, which covers the holes as in a drum; the velvet is cut through at various parts of each aperture, and folded round the edges of the holes, and lastly, every removed and covered inner piece, is pushed into its place, which stretches and smooths the edges of the velvet, and completes the work. As the central pieces are in three layers, the cells may be either of one-third or two-thirds the entire depth, at pleasure.

Mr. Lund's saw machine was constructed and used in 1828.

grinding frame, and the saw derives its motion from an eccentric carried by one of the ordinary grindstone spindles. This eccentric is a pulley of hardwood cut in half and screwed against the face of the mahogany pulley. A loop of wire embraces it, and connects it with the lower spring, so that when the spindle revolves the spring is thrown into rapid vibration; the springs are of wood, 21 inches long and $2\frac{1}{2}$ inches broad.

The saw is clamped at each end in a small iron clamp; the lower clamp is joined to the lower spring by the same steel pin that carries the loop of wire. The upper clamp has several hooks filed in its edge, any one of which can be hooked on a steel pin fixed to the upper spring. Thus the saw is carried and stretched at the same time by the two springs, and can be readily disengaged, either by unhooking the upper clamp or by unclamping either end. The lower spring is fixed to the frame, the upper is fixed to a separate piece of wood that can be adjusted to different heights, and the platform is 12 inches above the bearers.

The only point that requires further consideration is the adjustment of the saw in the springs, so that it may traverse as nearly as possible through one and the same point of the platform, notwithstanding that the ends of the springs nearly describe arcs of circles, and therefore carry the extremities of the saw slightly to and fro during its movements.

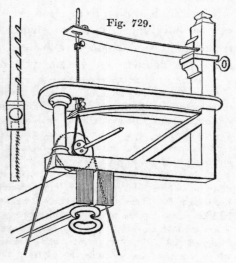

Fig. 729.

The vertical distances between the springs at their roots, where they are fixed to the framing, and at their pins where they carry the saw, must be so adjusted, that when the saw is at the top of its stroke, the lower spring is horizontal; and when at the bottom of its stroke the upper spring must be horizontal; and the platform midway between the two horizontal lines. In this condition, with a range of two or even three inches, the one curvature will neutralise the other at the platform, as in some of the parallel motions, which may be proved by a diagram carefully drawn on paper.

Professor Willis has used this machine extensively for cutting out in thin wood, models of Gothic tracery, also mathematical curves in illustration of the teeth of wheels and other elements of mechanism. To adapt the machine to take either short or long strokes as required in buhl cutting, without discontinuing the motion of the foot-wheel, Prof. Willis proposes to apply a contrivance to the eccentric, analogous to that explained in his Treatise on the Principles of Mechanism, p. 445.

A very curious sawing machine, the connecting link between rectilinear and circular saws, was patented by Mr. Newbury in 1808, and is thus described:—" Mr. Newbury's engine is formed by a long and very flexible blade of a similar nature to a clock-spring, which passes over two rollers of considerable diameter, placed in the same plane, and whose extremities are united so as to form a band round the two rollers. When this blade is intended to act as a saw, one of its edges is cut into teeth of the usual shape, and the substance to be sawed is placed on a stage, through which the blade passes, and is pressed against the blade with the necessary force, and in the direction proper to produce the shape required for it."* Guides for cutting rectilinear, curvilinear, and circular pieces are alluded to, the description does not however state the most difficult point of the construction, namely, the mode adopted in joining the ends of this elastic blade, or *ribbon saw*.

SECT. V.—COMMON APPLICATIONS OF CIRCULAR SAWS TO SMALL WORKS.

The remainder of the present chapter will be devoted to the consideration of machinery for circular saws; and in treating this

---

* See Retrospect of Philosophical Discoveries, 1808, Vol. IV, p. 222. The following paragraph respecting Newbury's flexible saw, appears on page 527 of the last edition of Belidor's *Architecture Hydraulique, avec Notes, par M. Navier,* Paris, 1819 :—

" *Scie à lame flexible et sans fin.*"—"*Cette invention a été proposée en Angleterre, mais il paraît qu'on y doutait de son succès. Elle a été employée avec avantage en France par M. Touroude pour refendre les liteaux qui composent les tuyaux des vis d'Archimède. (Bulletin de la Société d'Encouragement, Juillet 1815.) Le modèle de sa machine est déposé au Conservatoire des Arts et Métiers.*

extensive subject, it is proposed to present the matter in the following sections.

V. Common applications of circular saws to small works.

VI. Common applications of circular saws to large works.

VII. Less common, or specific applications of circular saws.

VIII. Circular saws and machinery for cutting veneers.

It is further to be observed that in the present or fifth section, in speaking of the construction and application of small sawing machinery, or that which may be conveniently used by the amateur, the matter will be arranged under the following subdivisions.

1. Lathe chucks for very small saws.

2. Spindles for saws of medium size.

3. Platforms, or tables and benches, for saws of medium size.

4. Stops to prevent the vibration of flexible saws.

5. Parallel guides.

6. Sawing the sides of rectangular pieces.

7. Sawing grooves, rebates and tenons.

8. Sawing or cross cutting, the ends of pieces, either square or bevilled; or those works in which the angular variations are in the horizontal plane.

9. Sawing bevilled edges, and prismatic pieces; or those works in which the angular variations are in the vertical plane.

10. Sawing geometrical solids and irregular pieces; or those works in which the angular variations are in both the horizontal and vertical planes.

The sub-divisions 1 to 10, when a little modified, denote also the arrangement followed in Sections VI. and VII.

------

1. *Lathe chucks for very small saws.*—Circular saws not exceeding one or two inches diameter, are occasionally mounted on lathe chucks, similar to that represented in fig. 730, which is not only the most simple, but probably one of the earliest modes in which the circular saw was used. The chuck should be of moderate length, with a tenon to fit the hole in the saw, and a central screw or nut to fix the same, as represented.

Opticians use this mode for the small thin saws with which they cut the notches in the tubes serving as springs in pocket telescopes. Carvers in ivory and similar materials employ small but thick saws, the edges of which are of round, angular, or other sections. In each art the objects are mostly applied by the hands alone.

For cutting the notches in the heads of screws for mechanical construction, thick saws are similarly employed. The screw is held in a socket, fig. 731, the end of which is tapped to receive the thread of the screw, and in cutting the notch, the socket is supported an inch or more from its extremity, upon the edge of the rest for the turning tool. The socket is wriggled up and down as a lever, to make the bottom of the notch tolerably straight, instead of concave, and the precautions to make the cut diametrical will be found at the beginning of page 723.

The gas-burners designated as *bat's-wing burners* have a narrow slit through which the gas issues: these are cut in a similar manner by thin circular saws ; and Mr. Milne, gas-fitter of Edinburgh, serrates such saws with a screw-cutter or tap, as in making the teeth of a worm-wheel, (see pages 591-2) ; but the cutter should for the present case have one side of the thread perpendicular, to produce saw teeth of the customary form.

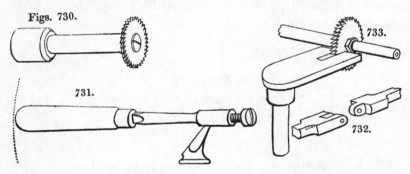

Figs. 730.

731.

733.

732.

In cutting the knuckles and tenons for joints, fig. 732, the work is usually supported on a small iron platform, fig. 733, the surface of which is horizontal, with a notch to receive the saw, and a cylindrical stem to adapt the platform to the bed piece of the common rest. The platform is fixed a little below the axis, to place the knuckles exactly central to the saw, so as to make the notches equally deep on both sides ; and if the surface of the platform is parallel with the axis of the spindle, the notch is sure to be perpendicular or square to the side of the work.

Sometimes two saws are used upon the same chuck or spindle,

3 c

to ensure parallelism in the sides of the middle piece or tenon; and similar methods are commonly used in sawing, notching and drilling, the small wooden mechanism of piano-fortes. For some of these works, especially those in metal, the saws are not always mounted on lathe chucks, but occasionally on small spindles similar to that drawn in the next figure.

---

2. *Spindles for circular saws of medium size.*—For sawing ordinary works in wood, the above arrangements are mostly insufficient; as the saw should be, both further removed from the pulley or lathe head to enable pieces of moderate width to be cut off, and also larger in diameter to serve for thicker pieces. The saw is then mounted on a spindle such as that shown in section in fig. 734 : the saw plate fits upon the cylindrical neck of the spindle, and is grasped between the two flat surfaces of the flange and loose collar, (which latter is shaded) and pressed forward by the nut. A steady pin, or a small wire (represented black) is inserted obliquely in the spindle, and passes through a corresponding notch in the saw. The steady pin constrains the saw always to travel with the spindle, without depending on the grasp of the nut alone.

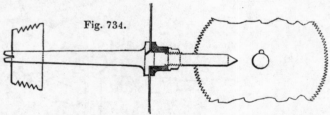

Fig. 734.

The saw spindle, fig. 734, is frequently squared at one end, and has a center at the other, to admit of being supported in the lathe at its extremities, by the square hole chuck and popit head respectively, so as to revolve together with the mandrel. When the saw spindle is used independently of the lathe, it has a center at each end for the center screws then employed, and also a pulley to receive the band from the foot wheel or other motive apparatus. In regard to the proportions of circular saws and some other particulars concerning them, the reader is referred to the table on page 784, near the commencement of the following or sixth section of this chapter.

3. *Platforms or tables, and benches.*—Wooden platforms employed for supporting the work have sometimes iron stems, and are in fact, extensions of fig. 733, except that they are placed above the center, so that one-third the saw-plate protrudes perpendicularly through the center of the platform. But a large platform thus constructed is very weak, from being attached only at one point; and every time the platform is fixed, there is the trouble of placing the saw-kerf exactly parallel with the saw, otherwise great friction ensues.

The saw platform and apparatus in fig. 735, are made almost entirely in wood; they are applicable to the ordinary turning lathe, and to saws not exceeding about 8 to 10 inches in diameter. The wooden platform is supported at the front and back, nearly throughout its width, upon the edges of the wooden box, the position of which is defined by a tenon fitting between the lathe bed, and secured by a bolt passing through the same. The platform is hinged to the back of the box, thus constituting as it were a large and overhanging cover. The last process in the construction of the apparatus, is to fix it upon the lathe bearers, and to allow its own circular saw to cut the saw-kerf or slit in the platform, which thence becomes exactly parallel with the saw.

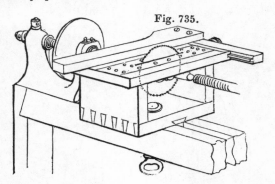

Fig. 735.

In refixing the apparatus ready for work, the wood frame is first placed loosely on the bearers, and the platform is turned up; the saw spindle is then adjusted between the centers, and lastly, the platform is shifted sideways until the saw enters the kerf, the entire wood frame is then secured by its bolt and nut; but owing to the tenon beneath, there is no risk of the groove being otherwise than parallel with the saw. Occasionally that part of the

3 c 2

platform which is contiguous to the saw, is covered with a thin plate of brass to increase its durability.

The sawing apparatus, fig. 735, although made principally in wood, will be found a very convenient appendage to the turning lathe; or the same parts may be used independently of the lathe, upon a wooden bench or frame with a wheel and treadle, much the same as that partly represented in the succeeding figure, except that the wooden standards are then required to extend above the bearers, so as to carry the center screws for the saw spindle. The back board for receiving any parts of the work under progress, and the drawer for the saws, are convenient for their respective purposes, but by no means important.

The sawing machinery represented in fig. 736, although generally similar to the last, is made entirely in metal, except the wooden frame. The principal piece in fig. 736, or the bed piece, is planed flat on its underside, and has a fillet to adapt it to the lathe bearers or other frame; the ends of the casting are formed as popit heads, and are tapped for the reception of the center screws, which support the saw spindle. The middle of the bed piece is formed as the box or trough to which the platform is hinged, by two center screws, tapped into projections on the underside of the platform, the front part of which rests upon the supporting screw, fitted into the bed piece.

Fig. 736.

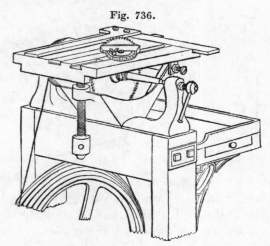

In general construction the iron machine fig. 736 is a great improvement on that in wood, fig. 735, in respect to strength and permanent accuracy; and as the supports for the spindle and platform, are all united in one iron casting, the mechanism is not subject to derangement, and is quite independent of the frame or bench, which may be either that partly represented in the figure, or the frame of an ordinary foot lathe after the removal of the headstocks; or on any bench whatsoever, provided motive power from any source can be conveniently applied to the saw spindle. And in the course of the following descriptions it will be seen, that the latter machine, with certain additional mechanism, is capable of performing, within the limitation of its size, almost any kind of work to which the circular saw is applied.

---

4. *Stops to prevent the vibration of flexible saws.*—When the diameter of the circular saw is considerable, compared with the diameter of the flange on the spindle, the blade becomes very flexible, and may be easily diverted sideways from the true plane; the prevention of this is accomplished in many ways.

The saws used for slitting the thin wood of which cedar pencils are made, are from about 4 to 6 inches diameter, and very thin, so as to act rapidly and with little waste; such saws have frequently supplementary collars, or thick flat plates of brass, fitted to the cylindrical neck of the spindle, and extending to within $\frac{1}{2}$ or $\frac{3}{4}$ of an inch of the edge of the saw, which thereby nearly acquires the stiffness of the collars themselves. But as saws are in general required for thicker wood, such large flanges are mostly inadmissible, and other methods must be employed.

For small saw machines having wood platforms, it is generally considered sufficient, that the saw should work in a narrow cut or groove made by the revolving blade in the platform, and which allows the saw but very little lateral play; as the teeth can no longer cut when the smooth part of the blade rubs against the slit. The friction will in time wear away the wood until the slit becomes inconveniently wide, but a fresh piece of wood can be then inlaid, and another notch made by the saw as at first.

Metal platforms are sometimes made in two parts for the convenience of forming the slit for the saw, but friction against the metal would blunt the teeth, and should be avoided. In such cases, the inner edges of metal platforms made in two pieces are usually tapped for small screws, which are adjusted very nearly to grasp the smooth part of the saw, just within the line of its teeth.   The platform fig. 736, is made in only one piece, with a wide shallow groove in its upper surface, which is again filled up flush with a bar of iron, in the end of which is a deep notch to admit the saw, and at right angles thereto the stop screws are inserted laterally in the bar.   The latter can be adjusted in the groove, to place the stop screws just within the line of the teeth, after which they are twisted by their capstan heads until they nearly touch the saw plates.

But stop screws, howsoever constructed, give rise to noise, and are somewhat liable to wear the saw into grooves.   A preferable mode for small saws, is to inlay a piece of ivory or hard wood in the groove on the top of the platform, and allow the saw to cut its own slit ; or else to fit two pieces of ivory into dovetail grooves, made transversely in the under sides of the platform, and to advance them to the saw by adjusting screws, but which, although a more costly method, is no better, as in every case the stops should be as nearly as possible flush with the platform ; various other stops will be described in speaking of large sawing machinery.

---

5. *Parallel guides for small circular saws.*—Saw machines of every kind depend very materially for their usefulness on the various *guide principles* introduced into their several constructions, and upon the advantage of which principles, as applied to cutting tools generally, some preliminary observations were offered in pages 463 to 471 of the volume now in the reader's hands.

In circular sawing machinery, the table or platform being a flat surface, and the saw-blade at right angles thereto, all pieces that lie tolerably flat on the saw-bench are sure to be so *guided* as to be cut *out of winding*, and square with the face on which they lie.   But to guide them across in a right line, it is requisite to have some kind of rectilinear guide parallel with the saw; the width of the piece sawn off then becomes equal to the distance between the saw and guide, and any number of succeeding pieces may be produced exactly of the same width.

The guides for parallelism are constructed in many ways, three of which, available for small sawing machines, will be noticed at this place; the jointed parallel rules are also used, and will be described in subdivision 5 of the next section.

The most simple parallel guide, is a straight bar of wood fixed to the platform by a screw clamp at each end, or by two screws passing through transverse mortises in the ends of the bar ; but two sets of graduations are then required on the platform, to place the straight fence or bar exactly parallel with the saw.

Sometimes a shallow groove, inclined 30 to 40 degrees with the saw, is made in the top of the platform, and fitted with a slide, the overhanging edge of which is also inclined 30 to 40 degrees, so as to be always parallel with the saw ; the variation of width arises from placing the guide in different parts of the groove. This may be considered a modification of the principle employed in the Marquois scales and parallel rule, but as a saw-guide the range is rather too limited.

A more convenient guide was suggested by Professor Willis of Cambridge, and is shown in figs. 735 and 736. The first is simply a square, the two bars of which are not in the same plane, as the one bar lies upon the platform, the other is flush with it, and fitted to the back edge of the platform by a groove and tongue joint: a screw-clamp is there situated, to fix the one bar of the square to the platform, after the position of the other bar has been adjusted to the width required in the works. This parallel guide may be allowed to extend altogether beyond the sides of the platform, so as to have fully twice the range of the jointed parallel rules, to be described hereafter, and is besides steady alike in every position, provided the surfaces by which the two bars are united are sufficiently large, and firmly joined. The parallel guide in fig. 736, is made in iron, and also after Professor Willis's plan ; but the back bar, then lies in a rebate in the platform, and is secured by a small clamp and screw, partly seen.

---

6. *Sawing the sides of rectangular pieces.*—Before commencing to saw a piece of wood with the circular saw, it is desirable, in order to ensure accuracy in the result, that two neighbouring faces of the work should be moderately straight, to serve as the basis from which to commence; otherwise as the work is thrust past the saw with the hand, it may assume different positions in its course, and thereby give rise to enormous friction against the saw, and may also present, when finished, curved instead of flat surfaces.

Round wood is in general too large to be cut up with the

small saw-machines here referred to, but particulars of the mode adopted in large machines, are given in the corresponding subdivision of the next section. It may however be observed, that when the first cut is *diametrical*, small round wood may be held with tolerable facility to the saw, and it is sometimes sawn at twice, or with two radial cuts, from opposite sides, but which cannot be expected exactly to meet. When the first cut is required to be on one side the center, it is much the best plan to flatten some part of the wood with the handsaw or plane, to serve as the bed on which the work may rest upon the platform.

In sawing up pieces of plank-wood, the broad surfaces left by the pit-saw will in general be found sufficiently accurate for their guidance in that plane, so that the edges alone then require examination, and one of these is sometimes corrected with a jack plane, for greater exactness.

When the saw has been put in rapid revolution, and so that the teeth near the operator descend, the work is laid flat on the platform and against the parallel guide, and is then gradually advanced towards the saw. If the work be thrust forward too quickly, the saw may be altogether stopped from the excessive work thrown upon it, and if it be not advanced at an uniform rate, the markings left by the saw will present corresponding irregularities.

In dividing a piece of wood that is long compared with its width, it occasionally springs open as a fork when sawn, so that the outside or guiding edge of the work, from having been originally straight becomes a little concave. This is sometimes allowed for by making the face of the parallel guide to consist of *two* straight lines, a little distant one from the other, instead of *one* continuous line, by fixing a thin plate to the principal piece by countersunk screws. The set-off in the guide usually occurs a little behind the cutting edge, and allows the work to escape the saw, so as not to be scored by the ascending teeth at the back part of the plate, and which are otherwise apt to catch up the work, if small, and throw the pieces in the face of the operator.

It usually happens that many similar pieces are cut in immediate succession; in such cases, the succeeding piece is frequently made to push forward that which is nearly sawn through, by which mode the risk of hurting the fingers with the saw is obviated; otherwise the piece is thrust towards the conclusion with a stick of wood, having a rectangular notch at the end.

The jointed platforms are very convenient, as they can be turned up to shoot off any accumulation of work or sawdust, and also for the removal of any little pieces of wood, which may occasionally become wedged in the cleft beside the saw.

---

7. *Sawing grooves, rebates, and tenons.*—When the platform of a circular saw machine does not admit of any change of elevation, as in that shown on page 765 and many others, the quantity the saw projects through the table can only be varied by selecting saws of different diameters, or by placing supplementary beds of different thicknesses upon the platform ; the latter method generally interferes with the action of the parallel rule.   But in the machine, fig. 736, constructed in iron, the hinged platform may be adjusted by the regulating screw in front, so that the projection of the saw through the table may, if required, barely exceed the thickness of the wood to be operated upon, or the saw may be only allowed to cut to a limited depth, and to form a groove either in the side or edge of the work.

By making two incisions on the contiguous faces of the wood, the solid angle may be removed, as in the formation of a rebate, fig. 737, the same cuts again repeated would form the tenon, fig. 738 ; but this process requires that the end of the wood should have been previously cross-cut exactly square, in the mode explained in the following subdivision of this chapter.

---

8. *Sawing or cross-cutting the ends of pieces, either square or bevilled ; or those in which the angular variations are in the horizontal plane.*—The most general guide for cutting the ends of work either square or oblique, is shown in fig. 736, and also in plan in figs. 740, 741, and 742 ; it is applicable to every angle.   An undercut groove is made in the platform parallel with the saw, for the reception of a slide that carries a semicircular protractor, which latter is graduated, and may be fixed at any angle by the thumb-screw passing through its semicircular mortise into the slide beneath.   The slide has sometimes V grooves made in its two sides, and the platform is then in two parts with bevilled edges, corresponding with the V grooves.   The work to be sawn is held by the fingers in contact with the straight fence of the guide, and the two thus grasped are slid together past the saw.

The guide for angles is represented in fig. 740, in the position for cutting rectangular pieces from the end of a long bar, and the edge $p\ p$ of the parallel guide, then serves as a stop for the width of the blocks thus removed. By the similar employment of an oblique position, such as that shown in fig. 741 ; rhomboidal pieces of any angle and magnitude, may be as readily produced.

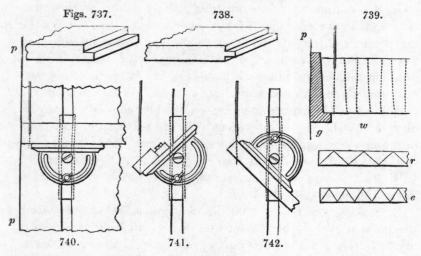

Figs. 737.   738.   739.

740.   741.   742.

When the pieces are not cut from the end of a long rod, but are small, and only require to be reduced to any exact size, it is more convenient, to affix the stop for width upon the fence or the semicircular protractor, as in fig. 741, and in this manner small pieces can be easily sawn into regular or irregular polygons of any particular angles and numbers of sides.

In cutting mitres, as for picture-frames, the one piece would be cut by placing the semicircular fence in the position, fig. 741, but for the other piece of the mitre, it is necessary to place the semicircle as in fig. 742, so that the guide may precede the work that is to be sawn ; consequently, unless the slide will admit of being withdrawn from the groove, and replaced the other end foremost, there should be two holes for the thumb-screw, and two indexes for the graduations.

Although the oblique fence may be placed at the smallest angle, and even parallel with the saw, yet when the pieces are required to be thin and acute, it is more generally convenient to prepare with the apparatus, fig. 740, a wooden guide of the particular angle, and of the form shown in fig. 739 ; p, being the parallel rule ; *g*, the guide or bevilled block, and *w*, the work. A separate wooden block is necessarily required for every angle, and the parallel guide is still available in determining the general width or thickness of the works.

When pieces are parallel in one direction and bevilled in the other, they may be cut out without any waste beyond that arising from the passage of the saw.   In such cases the work is prepared as a parallel piece equal in thickness to the parallel measure of the objects, and the work is turned over between every cut so as to saw the pieces " heads and tails," or the wide end of the one from the narrow end of the other, as shown by the dotted lines in fig. 739.   This mode is employed for ivory knife-handles, and for the thin slips for covering the keys of pianofortes, which are made thicker in front, where the principal wear occurs.

Triangles may be sawn out of parallel slips in a similar manner; thus, by using guides at the angle of forty-five degrees, and turning the work over each time, right-angled triangles *r*, are produced exactly of one size ; with sixty degrees, equilateral triangles *e*, and so on for all others having two equal sides, a half triangle at each end being the only waste. In manufactories where large quantities of bevilled works are sawn, it is usual to employ a wooden bevil guide for every different angle required ; both from motives of economy, and also to prevent the accidental misadjustment of variable guides ; and sometimes the unchangeable guides are made in metal.

---

9. *Sawing bevilled edges and oblique prisms ; or those in which the angular variations are in the vertical plane.*—In cutting pieces with bevilled edges, a supplementary bed of metal, the hinge of which is quite close upon the saw-platform and against the saw, is occasionally employed; this may be set at all angles by a stay and binding-screw.   But the more simple and usual plan is to employ supplementary wooden beds planed to the definite angles required, and through which beds, the saw is allowed to cut a thin kerf as usual.

A pretty example of the use of inclined saw-beds is seen in the so-called mosaic works, consisting of groups either of triangles, rhombuses, or of squares, cut in different coloured woods, and arranged so as to constitute various patterns, which it is proposed to distinguish as triangular mosaics and square mosaics. Mr. James Burrowes, of Tonbridge Wells, informs the author that nearly every sort of wood is used, both English and foreign, and also many sap-woods, but principally holly and ebony for white and black ; and bar-wood, barberry, beech, cam-wood, cherry, deal, fustic, green-ebony, king-wood, laurel, laburnum, lilac, mulberry, nutmeg, orange, partridge, plum, purple, yew, and walnut, for various colours. Mr. Burrowes adds, that he was the first to introduce this work in Tonbridge-ware turnery, boxes, and toys, although striped, feathered, and tesselated works some- what of the same kind, were used long prior, in the bandings and stringings of ornamental cabinet-work.

For the triangular mosaics, beds of the angles of 45 and $22\frac{1}{2}$ degrees are principally used, but others of 15, 30, 60, and 75 degrees are also occasionally employed ; they require guides for parallelism, either to be applied to the inclined beds themselves, or to be added to the parallel rule, with the power of adjustment vertically as well as horizontally ; very thin saws are used, and they project but little through the beds.

Figs. 743.   *a*   *b*   *c*   744.

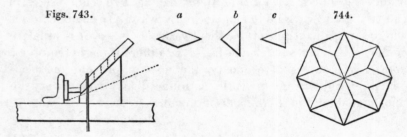

The wood is cut in pieces six or seven inches long, first into veneers of appropriate thickness, the formation of which into slender squares requires no explanation. Figure 743 shows that a bed of 45 degrees, will at one cut for each piece, convert the veneer into rhombuses figured separately at *a*, the acute angles of which measure 45, the obtuse 135 degrees each ; and when the wood is turned over between each cut, right-angled triangles *b*, are produced, with the same bed. When, as in the dotted line fig. 743, the bed measures $22\frac{1}{2}$ degrees, and the work is also turned over, triangles are produced such as *c*, and from which three figures, *a, b, c*, almost all the work is compounded.

Such of the pieces as are required to form the pattern, are selected and carefully arranged in groups on the bench : one man picks up a small group, brushes them over quickly with thin glue, and hands them to another workman, who dexterously arranges them in their required positions; and further quantities of the pieces are handed up by the first workman, until all that constitute the first glueing are arranged. The stick, or faggot, is then tightly bound with string, and before the last coils are strained around the mass, any pieces which stand out beyond their true positions, are rapped with the hammer along the side of the faggot.

Generally, eight rhombuses, *a*, constitute the central group, as in fig. 744, and the eight angles are then filled up by right-angled triangles, *b*, thus producing an octagon, which is allowed to dry. At other times, the eight rhombuses, *a*, are combined for the central star, the hollow angles of which are filled in by eight squares, which themselves produce eight new angles, A B, fig. 745, each measuring 135 degrees. Sometimes each angle

Figs. 745. 746.

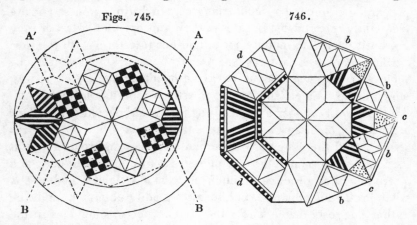

A B, is filled by the obtuse angle of one rhombus, *a*, and this also produces an octagon. At other times, each angle, A' B', is filled by the three acute angles of three rhombuses, *a*, which together measure 135 degrees also (one group being striped, the others only dotted), and afterwards 16 right-angled triangles, *b*, complete a nearly circular figure. The whole of the latter group would be combined at one glueing by dexterous workmen; except when the squares or other pieces are themselves compounded of little bits, which is a preparatory process.

The central octagon, fig. 744, when dry, is often surrounded by other sectional groups, as in fig. 746, either eight compounded triangles, such as *c*, with the new spaces filled by eight right-angles, *b*, to reconstitute the octagon, or else eight wedge-form pieces, *d*, are alone used. The edges of the sections are glued, and quickly placed around the octagonal nucleus, after which the whole is sometimes fixed between powerful clamps, or wedged within external rings; at other times, string is again used to bring the parts together.

The blocks, when finished, are allowed to dry for some weeks, and are ultimately cut into thin veneers, and glued upon round boxes. Octagons of different patterns are united side by side, and the spaces filled in with right-angled triangles, so as to constitute straight patterns, for the centers and borders of rectangular boxes. Small round sticks are occasionally turned into little ornaments, and the curvilinear surfaces so obtained present various pretty effects when the intersections are accurate.

The compounded sections of the wooden mosaics are in general prepared beforehand of small triangles, as a distinct process, and are frequently screwed fast in cauls of their appropriate angles, or they are built up as laminated sheets, and cut into form with the saw.

The chequered squares are prepared from slips of veneer one inch or more wide, so as to avoid handling the little squares, which could scarcely be tied up in true rectangular arrangement. The pieces of veneer are glued together, either white and black alternately, or in any arrangement that the pattern may require; strips cut off the edges of the laminated pieces and reversed as at *a*, fig. 747, produce the chequered squares, cut obliquely and alternated they produce rhombuses *b* ; and striped rhombuses *c*, triangles *d*, and squares, can be also readily obtained, and the author suggests that *b*, *c*, *d*, and similar pieces, should as in the diagrams, figs. 745 and 746, be mingled with the present patterns,

a   Fig. 747.   *b*   *c*   *d*

many of which are much elaborated, principally from small triangles alone, without a sufficient regard to the general design or drawing of the figure. The author possesses however, a very good specimen of mosaic work composed almost entirely of triangles, which in a diameter of $3\frac{1}{4}$ inches, contains no less than 808 separate pieces of wood, combined with very good effect.

The square wood mosaics, called also Berlin mosaics, from their assimilation to worsted works, are more recent than the triangular. Figures of vases, animals, and running patterns, are composed entirely of little squares of various coloured woods which are glued up like the chequered works. Supposing the entire pattern to constitute a rectangle composed of 20 squares in width, and 30 in length, 30 slips of veneers of appropriate colours and an inch wide, are first glued together, and this is repeated 19 times, making one laminated block A, for every line of the figure. A veneer B, is then cut off from each of the 20 blocks A ; and these striped veneers B, are glued side by side to constitute the group c, of 600 slender squares; the thin leaves cut off from the end of this last constitute the mosaic pattern D.

The accuracy of the work greatly depends on the exact similitude of the veneers as to thickness; and as the blocks A, will each produce some 15 or 20 repetitions of B and c, the persevering care required in the formation of a single specimen, will also effect a vast extent of repetition of the same pattern or D.

The small square mosaics for borders and other works are usually inlaid in slips of holly as running patterns, by aid of the buhl saw. Very large mosaics are usually made in 6, 9, or 12 sections, glued up separately into squares, and then combined. One example, thus formed by Mr. Burrowes, represents the Prince of Wales's feathers, arms, and motto; it measures $3\frac{1}{2}$ by $2\frac{1}{2}$ inches, and consists of between 8000 and 9000 squares; the block was prepared in 12 sections, that were afterwards united.*

---

* From the researches of Winkelmann, Wilkinson, and others, there appears to be no doubt but that, 3300 years ago, the ancient Egyptians were wonderfully successful in making Mosaics of minute cylinders, squares, and filaments of glass, united by partial fusion and pressure ; and that from the end of the mass, slices, about one-sixth of an inch thick, were cut off and polished, much the same as above described.

Various specimens are referred to, in which the pictures are said to be very perfect and exactly alike on opposite sides, showing them to run through ; the mode of construction is apparent, from the joinings being just visible in a strong light, and from the colours having in some places run into one another, from the partial excess of the heat employed in uniting them.

The Egyptians also appear to have made other mosaics, by cementing pieces of glass, stone, and gems on backgrounds, just the same as since practised by the ancient Romans, and by the artists of Italy and other countries in our own times. —*See* Wilkinson's Manners and Customs of the Ancient Egyptians, 1835, Vol. ii., pages 94—97, &c.

In sawing the regular prisms of from 3 to 12 sides, it is necessary the inclined beds should meet the saw-plate, at the same angle as that at which the sides of the polygon meet, or their exterior angles. It is therefore proposed as an example for all prisms, to trace in fig. 748 the formation of the hexagon, or 6-sided prism, from a round or irregular piece of wood, upon which, as a preparatory step, one plane surface has been cut in any manner, either by the saw or plane. The following table contains the several angles required.

In regular prisms of .	3	4	5	6	7	8	9	10	11	12 sides.
Their external angles measure . . . . }	60	90	108	120	$128\frac{4}{7}$	135	140	144	$147\frac{3}{11}$	150 deg.
The supplements to the external angles, or what they fall short of 180 degrees, are . . . }	120	90	72	60	$51\frac{3}{7}$	45	40	36	$32\frac{8}{11}$,	30 deg.

Referring to the above table it is seen the external angle of the hexagon is 120 degrees (represented by the dotted arc A),

Figs. 748.

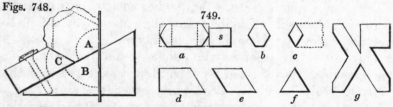

749.

and that the supplement to the latter is 60 degrees, therefore the inclined bed should also meet the saw at an angle of 60 degrees (represented by the dotted arc, B); by means of this bed alone, the second side of the prism would be cut on the piece of wood. But in cutting the remaining four sides, it would be required to introduce some guide, to ensure the parallelism and equality in width of the sides; and this is done by laying a second angle upon the first, also equal to the supplementary angle of 60 degrees (represented by the dotted arc C). Then B, and C, which are of the same angle, together constitute a trough, and the width of the side of the trough near the saw, must be equal to the side of the required hexagon; but the second piece C, is not adjusted to its position until after the first two sides of the prism have been sawn. The angle of the inclined beds must be very exact; as any error that may exist, becomes accumulated, or is six times multiplied in producing a hexagon.

Irregular polygons have frequently the angles alike, but the sides dissimilar; thus it may be considered that in *a*, fig. 749, a parallel piece is added between the halves of the regular hexagon, whereas in *b*, a piece is abstracted, and in *c*, two of the sides disappear. These and the entire group, *a* to *g*, fig. 749, may be sawn with the bed B, fig. 748, of 60 degrees.

It is most convenient, especially when many pieces are wanted, to prepare for *a*, a rectangular prism, and then to cut off the four dotted triangles at four cuts, leaving the stop *s*, in the same position throughout; *b* may be treated in the same manner as *a*, or else as in *c*, the two exterior cuts may be made on the edge of a wide piece of board, and then two interior cuts remove the rhombus *c*, and leave a hollow angle of 120 degrees, as explained by the dotted lines.

The several inverted angles of the piece *g*, may be also produced in this manner by two cuts each ; two of the cuts in *g*, are however made on the horizontal table, and not the inclined bed, B. The inverted angles are convenient as troughs, to support prismatic pieces on their angles, instead of their surfaces.

Pieces analogous to those, *a* to *g*, may be cut on beds of any other angles ; but when the prismatic pieces have dissimilar angles, unless they are complementary one to the other, separate inclined beds are generally required for every angle.*

---

10. *Sawing geometrical solids and irregular pieces, or those in which the angular variations, are in both the horizontal and vertical planes.*—It is proposed to illustrate this part of the subject, by some remarks on the formation of various solids illustrative of geometry, and crystallography; such as erect and oblique prisms, pyramids, double pyramids, the five regular solids or platonic bodies, (namely, 1st, the tetrahedron, 2nd, the hexahedron, 3rd, the octahedron, 4th, the dodecahedron, 5th. the icosahedron,) and some other polyhedra. And, although in the formation of the models of these solids, various modes are employed, those methods will be selected, in which all, or nearly all the work,

---

* It will be shown in the succeeding section that, in some cases, prismatic works are mounted upon an axis, placed at various angles by a dividing plate, and then applied to the saw. And in the subsequent volumes, it will be likewise explained that most lathes for ornamental turning, possess very ready means of producing, both in wood and metal, an infinite variety of polygonal and polyhedral works, with great precision and smoothness.

may be performed by the saw machine alone, independently of the various other means.

The models above referred to, are generally made in sycamore, maple, or horse chesnut, and in the majority of cases, the wood is prepared as prisms, the sawing of which has been fully described. Sometimes, before the subsequent processes, the prisms are very carefully planed in angular beds, mostly so arranged, that the surface to be planed is horizontal.

A long prismatic rod, carried to the saw at right angles, is readily cut into short erect prisms of various heights; and the same prisms, carried obliquely to the saw, become oblique prisms.

For pyramids of 3 to 12 sides, long prisms should be first prepared also of 3 to 12 sides, the sections of which are exactly equal to the bases of the required pyramids.

The prisms are usually cut into short pieces equal to the vertical height of the pyramids, and one guide-block suffices for making all pyramids the sides of which meet at the same angle. The ordinary guide or gage-block, is simply a piece of wood having at the end a rectangular and perpendicular notch B C D, fig. 755, which may be made at the saw machine by aid of the protractor. For pyramids, the sides of which meet at 60 degrees, as in fig. 750, the side B C, of the notch in fig. 755, measures 30 degrees with the principal edge A B, of the guide; for pyramids of 40, 50, or 70, the angle of the guide is respectively 20, 25, and 35 degrees, or half the angles at which the sides meet.

The side A B, of the guide is placed in contact with the parallel rule, and the short prism is placed in the nook, so that in every case the base of the prism rests against the face C D, and one of its sides, *whatsoever their number*, touches the *vertical face* B C; the parallel rule is then adjusted to direct the saw *s s*, through the dotted line proceeding from the apex to the base of the pyramid. One cut having been made, the guide and work are quickly withdrawn, the waste piece removed by the saw, is thrown away, and the block is shifted round until the succeeding face of the prism, (or so much of it as remains,) touches the face B C, and so on to the last face of the pyramid.

Sometimes, as in fig. 751, a pyramid is cut at each end of a prism, the method is almost the same; but the wood and guides are each longer, as in fig. 756. The square end of the prism is placed against the stop, and the first pyramid having been cut, the piece is changed end for end, and the process is repeated; in cutting the second pyramid, the point of the first touches the stop, or a notch may be made in the stop to prevent the extreme point of the prism from being bruised.

When the pyramids meet base to base, as in fig. 752, other methods are pursued, dependent on the parallelism of the opposite sides or angles of equal pyramids. Sometimes the prism is cut off to the exact length of the double pyramid; and the first pyramid having been cut as shown in fig. 756, the second pyramid is produced as is fig. 753, by laying the sides of the first pyramid against the parallel rule, and placing a wedge beneath the point of the first pyramid, to support the axis of the piece horizontally.

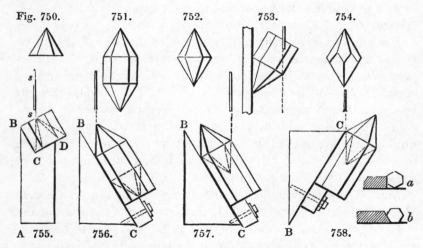

Fig. 750.   751.   752.   753.   754.

A 755.   756.   C   757.   C   B   758.

A much easier and more accurate way of cutting the second pyramid, is suggested by the author in figs. 757 and 758. The prism is in all cases to be left longer than the two pyramids, the first of which is cut as in fig. 756. Then leaving all matters as before, for pyramids of 4, 6, or 8 sides, simply to remove the parallel guide sideways, so as to change the position of 756 into 757, in order that the saw may enter the opposite side of the prism, at the base of the first pyramid, and proceed into the solid prism as far as its center. In a 4, 6, or 8-sided prism, the 4, 6, or 8 cuts release the double pyramid in 757, from its hollow bed, or inverted pyramid, or that which is sometimes termed, by mineralogists, its *pseudo-morphous crystal*.   It is needful the saw should penetrate slightly beyond the apex, and the crystal will jump out of its bed when the last side is nearly cut through, leaving a trifling excess on the last side, just at the point; but if the inverted cuts are extended much beyond the apex, the model will be released before the last side is completed.

For double pyramids of 3, 5, or 7 sides, meeting base to base, as in fig. 752, the position of the saw in fig. 757, cannot be employed in cutting the second pyramid ; because in a pyramid with uneven sides, the saw then would enter at one of the *angles* instead of at one of the *faces* of the first pyramid.   Consequently the angular guide, fig. 756, is changed end for end, as in fig. 758, and all the sawing is done on the same side of the axis of the prism.   The position fig. 758, might be used for all second pyramids, whether of odd or even sides, but for the latter the guide fig. 757, is more conveniently placed.

Sometimes however, it is required that the face of one pyramid should meet the edge of the opposite, as in fig. 754, thus producing what is termed in mineralogy, a *macled* or twisted crystal.   Macled double pyramids with 3, 5, or 7-sides, are cut by pursuing throughout the method prescribed for ordinary double pyramids with 4, 6, or 8 sides; namely, using the one guide, after the mode fig. 756 for the first, and after the mode fig. 757 for the second pyramid, and then with pyramids of uneven sides the required displacement is obtained.

Macled double pyramids, with 4, 6, or 8 sides, require the face B C, of the first guide fig. 757, to be perpendicular as in the reduced figure *a* 758, and the face B C, 757, for the second pyramid, to be inclined $22\frac{1}{2}$, 30, or 45 degrees respectively, as at *b*, or half the supplement to the external angle of the respective polygons. For macled *hexagonal* pyramids, the side B C, may continue perpendicular, provided that in sawing the second pyramid, the *edges*, and not the *faces*, of the six-sided prism are placed against B C, fig. 757.

Irregular prisms may be sawn into *irregular* pyramids, but certain corrections are sometimes required.   Thus, the prism beneath fig. 759, which is more, and fig. 760, which is less than a regular hexagon, produce the irregular pyramids respectively annexed; the sides of each of which meet on one base line.   In the first pyramid, fig. 759, the plain ridge is equal to the central piece added to the hexagon: in the second pyramid, fig. 760, the central face that corresponds to the narrow side of the hexagon, terminates below the extreme point. The six faces might in either case be made to converge exactly to one point, by the employment of a second guide adapted to the irregular side.

Figs. 759.   760.   761.   762.   763.

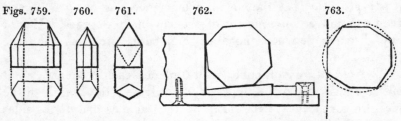

Irregular pyramids, having, as in fig. 763, *equal* sides, but *unequal* angles, produce pyramids, that converge exactly to a point.

Thus fig. 761 shows the result when the rhombic prism is cut into a pyramid, the bases of the sides also meet on one plane, and when the piece is released by cutting the inverted pyramid by the method shown in fig. 757, the solid that results is an irregular octahedron, the section of which is rhombic in both planes.

To produce an *irregular* octagonal pyramid from a *regular* octagonal prism, a wedge is placed beneath the prism, as in fig. 762, which now represents the guide; the point of the wedge is to the left, in cutting the sides 1, 3, 5, 7, of the octagon, and the point of the wedge is to the right, in cutting the sides 2, 4, 6, 8. By this *twisting* of the axis, the *regular* prism yields an *irregular* pyramid of the section shown at fig. 763, and the departure of the latter from the true polygon, is shown by the angular space, between the true polygon, and the vertical face in fig. 762, which space represents the piece removed in virtue of the subjacent wedge, the angle of the two being alike.

When the inverted irregular pyramid is similarly cut, the line of junction of the two is in *one plane*, when the more obtuse edges of both pyramids meet; but the line of junction becomes zig-zag or macled, when the more obtuse angles of the one octagon meet the less obtuse of the other.

The same method pursued with the 4 or 6-sided prisms produces similar results, subject however to certain displacements of the edges and points, the modes of correcting which will be sufficiently manifest to those who take up these matters practically.

It is now proposed to show how, by pursuing the methods of cutting various pyramids, the five regular solids, and many others, can be obtained with the saw-machine.

The *tetrahedron*, with 4 planes each an equilateral triangle, is cut from a regular triangular prism inclined $19\frac{1}{2}$ degrees,* and it is best to cut it at the end of a long piece, as in fig. 756, and then to remove it by one cut of the saw at 90 degrees, which at any distance between the apex and base, produces the true tetrahedron.

The *hexahedron* or cube, with 6 planes each a square, is cut off from a square prism, held at 90 degrees ; the length of the piece removed, must necessarily be the same as that of the sides of the prism.

The regular hexahedron or cube, may be also viewed as two triangular pyramids, the faces of which are interposed or macled, or so placed, that the face of the one pyramid meets the angle of the opposite, as before explained in fig. 754. And pursuing this method, the cube may be sawn from a triangular prism by the positions figs. 756 and 757, provided the prism is inclined exactly $35\frac{1}{4}$ degrees to the saw. † The cube, when produced in this manner from the triangular prism, is however very small, as viewed diagonally, (and in which direction it is cut,) the cube appears as a hexagon, three angles of which touch the centers of the triangular prism. It is better to use the hexagonal prism, and to place its alternate sides 1, 3, 5, successively upon the platform, both for the first and second processes, figs. 756 and 757 ; in which case the hexagonal outline of the cube, may be as large as the section of the hexagonal prism from which it is sawn.

Any other inclination than $35\frac{1}{4}$ degrees produces an oblique hexahedron, or rhomboid, with six equal rhombic faces. For instance, the very dissimilar figures 764, 765, and 766, were cut from hexagonal prisms of the same size, and respectively as large as the prisms would permit. In fig. 764, which is an acute or elongated rhomboid, the angle at which the prism met the saw was 10 degrees ; and in fig. 766, an obtuse or compressed rhomboid, the angle was 80 degrees. Viewed along the dotted line, or through their common axis, the three figures all appear as equal hexagons, and show the three pyramidal planes of each solid as equal rhombuses, as in the figure 767 ; but the axis of

---

* Mathematically 19°. 28′. 17″. † Mathematically 35°. 15′. 52″.

fig. 764 is about four times as long as that of the cube 765, the axis of 766 is only about one eighth as long as the cube, and its edge is acute like a knife.

Figs. 764.   765.   766.   767.

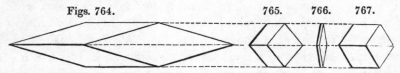

The *octahedron*, with 8 planes each an equilateral triangle, may be viewed as a double square pyramid, cut off at an angle of 35¼ degrees,* and is produced in that manner with very little difficulty from a square prism.   When the prism meets the saw at a smaller angle than 35¼ degrees, the octahedron is said to be acute or elongated; and when the angle is greater, the octahedron is obtuse or compressed, as recently explained in regard to the rhomboids figs. 764 and 766.

It has been considered unnecessary to represent the regular tetrahedron, hexahedron, and octahedron, which are simple, and familiarly known; and the subsequent figures 768 to 771, of the dodecahedron, the icosahedron, and trapezohedron, are to be viewed as explanatory diagrams, and not as faithful representations of these respective polyhedra.

The *dodecahedron*, fig. 768, with 12 planes each an equilateral pentagon, may be viewed as frusta of two pentagonal pyramids, the sides of which are interposed or macled, and the pyramids being truncated form the two remaining pentagons.   The double 5-sided pyramids, are first cut at the angle of 26½ degrees,† and discontinuously, by means of the positions shown in figs. 756 and 757, the sides of the pyramids will then be found to meet at 36°, the angle made by the first and third sides of a pentagon.   The outer plane is obtained by cutting off the point of the pyramid at right angles to the prism, and extending it by trial, until the terminal pentagon itself, and the 5 pentagons near it, become equilateral.   The second pyramid, not having been cut so far as the center, the solid is now removed from its matrix or prism, by one cut at right angles to the prism, and so far removed from

---

* Mathematically 35°. 15′. 52″., or half the supplement to 109° 28′ 16″, the angle at which the pyramidal planes of the octahedron meet.   See Brooke's Crystallography, page 116.

† Mathematically 26°. 33′. 54″.

the angles of the zig-zag line on which the pyramids join, as the corresponding pentagon, at the outer end of the solid.

The above, or the pentagonal dodecahedron, is also called the Platonic dodecahedron; but there is another kind named the *rhombic* dodecahedron, which is more referred to by mineralogists. The rhombic dodecahedron, fig. 769, has 12 faces, each an equilateral rhombus, and may be viewed as a hexagonal prism with a shallow triangular pyramid at each end.

The *rhombic dodecahedron* may be therefore sawn from the hexagonal prism, provided, that first three pyramidical planes are cut at the angle of $54\frac{3}{4}$ degrees,* and that the solid is then released from the prism, by three similar but inverted cuts on the intermediate angles of the hexagon, so much of the central prism being left, as will make six rhombuses equal to those terminating the original prism.

Figs. 768.   769.   770.   771.

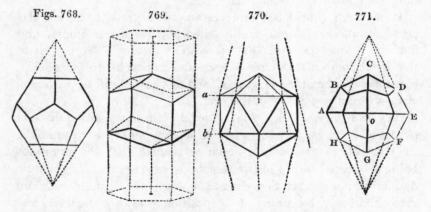

The rhombic dodecahedron may be also viewed as a square prism terminating in two square pyramids cut off at an angle of 45°; but as these planes run on to the angles of the prism, it is needful the bed should be inclined 45° horizontally, for the pyramids, and also 45° vertically, for their displacement.

The *icosahedron*, fig. 770, with 20 planes each an equilateral triangle, may be viewed as two obtuse pentagonal pyramids, united by frusta of two other pentagonal pyramids *a* to *b*, the sides of which are very acute and interposed. The icosahedron may be sawn from the pentagonal prism nearly in the manner of

---

* Mathematically, 54°. 44'. 8''.

the last; the first guide is the angle of $10\frac{3}{4}$ degrees,* and suitable to cutting the two central frusta. This guide is first employed as in fig. 756, and then shifted as in fig. 757, the 10 cuts produce the 10 angles, each of 60°, constituting the central zone of the figure. The extreme end of the piece is then sawn at five cuts on a bed of $52\frac{1}{2}$ degrees,† so that the five planes of the outer pyramids, constitute equilateral triangles exactly terminating on the line a, or on the sides of one series of five triangles, and the points of the other series, constituting the central zone of the solid. The icosahedron is removed from the prism by placing the guide block as in 757, and cutting the second pentagonal pyramid, which similarly to the first, falls on the line b, and just meets both the sides and angles of the 10 central triangular faces; when the work is accurately performed, every point is the center of a group of five equilateral triangles.

The solid fig. 771, with 24 equal trapezoidal planes, may be viewed as two frusta of octagonal pyramids, joined base to base with continuous edges, and surmounted by two obtuse four-sided pyramids. This solid belongs rather to mineralogy than geometry, and occurs with various angles; its usual name is an *icositessera-hedron*, but it has been sometimes termed a *trapezohedron*, from the shape of its faces: three of its varieties will be noticed. In the first, the three quadrantal sections, namely, through A -o E, through C o G, and through A B C D E F G H, are all regular octagons, and the angles of the solid are throughout alike; this variety may be therefore called the regular trapezohedron. In others the three sections are irregular octagons, and the alternate angles dissimilar; these may be called irregular trapezohedra, and two of these varieties that occur in mineralogy are referred to in the annexed table.

The *regular trapezohedron* may be sawn from the *regular* octangular prism, by means of two beds, one of them inclined in *two directions*. The first bed for the frusta of the two central pyramids, is inclined 21 degrees horizontally, or on the line B C, fig. 756. The second bed for the two exterior four-sided pyramids, is inclined $59\frac{1}{2}$ degrees horizontally on the line B C, fig. 756, and $22\frac{1}{2}$ degrees vertically, as at b, in the same group, in order to twist the prism on its axis, because the four terminal planes run on to the angle of the octagon.

---

* Mathematically, 10°. 48'. 44".　　　　† Mathematically, 52°. 37'. 21".

The four planes of the terminal pyramid produce trapeziums, and which are increased, by trial, until they just equal the eight trapeziums formed by the partial obliteration of the central pyramidal faces.   The second four-sided pyramid, which completes and releases the solid, is merely an inversion of the first.

The irregular or mineralogical trapezohedra, may be produced from the regular octangular prism, nearly in the manner just explained, by the employment of different angles, that are stated exactly in the annexed table, which shows the comparison of the three varieties of this solid selected for illustration.*

	Alternate angles of the solids.		Beds for the central parts.		Beds for the terminal parts.	
	A. C. E. G.	B. D. F. H.	Hor. angles.	Wedge.	Hor. angles.	Vert. angles.
Reg. Trapezohedron	135°. 0′.	135°. 0′.	20°. 56′.	none	59°. 38′.	22°.30′.
Irreg. ————	126°. 52′.	143°. 8′.	24°. 6′.	8°. 8′.	54°. 44′.	22°.30′.
——— ———	143°. 8′.	126°. 52′.	17°. 33′.	8°. 8′.	64°. 46′.	22°.30′.

The table supposes the regular octangular prism to be in every case used, but to produce the *irregular* pyramid from the *regular* prism, requires the use of a wedge, as explained in page 773, and the angle of the wedge is half the difference between the two external angles of the prisms, which are simply the reverse one of the other.   The wedge becomes unnecessary, if prisms are prepared, having the same *irregular section* that occurs in the second and third solids, and which is the preferable mode.   If the lathe with revolving cutters and dividing plate is used for preparing the prisms, as hereafter recommended, instead of stopping the lathe at eight equal spaces, or taking 45° each time, the angles taken alternately, are the supplements to the two external angles of the prism, common to the second and third solids, namely 53°. 8′. and 36°. 52′., which together are equal to 90°. †   When

* The irregular trapezohedron, in another of its sections is a regular hexagon, as
Fig. 772.

illustrated by the figure 772 ; six of the trapeziums then constitute parts of the original prism, three trapeziums at an obtuse angle form the summit of the crystal, and three pairs of trapeziums are situated more acutely and intermediately. The trapezohedron might be therefore also worked from the hexagonal prism, by aid of two beds of the particular angles, one of them having a double inclination.

† The angles for the dividing plate are consecutively as follows :

| 1—53°. 8′. | 3—143°. 8′. | 5—233°. 8′. | 7—323°. 8′. |
| 2—90°. | 4—180°. | 6—270°. | 8—360°. |

Unless the lathe has an index with an adjusting screw, the 8′ must in each case be neglected, but it is an admissible error.

the wedge is thus dispensed with, the vertical angle 22°.30'., suitable to the regular prism, becomes 18°. 26'. for the second, and 26°. 34'. for the third solid in the table, or half the supplements.

The order of proceeding given, in reference to producing the various solids with the circular saw, namely, first to saw the central parts of the solids, and then the terminal planes or pyramids, is in all cases advisable when only one or two solids of a kind are made, as the equality of the faces is then arrived at by *two* adjustments in place of *four*. The two central portions are simply inversions one of the other, and necessarily agree *without trial;* the central part thus produced, serves as the base from which to determine the two adjustments for the terminal parts.

As however, every step of this process depends on the primary accuracy of the prism, which serves as the means both of guiding and holding the pieces whilst under formation, it is desirable, as regards the more complicated polyhedra, that those who possess the lathe with revolving cutters, for ornamental turning, should make, or at any rate finish the prisms therewith, which will thence acquire an unexceptionable degree of accuracy. The trouble of preparing the wooden prisms, may be entirely saved, if metal prisms of the several sections, each with a conical hole to serve as a driving chuck, are prepared. The pieces of wood for the solids are then roughly turned, as cylinders with conical stems, which are driven into the prisms for their attachment. The metal prisms may be used for an indefinite number of pieces; they save much trouble and uncertainty, and are especially desirable in the more complex polyhedra.

There are other and very different ways of making the geometrical and crystallographical solids. Sometimes the wood is prepared with the plane alone, into prisms of *unequal sides and angles*, so arranged, that two or four of the sides of the solid, may be parts of the surfaces of the original prism, and that some of the edges of the solids may fall on the remaining faces of the prism. The plane is then used subsequently to the saw machine, in perfecting and smoothing all the faces.

These modes do not admit of the same generalisation or facility of method as that described, which the author believes to be original, and that may be called *the method of double pyramids;* and which he was led to work out practically to the extent set forth, in order to show how much may be done by the saw-machine and various simple adjuncts.

The author has now the pleasing duty to acknowledge the kindness of Professor Willis, who has examined the several details mathematically, and furnished the corrected angles that are given in the notes and table.

Many crystals that occur in mineralogy are considered to be derived from the primary solids, especially from the tetrahedron, cube, octahedron, and the rhombic dodecahedron, by the obliteration of some of their edges and angles in various ways; or as it is said in mineralogy, the edges are bevilled or *replaced*, the points or angles are *truncated*. By way of general illustration of the method of producing these secondary crystals from their primaries, a few of those derived from the cube are demonstrated by figs. 773 to 778, but numerous other crystals, from this and other primary solids, might be advanced.

The cubes are first prepared as described on page 774, and their faces are rubbed smooth; in cutting their edges and angles, beds similar to fig. 779 are required. The latter may be made entirely with the saw; for example, the rectangular block is supported on the face A, and two incisions *a b*, each at 45 degrees, are made by means of the saw and protractor; then the piece being placed with B downwards, and with the face A, against the parallel rule, the perpendicular notch *c*, is sawn; the three cuts release a piece of wood, leaving a cubical matrix.

Figs. 773.   774.   775.   776.   777.   778.

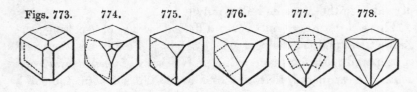

Fig. 773, the cube with bevilled edges, requires that the edges of the cube should be parallel with the saw, and the guide is then placed, as in fig. 781; that is, before the protractor, which is set at zero, and *s* is the stop for the quantity each of the 12 edges is bevilled or truncated. Cubes with two bevils or planes on each edge, may be bevilled with the position 781, provided the guide is tilted up some 20 degrees, by fixing a wedge of 20 degrees beneath the guide, as dotted in fig. 779 ; or otherwise by making a similar bed, fig. 780, with the angles 25 and 65 instead of 45, which will make a rectangular notch, inclined 20 degrees, as in fig. 780, so that the wedge may be dispensed with.

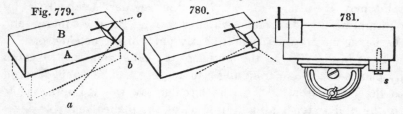

Fig. 779.   c   780.   781.

B

A   b

a

Fig. 774, the cube with three bevilled planes at each angle of the cube, (one angle only being shown,) is obtained with the position of fig. 781; but the protractor is then set about 10 degrees from 90, so as to cut off every edge of the cube by two cuts slightly inclined. The square face of the cube then becomes an octagon, if the facets meet as represented in dotted lines, or a dodecagon when the bevils do not meet. The bed, if also inclined vertically, as by the wedge in fig. 779, will duplicate the angular chamfers, and it is clear this elaboration may be carried systematically to any required extent.

Fig. 775, in which the *angles* of the cube are truncated on the diagonal, require that the bed, fig. 781, should be placed at $35\frac{1}{4}$ degrees *, and then the angles of the cube will be cut off nearly at $54\frac{3}{4}$ degrees to every plane, or at right angles to the diagonal, and this little facet, in like manner to the above, may be converted into three planes, somewhat after the manner of fig. 774, if so required.

When, as in fig. 776, the angles of the cube are so far obliterated, that the eight little triangular planes exactly meet, the cube is converted into the *cubo-octahedron*, a solid having six square faces and eight triangular faces, the whole of which are equilateral; one only of each is represented, to avoid confusion.

By pursuing the last method a little further, so that the triangular faces encroach upon each other, they first produce a little ridge intermediate to the neighbouring facets, and carried to the proper extent, convert each of the triangular faces, in fig. 776

---

* Mathematically, 35°. 15'. 52''. the same angle as that employed to produce the cube from the regular prism with 3 or 6 sides, by six pyramidal cuts ; and also the regular octahedron from the square prism.

into equilateral hexagons, in fig. 777; the six little square faces are all that remain of the original cube, and these squares are united by eight hexagons, all equilateral. The name of fig. 777 when perfected, is the *ex-octahedron*, and which implies that this solid may be also obtained *from* the regular octahedron, by obliterating its six points, which develope the six squares, and the hexagons are then consequently parts of the octahedron.

If, as in fig. 778, all the angles of the cube could be truncated by planes extending from angle to angle, the cube would descend to the octahedron. With the circular saw this is impracticable to the full extent, although some of the planes may be developed; but the mineralogist produces the octahedron from cubes of fluor spar, which splits diagonally from every point of the cube with great facility.

When the octahedron is produced by the cleavage of fluor, further reduction only makes a smaller octahedron, which form is thence described as the primary crystal of this mineral. In other minerals, the cube is the primary to the octahedron.

It is expected that enough has been said to show that, with a little contrivance in the carrying out of the methods advanced, a vast number of even the most complex models of geometrical and crystallographical solids, with plane surfaces, may be produced with comparative facility and great exactness, by the saw-machine; and the mechanical amateur will find it a somewhat fascinating study, especially if he be likewise interested in geometry or crystallography.

The circular saw should be rather stiff, and have fine teeth, as then the planes developed by the instrument will be tolerably smooth, and merely require to be rubbed slightly on a sheet of fine glass-paper, laid on a flat board or metallic surface; they are sometimes cleaned off on a wooden face wheel, on which powdered glass or flint is glued after the manner of glass-paper.

In concluding this section, the author begs to add that the whole of the various works described, subsequently to page 766, may be executed by the amateur with the machine represented on that page, aided by the simple additions described. The remainder of the chapter refers to larger sawing machinery, principally used by manufacturers.

SECT. VI.—COMMON APPLICATIONS OF CIRCULAR SAWS TO LARGE WORKS.

In the present section, it is proposed to describe the principal points of construction in large circular sawing-benches, such as are in general driven by steam power, and used for various manufacturing purposes. Some remarks are first offered on the conditions and proportions of the circular saws themselves, and the subsequent matter is arranged under the sub-divisions employed in the last section and enumerated on page 752.

1. *Conditions and proportions of circular saws.*—It appears to be uncalled for to enter into particulars on the manufacture of circular saws, especially after the remarks already offered (pages 683—698 of this Volume,) on the modes of constructing, sharpening, and setting rectilinear saws, as the methods are nearly similar for both kinds; and some remarks on the circular saw in particular, are given on the first and last of the pages quoted.

As regards the methods of hammering and blocking circular saws, to give them the right degree of flatness and tension, a point of considerable importance, the reader is referred to the section, "On the principles and practice of flattening thin plates of metal with the hammer," (vol. i., p. 414—422,) and particularly to the remark, (p. 419—20,) on the propriety of keeping the edge of the saw "rather tight or small" prior to its being set to work. So that the heat communicated to the edge in the course of work may, by *stretching* the edge, render the blade *tense alike throughout ;* whereas had the saw been at first rather large or loose on the edge, the expansion at that part would render it so loose or flaccid on the edge, as to cause it to vibrate when at work, which is a great disadvantage.

The teeth of both circular and rectilinear saws have been considered at some length, both as regards their outlines, (pages 683—687,) and in respect to the modes of sharpening and setting them (pages 688—698,) but on the whole it may be said that the teeth of circular saws are more *distant*, more *inclined*, and more *set*, than those of rectilinear saws.

The teeth of circular saws are *more distant* than those of straight saws, because their greater velocity causes the teeth to follow in such rapid succession, that their effect is almost continuous ; the distance is carried to the extreme in Mr. R. Eastman's circular saw,

TABLE OF THE DIMENSIONS OF CIRCULAR SAWS.

The columns, " Gage of Plate," refer to the Birmingham sheet-iron gage ; for the comparison of which with ordinary linear measure, see Appendix.
The columns, " Form of Tooth," refer to the diagrams on page 684.
The columns, " Revolutions per Minute " and " Horses' Power," required for the maximum of effect, are from the experience of Mr. Ovid Topham, Engineer.

(1.) SINGLE PLATES OF EQUAL THICKNESS THROUGHOUT.

Generally called Bench Saws, and used either for thick or thin Wood.
Intermediate sizes used, and also thick Saws for cutting Grooves.

Diameter.	Gage of Plate.	Form of Tooth.	Space of Tooth.	Revolutions per Minute.	Horses' Power.
2 inch	23 to 28	644 to 646	$\frac{1}{30}$ to $\frac{1}{10}$ in.	2000	
3 —	21 – 27	— —	$\frac{1}{24}$ – $\frac{1}{8}$ –	1800	
4 —	20 – 26	— —	$\frac{1}{16}$ – $\frac{1}{5}$ –	1600	
6 —	19 – 24	— —	$\frac{1}{12}$ – $\frac{1}{4}$ –	1400	
9 —	17 – 22	644 to 653	$\frac{1}{8}$ – $\frac{1}{3}$ –	1200	
12 —	15 – 21	— —	$\frac{1}{6}$ – $\frac{1}{2}$ –	1100	1
15 —	14 – 20	— —	$\frac{1}{4}$ – 1 –	1000	1½
18 —	13 – 18	— —	$\frac{1}{3}$ – 1½ –	900	2
24 —	12 – 16	— —	$\frac{5}{8}$ – 1½ –	750	2½
36 —	10 – 14	— —	1 – 2 –	500	3
48 —	8 – 12	— —	1½ – 3 –	390	3½
60 —	6 – 9	— —	2 – 4 –	330	4

(2.) SINGLE PLATES BEVILLED ON THE EDGE.

Generally called Bevilled Saws, and used for Veneers.
The largest, medium, and smallest of the ordinary sizes alone are given.

Diameter.	Width of Bevils.	Gage of Plate.	Gage of Edge.	Form of Tooth.	Space of Tooth.	Revs. per Minute.	Horses' Power.
8 inches	2 to 3 in.	12 to 15	22 to 28	644 or 645	$\frac{1}{8}$ to $\frac{1}{4}$ in.	1300	
22 —	3 – 5 –	10 – 13	20 – 25	— —	$\frac{1}{4}$ – $\frac{1}{3}$ –	800	1
36 —	4 – 6 –	8 – 11	18 – 22	— —	$\frac{1}{3}$ – $\frac{3}{4}$ –	550	2

(3.) SEGMENTS FIXED TO A DISK, AND BEVILLED ON THE EDGES.

Generally called Segment or Veneer Saws, and used for Veneers and thin Wood.
The largest, medium, and smallest of the ordinary sizes alone are given.

Diameter.	No. of Segments.	Width of Segments.	Width of Bevil.	Gage of Plate.	Gage of Edge.	Form of Tooth.	Space of Tooth.	Revs. per Min.	Horses' Power.
5 ft.	10 to 15	5 to 8 in.	2 to 3½ in.	11 to 12	24 to 28	644 or 645	$\frac{1}{5}$ to $\frac{1}{4}$ in.	320	3
12 —	15 – 20	5½ – 9 –	2½ – 4½ –	10 – 11	22 – 26	— —	$\frac{1}{4}$ – $\frac{1}{3}$ –	130	5
18 —	20 – 30	6 – 10 –	3 – 5 –	9 – 10	20 – 24	— —	$\frac{1}{3}$ – $\frac{3}{8}$ –	85	6

Bench Saws, below about one foot diameter, are usually mounted on spindles running on conical steel centers, and driven by catgut bands ; those above one foot, on spindles running in cylindrical brass bearings, and driven by leather straps.

Compared with the diameter of the saw, and speaking generally, the hole or eye may be considered to measure from $\frac{1}{8}$ to $\frac{1}{18}$ part of the diameter ; that of the flange of the spindle, from $\frac{1}{4}$ to $\frac{1}{6}$ part of the diameter ; of the pulley for leather straps, about $\frac{1}{3}$; and for the catgut, $\frac{1}{2}$ the diameter of the saw.

The velocity of the edge of the saw varies from about 4500 feet to 5000 feet per minute ; and the greatest thickness of work done can scarcely exceed $\frac{1}{3}$ the diameter of the saw, and is generally below $\frac{1}{4}$ the diameter.

with only eight sectional teeth (see fig. 791, p. 796). The teeth of circular saws are *more inclined*, because such teeth cut more keenly, and the additional power they require is readily applied, by the great velocity and momentum that may be given to circular saws. The teeth of circular saws are *more set,* to make a wider kerf, which is required, because the large circular plate, can neither be made nor retained, so true as the narrow straight blade. The general proportions of circular saws are given in the annexed table.

It is generally politic, to use for any given work, a saw of as small diameter as circumstances will fairly allow, as the resistance, the surface-friction, and also the waste from the thickness, rapidly increase with the diameter of the saw. But on the other hand, if the saw is so small as to be nearly or quite buried in the work, the saw-plate becomes heated, the free escape of the dust is prevented, and the rapidity of the sawing is diminished.

Hassenfratz, Emy, and other French writers on carpentry, have described the mode of cutting thick logs of timber, as in fig. 782, by means of two comparatively small saws, each extending alone to the center of the log. The saws are in the same plane, but one above and the other below the log, and a little removed to avoid the contact of their teeth; but from the reasons above stated, and some others, the plan is but rarely if at all adopted.

Figs. 782.   783.

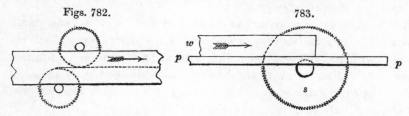

Under most circumstances, it is best to employ that part of the saw which is nearest to the center, and it may be stated generally that, as in fig. 783, the diameter of saw *s*, should be about four times the average thickness of the wood *w*, and that the flange on the spindle, should be as nearly as practicable flush with the saw table or platform *p p*.

In addition to various other particulars in the table on circular saws, an attempt has been made to tabulate the velocities proper for different saws, and the amount of power severally required, but these numbers must be received with some latitude, because they are very much influenced by accidental circumstances. Amongst these are the particular quality of the wood or other material, as to its hardness and grain, its greater or less freedom from moisture, or from gummy or resinous matters, also its magnitude, and the degree of smoothness desired in the surfaces left by the saw; all these circumstances demand certain variations in the proportions and conditions of the saws used. A few words will be therefore added respecting each of these conditions.

The *harder* the wood, the smaller and more upright should be the teeth, and the less the velocity of the saw; hence it follows that the rate of sawing is proportionally slow.

In cutting *with* the grain, or lengthways through the fibres, the teeth should be coarse and inclined, and the speed moderate, so as rather to cut the removed wood into shreds than to grind it into powder; as the more minute the saw-dust, the greater the power that must be expended in its production.

In cutting *across* the grain, the teeth should be finer and more upright, and the velocity should be greater than in the last case; so that each fibre of the wood may be cut by the passage of some few of the consecutive teeth, rather than be torn asunder by one tooth only.

Wet wood is softer than *dry*, and is therefore more easily cut, but the saw is required to be keener and more coarsely set; the waste is consequently greater.

For *gummy* or *resinous* materials, and for *ivory*, the saw teeth are required to be very keen, and the velocity comparatively slow, to avoid the dust becoming softened and rendered adhesive, as it will then stick to the blade. This disposition is lessened by lubricating the saw either with a tallow candle, solid tallow, lard, or oil applied with a brush.

When the object is to get through as much work as possible, the rapidity with which the wood is then advanced, will prevent regularity in its progress, and consequently likewise in the saw marks on the wood. The saw is then liable to be over-loaded; if so, it vibrates rapidly sideways with great noise, requires greater force, but nevertheless proceeds through the wood slowly and leaves it full of coarse ripple marks.

Smooth sawing requires the work to be regularly advanced towards the saw, and the latter must be keen and very uniformly set; as one tooth projecting beyond the general line, is sufficient to score or scratch the work. It is a proof that the saw was in most excellent order and well applied, when the portion cut in every revolution of the saw, cannot be detected by the corresponding marks left on the wood or other material.

---

2. *Spindles for circular saws exceeding about one foot diameter.*— Saws of this magnitude are seldom used on spindles mounted between pointed centers, as represented on page 764, but on those resembling the sections figs. 784 and 785. These spindles revolve in bearings or brasses *b b*, made in halves, and securely united to the stationary framework of the saw bench. The *end-play*, or end-long motion of the spindle, is usually prevented alone by the two collars or projections *c c*, which embrace the one bearing; sometimes however the one collar *c'*, fig. 785, is screwed on the spindle to admit of adjustment, and has a side screw to retain its position; or else the collar *c'*, is in the solid, as usual, and a fixed screw *s*, exterior to the pulley, is made to bear on the end of the spindle.

Each spindle has a wooden or iron pulley of about one-third the diameter of the saw, for the driving strap, but in mills driven by power, a fast and a loose pulley of equal diameter are placed on each spindle, as in fig. 786, so that the spindle may be disconnected with the engine by throwing the strap on the *loose, free,* or *live* pulley.

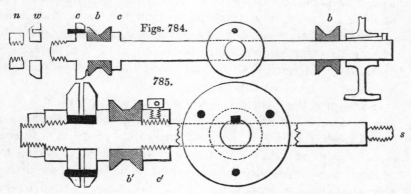

Figs. 784.

785.

Saws below about 20 inches diameter, are commonly held like those previously described, between the flat surfaces of the collar or projection *c*, that is forged in the solid with the spindle, and the surface of the loose collar or washer *w*, as in fig. 784; one steady pin then suffices, and which is fixed near the periphery of the flange. Large saws require flanges, say from 5 to 10 inches diameter, and which are then added to the spindle, as in fig. 785; the one is fixed by a feather or parallel key, and carries three steady pins; all the steady pins are represented black in the figures.

The loose flange is sometimes pressed up by only one screwed nut *n*, but it is preferable to have two, of different threads, that the second may prevent the first from being accidentally loosened; as the two then unwind at different rates and check each other's motion. Either the one nut is right and the other left-handed, as in Collinge's patent axletrees, or else both nuts have right-handed threads, which differ in pitch as well as diameter.

---

3. *Benches and platforms for large circular saws.*—These are in general framed together very strongly in wood, in the ordinary manner of carpentry; they measure from about 4 to 12 feet long, $2\frac{1}{2}$ to 4 feet wide, and $2\frac{1}{2}$ to 3 feet high. The bearings for the saw are placed close beneath the platform, and at about the middle of its length; the central part of the bench is represented in plan in fig. 786.

To arrive at the saw spindle for the purpose of changing the saw, there is frequently inlaid in the platform, a rectangular frame of cast iron with a rebate on the inner edge, fitted with a loose iron panel in two pieces to form the cleft for the saw. The panel is supposed to be removed to show the nuts and stops for the saw, and before the saw can be changed, it is also needful to lift out the wooden bar, which lies across the end of the spindle and against the saw; the bar is added for the purpose of carrying the stops *s s*, to be explained.

Sometimes the bench is nearly covered with plates of iron to lessen the friction of the timber upon it; and in benches for heavy work, the half of the platform in front of the saw is occasionally made as a slide, with a rack, pinion and winch handle, by which it is moved endlong. The work is in such cases placed against a ledge or cross piece on the slide, and is carried to the saw with great facility. A few saw benches, for some specific kinds of work, are constructed entirely in iron.

---

4. *Stops to prevent the vibration of large saws.*—These are in

many cases inlaid in the wooden bed of the machine, beneath the iron plate by which access is obtained to the saw, as shown in fig. 786. The two grooves *s s*, nearest the periphery of the saw, are in some instances each entirely filled with a block of hard wood, kept in position by the top plate, and set forward from time to time by pieces of card or veneer placed behind them, to compensate for the portion worn away by the saw. At other times, the grooves are fitted with blocks of wood or metal, which have mortises for fixing screws, as shown on a larger scale at *s′ s′*; these admit of adjustment and fixation. Screwed holes are also used, especially in the iron framings, cylindrical wooden plugs from $\frac{3}{8}$ to $\frac{3}{4}$ inch diameter are then screwed into the holes and set forward to meet the saw.

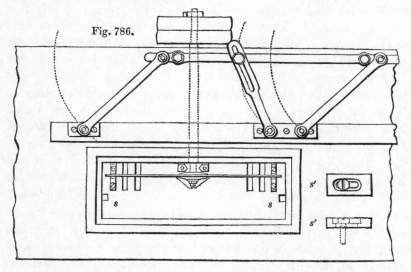

Fig. 786.

Large saw machines have sometimes wedge-form pockets beside the saw plate, which are filled with greasy hemp; the downward motion of the saw carries the hemp into the narrow part of the pocket, and pressing it against the saw, checks the vibration. This method, although it causes more friction, is nevertheless much approved of, as the elasticity of the packing enables the saw to be at all times closely gripped; which on account of its small irregularities, cannot be the case when rigid metallic or wood stops are used; but hemp is less suitable than wood for small saws. Frequently the stops are applied to both the front and back edges of large saws, as shown in the figure.

5. *Parallel Guides for circular saws.*—The parallel guide mostly added to large saw benches, closely resembles the ordinary parallel rule used for drawing, as will be seen on the inspection of fig. 786.   The principle requires that the four centers of the parallel rule should constitute the four angles of a parallelogram, or that the four sides should be exactly two pairs, with which view the two radius bars are clamped together and drilled as a solid bar, and so likewise are the long bars.   Unless the centers or pins fit accurately, it will be found that when the bars lie very obliquely, that the front bar or fence will have a rolling motion, as on a center, instead of being firm and parallel.

In some few cases the long metal bars are dispensed with; iron ears or plates, for two of the centers, are then fixed to the wooden fence or rail, and the back centers are similarly attached to the platform itself, through which a circular mortise, parallel with the paths of the radius bars, is sometimes made for the clamping screw that fixes the rule.   It is however, better the rule should be constructed as in the figure 786, and quite independently of the platform, to admit of ready detachment. The long back rod is then essential, and also a fixing bar, placed as a chord to the arc described by the radius bars, and retained by a screw and nut passing through a mortise in the bar.

In the above construction, the long fence moves in an *arc*, like those described by the radius bars, and shown by the dotted lines, but the three-bar parallel rule, is sometimes employed, because it may be opened in a *right line*, and therefore moves simply sideways to the saw; its path is directed by a pin in the long bar or fence, which enters a straight groove made transversely in the platform.   The construction of the three-bar parallel rule, is nearly a duplication of the former, and as it is equally important that the centers of the similar parts should be equidistant, the four radius bars are drilled together, to ensure their similitude, and so are also the three long bars.   In the two and three-bar parallel rules, two slit clamping bars are occasionally used, which entirely restrain any wriggle, as they secure both ends of the fence; the perpendicular height of which varies from two to ten inches, according to the nature of the work to be sawn.

6. *Sawing the sides of rectangular pieces.*—In both small and large sawing machines, the work is applied much in the same manner ; but in saw-mills two individuals are commonly employed, one to hand up and thrust forward the work, and another to assist by dragging and afterwards removing the work from the bench.   When the pieces are short, the person who pulls commonly uses a *tomahawk*, which is like the half of a small pickaxe, the point of which is struck into the wood to serve as a handle.

When a log or round piece of wood is applied by the hands alone to the circular saw, it is difficult to get the first cut exactly true, as the wood is apt to roll on the two or three points at which it may touch the platform; but when the saw has penetrated a little way, the blade itself materially assists the holding of the work.   One cut having been made, the flat side is placed downwards, and a second cut is made from either of the edges, and provided the first side is moderately true, the second will become at right angles to the first; the third and fourth sides will be found to present no difficulty.

As a ready means of adapting the parallel guide to works of different widths, a parallel piece of wood is often placed alongside the object to be sawn.   Thus in cutting the blocks for wood-paving, the round larch timber is first cut into pieces about 3 feet 6 inches long, and these are, for the most part, sawn into pieces six inches square ; but should any of them fail to hold that size, a parallel board half an inch thick, is placed alongside the work, which is then reduced to the next following size, or $5\frac{1}{2}$ inches square.   And in the same manner, pieces of two dimensions, as of 2 by 1 inch in section, are in some cases cut by setting the parallel rule to 2 inches, and packing the work the thin way, with a piece 1 inch thick. *

---

* In reality, the standard size of the squared timber for the blocks of the Metropolitan Wood-Paving Company, is $5\frac{1}{2}$ by 6 inches ; but the round logs are cut as large as they will respectively hold, the one measure being always half an inch more than the other.   The wood is used very soon after it is felled, and is so wet, that the men find it needful to suspend a board over the saw and at right angles to it ; this arrests the saw-dust, which if allowed to drive against the attendant, soon wets him to the skin.

In some wood-cutting processes, a screen of wire-gauze is placed between the work and the workman, that he may be enabled closely to watch the operation without risk of the shavings entering his eyes.

SECT. VII.—LESS COMMON OR SPECIFIC APPLICATIONS OF
CIRCULAR SAWS TO LARGE WORKS.

It may be considered that in the last section, the remarks on
the structure and use of the circular saw-bench, were concluded,
so far as concerns its ordinary application to the conversion of
timber into scantling, or squared pieces of various sizes. But it
still remains to notice, in continuation, some of the miscellaneous
and large applications of circular saws, which so far as admissible, will be introduced in the order formerly adopted, as the
subdivisions 7, 8, 9, and 10, will be repeated, to which will be
added the sawing of curvilinear works, and some other less clas-
sifiable matters.

Part of the contrivances for these works, are merely additions
to the ordinary saw-bench, others are machines expressly constructed for their respective purposes; but to save unnecessary
subdivision, they will be collectively and briefly noticed; as the
principles rather than the mechanical details will be advanced,
together with references to such published descriptions of them,
as have come under the author's notice. Two contrivances for
obtaining an accurate base to work from, in pieces not originally
straight, will be first referred to.

The late Mr. Smart, in obtaining the first true side in irregular
pieces three or four feet long, intended for the staves of casks,
attached the pieces to an external fence or guide. The wood was
grasped by its extremities, somewhat as between the centers of a
lathe, in a kind of trough made of two boards united at right
angles ; one end of the trough had a solid block of wood, that
could be fixed at variable distances ; the other end had an iron
bar, roughened at its extremity, and brought up by a rack and
pinion, so as to stick into the ends of the wood, the grasp being
secured by a ratchet.

The trough was considerably longer than the length of the
wood to be sawn, and two studs projected from its extremities
beyond the side of the work. These projections were made
to rub against the face of the parallel rule, and avoiding the
saw, to direct the cut exactly in a right line, and produce,
on the irregular wood, one flat surface that might serve as
the base for the subsequent operations.* The same end is

---

* See Trans. Soc. of Arts, Vol. 47, plate 8.

differently obtained, and on larger pieces of timber, in the following method.

In the Ravensbourne wood-cutting mills at Deptford, battens 10 or 12 feet long, and intended to be sawn and planed for flooring-boards, are grasped by their upper and lower edges, and without strain, by screw-teeth or dogs built out from a carriage which runs in V bearings; the slide is carried by a self-acting rack and pinion movement, past a circular saw revolving in a vertical plane, which skims the side of the batten, and leaves it as straight as the V slide itself. The traversing carriage or *drag* of this machine, is closely analogous to that of the veneer saw to be hereafter noticed.

---

7. *Sawing grooves, rebates, and tenons.*—These works may be accomplished in the large way, in the modes already described on page 771. The flooring boards of the warehouses in the St. Katherine's Docks, London, were grooved on each edge upon an ordinary saw bench, for the reception of strips of hoop-iron used as tongues to prevent dust falling through the joints; and the frames for doors are occasionally grooved for the panels in the same manner, but with thick saws. The still wider rectangular grooves in the blocks for wood pavement, are cut out with two ordinary saws on the same spindle, having two or more intermediate chisels, to cut the bulk of the removed wood into chips.

The mortises in the shells of ship's blocks, for the reception of the sheaves, are cut by small double circular saws; a hole is first bored through the shell at each end of the mortise, and the saws are then made to penetrate from each side, and nearly complete the mortise, in a less expensive manner than with the mortising engines in Portsmouth Dockyard.

The squares or tenons of the steel pins for harps, by which the strings are tuned, are also cut by means of two thick saws, separated to the extent of the side of the square; the pin is presented twice to the saws, the second position being at right angles to the first. The equality in size of the squares is also ensured by this method, so that they all fit the same tuning key.

Rebates, may of course be cut upon the ordinary saw bench at two processes, as before explained, but they are also made by two saws mounted on separate spindles, and placed in the exact directions of the two cuts required; one saw spindle is a little before the other, to avoid the contact of the teeth. The angular grooves or rebates in the blocks for wood pavement, are thus made at one operation, in a machine with two saws at right angles to each other.

The combination of two saw spindles was first employed by the late Mr. Smart, in cutting the tenons for the construction of his patent hollow mast. The small pieces of wood were first squared on all sides to the proper measures, each small block was then rebated, first on the one angle, it was then turned over, and the formation of the second rebate completed the tenon. Another part of the same machine carried a mandrel and center bit, so that by the aid of a guide, the holes in the tenons could be also made exactly true and alike.*

Two saws mounted on the same spindle are used in cutting the teeth of combs, which may be considered a species of grooving process. One saw is in this case larger in diameter than the other, and cuts one tooth to its full depth, whilst the smaller saw, separated by a washer as thick as the required teeth, cuts the succeeding tooth part way down, on the same principle as in the *stadda*, and rack saws, figs. 703 to 706, page 723.

A few years back, Messrs. Pow and Lyne invented an ingenious machine for sawing box wood and ivory combs. The plate of ivory or box wood, is fixed in a clamp suspended on two pivots parallel with the saw spindle, which has only one saw. By the revolution of the handle, a cam first depresses the ivory on the revolving saw, cuts one notch, and quickly raises it again; the handle in completing its circuit, shifts the slide that carries the suspended clamp to the right, by means of a screw and ratchet movement. The teeth are cut with great exactness, and as quickly as the handle can be turned; they vary from about 30 to 80 teeth in the inch, and such is the delicacy of some of the saws, that even 100 teeth may be cut in one inch of ivory; the saw runs through a cleft in a small piece of ivory, fixed vertically and radially to the saw, to act as the ordinary stops, and prevent its flexure or displacement sideways. Two combs are usually laid one over the other and cut at once; occasionally the machine has two saws, and cuts four combs at once.

---

* See Gregory's Mechanics, 1807, Vol. II, page 328, plate 26.

8. *Sawing or cross-cutting the ends of pieces, either square or bevilled ; or those in which the angular variations are in the horizontal plane.*—The saw-bench is not much employed in cross-cutting the ends of long timber for the general purposes of carpentry ; but short pieces are sometimes guided to the saw, as in the small machines, by the intervention of either a wooden square or bevil, the one edge of which rests against the parallel rule, the other thrusts forward the work. In cutting the square scantling for wood pavement into oblique prisms, a wooden slide is sometimes added to the saw-bench, with a trough exactly at the required angle, and in this case, as well as the last, the parallel rule serves as the guide for the length of the blocks.

The Metropolitan Wood Paving Company employ for this purpose, an iron machine which has a slide running in V bearings or angular grooves, planed in the bed of the machine and parallel with the saw ; the cast-iron slide is constructed to serve as the inclined trough to receive the squared wood, and has an adjustable stop to determine the length of the blocks.*

The three following diagrams are intended to show the principles of different circular saw machines for cross-cutting ; the wood is shaded in each of the examples, and the arrows denote the movements for following up the cuts of the revolving saws.

In cross-cutting the round logs of lignum vitæ for the sheaves of ship blocks, Messrs. Esdailes use a wooden saw bench, the sliding platform of which is inclined, and has at its lower end a perpendicular rail, as in fig. 787. The log of wood is laid in the nook, and the entire platform is then thrust by the hands past the saw, which revolves on a fixed axis as usual, and thus the log is sliced into pieces, their thickness being determined by a wooden stop ; but it is necessary, in this machine, that the saw should have rather more than twice the diameter of the log.

In the block machinery at Portsmouth, a somewhat elaborate machine is used for the same purpose, which is so constructed that the saw *s*, need only be large enough to penetrate to the

---

* The angle specified in the *Count de Liles's* Patent is 63° 26′ 6″, every block is afterwards chamfered on three edges, grooved on the face, and drilled with four holes for the dowels, in appropriate machines, nearly the whole of which are constructed in iron and driven by two steam-engines each of twelve horses' power. The thirteen various machines, are managed by sixteen men and fifteen boys, and in one week of seventy-two working hours, produce on the average 30,000 blocks, or 800 square yards of paving.

center of the log, as explained in fig. 788. A short log of lignum vitæ is mounted on a kind of lathe mandrel; the saw spindle is then traversed sideways until the teeth cut to the center of the wood, and the mandrel is afterwards rotated once on its axis by a wheel and pinion, to extend the cut around the log. One slice having been removed, the saw is withdrawn sideways to the dotted position *s'*, and the mandrel and wood are set forward through the collars, as much as the thickness of the sheave, by a screw at the back of the mandrel, preparatory to the next slice being removed.

Figs. 787.   788.   789.

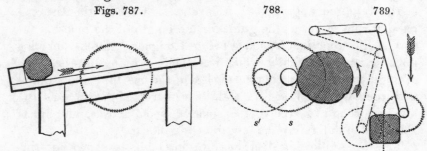

Another cross-cutting machine, after the manner of fig. 789, and also contrived with a view of using a saw for work of nearly its own diameter, is used at Portsmouth, for cross-cutting the butts of round elm timber, into short pieces used for the wooden shells of the blocks. In this latter case, the timber is fixed horizontally and immoveably, and the saw is carried in one plane, first down the one side of the timber and then the other.   To accomplish this, the saw spindle is mounted at the end of a double swing frame, near the centers of which are placed guide pulleys, for the strap that connects the saw with the steam-engine. The parts of the wooden swing frame, are double and strongly braced with iron bars, and the angular movements of the frame are governed by racks and pinions, but the various details are altogether omitted in the diagram.*

9. *Sawing bevilled edges and prismatic pieces; or those works in which the angular variations are in the vertical plane.*—The most

---

* The two machines, figs. 788 and 789, were invented by Mr. (now Sir M. I.) Brunel. and are fully described and figured in Rees's Cyclopædia, article " Machinery for Manufacturing Ships' Blocks ;" and also in Encycl. Metrop. part Manufactures, articles 533 and 535.

simple and usual method of accomplishing this class of work, is by the employment of oblique supplementary beds, as explained in fig. 748, page 768; the hexagonal blocks for wood paving have been cut on the common saw-bench, precisely in the mode there described for small hexagonal and other prisms : indeed, the whole of the remarks already given on bevilled or prismatic works, are applicable alike to the small saw machines and the full sized saw-benches.

In the sawing machine invented by Mr. Robert Eastman, of America, for cutting feather-edged or weather-boards, &c., (as in fig. 790,) the round log of timber is held horizontally, between centers inserted in the end of a long rectangular frame or carriage, which has rollers that run on fixed bars or rails. The round timber is placed above the revolving saw, which makes a vertical and radial incision into the timber; the slide then runs quickly back, and the wood is afterwards shifted on its axis for a new cut, by means of a dividing plate and appropriate mechanism. The machine is automatic, or self-acting, so that, the primary adjustments having been first made, the entire tree is cut into radial feather-edged boards without further attention. The rough exterior edges of the board are also cut away by *sappers,* or chisels *c,* screwed near the center of the saw-plate, which cut away the sap or waste wood, and reduce the tree to the cylindrical form; sometimes, if the tree is large, two series of radial boards are cut.

Figs. 790.   791.   792.

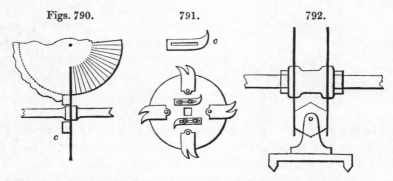

The account further states that ordinary steel saws, toothed all round as usual, were found to heat and choke when thus employed, on account of their being so deeply buried in the wood, the inventor, therefore, contrived what he termed sectional teeth,

shown in fig. 791.   An iron plate of one-eighth of an inch thick
had four dovetail notches, fitted with four pieces of steel, each of
which constituted two teeth in the form of the "hawk's bill,"
the paucity of teeth, was compensated for by giving the spindle
a velocity of 1000 to 1100 turns per minute, and the saw is said
to have penetrated with facility eight inches deep into white
Canada oak. The radial boards are described to be, (as explained
in the former volume,) much less liable to split in shrinking than
those cut out in the ordinary way.*

A mode, somewhat resembling the above, for cutting hexagonal blocks for wood pavement, has been recently proposed by
Messrs. Randolph, Elliot, & Co., of Glasgow, and is illustrated
by fig. 792.   In this case, two saws are employed on the same
horizontal spindle, and the headstocks, which are of iron and just
like those of a lathe, pass exactly between and beneath the saws,
which thus produce two parallel cuts at once. The round timber
being shifted twice, and one-third of the circle each time, becomes
an exact hexagonal prism, three or four feet long, and is afterwards cross-cut into the proper lengths.†

Professor Willis is in the habit of using the circular saw for
blocking out Gothic and other mould-
ings, for the illustration of architec-
tural science. For example, if in the
moulding, fig. 793, the several cuts
are made that are denoted by the
surrounding lines, the fillet and chamfers are definitively produced, and
the margins of the curvilinear parts
are accurately blocked out or defined,
so that the mouldings may be easily
and faithfully finished by moulding
planes.

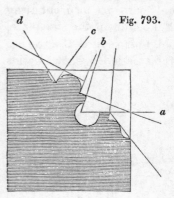

Fig. 793.

The wood in such cases, is marked at one end with the sectional
and formation lines, as in the figure, and then mounted between
centers in a species of lathe, with a dividing plate, so that the
line *a*, first becomes horizontal.   The saw, which is also hori-

---

* The full description of this machine, with figures, is transcribed from Professor
Silliman's American Journal of Science and Art, into Gill's Technological Repository, 1822, vol. ii. page 217.

† Practical Mechanic and Engineers' Magazine.   Glasgow, 1843, page 57.

zontal, is attached to a kind of slide-rest, with three adjustments; a vertical and a lateral adjustment, to adapt the saw also to the line *a*; and a longitudinal adjustment, by which the saw is then traversed the entire length of the moulding. The work is then adjusted on its axis by the dividing plate, until *b* becomes horizontal, and the saw having been as before adjusted to *b*, is swept the length of the moulding, and the two incisions remove the angle of the square block. The cuts *c* and *d*, similarly treated, remove another portion of the wood that is in excess, and so on to the end; all the cuts thus made become strictly parallel, or in prismatic relation to one another.

When the mouldings run on to a chamfered base or plinth, which commonly occurs in Gothic architecture, the plinth is first of all removed by a transverse and oblique incision of the saw, after which the mouldings are made, and finally the removed plinth is replaced without alteration, and the work is complete.

---

10. *Sawing works, in which the angular variations are in both the horizontal and vertical planes.*—All the observations and instructions given in the former and corresponding subdivision, are in truth applicable to large saw-benches; but the machine now to be described is more suitable to large works of this class.

In Mr. Donkin's saw-bench, fig. 794, the half of the platform in front of the saw is hinged like the flap of a table, and has quadrants, somewhat after the manner of the sketch, by which it may be fixed for cutting any bevils within its range. The parallel rule is available for setting out the widths of the works; and the saw is mounted upon a swing-frame of cast iron, shown separately in fig. 795. So that the quantity the saw projects through the table, as for sawing rebates, can be regulated by a cam *c*, upon which the one end of the swing-frame rests.

In cutting small bevilled works, such as those for the wooden cogs of cast-iron mortise wheels, and various other pieces, Mr. Donkin employs a supplementary carriage, running upon three iron rollers, and guided by the hands against the parallel rule. An idea of the carriage is also conveyed by fig. 794. It is made in cast-iron, and rectangular, but deficient of the half of the lower side; and carries a center screw, a dog or prong chuck, and a dividing plate, much as in a lathe; but the axis of these parts, although sometimes horizontal, is generally vertical.

The small pieces of wood are cut out square as usual, but somewhat too large ; they are then grasped between the dog and center screw.   If the pieces are parallel or *prismatic,* the saw-table remains horizontal as usual; if the pieces are taper or *pyramidal,* the table is inclined, and which throws the guiding carriage to any required obliquity.   The parallel rule is next adjusted to enable the saw to cut the first side ; and should the object have four, six, or more sides, the dividing plate is brought into requisition, for giving the four or more angular positions. The parallel rule determines the respective distances of each side from the axis on which the work is shifted.

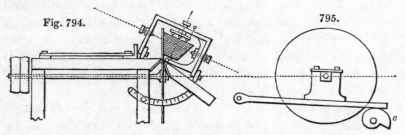

Fig. 794.   795.

In this ingenious manner, by the changing of the horizontal and vertical angles, by the adjustment of the parallel rule, and by the projection of the saw through the platform, almost any piece, having plane surfaces, may be sawn ; and the settings once adjusted, an unlimited number of similar pieces may be produced, as it is only necessary to make the first cut, throughout every piece of the entire number, then the second cut throughout the whole, the third, and so on.   This is accomplished by leaving every adjustment undisturbed whilst the first cut is repeated throughout all the pieces, except the removal of the one block of wood from between the centers and the insertion of the next, and so on with each of the succeeding cuts.   The indentations made by the center screw and dog, ensure the similitude of position throughout the entire operation.

11. *Sawing Curvilinear Works.*—The trephine saw used in surgery, and represented nearly full size in fig. 796, appears to have been by far the earliest of the circular saws of this kind.   It consists of a thin tube of steel, with teeth cut on the edge, of the peculiar form represented, and at the opposite end of the tube is fixed, by small side screws, the stem by which it is attached to the mechanism whereby it is worked.

The motive apparatus of the trephine saw, is usually a cross handle like that of a corkscrew, or a revolving brace like that used in carpentry. To guide the first entry of the trephine saw, the shaft is drilled and fitted with a drill point pp, which is fixed by a side screw s. In the commencement, the point makes a small central hole, and when the saw has once fairly penetrated, the point is loosened and allowed to fall back into the stem of the saw.

In another modification the center of the trephine saw is dispensed with, as the "guide principle" is effectually introduced. The saw is fixed at the one extremity of a cylindrical stem, which at the other has a winch handle; the stem works freely in a vertical tube or socket with three legs, constituting a tripod stand, therefore the axis is kept steady and vertical by the left hand; and whilst the teeth fulfil their office, the saw advances through its fixed collar by the pressure of the right hand, with which the winch handle is turned.*

---

* The art of surgery has given rise to an enormous variety of instruments, a most complete collection of the representations of which, both of the earliest and latest times, was published by A. W. H. Seerig, in a work entitled *Armamentarium Chirurgicum ; oder möglichste vollstandige Sammlung von Albildungen chirurgischer Instrumente älterer und neuerer Zeit.* The work contains 145 large and crowded lithographic plates, and was published at Breslau, in 1835.

It appears from plate 75 of this collection, that the trephine saw was known in the time of Hippocrates, and that both the blades and the mechanism for moving them, have since assumed numerous varieties of form.

The amputating saws set forth in this work as having been contrived or used by various eminent surgeons, are modifications of the bow, frame, and piercing saws for metal, and the tenon and dovetail saws for wood ; they vary from about 14 to 4 inches in length. Some of the small saws analogous to the dovetail saw, have edges more or less curved, and the smallest of these dwindle down to a nearly circular plate of steel less than one inch in diameter, serrated around the edge, except where a slender wire, terminating in a wooden handle, is rivetted to the edge of the saw-plate. These last are known as Hey's saws, and are principally used for the cranium and the metacarpal bones.

A saw, intended for dividing deeply-seated bones, is formed like the chain of a table clock, but with the one edge serrated ; it is worked with two cross handles by the alternate motion of the two hands. One of the handles is detached, whilst the end of the chain saw is passed beneath the bone, by a kind of semicircular needle. The chain saw was invented by Dr. Jeffrey of Glasgow.

A nearly similar chain saw is arranged as an endless band, passing around the grooved edge of a taper staff like the blade of a poniard, but terminating in a small semicircle. There are guards to cover up portions of the edge, and a prop or strut to steady the instrument, whilst the endless chain is put in motion by a winch handle attached to a pin wheel, around which also the chain circulates. This

The trephine saw has given rise to various larger applications of the same kind of instrument, having teeth of the ordinary form, and known as *crown* saws, *annular, curvilinear, drum,* and even as *washing-tub* saws, the respective merits of which names it would be useless to discuss. Small saws of this kind, when mounted upon the lathe, are often employed for cutting out disks of metal and wood; the material is in general thrust against the saw, by a block of hardwood fitted to the front center of the lathe, and frequently, as in making buttons, the cutting out is combined with the shaping of the two faces of the button.

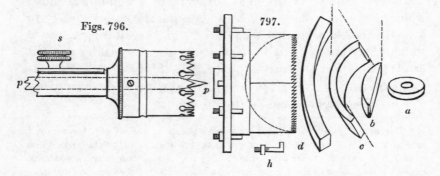

Figs. 796.   797.

In the block machinery at Portsmouth the crown saw is used for rounding the sheaves, which are cut out of transverse slices of lignum vitæ; the wood is held at rest by its margin whilst the

singular instrument is ascribed to S. Heine, and is figured on plate 60 of Seerig's work, which also contains several schemes for using small circular saws, but some of the mechanical arrangements are not clearly defined in the figures.

A circular saw proposed for cutting deeply-seated bones, and as an occasional substitute for the trephine saw, was invented by Mr. Thomas Machell of Durham, surgeon, and is accurately described in the Trans. Soc. of Arts for 1812, Vol. xxx, page 150. In Mr. Machell's saw the axis of rotation is constructed *within the thickness of the blade,* so that two thirds the area of the circular saw may be depressed in the saw cut. The saw is worked by a pin wheel, the pins of which enter notches in the edge of the saw blade, the pin wheel has teeth, and is itself moved by a larger and more distant toothed wheel, having a small winch handle.

The great difficulty encountered in almost all the surgical saws, arises from the removed particles of bone becoming mixed with the fluids, and forming a thick paste which clogs and nearly stops the action of the blades. To remedy this inconvenience, Mr. Weiss suggested that slits terminating in round holes should be cut in the edges of such blades as admit of these receptacles being made.—*See* Weiss on Surgical Instruments, page 10, plate 18 ; and figure 796 in the text. Small bones are now more frequently cut by strong nippers than by saws, and many nippers are drawn on Seerig's plate 134.

revolving mandrel, which carries the crown saw and also a drill, is advanced through its collars, and rounds and bores the sheaves *a*, at the one operation, ready for the coaking-engine, turning-lathe, &c. *

Crown saws, as large as 5 feet diameter and 15 inches deep, constructed somewhat after the manner of fig. 797, are employed at Messrs. Esdailes' saw mills. The three or four pieces of steel then constituting the hoop, are rivetted to the outside of a strong ring, and very carefully hammered, so that the plates exactly constitute one continuous cylinder; although the ends of the plates are not united, but simply make butt joints. The ring is fixed to the surface-chuck of a kind of lathe-mandrel, by means of hook-bolts *h*, and the work is grasped in a slide rest, which traverses within the saw, and parallel with its axis.

The saws of about 2 feet diameter are used for cutting the round backs of brushes *b*, and the larger saws are employed for felloes of wheels *d*, and similar curved works. If the wood is applied obliquely, the piece also becomes oblique, in the manner explained by the diagram *c*, which represents the sloping and hollowed back of a chair thus produced. It is, however, much more usual to saw curvilinear works of the kinds referred to, with the felloe or pit-turning saw, (see page 707), the chairmaker's and wheelwright's saw (p. 725), and the turning sweep, or bow saw (p. 728), the respective applications of which have been already noticed at the pages referred to.

Mr. Trotter proposed for curvilinear sawing, the employment of a saw plate *s*, fig. 798, which instead of being a flat plate, as usual, was dished as the segment of a large sphere. The fence *f*, which was made as the arc of a circle, had a conductor *c*, to receive the work *w*; the circular fence was attached to a three-bar parallel rule, so as always to keep the curvatures of the fence, conductor, and saw, which were equal, truly parallel with each other. The construction of the spherical saw blade is difficult, and its advantage questionable, especially as the edges of the pieces when left from the saw, would be curvilinear in width as well as length, or part of a spherical surface, of the same radius as the saw. This form is seldom required in the arts, and its conversion into the simple arch-like form with square edges, (proposed to be

---

* Rees's Cyclopædia, art. "Machinery for Manufacturing Ships' Blocks."— Encyc. Metropolitana, vol. Mechanics, art. 376.

approached by inclining the work,) would fully cancel the intended
economy of the spherical saw, which is however curious, as one of
the links in the chain of contrivances under consideration.*

Much ingenuity has been displayed in cutting the curvilinear
and bevilled edges of the staves of casks by circular saws. The
late Sir John, (then Mr.) Robinson, proposed many years back that
the stave should be bent to its true curve against a curved bed,
shown in two views in fig. 799, and that whilst thus restrained
its edges should be cut by two saws *s s*, placed as radii to the
circle, *the true direction of the joint*, as shown by the dotted circle
representing the head of the cask. The principle is perfect, but
the method has been found too troublesome for practice.

Figs. 798.   799.   800.

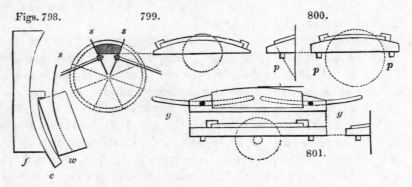

801.

Mr. Smart cut the edges of thin staves for small casks *on the
ordinary saw bench*, by fixing the thin wood by two staples or
hooks to a *curved* block, fig. 800, the lower face of which was
bevilled to give the proper chamfer to the edges. One edge having
been cut, the stave was released, changed end for end, and refixed
against two pins, which determined the position for cutting the
second edge, and made the staves of one common width. The
curved and bevilled block, was guided by two pins *p p*, which
entered a straight groove in the bench parallel with the saw.

This mode of bending was from various reasons found inapplicable to large staves; and these were cut, as shown in three
views in fig. 801, whilst attached to a *straight* bed, the bottom of
which was also bevilled to tilt the stave for chamfering the edge.
To give the curve suitable to the edge, the two pins on the
under side of the block then ran in two curved grooves *g g*, in the

---

* Trans. Soc. of Arts, 1805. Vol. xxiv., p. 114.

saw bench, which caused the staves to sweep past the saw in the arc of a very large circle, instead of in a right line, so that the ends were cut narrower than the middle.   Mr. Smart observes, that in staves cut whilst straight, the edges become chamfered at the same angle throughout, which although theoretically wrong, is sufficiently near for practice; the error is avoided when the staves are cut whilst bent to their true curvature.*

SECT. VIII.—CIRCULAR SAWS AND MACHINERY FOR CUTTING
VENEERS.

Valuable and beautiful woods are seldom used in the solid state for decorative furniture, but are cut into veneers or thin plates, to be glued upon fabrics made of less expensive woods, an art successfully practised by the Romans, as formerly adverted to (Vol. i., page 64).   Until of late years the cutting of veneers was generally accomplished, either at the saw-pit with very thin plates strained in the ordinary pit-saw frame, (see Vol. ii., page 703), or by the cabinet-maker with the smaller frame saw, (page 726).   In this latter mode, which is still much practised on the continent, the wood is fixed perpendicularly, and the saw is also guided by two men.   Expert pit-sawyers could cut six veneers out of each inch of wood, and cabinet makers seven or eight from smaller pieces, but the difficulty of these methods rapidly increases with the size of the veneers.

Small veneers for the backs of brushes and other works, have been split or planed from small pieces squared to the respective sizes.   Pine, willow, and other woods, are planed into thick con-

---

* See the original paper, Trans. Soc. of Arts, Vol. xlvii., pp. 121-7.   In the year 1833, Mr. Samuel Hamilton took out a patent for " certain machinery for sawing, boring, and manufacturing wood for various purposes, such as bevilled timber for ship-building, tenon cheeks, felloes of wheels, the circular rails of chair backs, chair legs, and other works of the same description, either square on the face, or bevilled to any required angle, or in any required radius or diameter of a circle."

The specification is very complex, but it may be said briefly, that the felloes are cut by a vertical reciprocating saw worked by a crank, and the edge of the work is guided either by a fixed circular fence, or by radius bars ; for bevilled works the table of a similar machine is tilted to any angle.   For other classes of work, the saw frame is jointed, and may be brought down by a swing-frame in the arc of a circle, to penetrate to any assigned depth.   The work is grasped by numerous arrangements of parts, that hold any successive number of pieces exactly in the same position.—*See* Newton's *London Journal and Repertory, &c.*, Vol. vii., p. 1.

tinuous shavings called scale-boards, for making hat and bonnet boxes (Vol. ii., p. 504). And of late years oak, when softened by steaming, has been split into staves for casks (foot-note, Vol. i., page 32). All these processes are accomplished without waste of the materials, but they are only applicable to pieces of limited dimensions.

In 1806, Mr. Brunel took out a patent for splitting veneers, of considerable size, by means of a horizontal knife, the length of which exceeded the length of the block to be converted. The knife was composed of several pieces of steel, placed exactly in a line on their lower surfaces, but with edges faintly rounded and very keen. The compound knife received a short recipro-cating or sawing action, and the block of mahogany or other wood was carried slowly sideways, and beneath the knife by a strong screw slide, worked with a spoke wheel, like that by which a ship is steered. After one veneer had been cut off, and the log brought back again to its first position, it was raised in exact parallelism, by a system of two right and two left-handed screws at the four angles of the frame, which were simultaneously moved with one winch handle, by aid of appropriate mechanism. *

This machine for cutting or splitting wood into veneers, the precursor of the segment veneer saw, is said to have answered moderately well with straight-grained and pliant woods, such as Honduras mahogany, but there were serious objections to its use for woods of irregular, harsh, and brittle grain, such as rosewood ; as the veneer curled up considerably on removal, and the wood if harsh and brittle had a disposition to split and become pervious to the glue.† This is to be regretted, as the splitting-machine converted the *whole* of the wood into veneer without waste, whereas the veneer saw, on the average, cuts one-third of the wood into sawdust.

As already explained, the ordinary circular saw will not, in general, serve for work exceeding in thickness about one-third the diameter of the saw, and the larger the saw, the thicker it is required to be, to give a proportionate degree of stability. These two conditions, joined to the impracticability of obtaining

---

* See the drawing and description in the Rep. of Arts for 1810, Vol. xvi., p. 257.

† The Russian machine for cutting the entire tree into one spiral veneer, (see Vol. i., p. 154,) seems open to the same objection in regard to brittle woods, neither does it expose the most ornamental section of the tree.

plates of steel exceeding some 4 or 5 feet diameter, limit the application of the circular saw under ordinary circumstances.

But when this instrument is employed for veneers, advantage is taken of the pliancy of the thin leaf or veneer, and the saw is consequently made thick and strong towards the center, to give it the required stability, but towards the edge it is thinned away almost to a feather edge, as at *s s,* in the diagram, fig. 802.   Therefore

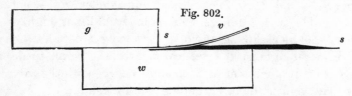

Fig. 802.

the solid block of wood or ivory *w,* which is unyielding, can pass along the parallel guide *g,* and across the flat face of the saws *s s,* whilst the thin pliant veneer *v,* separates so much as to form an opening that admits the wedge-formed edge of the blade, and the veneer proceeds along the conical back of the saw without fracture or interruption ; circumstances that would be impracticable were both parts of the material when sawn, alike unyielding.

In the small application of this principle, as for sawing blocks of ivory into leaves for miniatures, and small square pieces of wood into veneers for brushes and small works, the veneer saw is made as a single plate of steel, from 6 to 36 inches diameter. In the large application of the principle, as for cutting logs of square or round wood into veneers, the saw is composed of many segments or plates, and commonly varies from about 5 to 18 feet diameter.   But as the segment saws are occasionally made as small as 20 inches diameter, the two kinds constitute an unbroken series, and their principal applications will now be described, beginning with the smallest.

The single plate veneer saw (described in section 2 of the table, on page 784), is thick and parallel at the center for about one-half its diameter, the edge is ground away, as a cone, almost to a feather edge ; at other times the edge is thin, and nearly parallel for about an inch, and is then gradually coned, making the section somewhat concave.   The edge is required to run exceedingly true, and the teeth must be sharp and very faintly set.

Saws of six to ten inches, are sometimes used in machines such as that shown on page 766, for very small pieces of ivory veneer and for slicing up wooden mosaic works, but it is more usual to employ larger saws for miniature leaves, say those from fifteen to twenty inches diameter, and consequently larger machines are also required, which are driven either by a hand fly-wheel or other motive power. The principal variations between veneer saw-benches, and those for ordinary and thicker works, is in the parallel guide, which, for veneers, is made fully as high as the width of the block to be sawn, by screwing a parallel piece of wood or metal against the vertical face of the parallel rule, and cutting it off in a circular arc, exactly to agree with the curvature of the saw, and without extending at all behind it. In many cases the parallel guide is constructed with a set screw, that it may be adjusted for distance very minutely, after which it is fixed as usual. When, therefore, the block of ivory or wood is placed against the parallel rule, and pressed towards the saw by hand, the thin leaf bends away as cut from the block, or yields sufficiently to pass behind the saw without impediment.

In bevilled or veneer saws for ivory, the teeth should be finer, and the rate of motion slower than for wood, say, three-fourths the speed, as when a considerable velocity is used the saw becomes heated, and this, from the gelatinous nature of the material, causes the saw-dust to adhere to it; the heat also tends to split the thin leaves of ivory. These sources of mischief are avoided by giving to the saw-blade a subdued rate of motion, and keeping it moderately anointed with tallow or lard.

Some idea of the delicacy of veneer saws for ivory, will be given by the inspection of the annexed scale, which shows the average numbers of veneers or leaves cut from each solid inch of ivory :—

When the width of the ivory is	1	2	3	4	5	6	7 inches,
Each inch of ivory is cut into	30	27	24	22	20	18	16 leaves.

The leaves from 1 to 2 inches wide and 2 to 3 inches long, are used for memorandum books, the larger sizes for miniature leaves, the lengths of which are about one-third more than their widths. When scraped and prepared ready for the artist, the 30, 27, or 16 leaves, respectively measure about half an inch in total thickness, showing the waste in sawing and scraping to be equal to about one-half the original material. The leaves might be cut still thinner, but this would be objectionable as regards their intended purposes.

The bevilled or veneer saws, when used for wood, have greater diameter, coarser teeth, are used without grease, and at a higher velocity than for ivory ; but the single plate-veneer saws are not frequently made of the full-size named in the table, nor are they used for wood exceeding about six inches wide, or that has not been previously squared into small pieces.*

In the larger applications of the veneer saw, it is built up of segments or separate plates of steel, screwed to the edge of a metal disk or chuck. Some few of the smallest segment saws are even less than two feet diameter, and those not exceeding about four feet diameter are generally used in the ordinary saw-benches, with fixed horizontal platforms, the work being then fed by hand as usual.

But when the segment veneer-saw exceeds about four feet diameter, the horizontal platform or table is rejected, and the guidance of the wood is entirely effected by machinery, called the *dray;* the arrangement of this construction, which is known both as the *veneer mill* and the *segment saw*, is shown in the perspective figure 804, page 812. The veneer almost always proceeds from the edge of the saw, through a curvilinear trough parallel with the back of the saw ; but in the figure the veneer is represented as if bent almost at right angles, so as to quit the

---

* A manufacturer, experienced for thirty years in cutting miniature leaves, generally employs single plate saws from sixteen to twenty inches diameter. He also uses a segment saw, measuring the larger diameter, when new, and composed of six segments, attached to a gun-metal chuck, the edge of which is very thin, and the center enlarged into a boss cut with a hollow screw, for its attachment to the saw spindle, which runs in a collar and center, exactly after the manner of a lathe mandrel. He prefers about eight to ten points per inch, and an average velocity of about 600 to 700 revolutions per minute ; in topping the teeth, he uses a steel turning tool, and sets the teeth before sharpening them.

He adds, that when the blocks of ivory are cut into lengths, prior to being sawn into veneers, loss occurs, because the central and wider leaves require to be longer than those from the same block, which are exterior and narrow. Sometimes the entire tooth, or a large portion of it, is cut into veneers with the large segment saws, having the drag, (to be described) ; this is better as regards the cutting of the leaves into squares ; but the apparent economy is again lost, as these saws being intended for wood, have coarser teeth, and will not leave such smooth surfaces as the saws exclusively used for ivory, neither will they produce more than about fourteen or fifteen veneers from each inch of ivory.

saw in front; this construction is far less common, but was selected for the present illustration, as it affords a more conspicuous view of the entire process.

In the veneer saws furnished with the drag, the axes run in massive brass bearings, which are fixed on brick or stone piers; the edges of the larger saws dip below the ground into a pit lined with brickwork or masonry.

The axis of the saw is connected or disconnected with the steam-engine at pleasure, by means of a fast and loose pulley; and in bringing the saw to a state of rest, the brake wheel at the end of the axis is strongly grasped by a friction-hoop, as in some cranes. Between the driving pulleys and the cone for the saw is placed a bevelled pulley, for a catgut band or rope that is used in feeding the cut, as will be hereafter explained. The saw, which is the all-important part of the machine, is made of great strength, and consists of three parts, shown in the section of the edge, fig. 803, of which the shaded part *c* to *c* is of cast-iron, the white part *s* to *s* of soft steel, and the black *h* to *h* of hardened steel.

Fig. 803.

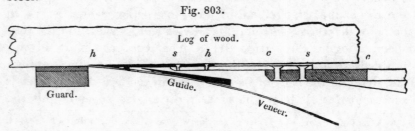

The saw is composed, first, of a cast-iron wheel or chuck, with from six to eighteen arms, which are taper, so as to constitute a cone, the thickness of which at the center is about one-twelfth the diameter. The rim of the wheel *c c*, is flat and turned smooth on the face to receive a series of 6 to 18 segments of *soft steel*, about one-quarter of an inch thick, marked *s s*, which are fixed to the cast-iron by strong rivets; the segments project from 5 to 8 inches beyond the cast-iron, and are chamfered at the edge. To the soft-steel segments *s s*, are affixed a second series *h h*, consisting of about twice the number; these are *hardened and serrated*, so as to constitute the cutting edge of the saw.

The tempered plates are technically called the *hard*, and are attached to the soft segments by numerous countersunk copper screws, tapped into *s s.* When new, the hard segments project from 4 to 6 inches beyond the soft; so that the angle then formed by the three parts, *h* to *c*, considered collectively, is only about 4 to 6 degrees with the flat face of the saw, and the veneer will readily yield to more than that extent from the log without splitting. To prevent the risk of accident from the exposed spokes of the wheel or chuck, and also the current of wind caused by their rapid rotation, the spaces intervening between them are filled up on the face with wood, and an entire cone of thin boards is attached to the back of the chuck.

The log to be sawn sometimes requires to be previously adzed all over, to remove the sand and dirt that would soon blunt the saw ; it is then partially levelled with the adze or plane, to adapt it to the vertical face of the drag. The drag has three long bars of *wood*, in order that the revolving saw may cut or prepare for itself the surface against which the log is fixed. The sharp ends of the iron dogs are driven a little way into the log, and the dogs are then drawn down by screw bolts as represented.

Sometimes the log is only temporarily held by the iron fastenings or dogs, whilst its surface is partially levelled with the saw, after which it is glued on a wooden frame, that is full of transverse and oblique bars, and has been also levelled with the saw ; the log and frame are afterwards bolted to the drag. In this case the entire body of the wood can be cut into veneer without interruption from the fastenings, and the glue joint is safe so long as the log does not project more than the width of the glued surface.

The timber requires two motions to be impressed upon it ; the one motion, longitudinal, to carry it across the face of the saw ; the other motion, lateral, to advance it sideways between each cut, the exact thickness of the intended veneer.

For the first or cutting motion, a long railway extends across the face of the saw, and supports the drag, which is carried past the saw by means of a rack and pinion, actuated by a cord proceeding from one of the grooves of the cone pulley on the mandrel, down to the pinion axis, which is beneath the surface of the ground, and not represented. On the pinion axis there is a double train of toothed wheels, and a clutch box, by the three positions of which latter, the drag is left at rest, or it is carried slowly past the saw in the act of cutting, or quickly back preparatory to the succeeding cut. The gearing lever, by which the three positions of the clutch box are given, is perpendicular, and passes downwards through a trap-door, situated close behind the little stool on which the attendant is seated.

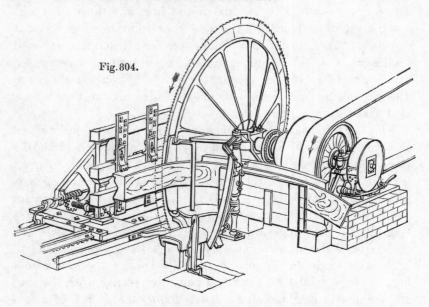

Fig. 804.

The second motion of the log, or its lateral adjustment, is thus effected. The slide that runs on the railway has a horizontal plate, which carries three or more triangular standards, like buttresses, to the perpendicular faces of which are fixed the three wooden bars against which the wood is clamped.

The horizontal plate that carries the triangles, is united at each end to the lower piece of the drag, by a chamfer slide with an adjusting screw and nut, one of each alone being seen. The adjusting screws have worm wheels at the one end, and are simultaneously moved by means of a winch handle w, at the extremity of a long rod, having two worms taking into the two worm wheels fixed on the adjusting screws. From 50 to 60 turns of the handle are required to advance the log of wood one inch; the attendant can therefore determine with great facility, the number of veneers cut out of each inch of wood, or he can cut the veneers to any particular pattern for thickness.

There is no impediment to the passage of the log across the rectilinear face of the saw; but for the guidance of the veneer around the back of the cone, some particular arrangements are required.　To enable the veneer to avoid the edge of the soft steel segments, to which the serrated blades are fixed, a feather-edged guide-plate, usually of brass, and extending around about one-sixth or eighth of the circle, is fixed *almost in contact with the blade*, by screw bolts and nuts, which, as seen in fig. 804, unite it to the stationary framing of the machine; the guide is represented black in the sectional view, fig. 803.　As the veneer is sawn off, the attendant leads the veneer on to the guide, by means of a *spud*, or a thin blunt chisel, the veneer then slides over the guide, as shown, and proceeds through a curvilinear wooden trough, usually extending round the back of the cone, and the veneer is pulled out on the other side by an assistant, and stacked on the heap.　Sometimes the veneer is bent nearly at right angles, and quits the saw in front, as in the figure : this arrangement is less usual, but was selected for the illustration, as it offers a more comprehensive view of the several parts.

Before running back the drag, preparatory to a new cut, the handle w, is unwound two or three turns, to remove the log beyond the reach of the saw, and prevent its being scratched by the saw teeth, these turns are afterwards moved in addition to those required for the new thickness : the handle is managed by a boy, who stands outside the railway.

Whilst the saw is in the act of cutting, the principal attendant applies a soft deal *freeing-stick*, on the right and left of the blade beneath the timber, in order to clear the sawdust out of the teeth.　The speed at which the table is fed is easily adjusted, by the selection of an appropriate groove of the cone pulley on the main shaft, which communicates with the driving pinion beneath the floor; and this adjustment of the feed is jointly dependent on the condition of the saw as to sharpness, and the general quality, hardness, and size of the wood.

The veneer saw may be used for logs of wood measuring as much as 24 feet in length and $5\frac{1}{2}$ feet in breadth, but which sizes are rarely or never met with in the same log.　It may be added, that the number of veneers cut out of each solid inch of wood, varies with the width and the intended purpose of the veneers; but that on the average—

When the width of the wood is	6	12	18	24	30	36	48	60 inches,
Each inch of wood is cut into	15	14	13	12	11	10	9	8 veneers ;

and, as about one-third of the wood is wasted in sawdust, the respective veneers are about two-thirds the 15th, 14th, &c. of an inch in thickness.

The veneer saw is also applied to cutting cedar wood for making pencils ; *bead stuff*, or thin wood for making the beadings in cabinet work ; *quarter stuff*, or wood $\frac{1}{4}$ inch thick ; and occasionally also to wood nearly $\frac{1}{2}$ inch thick ; and this may be considered the point of meeting, between the veneer saw and the upright frame saw, page 742, in which ten or a dozen saw-blades are occasionally used for deals. But the veneer saw works with greater accuracy, and is almost always used for such thin boards of mahogany as are not cut by hand at the saw-pit.

For sawing thin boards, the segments should be nearly new or very wide, in order that the angle made by the removed board may be slight.   But as the board in riding over the guard, (page 810,) near the edge of the saw, is nevertheless somewhat strained open, it becomes needful to apply a contrivance called a *guard*, to prevent the thin board from being at all split off, instead of being entirely separated by the saw.   This is accomplished by a curvilinear arm, equal in size and form to the feather-edged guide which lies against the hardened saw plates, but the guard is very much thicker and stronger, and is covered with a thin plate of brass.

It will be further perceived in the perspective figure, page 812, that the guard is attached to a column, and is represented turned back, or out of work, which is the case whilst veneers are being cut; but in sawing boards, the guard is placed parallel with the edge of the saw, just external to its teeth, (as dotted,) and is adjusted by set screws to rest in hard contact with the face of the wood which is sliding past it, the removed board is consequently held securely unto within half an inch of the saw teeth, or the line of separation, as shown by the diagram, fig 803.

In sharpening the veneer saw, the workman first applies a lump of grindstone very cautiously upon a proper support, against the edge of the teeth as the saw revolves, so as to reduce the few points extending beyond the circle.   The saw having been stopped, he then stands on a stage and rests his left arm, which is guarded by a wooden board, or leather shield, upon the teeth of the saw, whilst he manages the triangular saw-file with both hands.   The saw teeth are afterwards set by a hammer and a small flat stake held in the left hand.   The necessity for the recurrence to sharpening and setting depends much on the hardness of the wood, but it is commonly needed several times each day that the saw is in constant work.

When the edge becomes too thick and wasteful, it is ground by means of revolving laps of lead or iron fed with emery, one lap on the face, another on the back of the saw; the laps are placed one below the other, to prevent their faces touching, and are kept in rapid motion, whilst the saw traverses between them, as in cutting, so that all parts of the circumference, of this most stupendous and accurate of saws, may be ground alike.*

Notwithstanding the very considerable length to which the chapter on saws has been extended, the subject may be considered as very far from exhausted. Thus the great majority of the applications of the saw hitherto noticed have been for manufactures in wood, but toothed saws are also employed for many other purposes, and different materials, some few of which will be glanced at by way of conclusion.

Both reciprocating and circular saws are occasionally employed in cutting off piles beneath the surface of water, when to draw them, (by the aid of the hydrostatic press,) would endanger the safety of the foundations. Two methods of thus using *rectilinear* saws have been described, to which the reader is referred.†

The *circular* saw, when used for piles, is commonly placed at the bottom of a long vertical shaft, the top of which is driven by a winch, through the medium of a pair of mitre wheels. The shaft is attached to a swing-frame, like a gate, or to a traversing platform, connected with such of the piles as may with safety be ultimately drawn up; in every case the erection of machinery for sawing piles is troublesome, and the process tedious.

In the American steam-pile driving machine, intended principally for constructing the foundations of railways, two piles are driven at the same time, in the respective track. After which, they

---

* The author is greatly indebted to Messrs. Esdaile and Margrave, of the City Saw Mills, for the free access they permitted him to their establishment, which contains eleven veneer saws, from 17 ft. 6 in. to 5 feet diameter, and also nearly every kind of machine-saw and shaping-engine for wood that is extensively used.

Many of the practical details, on sawing ivory veneers, were derived from the experience of Mr. Donald Stewart.

† See Encycl. Metro. Part Mechanics, article 536 ; also, Civil Eng. and Arch. Journal, 1843, vol. vi. page 439.

are sawn off by a circular saw four feet in diameter, the spindle of which is mounted on the end of a strong horizontal frame, moving on a joint, so as to cut first the one pile and then the other. Notwithstanding the irregularities of the ground, the piles may be cut either to a dead level or to any particular inclination.*

Circular saws are used in cutting sheets of slate into rectangular pieces, many of which are afterwards planed by machinery (vol. i. page 165). Slate is also grooved with thick circular saws, for making a particular kind of roofing, the joints for cisterns, and other works; and more frequently two thinner saws are used, and the intermediate substance is chiselled or *tooled* out. Rectilinear toothed saws, driven both by hand and machinery, are likewise used for blocks of slate and soft building stone.

A saw machine is used at the Butterley Iron Works, Derbyshire, in cutting off the ends of railway bars whilst red hot; in fact, the moment they leave the rollers. The two saws are exactly like those for wood, of three feet diameter, with flanges of two feet, they travel at upwards of 1000 revolutions per minute, and their lower edges dip into water. The bar is brought up to the saws by machinery, and both ends are cut off simultaneously, in twelve to fifteen seconds, to the precise length required.†

If the customary applications of the saw machine to works in *metal* had been touched upon in this chapter, they would almost inevitably have trenched upon the fifth volume; as it would have been difficult, to avoid proceeding from the circular saw, used simply for dividing works, to circular cutters with plain edges, used in cutting grooves, and to cutters with curvilinear or figured edges, used for the teeth of wheels, and various other analogous works, subjects that are for the present held in reserve.

By analogy, it might also have been shown, that in some of the various apparatus employed in ornamental turning, revolving cutters of all kinds, with plain or figured edges, are likewise used. But in reference to these, it will be explained in the fourth volume, that the many teeth of the circular saw, or figured cutter, dwindle down to a single radial tooth; and that the solitary cutting edge makes up for its apparent deficiency, by the extreme rapidity with which it is in general driven.

---

* Civil Eng. and Arch. Journal, vol. v. page 1.
† Trans. Inst. Civil Engineers, vol. iii., p. 197.

CHAPTER XXVIII.—FILES.

SECT. I.—GENERAL AND DESCRIPTIVE VIEW OF FILES OF USUAL KINDS.

THE file is a strip or bar of steel, the surface of which is cut into fine points or teeth, that act by a species of cutting, closely allied to abrasion. When the file is rubbed over the material to be operated upon, it cuts or abrades little shavings or shreds, which from their minuteness are called *file-dust,* and in so doing, the file produces minute and irregular furrows of nearly equal depth, leaving the surface that has been filed more or less smooth according to the size of the teeth of the file, and more or less accurately shaped, according to the degree of skill used in the manipulation of the instrument. In treating this subject, it is proposed to divide the matter into the following sections:—

   I. General and descriptive view of files of usual kinds.

  II. General and descriptive view of files of less usual kinds.

 III. Preliminary remarks on using files, and on holding works that are to be filed.

 IV. Instructions for filing a flat surface, under the guidance of the straight-edge, and of the trial-plate, or *planometer.*

  V. Instructions for originating straight-edges and trial-plates, or planometers.

 VI. Instructions for filing rectilinear works, in which several or all the superficies have to be wrought.

VII. Instructions for filing curvilinear works, according to the three ordinary modes.

VIII. Comparative sketch of the applications of the file, and of the engineer's planing machine, &c.

The files employed in the mechanical arts are almost endless in variety, and which is to be accounted for by there being some four, five, or six features in every file, that admit of choice, in order to adapt the instrument to the several kinds of work for which the file is used ; and most of the names of files express these different features, for instance the three following files are in common use :—

6 inch,	blunt,	single-cut,	Sheffield,		saw-file,
9 inch,	taper,	smooth,	Lancashire,		half-round file,
12 inch,	parallel,	rough,	Sheffield,	safe-edge,	cotter-file.

From the perusal of these compounded names it will be seen, that six sources of variation have been noticed, and upon which several characters a few observations will be offered.

1. *Length.*—The length of files is always measured exclusively of the tang or spike, by which the file is fixed in its handle, and the length and general magnitude of the file require to be proportioned to the work to be performed. When the works are both large and coarse, the file should be long and strong, that the operator may be able to exert his entire muscular force in using the instrument; when the works are minute and delicate, the file should be proportionally short and slender, so that the individual may the more delicately feel the position of the file upon the work; as the vigorous employment of force, and the careful appreciation of position or contact, are at opposite extremes of the scale. Thus, it may be said, the watchmaker frequently uses files not exceeding three quarters of an inch in length, and seldom those above 4 or 5 inches long; artizans in works of medium size, such as mathematical instrument makers and gunmakers, employ files from about 4 to 14 inches long; and machinists and engineers commonly require files from about 8 to 20 inches long, and sometimes use those of 2, 3, feet and upwards in length.

The lengths of files do not bear any fixed proportion to their widths; but speaking generally, it may be said the lengths of square, round, and triangular files, are from 20 to 30 times their widths, measured at the widest parts; and the lengths of broad files, such as flat files, half-round files, and many others, are from 10 to 12 times their greatest widths.

2. *Taper, blunt, and parallel files.*—Almost all files are required to be as straight as possible in their central line, and are distinguished as taper, blunt, and parallel files; a very insignificant number of files are made curvilinear in their central line, as in the rifflers used by sculptors and carvers, and some other files.

The great majority of files are made considerably taper in their length, and to terminate nearly in a point, such are called taper files; others are made nearly parallel, and known as " *blunt pointed*," or simply as *blunt* files; but in each of these kinds the section of the file is the largest towards the middle, so that all the sides are somewhat arched or convex, and not absolutely straight. A very few files are made as nearly parallel as possible, and have consequently, nearly straight sides, and an equal section throughout; such are designated as parallel files, and by some, as *dead parallel files*, just as we say " *dead level*" for a strictly level surface, but it is very far more general for the so-called parallel files to be slightly fuller in the middle.

3. *Lancashire and Sheffield files.*—In England the principal seats of the manufacture of files, are Sheffield and Warrington; those made at the latter place being more generally designated as Lancashire files. The Sheffield files are manufactured in very much the larger quantity, and for nearly every description of work, both large and small. The Lancashire files are less used for large than for small works, including watch and clock-work, some parts of mathematical instruments, and the finer parts of machinery.

Formerly all the Lancashire files bore a great pre-eminence over the Sheffield, in respect to the quality of the steel from which the files were made, their greater delicacy of form, the perfection and fineness of their teeth, and the success with which they were hardened; these circumstances rendered the Lancashire files more expensive, but also much more serviceable than the Sheffield. Of later years, this superiority is generally considered more particularly to apply to the smaller Lancashire files, not exceeding about 8 or 10 inches in length, as from the steady improvement amongst the best of the Sheffield file manufacturers, in respect both to the quality of the steel, and the workmanship, it now results, that the larger files made both in Lancashire and Sheffield, assimilate much more nearly in their respective qualities than formerly.

4. *The teeth of files.*—Many files that are in all other respects alike, differ in the forms and sizes of their teeth. Three forms of teeth are made, those of *double-cut files*, those of *floats*, or *single-cut* files, and those of *rasps*. The floats and rasps are scarcely used but for the woods and soft materials; the double-cut files are used for the metals and general purposes; and when the file is spoken of, a double-cut file is always implied, unless a single-cut file, or a rasp, is specifically named.

In a double-cut file, the thousands of points or teeth occur from *two* series of straight chisel-cuts crossing each other; in a single-cut file or float, the ridges occur from the *one* series of chisel-cuts, which are generally square across the float; and in a rasp the detached teeth are made by solitary indentations of a pointed chisel or punch, a subject that will be further noticed when the cutting of files is adverted to.

Double cut files are made of several gradations of coarseness, and which are thus respectively named by the Lancashire and Sheffield makers:—

LANCASHIRE FILES.	SHEFFIELD FILES.
1.　Rough.	1.　Rough.
2.* Middle-cut.	2.　Bastard.
3.　Bastard.	3.　Second-cut.
4.* Second-cut.	4.　Smooth.
5.　Smooth.	5.* Dead-smooth.
6.　Superfine.	

The sizes marked with asterisks are not commonly made, and this reduces each scale of variety of cut to four kinds, of which the Lancashire are somewhat the finer. The above names afford, however, but an indifferent judgment of the actual degrees of coarseness, which, for all the denominations of coarseness, differ with every change of length; but the numbers in the annexed table may be considered as pretty near the truth:—

Approximate Numbers of Cuts in the Inch of Lancashire Files.

Lengths in Inches.	4	6	8	12	16	20
Rough-cut　． ．	56	52	44	40	28	21
Bastard-cut　． ．	76	64	56	8	44	34
Smooth-cut　． ．	112	88	72	72	64	56
Superfine-cut ． ．	216	144	112	88	76	64

Of floats and rasps, but two denominations are generally made, and which are simply distinguished as coarse and fine; the fine are also called cabinet floats and rasps; and as with the files, the

---

* The numbers in the Table, were counted from the engravings of the teeth of files in Mr. Stubs' pattern book. These engravings were laid down with great care from the files themselves, and it is somewhat curious the numbers should so nearly fall in regular series. The second courses of teeth were in each case counted, and which are somewhat finer than the first course, as explained on page 829.

One of the smallest and finest Lancashire files, was found by the author to contain from 290 to 300 cuts in the inch, which is confirmatory of the above numbers.

two nominal sizes of the teeth of floats and rasps, differ for every variety of length in the instruments.

5. *Safe-edges.*—Some files have one or more edges that are left uncut, and these are known as *safe-edges*, because such edges are not liable to act upon those parts of the work against which they are allowed to rub, for the purpose of guiding the instrument. The safe-edge file is principally required in making a set-off, or shoulder, at any precise spot in the work, and in filing out rectangular corners; as whilst the one side of the notch is being filed, the other side can be used to direct the file. Occasionally the edges alone of files are cut, and the sides are left safe or smooth, as in some warding files, which nearly resemble saws.

6. *The names of files.*—These are often derived from their purposes, as in saw files, slitting, warding, and cotter files; the names of others from their sections, as square, round, and half-round files.

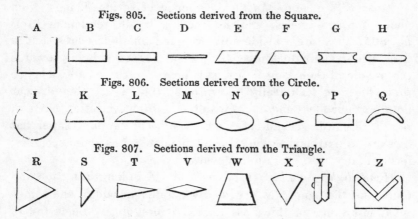

Figs. 805. Sections derived from the Square.

Figs. 806. Sections derived from the Circle.

Figs. 807. Sections derived from the Triangle.

Files of all the sections represented in the groups, figs. 805, 806, and 807, are more or less employed, although many of them are almost restricted to particular purposes, and more especially to the art of watchmaking, for which art indeed, very many of the files have been originated. The sections may be considered to be derived from the square, the circle, and the equilateral triangle, as will be detected by the eye without description.

To avoid wearying the reader by attempting to describe all the various files that are made, the eight or nine kinds which are of most extensive application, will be briefly adverted to, and these will be placed in the supposed order of their usefulness, as derived partly from the author's observation, and partly from the relative quantities considered to be manufactured of each kind in two large establishments. After this, a few remarks will be given on some of the files to which the sections 805 to 807 refer, and this, or the first division of the chapter, will be concluded by a short account of the mode of forming the teeth of files, and some other particulars of their construction.

It may be considered that in nearly every branch of art in which the file is used, that the following constitute the basis of the supply; namely, taper files, hand files, cotter and pillar files, half-round, triangular, cross, and round files, square, equalling, knife and slitting files, and rubbers: a short explanation will be given of all of these varieties, in the course of which, reference will be occasionally made to the sections A to Z just given.

Taper files, or *taper flat files*, are made of various lengths from about 4 to 24 inches, and are rectangular in section as in B fig. 805; they are considerably rounded on their edges, and a little also in their thickness; their greatest section being towards the middle of their length or a little nearer to the handle, whence these files are technically known to be "bellied;" they are cut both on their faces and edges with teeth of four varieties, namely, rough, bastard, second-cut, and smooth-cut teeth. Taper flat files are in extremely general use amongst smiths and mechanics, for a great variety of ordinary works.

Hand files or *flat files*, resemble the above, in length, section and teeth, but the hand files are nearly parallel in width, and somewhat less taper in thickness than the foregoing. Some few of them are called parallel-hand-files, from having a nearer equality of thickness, and parallelism of sides. Engineers, machinists, mathematical instrument makers and others, give the preference to the hand file for flat surfaces and most other works, except in filing narrow apertures and notches, as then the small end of the taper file, first described, may be employed in the commencement, gradually the central and wider part, and then the entire length of the instrument, as the space or notch to be filed becomes wider; the taper form, thus enables a larger and stronger file to be used in the commencement, but for other and accurate purposes, the hand file is esteemed preferable to the taper.

Cotter files, are always narrower than hand files of the same length and thickness; they are nearly flat on the sides and edges, so as to present almost the same section at every part of their length, in which respect they vary from 6 to 22 inches. Cotter files are mostly used in filing grooves, for the cotters, keys or wedges, used in fixing wheels on their shafts, whence their name. The *taper cotter files*, or as they are also called *entering files*, are entirely different from the above, as they are taper both in width and thickness, and almost without any swell, or pyramidal, in which respect alone they differ from ordinary taper files that are usually much swelled or bellied.

Pillar files, also somewhat resemble the hand files, but they are much narrower, somewhat thinner, as in C, and are used for more slender purposes, or for completing works that have been commenced with the hand files. Pillar files have commonly one safe edge, and vary from 3 to 10 inches in length.

Half round files, are nearly of the section L, notwithstanding that the name implies the semicircular section; in general the curvature only equals the fourth to the twelfth part of the circle, the first being called *full* half round, the last *flat* half round files. The half round files, vary from about 2 to 18 inches in length, and are almost always taper. The convex side is essential for a variety of hollowed works, the flat side is used for general purposes.

Triangular files, commonly misnamed " *three-square*" files, are of the section R, and from 2 to 16 inches long; they are used for internal angles more acute than the rectangle, and also for clearing out square corners. One of the greatest uses of triangular files from 3 to 6 inches long, is the sharpening of saws, the greater number of which have teeth of the angle of 60 degrees; an angle doubtless selected, because it appertains to all the angles of the equilateral triangular file, the three edges of which are therefore alike serviceable in sharpening saws. In the southern parts of England, saw files with single-cut teeth, are in more general use, from the idea that they ' *cut sweeter*'; in the midland and northern counties, the double-cut files of the same dimensions are more in vogue, being esteemed more durable. Small saws for metal, which are harder than those for wood, are always sharpened with double-cut files, the Lancashire being preferred.

Cross files, or crossing files, sometimes called double half-rounds, are of the section M, or circular on both faces, but of two different curvatures, they are used for concave or hollowed forms the same as the convex side of the half-round; but crossing files are on the whole shorter and less common than half round files, and are probably named from the files being used in filing out the crosses or arms of small wheels, as in clock-work, in which case, the opposite sides present a two-fold choice of curvature in the same instrument, which is convenient. Those cross files which are principally known as double half-rounds, are fuller or more convex on both faces than ordinary cross files, and are employed by engineers.

Round files, of the section I, range from the length of 2 to 18 inches; they are in general taper, and much used for enlarging round holes. The round file is better adapted than the so-called half-round file, to works the internal angles of which are filled in or rounded, as the round file is much stronger than the half-round of the same curvature. Small taper round files, are often called *rat-tail* files, and the small parallel round files, are also called *joint* files, as they are used in filing the hollows in the joints of snuff boxes and similar objects, for the reception of the pieces of joint wire, (vol. i. page 429,) that are soldered in the hollow edges of the work for the joint pin or axis.

Square files, are used for small apertures, and those works to which the ordinary flat files are from their greater size less applicable. The square files measure in general from 2 to 18 inches long, and are mostly taper; they have occasionally the one side safe or uncut.

Equalling files, are files of the section D; in width, they are more frequently parallel than taper, in thickness, they are always parallel. They are in general cut on all faces, sometimes, as in the warding files for locksmiths, the two broad surfaces are left uncut or safe, and they range from 2 to 10 inches long.

Knife files, are of the section T, and in general very acute on the edge, they are made from 2 to 7 inches long, and are as frequently parallel as taper. The knife files are used in cutting narrow notches, and in making the entry for saws, and for files with broader edges; knife files are also employed in bevilling or chamfering the sides of narrow grooves.

Slitting files, called also *feather-edged files*, resemble the last in construction and purpose, except in having, as in section V, two thin edges instead of one; they are almost always parallel.

Rubbers, are strong heavy files generally made of an inferior kind of steel, they measure from 12 to 18 inches long, from ¾ to 2 inches on every side, and are made very convex or fish-bellied; they are frequently designated by their weight alone, which varies from about 4 to 15 lbs. Rubbers are nearly re-stricted to the square and triangular sections A and R. Some few rubbers are made nearly square in section, but with one side rounded, as if the sections K and B were united, these are called *half-thick*. Rubbers are scarcely ever used by machinists and engineers, but only for coarse manufacturing purposes, where the object is rather to brighten the surface of the work, than to give it any specific form. Rubbers were formerly made only of bar or common steel, but are now also made of cast-steel, and in a more careful manner.

Many artizans, and more particularly the watchmakers, require other files than those described, and it is therefore proposed to add the names of some of the files to which the sections refer, premising that such names as are printed in *Italics*, designate small files especially used in watchmaking.

Names of some of the Files, corresponding with the Sections A to Z,
(represented on page 821).

A.—Square files, both parallel and taper, some with one safe side; also square rubbers.

B.—When large, cotter files; when small, *verge* and *pivot* files.

C.—Hand files, parallel and flat files; when small, *pottance files;* when narrow, pillar files; to these nearly parallel files are to be added the taper flat files.

D.—When parallel, equalling *clock-pinion* and *endless-screw* files; when taper, slitting, entering, warding, and *barrel-hole* files.

E.—*French pivot* and *shouldering files* which are small, stout, and have safe-edges; when made of large size and right and left they are sometimes called parallel V files, from their suitability to the hollow V V's of machinery.

F.—Name and purpose similar to the last.

G.—Flat file with hollow edges, principally used as a nail file for the dressing case.

H.—Pointing mill-saw file, round-edge equalling file, and round-edge joint file; all are made both parallel and taper.

I.—Round file, gulleting saw file, made both parallel and taper.

K.—Frame saw file, for gullet teeth.

L.—Half round file. *Nicking* and *piercing* files, also cabinet floats and rasps; all these are usually taper. Files of this section which are small, parallel, and have the convex side uncut, and have also a pivot at the end opposite the tang, are called *round-off files*, and are used for rounding or pointing the teeth of wheels, cut originally with square notches. The pivot enables the file to be readily twisted in the fingers to allow it to sweep round the curve of the tooth to be rounded.

M.—Cross, or crossing files, also called double half rounds.

N.—Oval files; oval gulletting files for large saws, called by the French *limes à double dos*. *Oval-dial file* when small.

O.—*Balance-wheel or swing-wheel files*, the convex side cut, the angular sides safe.

P.—Swaged files, for finishing brass mouldings; sometimes the hollow and fillets are all cut.

Q.—Sir John Robison's curvilinear file, to be hereafter described.

R.—Triangular, three-square, and saw files, also triangular rubbers, which are cut on all sides. Triangular files are also made in short pieces, and variously fixed to long handles, for works that are difficult of access, as the grooves of some slides and valves, and similar works.

S.—Cant file, probably named from its suitability to filing the insides of spanners, for hexagonal and octagonal nuts, or as these are generally called, six or eight *canted* bolts and nuts; the cant files are cut on all sides.

T.—When parallel, *flat-dovetail, banking* and *watch-pinion* files; when taper, knife-edge files. With the wide edge round and safe, files of the section T, are known as moulding files, and *clock-pinion* files.

V.—Screw-head files, feather-edged files, *clock and watch-slitting* files.

W.—Is sometimes used by engineers, in finishing small grooves and key ways, and is called a valve file, from one of its applications.

X.—A file compounded of the triangular and half-round file, and stronger than the latter; similar files with three rounded faces have also been made for engineers.

Y.—Double or checkering files, used by cutlers, gun-makers and others. The files are made separately and riveted together, with the edge of the one before that of the other, in order to give the equality of distance and parallelism of checkered works, just as in the double saws for cutting the teeth of racks and combs, see p. 723.

Z.—Double file, made of two flat files fixed together in a wood or metal stock; this was invented for filing lead pencils to a fine conical point, and was patented by Mr. Cooper under the name of the *Styloxynon*.

The manufacture of files.—The pieces of steel, or the blanks intended for files, are forged out of bars of steel, that have been either tilted or rolled as nearly as possible to the sections required, so as to leave but little to be done at the forge; the blanks are afterwards annealed with great caution, so that in neither of the processes the temperature known as the blood-red heat may be exceeded. The surfaces of the blanks are now rendered accurate in form and quite clean in surface, either by filing or grinding. In Warrington, where the majority of the files manufactured are small, the blanks are mostly filed into shape as the more exact method; in Sheffield, where the greater number are large, the blanks are more commonly ground on large grindstones as the more expeditious method, but the best of the small files are here also filed into shape: and in some few cases the blanks are planed in the planing machine, for those called *dead-parallel files*, the object being in every case to make the surface clean and smooth. The blank before being cut is slightly greased, that the chisel may slip freely over it, as will be explained.

The file cutter, when at work, is always seated before a square stake or anvil, and he places the blank straight before him, with the tang towards his person, the ends of the blank are fixed down by two leather straps or loops, one of which is held fast by each foot.

The largest and smallest chisels commonly used in cutting files are represented in two views, and half size in figs. 808 and 809. The first is a chisel for large rough Sheffield files, the length is about 3 inches, the width $2\frac{1}{4}$ inches, and the angle of the edge about 50 degrees, the edge is perfectly straight, but the one bevil is a little more inclined than the other, and the keenness of the edge is rounded off, the object being to indent, rather than cut the steel; this chisel requires a hammer of about 7 or 8 lbs. weight. Fig. 809 is the chisel used for small super-fine Lancashire files, its length is 2 inches, the width ½ inch, it is very thin and sharpened at about the angle of 35 degrees, the edge is also rounded, but in a smaller degree; it is used with a

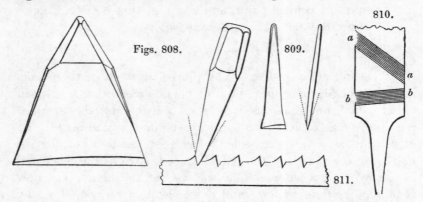

Figs. 808.   809.   810.

811.

hammer weighing only one to two ounces, as it will be seen the weight of the blow mainly determines the distance between the teeth. Other chisels are made of intermediate proportions, but the width of the edge always exceeds that of the file to be cut.

The first cut is made at the point of the file, the chisel is held in the left hand, at an horizontal angle of about 55 degrees, with the central line of the file, as at *a a* fig. 810, and with a vertical inclination of about 12 to 4 degrees from the perpendicular, as represented in the figures 808 and 809, supposing the tang of the file to be on the left-hand side.* The blow of the hammer upon the chisel, causes the latter to indent and slightly to drive forward the steel, thereby throwing up a trifling ridge or *burr*, the chisel is immediately replaced on the blank, and slid from the operator, until it encounters the ridge previously thrown up, which arrests the chisel or prevents it from slipping further

---

* A foreman, experienced in the manufacture of Sheffield files, considers the following to be nearly the usual angles for the vertical inclination of the chisels : namely, for rough rasps, 15 degrees beyond the prependicular; rough files, 12 degrees ; bastard files, 10 degrees ; second-cut files, 7 degrees ; smooth-cut files, 5 degrees ; and dead-smooth-cut files, 4 degrees.

back, and thereby determines the succeeding position of the chisel. The heavier the blow, the greater the ridge, and the greater the distance from the preceding cut, at which the chisel is arrested. The chisel having been placed in its second position, is again struck with the hammer, which is made to give the blows as nearly as possible of uniform strength, and the process is repeated with considerable rapidity and regularity, 60 to 80 cuts being made in one minute, until the entire length of the file has been cut with inclined, parallel, and equi-distant ridges, which are collectively denominated the *first course*. So far as this one face is concerned, the file if intended to be single-cut would be then ready for hardening, and when greatly enlarged its section would be somewhat as in fig. 811.*

Most files, however, are double-cut, or have two series or *courses* of chisel-cuts, and for these the surface of the file is now smoothed by passing a smooth file once or twice along the face of the teeth, to remove only so much of the roughness as would obstruct the chisel from sliding along the face in receiving its successive positions, and the file is again greased.

The second course of teeth is now cut, the chisel being inclined vertically as before or at about 12 degrees, but horizontally, only a few degrees in the opposite direction, or about 5 to 10 degrees from the rectangle, as at *b b*, fig. 810; the blows are now given a little less strongly, so as barely to penetrate to the bottom of the first cuts, and from the blows being lighter they throw up smaller burrs, consequently the second course of cuts is somewhat finer than the first. The two series or courses, fill the surface of the file with teeth which are inclined towards the point of the file, and that when highly magnified much resemble in character the points of cutting tools generally, as seen in fig. 811, for the burrs which are thrown up and constitute the tops of the teeth, are slightly inclined above the general outline of the file, minute parts of the original surface of which still remain nearly in their first positions.

If the file is flat and to be cut on two faces, it is now turned over, but to protect the teeth from the hard face of the anvil, a thin plate of pewter is interposed. Triangular and other files

---

* The teeth of some single cut files are much less inclined than 55 degrees, those of floats are in general square across the instrument.

require blocks of lead having grooves of the appropriate sections to support the blanks, so that the surface to be cut may be placed horizontally. Taper files require the teeth to be somewhat finer towards the point, to avoid the risk of the blank being weakened or broken in the act of its being cut, which might occur if as much force were used in cutting the teeth at the point of the file, as in those at its central and stronger part.

Eight courses of cuts are required to complete a double-cut rectangular file that is cut on all faces, but eight, ten, or even more courses are required, in cutting only the *one* rounded face of a half-round file. There are various objections to employing chisels with concave edges, and therefore in cutting round and half-round files, the ordinary straight chisel is used and applied as a tangent to the curve, but as the narrow cuts are less difficult than the broad ones, half-round and round files are generally cut by young apprentice boys. It will be found that in a smooth half-round file one inch in width, that about twenty courses are required for the convex side, and two courses alone serve for the flat side. In some of the double-cut gullet-tooth saw files, of the section K, as many as 23 courses are sometimes used for the convex face, and but 2 for the flat. The same difficulty occurs in a round file, and the surfaces of curvilinear files do not therefore present, under ordinary circumstances, the same uniformity as those of flat files, as the convex files are from necessity more or less polygonal.

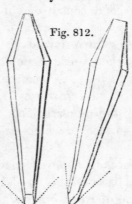

Fig. 812.

Hollowed files are rarely used in the arts, and when required it usually becomes imperative to employ a round-edged chisel, and to cut the file with a single course of teeth. Sir John Robison's curvilinear file will be hereafter noticed, in which the objections alluded to in both hollowed and rounded files are nearly or entirely removed.

The teeth of rasps are cut with a peculiar kind of chisel, or as it is denominated a punch, which is represented also half size, and in two views in fig. 812. The punch for a fine cabinet rasp is about $3\frac{1}{2}$ inches long, and $\frac{5}{8}$ square at its widest part. Viewed in front, the two sides of the point meet at an angle of about 60 degrees, viewed edgeways, or in profile, the edge forms an angle of about 50 degrees, the one-face being only a little inclined to the body of the tool. Different sized rasps necessarily require different sized punches, the ends of which would much resemble the ordinary point tools for turning wood or ivory, but that they are more obtuse, and that the edge of the punch is rounded, that the tool may rather indent than cut.

In cutting rasps, the punch is sloped rather more from the operator than the chisel in cutting files, but the distance between the teeth of the rasp cannot be determined as in the file, by placing the punch in contact with the burr of the tooth previously made. By dint of habit, the workman moves or, technically, *hops* the punch the required distance; to facilitate this movement, he places a piece of woollen cloth under his left hand, which prevents his hand coming immediately in contact with, and adhering to the anvil.

The teeth of rasps are cut in rather an arbitrary manner, and to suit the whims rather than the necessities of the workmen who use them. Thus the lines of teeth in cabinet rasps, wood rasps, and farriers' rasps, are cut in lines sloping from the left down to the right-hand side; the teeth of rasps for boot and shoe-last makers and some others, are sloped the reverse way; and rasps for gun-stockers and saddle-tree makers are cut in circular lines or crescent form. These directions are quite immaterial; but it is important that every succeeding tooth should cross its predecessor, or be intermediate to the two before it; as if the teeth followed one another in right lines, they would produce furrows in the work, and not comparatively smooth surfaces. Considering the nature of the process, it is rather surprising that so much regularity should be attainable as may be observed in rasps of the first quality.

In cutting files and rasps, they almost always become more or less bent, and there would be danger of breaking them if they were set straight whilst cold, they are consequently straightened whilst they are at the red heat, immediately prior to their being hardened and tempered.

Previously to their being hardened, the files are drawn through beer grounds, yeast, or other sticky matter, and then through common salt, mixed with cow's hoof previously roasted and pounded, and which serve as a defence to protect the delicate teeth

of the file from the direct action of the fire. The compound likewise serves as an index of the temperature, as on the fusion of
the salt, the hardening heat is attained ; the defence also lessens
the disposition of the files to crack or clink on being immersed
in the water, see vol. 1, page 253.

The file after having been smeared over as above, is gradually
heated to a dull red, and is then mostly straightened with a leaden
hammer on two small blocks also of lead ; the temperature of the
file is afterwards increased, until the salt on its surface just fuses,
when the file is immediately dipped in water.   The file is
immersed, quickly or slowly, vertically or obliquely, according to
its form ; that mode being adopted for each variety of file, which
is considered best calculated to keep it straight.

It is well known that from the unsymmetrical section of the
half-round file, it is disposed on being immersed, to become hollow or bowed on the convex side, and this tendency is compensated for, by curving the file whilst soft in a nearly equal degree
in the reverse direction ; by this compensatory method, the
hardening process leaves the half-round files nearly straight.

It nevertheless commonly happens, that with every precaution
the file becomes more or less bent in hardening, and if so, it is
straightened, not by blows, but by pressure, either before it is
quite cold, or else after it has been partially reheated in any convenient mode ; as over a clear fire, on a heated iron bar, over a
hooded gas flame, as in tempering watch-springs, or in any other
manner.   The pressure is variously applied, sometimes by passing the one end of the file under a hook, supporting the center
on a prop of lead, and bearing down the opposite end of the file ;
at other times by using a support at each end, and applying
pressure in the middle, by means of a lever the end of which is
hooked to the bench, as in a paring-knife.   Large files are always
straightened before they are quite cooled after the hardening,
and whilst the central part retains a considerable degree of heat.
When straightened, the file is cooled in oil, which saves the teeth
from becoming rusty.

The tangs are now softened to prevent their fracture ; this is
done either by grasping the tang in a pair of heated tongs, or by
means of a bath of lead contained in an iron vessel with a perforated cover, through the holes in which, the tangs are immersed
in the melted lead that is heated to the proper degree ; the tang

is afterwards cooled in oil, and when the file has been wiped, and the teeth brushed clean it is considered fit for use.

The superiority of the file will be found to depend on four points,—the primary excellence of the steel—the proper forging and annealing without excess of heat—the correct formation of the teeth—and the success of the hardening.   These several processes are commonly fulfilled by distinct classes of workpeople, who are again subdivided according to the sizes of the files, the largest of these being cut by powerful muscular men, the smallest by women and girls, who thereby severally attain great excellence in their respective shares of the work.

The manufacture of files, especially the cutting of the teeth, has been entered into much more largely than was at first intended, but it is hoped this may not be without its use; as notwithstanding the suitability of ordinary files to most purposes, still occasions may and do occur, in which the general mechanist or amateur may find some want unsupplied, which these hints may enable him to provide for, although less perfectly, than if the file in question had been manufactured in the usual course. The process of cutting teeth, is also called for in roughing the jaws of vices and clamping apparatus.*

Means of grasping the file.—In general the end of the file is forged simply into a taper tang or spike, for the purpose of fixing it in its wooden handle, but wide files require that the tang should be reduced in width, either as in fig. 813 or 814. The former mode, especially in large files, is apt to cripple the steel and dispose the tang to break off, after which the file is nearly useless; the curvilinear tang, 814, is far less open to this objection, and was registered by Messrs. Johnson, Cammell, and Co., of Sheffield.   Some workmen make the tangs of large files red hot, that they may burn their own recesses in the handles, but this is objectionable, as the charred wood is apt to crumble

---

* There is perhaps an equal mixture of philosophy and prejudice in the hardening of files : some attach very great importance to the coating or defence, others to the medication of the water, and all to the mode of immersion best calculated for each different file, in order to keep it as straight as possible, questions of opinion which it is impossible to generalize.   Mr. Stubs's process of manufacture is pretty much as above described, and although he has experimented with mercury at 8° F., as the cooling medium, as well as various fluids, he has arrived at the conclusion, that the salt principally acts as an antiseptic, and that fresh spring water at 45° is as effective as any fluid.

away and release the file : it is more proper to form the cavity in the handle, with coarse floats made for the purpose.

In driving large files into their handles, it is usual to place the point of the file in the hollow behind the chaps of the tail vice,

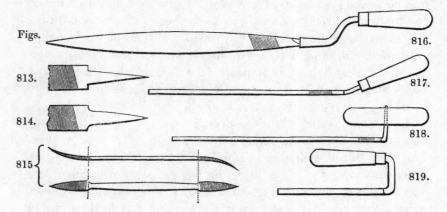

Figs.

813.

814.

815

816.

817.

818.

819.

and to drive on the handle with a mallet or hammer. Smaller files are fixed obliquely in the jaws of the vice, between clamps of sheet brass, to prevent the teeth either of the vice or file, from being injured, and the handle is then driven on. The file, if small, is sometimes merely fixed in a cork, or in a small piece of hazle rod, but these are to be viewed as temporary expedients, and inferior to the usual wooden handles turned in the lathe. Very small watch files are fixed in handles no larger than drawing pencils, and some few of them are roughened on the tang, after the manner of a float, and fixed in by sealing wax or shell lac.

Several of the small files have the handles forged in the solid, that is, the tang is made longer than usual, and is either parallel, or spread out, to serve for the handle, as in a razor strop; many of the watch files are thus made. In the double-ended rifflers, or bent files, fig. 815, used by sculptors and carvers, and in some other files, there is a plain part in the middle, fulfilling the office of a handle; and in several of the files and rasps made for dentists, farriers and shoemakers, the tool is also double, but without any intermediate plain part, so that the one end serves as the handle for the other.

In general the length of the file exceeds that of the object filed, but in filing large surfaces it becomes occasionally necessary to attach cranked handles to the large files or rubbers, as in fig. 816, in order to raise the hand above the plane of the work. Sometimes the end of the file is simply inclined, as in fig. 817, or bent at right angles, as in 818, for the attachment of the wooden handles represented; but the last two modes prevent the second side of the file from being used, until the tang is bent the reverse way. The necessity for bending the file is avoided, by employing as a handle, a piece of round iron ⅝ or ¾ inch in diameter, bent into the semicircular form as an arch, the one extremity, (or abutment), of which is filed with a taper groove to fit the tang of the file, whilst the opposite end is flat, and rests upon the teeth; in this manner, both sides of the file may be used without any preparation.

Fig. 819 represents, in profile, a broad and short rasp with fine teeth, used by iron-founders in smoothing off loam moulds for iron castings, this is mostly used on large surfaces, to which the ordinary handle would be inapplicable, and the same kind of tool when made with coarser teeth, will be recognised as the baker's rasp. For some slight purposes, ordinary files are used upon large surfaces, without handles of any kind, the edges of the file itself being then grasped with the fingers.

Cabinet-makers sometimes fix the file to a block of wood to serve for the grasp, and use it as a plane. Thus mounted, the file may also be very conveniently used on a shooting board, in filing the edges of plates to be inlaid.

Fig. 820 represents a very good arrangement of this kind by Mr. W. Lund, $a\,a$ is the plan and b the section of the file-stock, $c\,c$ is

Fig. 820.

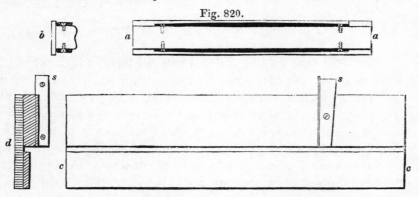

the plan of the shooting board and d its section. Two files, (that are represented black,) are screwed against the sides of a straight

bar of wood, which has also a wooden sole or bottom plate, that
projects beyond the files, so that the smooth edge of the sole may
touch the shooting board instead of the file teeth.   The shooting
board is made in three pieces, so as to form a groove to receive
the file dust, which would otherwise get under the stock of the
file; the shooting board has also a wooden stop *s*, faced with steel,
that is wedged and screwed into a groove made across the top
piece, and the stop being exactly at right angles, serves also to
assist in squaring the edges of plates or the ends of long bars,
with accuracy and expedition.   Mr. Lund prefers a flat file that
is fully curved on the face, as nearly half the file then comes into
action at every stroke.

   Short pieces of files, (or tools as nearly allied to saws,) are
occasionally fixed in the ends of wooden stocks, in all other
respects like the routing gages of carpenters, as seen in two
views in fig. 821; the coopers' *croze*, page 488, is a tool of
this description.

   Files intended for finishing the grooves in the edges of slides,
are sometimes made of short pieces of steel of the proper section,

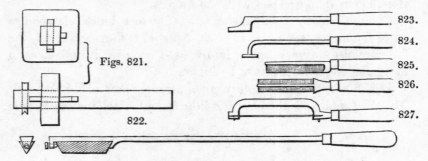

Figs. 821.

822.

823.

824.

825.

826.

827.

(see fig. 822,) cut on the surfaces with file teeth, and attached in
various ways to slender rods or wires, serving as the handles, and
extending beyond the ends of the slides.   Or the handle is at
right angles to the file, and formed at the end, as a staple, to clip
the ends of the short file, as in reaching the bottom of a cavity.
Files intended to reach to the bottom of shallow cavities are
also constructed as in figs. 823 and 824, or sometimes an inch or
more of the end of an ordinary file is bent some 20 or 30 degrees,
that the remainder may clear the margin of the recess.

   To stiffen slender files, they are occasionally made with tin or
brass backs, as in figs. 825 and 826; such are called dove-tail

files, evidently from their similitude to dove-tail saws; and thin equalling files, are sometimes grasped in a brass frame, fig. 827, exactly like that used for a metal frame-saw, by which the risk of breaking the instrument in the act of filing is almost annulled.

An equivocal analogy, both to the file and saw, is to be observed in some of the delicate circular cutters, used in cutting watch wheels and other small works. The teeth of such cutters are in many instances formed by cuts of a chisel, the same as the teeth of files, and the axis of the cutter becomes, by comparison, the handle of the circular file.

SECT. II.—GENERAL AND DESCRIPTIVE VIEW OF FILES OF LESS USUAL KINDS.

Notwithstanding the great diversity in the files alluded to in the foregoing section, it is to be remarked that all those hitherto noticed are made entirely of steel, and their teeth are all produced in the ordinary manner by means of the chisel and hand hammer; in the present section, a few of the less usual kinds of rasps, floats, and files, will be noticed, the teeth of which are, for the most part, produced by means differing from those already described.

The rifflers, fig. 815, used by sculptors, are required to be of numerous curvatures, to adapt them to the varying contour of works in marble. In general the rifflers are made of steel in the ordinary mode, but they have also been made of *wrought-iron,* and slightly case-hardened, in which case the points of the teeth become converted into steel, but the general bulk of the instrument remains in its original state as soft iron; consequently such case-hardened rifflers admit of being bent upon a block of lead with a leaden mallet, so that the artist is enabled to modify their curvatures as circumstances may require.

Several kinds of floats are made with coarse, shallow, and sharp teeth, which are in section like fig. 646, page 684; these teeth could not be cut with the chisel and hammer in the ordinary manner, but are made with a triangular file. Figs. *a* to *l*, 828, represent the sections of several of these floats, which have teeth at the parts indicated by the double lines; for instance, *a* is the float, *b* the *graille*, *c* the *found*, *d* the *carlet*, *e* the *topper*, used by the horn and tortoiseshell comb-makers; parts of the names of which floats are corrupted from the French language, indeed the art was mainly derived from French artizans. The floats, *f* to *i*, are used by ivory carvers for the handles of knives, and in

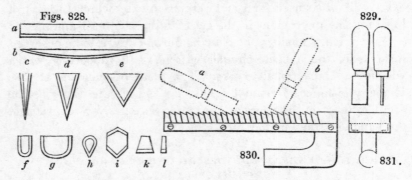

Figs. 828.

829.

830.

831.

the preparation of works, the carving of which is to be completed by scorpers and gravers; *k* and *l* are used in inlaying tools in their handles; *k* is made of various widths, and is generally thin, long, and taper; *l* is more like a key-hole saw. When the teeth of these floats have been formed with the triangular file, and made quite sharp, the tools are first hardened and very slightly tempered, just sufficiently to avoid fracture in use; but, when after a period the tools have become dull, they are tempered to a deep orange, or a blue, so as to admit of being sharpened with a triangular file.

The larger of the floats, such as those *a* to *e*, used by the comb-makers, are kept in order principally by the aid of a burnisher, represented in two views in fig. 829, the blade is about 2 inches long, 1 inch wide, and $\frac{1}{16}$ inch thick; the end is mostly used, and which is forcibly rubbed, first on the front edge of every tooth, as at *a*, fig. 830, and then on the back, as at *b*, by which means a slight burr is thrown up, on every tooth, somewhat like that on the joiner's scraper; but in this art the burnisher is commonly named a *turn-file*. When the teeth of the floats have become thickened from repeated burnishing, the triangular file is again resorted to, and then the burnisher for a further period; by these means the floats are made to last a considerable time.

The *quannet* is a float resembling fig. 819, but having coarse filed teeth, of the kind just described; it may be considered as the ordinary flat file of the horn and tortoiseshell comb-makers, and in using the quannet, the work is mostly laid upon the knee as a support. An ingenious artizan in this branch, Mr. Michael

Kelly, invented the quannet represented in figs. 830 and 831. The stock consists of a piece of beech-wood, in which, at intervals of about one quarter of an inch, cuts inclined nearly 30 degrees with the face, are made with a thin saw; every cut is filled with a piece of saw-plate. The edges of the plates and wood, are originally filed into the regular float-like form, and the burnisher is subsequently resorted to as usual. The main advantage results from the small quantity of steel it is necessary to operate upon, when the instrument requires to be restored with the file. From this circumstance, and also from its less weight, the wooden quannet, fig. 830, is made of nearly twice the width of the steel instrument, fig. 819, and the face is slightly rounded, the teeth being sometimes inserted square across, as in a float, at other times inclined some 30 degrees, as in a single-cut file.

A more elaborate, but less available, instrument was invented by Mr. White, probably during his residence in France, about the time of the Revolution (1793). It consisted of numerous parallel plates of steel, which were placed vertically and in contact, something like a pack of narrow cards, and were fixed in that position in an appropriate frame, and as the edges of the plates were all bevelled, they constituted a single-cut file. The most curious part of the contrivance was, the ingenious mode of chamfering the edges, as for this purpose the plates were loosened and arranged in a sloping direction, so that the chamfers then lay collectively in one plane, which was ground either on a grindstone, or a lead lap fed with emery ; the plates were replaced perpendicularly before use. Means were also described for placing the steel plates square across the instrument as in a float, or inclined to the right or left as in a file, according to the material to be wrought; and a drawing is also given of a circular float of similar nature for cutting dye-woods into small fragments. White's "*perpetual*" file, with moveable plates, is however scarcely known, and it is very questionable if it ever obtained more than the experimental application which led to its description having been published.*

The cutting of files by machinery is an operation that has engaged the attention of many persons, and the earliest attempt

---

* Published in *Déscriptions des Machines et Procédés specifiés dans les Brevets d'Invention*, &c. *Par M. Christian. Paris, 4to*, 1824. *Tome* 6, *p.* 33. Patent dated 6 Jan. 1795.

at the process that has come under the author's notice is that of *Thiout ainé*, which was figured and described in a work by his son in 1740; and this machine being based on the manual process, in all probability differs but little in its general features from most of those of more recent projectors.

According to the drawings referred to, the file is attached to a screw slide, which is suspended at the ends by pivots, and covered with a thin plate of tin; the slide rests upon a stationary anvil, and is actuated by a guide screw, which is moved at intervals, the space from tooth to tooth by a pin wheel, for which the ratchet wheel would be now substituted. The chisel is held by a jointed arm, beneath which is a spring to throw up the chisel from off the file, the moment after a drop hammer, which is also fixed on a joint, has indented the tooth. The movements of the slide and hammer are each repeated at the proper intervals, in every revolution of the winch handle, by which Thiout's machine is represented to be worked.*

The practical introduction of machinery for cutting files appears to be due to a Frenchman of the name of Raoul, at about the close of the last century, but the description of the machine has not been published, and the manufacture is now carried on by his son, some of whose files are in the possession of the author. They are certainly beautiful specimens of workmanship, being more strictly regular, and also less liable to clog or pin when in use, than files cut by hand, as usual.

His manufacture is principally limited to watch files with flat sides, and measuring from $\frac{3}{4}$ of an inch, to 5 or 6 inches long. When magnified, the teeth of the files, cut either by hand or machinery, appear as nearly as possible of the same character.†

Machines have been recently constructed in England for

---

* See Thiout's *Traité de l'Horlogerie*. Paris, 1740. Vol. 1, page 81 plates 33 and 34.

† Mr. Raoul was rewarded for his files by the *Lycée des Arts*, an institution that no longer exists, but which was founded soon after the French Revolution, for the reward of national discoveries and improvements. From the Report of the Lyceum of Arts it appears, that on the 10th Thermidor, year 8 of the Republic (July, 1800), an honorary crown was decreed to Citizen Raoul for the perfection of his files. And on a subsequent page of the report, is given the opinion of a Committee appointed to examine into the comparative merits of Raoul's files, from which report it appears, they were pronounced by the Committee to be equal, and even superior, to the best English files.

cutting both large and small files, and half a dozen or more at a time.* The details of the machines display great ingenuity and skill, especially in the arrangement for holding the blanks and the chisels, and also in the introduction of templets and other mechanism, by which, in cutting taper files, the hammer is less raised in cutting the ends of the file than at the middle, so as to proportion the force of the blow to the width and depth of the cut, at different parts of the file. Two machines were used for double-cut files, the bed of the one inclined to the right, of the other to the left, to give the different horizontal inclinations proper to these teeth; and a machine with a straight bed was used for single-cut floats, and for round and half-round files.

Considerable difficulty was at first experienced in the management of the chisels, which were then very frequently broken, but with more dexterous management it is ultimately considered that the chisels last for a longer time in the machines, than when used by hand. The machines make about 240 strokes in the minute, or three times as many as the file cutter, with the advantage of nearly incessant action, as unlike the arm of the workman, the machines are unconscious of fatigue; moreover, to save the delay of adjustment, two beds for the files are employed, so that the one may be filled whilst the blanks in the other are being cut, and two frames for the chisels are also alternately used. Taking all these points into account, each machine is considered by the proprietors, nearly to accomplish the work of ten men, but there are various drawbacks that prevent, under ordinary circumstances, any great commercial advantage in the machine over the hand process, from which considerations, the patent file cutting machines, are not at present used.

In concluding this section, there remain to be introduced, two propositions for the manufacture of files, suggested by a very talented and philanthropic member of the scientific world, the late Sir John Robison, K.H., F.R.S.E., late President of the Royal Scottish Society of Arts, &c., namely, his methods of making curvilinear files, and of cutting flat files with very fine teeth. The subjects cannot be better stated than by quoting Sir John's correspondence with the author; speaking of the

---

* Captain Ericcson's Patent File Cutting Machines, specified 1836, constructed by Messrs. Braithwaites of London, and carried into practical effect by Messrs. Turton & Sons, of Sheffield.

curvilinear files of the Section Q., page 821, he introduces the subject as follows:—

" I have just entered on a new project, of which I should be glad to know what you think. Having always found difficulty in filing hollow surfaces, from the scratches which the irregular cutting of even the best half-round, or round files, leave in the work, in spite of every care, I was lately led to consider whether half-round, or even round files, might not be made as perfect in their cutting as flat ones. It has occurred to me, that this object may be attained by cutting flat strips of rolled steel plate on one side, and then squeezing them into the desired curve by a screw press, and a block-tin or type-metal swage, and in the case of the round file, by pressing the plate round a cylindrical mandrel.

" I do not think that the files made in this way should cost more than those now made, as the surface would be cut by two courses of cuts, (as flat files are), intead of the numerous courses required to cover the surface of round files, the saving in this respect would make up for the time required in bending the plates." *   *   *   *

A valuable addition to Sir John's proposal occurred incidentally; Messrs. Johnson and Cammel, to whom the scheme was communicated, in the haste of putting it to trial, took a thin equalling file that had been previously cut on both faces. The equalling file was softened, bent, and re-hardened, and this produced a file, the convex and also the concave surface of which were both useful additions to the tools of the general mechanician.

But it was found that with a plate of equal thickness, the central part bent more easily than the edges, making the curve irregular. This was successfully obviated by making the blank thinner and more flexible at the edges, somewhat as a half-round file, and in which case the bending was quite successful, and the section became truly circular. *

Sir John Robison's second project in respect to the manufac-

---

* The Society for the Encouragement of Arts, of London, bestowed its silver medal on Sir John Robison for his invention of the curved file, which distinction it is to be regretted arrived as a posthumous honour. (See Trans. Soc. of Arts, vol. liv. p. 128.)   And the Royal Scottish Society of Arts presented, in November, 1843, a silver medal to Messrs. Johnson, Cammell, and Co., for the skilful manner in which they had carried out and perfected the above scheme, and introduced the curved files as a regular article of manufacture. (See the official report in the Edinburgh New Philosophical Journal for January, 1844, p. 86.)

ture of files, refers to a new mode of forming the teeth of very fine files, otherwise than by percussion; and without delaying the reader by referring to the earlier correspondence on the subject, the author gives a short extract from a letter received a few days before Sir John's death, and also the contents of the packet therein referred to.

" Lest my medical friends should be mistaken, and this malady increase so as to prevent my communicating my project for cutting fine files, I shall now make out a memorandum of my ideas on the subject, and making a sealed packet of it shall enclose it to you. If I get better and reach London, we can discuss the matter together, and if I am put *hors de combat*, you will consider it your own.　　*　　　　*　　　　*　　　　*　　　　*

" It appears to me that the graver may be applied with good effect in cutting the teeth of the finer classes of flat files, and that if a number of steel blanks were firmly embedded on a platform similar to the bed of a planing table, and made to move forward in their own plane by a micrometer screw, then if an equal number of gravers were to be fixed in a frame to lie over the platform, so that each graver point should be in a certain relative position to one of the blanks, on motion being communicated to the frame in a proper direction, and to a distance a little exceeding the breadth of the blank, a line would be ploughed out of the surface of each blank. If the frame were then brought back to its first position, and the platform advanced or receded by the micrometer screw, a second movement of the cutter frame would produce a line parallel to the first, and so on in succession.

" If the points of the gravers, instead of being set to cut

A  B

equilateral grooves as at A, were inclined so as to cut them as at B, then, by a proper proportioning of the depth of the cut, and the progressive movement of the platform, a regular cutting tooth of great sharpness may be given to the file.

" The movement to be given to the graver frame may be an oscillating one round a distant center, so that the short arc of the teeth may be sensibly a straight line.

" It is evident that the sharpness and smoothness of the

engraving must depend mainly on the way in which the cutter is presented to the work, and experience shows that the position of the tool in the hand of the engraver is the most favourable, both to the production of clean lines, and the preservation of the point of the tool; the graver must be supported endways, and not alone by fastenings in its middle, like the tool of a planing machine, or a slide rest cutter.

" The means of regulating the depth of the cut, and the other arrangements of the parts of such a machine, would of course require consideration by engravers and practical mechanics.

" (Signed)   John Robison.

" Edinburgh, 17<i>th February</i>, 1843."

The author much regrets that the multiplicity of his engagements, and especially those connected with these pages, should have prevented him putting the above project to experimental proof, but he would be well pleased to hear that the subject had been brought to successful issue, by any person more favourably situated for carrying out the suggestion.*

SECT. III.—PRELIMINARY REMARKS ON USING FILES, AND ON HOLDING WORKS THAT ARE TO BE FILED.

The use of the file is undoubtedly more difficult than that of the generality of mechanical tools, and the difficulty arises from the circumstance of the file possessing, but in a very inferior degree, the <i>guide principle</i>, the influence of which principle, in all tools, from the most simple cutting tool used by hand, to the most complex cutting machine or engine, formed the subject-matter of the introductory chapter of the present volume. The comparative facility of the manipulation of turning-tools, was shown to depend on the perfection in which the guide principle exists in the turning lathe. It was further stated at page 468—

" The <i>guide principle</i> is to be traced in most of our tools; in the joiner's plane it exists in the form of the stock or sole of the plane, which commonly possesses the same superficies that it is desired to produce. For instance, the carpenter's plane used for

---

* Since writing the above, the author learns that Captain Ericcson tried some experiments on cutting file teeth as with a graver, but that he was led to consider the mode less practical than that of cutting teeth by percussion. The subject appears, however, to deserve more extended trial.

flat surfaces is itself flat, both in length and width, and therefore furnishes a double guide. The flat file is somewhat under the same circumstances, but as it cuts at every part of its surface, from thousands of points being grouped together, it is more treacherous than the plane, as regards the surface from which it derives its guidance, and from this and other reasons it is far more difficult to manage than the carpenter's plane."

These points are recalled not to impress the amateur with the idea that the successful use of the file will be to him unattainable, but rather to call forth such a measure of perseverance, as may enable many to arrive at a practice which is confessedly difficult. It is proposed in the present section to notice certain preliminary and general topics, before attempting, in the next three sections, to convey the instructions for manipulating the file.

Commencing with the position of the work, it is in all cases desirable that the surface to be filed should be placed *horizontally*, and the general rule for the height of the work above the ground is, that the surface to be filed should be nearly level with the elbow joint of the workman, and which may be considered to range with different individuals from forty to forty-five inches from the ground. Some latitude is, however, required in respect to the magnitude of the works, as when they are massive, and much is to be filed off from them, it is desirable that the work should be a trifle lower than the elbow; when the work is minute and delicate, it should be somewhat higher, so that the eye may be the better able to add its scrutiny to that of the sense of feeling of the hand, upon which principally the successful practice depends. The small change of height is also in agreement with the three different positions of the individual in the act of filing ; for instance.

Firstly. In filing heavy works, or those which require the entire muscular effort, the file varies from about 12 to 24 inches long, and the length of the stroke is from about 10 to 20 inches, or nearly the full length of the file. The operator stands a little distant from his work, with the feet separated about 30 inches, which somewhat lowers his stature; he grasps and thrusts the handle of the file with his right hand, and bears forcibly near the end of the file with that part of his left hand which is contiguous to his wrist, so as to make the file penetrate the work, or *hang* to it. The general movement of the person is then an alternation of the entire frame upon the knee and ankle joints, the arms being comparatively fixed to the body, the momentum of which is applied to the file.

Secondly. In filing works of medium size, the file varies from about 6 to 12 inches, and the length of stroke is from about 4 to 9 ; the operator then stands nearer to the work and quite erect, with his feet closer together. The right hand grasps the file handle as before, but the extremity of the file is now held between the thumb and the first two fingers of the left hand, and the general movement is that of the arms, the body being comparatively at rest.

Thirdly. In filing the smallest works, the file is less than 6 inches long, and the stroke does not exceed 3 or 4, and sometimes is not one-tenth as much. When the work is fixed, the file is still usually held in both hands as last described, but frequently, in fact more generally, the file is managed with the right hand alone, the forefinger being stretched out as in holding a carving knife, and the work is held upon the support or filing block with the left hand, as will be explained. The act of filing is then accomplished by the movement of the elbow, or even of the fingers alone, but so little is the body moved, that the workman is usually seated as at an ordinary table.

It is apparent, and also true, that the most direct way of producing a flat surface with the file, would be to select a file the face of which was absolutely flat, and that should be moved in lines absolutely straight; but there are certain interferences that prevent these conditions being carried out. First, although it is desirable to employ files that are as nearly straight as possible, and that are also fixed straightly in their handles, yet very few files possess this exactitude of form, and although in the attempt to attain this perfection, some files are planed in the engineer's planing machine before being cut with teeth, still the cutting and the hardening so far invalidate this practice, that few even of these planed files can retain their perfect straightness, and either both sides become in a small degree irregularly tortuous, or the sides become respectively concave and convex. Therefore, as for the sake of argument, it may be almost taken for granted that no files truly possess the intended form, it is better purposely to adopt that kind of irregularity, which the least interferes with the general use of the instrument.

The file, if concave or hollow in respect to its length, in the manner coarsely exaggerated in fig. 832, might be used for works of corresponding *convexity;* but it would be impossible to file a flat surface therewith, as the concave file would only

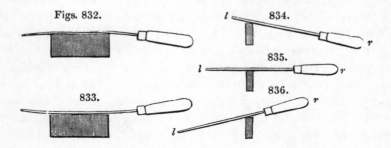

Figs. 832. 834. 835. 836. 833.

touch the surface at its edges, but the convex side of the same file might, as in fig. 833, be made to touch any and every part of the surface if moved in a right line.   On this account most files are made thicker and wider in the middle, or with both faces convex, and the error of hardening will then rarely make either side concave, but will leave both faces convex, although differently so; and consequently, both sides, notwithstanding some irregularity, are useable upon flat works, provided the operator can move them in a right line across the work.

In reference to the manipulation of the instrument, it is to be observed that the most natural movements of the hand and arm are in circular lines, the several joints of the limbs being the centers of motion; but, as in filing a flat surface, it is needful the hands should move very nearly in right lines, a kind of training becomes necessary.

If, however, the file were carried quite straight across a wide surface, the central part of the file would be alone used; but as the continual effort of the individual is to *feel* that the file lies in exact contact with the surface being filed, the hands imperceptibly depart so much from the exact rectilinear path as to bring all parts of the file from point to heel into use.

Again, it might be urged that the file, from being itself in the form of the arc of a large circle, would reduce the work to the counterpart form, or make it hollow in the opposite degree; it is true this is the tendency, and may by dexterity become the result, even on narrow pieces; but the contrary error is more common, so that the surface of the work becomes rounded instead of concave or plane.

If the surface to be filed is four or five inches or more in width, the risk of departing from the true figure becomes reduced, as the file has then a wide base to rest upon, and the pressure of the hands readily prevents any material departure from the right position of the file; but the difficulty becomes greatly increased when the surface to be filed is narrow.

The file held in the two hands upon the narrow work, may be then viewed as a double-ended lever, or as a scale beam supported on a prop; and the variation in distance of the hands from the work or prop gives a disposition to rotate the file upon the work, and which is only counteracted by habit or experience.

Assuming, for the moment, that in the three diagrams the vertical pressure of the right hand at r, and the left at l, to be in all cases alike, in fig. 834, or the beginning of the stroke, the right hand would, from acting at the longer end of the lever, become depressed; in fig. 835, or the central position, the hands would be in equilibrium and the file horizontal; and in fig. 836, or the end of the stroke, the left hand would preponderate; the three positions would inevitably make the work round, in place of leaving it plane or flat.

It is true the diagrams are extravagant, but this rolling action of the file upon the work is in most cases to be observed in the beginner; and those practised in the use of the file have, perhaps unconsciously, acquired the habit of pressing down *only* with the left hand at the commencement, and *only* with the right hand at the conclusion of every stroke; or negatively, that they have learned to avoid swaying down the file at either extreme, and which bad practice will necessarily result, if the operator have not at first a constant watch upon himself, to feel that the file and work are always in true contact, throughout the variable action of the hands upon the instrument.

When the work is fixed in the bench or table-vice, the file is almost always managed with both hands, as above described; but when the file is held in the one hand only, all the circumstances are altered, except the continued attempt to keep the work and file in accurate juxta-position; and to assist in this, the work when so small as to be filed with the one hand only, is almost invariably held on the filing-block with the left hand, occasionally through the intervention of a hand-vice, as in fig. 860, page 862. In this case the two hands act in concert, the right in moving the file, the left in adjusting the position of the work, until the individual is conscious of the agreement in position of the two parts.

Sometimes indeed the partial rotation of the work, in order to adapt the work to the file, is especially provided for, so as to compensate for the accidental swaying of the file; such is the case in the various kinds of *swing tools*, used by watchmakers in filing and polishing small flat works. A similar end is more rarely obtained, on a larger scale, when the file is required to be held in both hands. For example, *filing-boards* resembling fig. 837, and upon which the work is placed, have been made

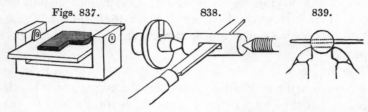

Figs. 837.   838.   839.

to move on two pivots, somewhat as a gun moves on its trunnions; consequently the works, when laid upon the swinging board, assume the same angle as that at which the file may at the moment be held.

A more common case is to be seen in filing a rectangular mortise, or key-way, through a cylindrical spindle, as in fig. 838 ; the hole is commenced by drilling three or four holes, which are thrown into one by a cross-cut chisel, or small round file ; and the work, when nearly completed, is suspended between the centers of the lathe, so that it may freely assume the inclination of the file. At other times, the cylinder is laid in the interval between the edges of the jaws of the vice, that are opened as much as two thirds the diameter of the object, which then similarly rotates on the supporting edges; this mode is shown in fig. 839.

These three applications are objectionable in some instances, as the file is left too much at liberty, and the works are liable to be filed hollow instead of flat, especially if the file be rounding, because the unstable position of the work prevents the file from being constrained to act on any particular spot that may require to be reduced.

Some general remarks will be now given on certain practices in respect to economising the wear of files; and these will be followed by other remarks on the modes of holding works that are to be filed, prior to giving, in the next sections, the practical instructions upon filing.

The exterior surfaces of iron castings are usually more or less impregnated with the sand of the foundry moulds, which is very destructive to the tools; and this is in many cases removed by pickling them with dilute sulphuric acid, which dissolves a little of the metal, and undermines and loosens the sand, as explained in vol. i., p. 375. Iron castings become moreover superficially hard from coming in contact with the moist sand of the foundry mould; so that a thin but hard skin envelops the entire object to the depth of the twentieth or thirtieth of an inch, and as this is very injurious to the files, it is usually chipped off with a chisel and hammer; the pickling is then less required.

The ordinary chipping chisel is about six or eight inches long, and three-fourths of an inch broad on the edge, which is a little convex, that the corners may not be liable to dig into the work. The bevils are ground to meet at an angle of about 80 degrees, and the hammer used with the chipping chisel varies from about two to three pounds in weight. Before commencing to chip the work, it is usual to rub both the face of the hammer and the end of the chisel upon the bench or floor, to remove any grease and leave them bright and clean, as were either of them greasy there would be risk of the hammer glancing off and striking the knuckles. A blow is first given with the hammer upon the angle of the work, to make a little facet upon which the first chisel-cut is made, about the thirtieth of an inch below the general surface of the casting, the chisel being then only raised some 30 degrees above the horizontal line. In continuing the cuts the chisel is elevated to about 45 degrees, the blows are given in quick succession, and the cuts are led gradually over the entire surface, the advance being always upon a line that is convex to the chisel.

Provided the casting is moderately flat, the edge of the chisel is kept at one uniform distance below the general surface of the work, which is occasionally examined with the straight-edge. Should the surface of the casting present any lumps or irregularities of surface, a thicker chip or two thin chips are removed from such high parts, to lessen the subsequent labour of filing, but which process is much less destructive to the file after the hard sand-coat has been removed by acid from the iron.

In some massive works, and also in cases where large quantities have to be chipped off certain parts of castings, much larger chipping chisels are used, which are called *flogging* chisels; they commonly exceed one foot in length, and are proportionally stout; one man holds the chisel in both hands, sometimes by means of a chisel-rod for greater security, whilst another strikes with a light sledge-hammer.   Where much has to be removed, it is also usual to employ *cross-cutting* chisels; these are about seven or eight inches long, a quarter of an inch wide on the edge, and an inch broad in the other direction; the cross-cut chisel is first used to cut furrows, half or three quarters of an inch asunder, to the full depth of the parts to be removed, and the intervening ridges are then easily broken off with the ordinary chipping chisel; but since the general employment of the planing-machine, and others of the engineer's tools, the chipping chisels are scarcely required.   When iron castings are so near to their required dimensions, that chipping would remove too much, they are either cleaned with a nearly worn-out file, or the outer coat is removed on the grindstone, means that are much less wasteful of the material.

Wrought iron is but seldom pickled previously to being filed, but is either cleaned with an old file, or is ground on a stone to remove the outer scale or oxydised surface; the chipping chisel is only in general required when the nature of the work prevents it from being forged so nearly of the required form as to bring it properly within range of the file.

Brass and gun-metal are, as already noticed in the first volume, p. 375, sometimes pickled, but with nitric acid, instead of the sulphuric acid which is employed for iron; and brass is commonly hammered all over to increase its density, unless a minute quantity of tin is added, say a quarter or half an ounce to the pound, which materially stiffens the alloy, so as to render hammering as unnecessary as it is with good gun-metal.

After a file has been used for wrought iron or steel, it is less adapted to filing cast iron or brass, which require keen files, therefore to economise the wear of the instrument, it is used for a time on brass or cast-iron, and when partially worn, it is still available for filing wrought iron or steel; whereas, had the file been first used on these harder materials, it would have been found comparatively ineffective for brass and cast-iron.

As a further measure of economy, the pressure on the file should be always relieved in the back stroke, which otherwise only tends to wear down or break off the tops of the teeth, as their formation shows that they can only cut in the ordinary or advancing stroke; the file should, in consequence, be nearly lifted from the work in drawing it back, but it is not usual actually to raise the file off the work, as it then becomes needful to wait an instant before the next stroke, to ensure the true position of the file upon the work being resumed; whereas, if it is brought back with inconsiderable pressure, the file is not injured, and the hand still retains the consciousness of the true contact of the file and work, without which the instrument is used with far less decision and correctness than it otherwise would be.

Some workmen smooth the work by the method called *draw-filing*, or by drawing the file sideways along the work, using it in fact, as a spoke-shave instead of a file : this certainly has the effect of smoothing the work, because in that position the file can only make slight and closely congregated scratches, but the teeth will not *cut* in this manner. Another mode sometimes employed is to curl the work with the file, by describing small circles with the instrument as in grinding or polishing, but neither of these practices employs the file teeth in the mode in which they are legitimately adapted to cut, and no great reliance should be placed upon them. When smooth surfaces are required, it is a better and quicker practice, as the work advances towards completion, to select files that are gradually finer, but always to use them from point to heel.

When it is desired to make the smooth files cut wrought-iron, steel, and other *fibrous* metals very smoothly, the file is used with a little oil to lubricate the surface, so that it may not penetrate to the same degree as it would if used dry ; the oil also lessens the disposition to the scratching and tearing up of the particles, which, should it happen, mostly produces a furrow or scratch, especially if the file be *pinny*, a circumstance now to be explained; but the oil should not be used on the coarser or preparatory files.

The particles removed from the materials operated upon, are

always more or less liable to clog the file, but which, particularly when the instrument is dry, are partially removed by giving the edge of the file a moderately smart blow on the chaps of the vice or the edge of the bench; but particles of wrought iron, steel, and other fibrous metals, are apt to *pin the file*, or to stick in so hard as to require to be picked out with a pointed steel wire, which is run through the furrow in which the pin is situated. The marking point, used in setting out works, is commonly employed for the purpose.

Files are sometimes cleaned with a *scratch-brush*, which is a cylindrical bundle of fine steel or brass wire, bound tightly in its central part, but allowing the ends of the wire to protrude at both extremities as a stiff brush. Occasionally also, a *scraper* is used, or a long strip of sheet brass, about an inch wide, a small portion of the end of which is turned down at right angles, and thinned with a hammer; the thin edge is then drawn forcibly through the oblique furrows of the file, and serves as a rake to remove any particles of metal that lodge therein.

But the best and most rapid mode of cleaning the file, is to nail to a piece of wood about two inches wide, a strip of the so-called *cotton card*, which is used in combing the cotton-wool preparatory to spinning; the little wire staples of the card that are fixed in the leather constitute a most effective brush, and answer the purpose exceedingly well. Some workmen, to lessen the disposition of the file to hold the file dust, or become pinny, rub it over with chalk; this absorbs any oil or grease that may be on the file, and in a considerable degree fulfils the end desired.

To remove wood-dust from files, floats, and rasps, some persons dip them for a few moments into hot water, and then brush them with a stiff brush; the water moistens and swells the wood, thereby loosening it, and the brush entirely removes the particles; the heat given to the file afterwards evaporates the trifling quantity of moisture that remains, so as to avoid the formation of rust. This plan, although effective, is neither general nor important.

The principal methods of fixing works, in order to subject them to the action of the file, will be now noticed. Many of the massive parts of machinery are so heavy, that gravity alone is sufficient to keep them steady under the action of the file, and

for such as these, it is therefore only needed to prop them up
in any convenient manner, by wedges, trestles, or other supports,
so as to place them conveniently within reach of the operator.
But the great majority of works are held in the well-known
implement, the smith's bench-vice, or tail-vice, the general form
of which is too familiar to require description; but the annexed
figures represent the front and side views of a less known modification of the same, called a *taper-vice*, which presents some
peculiarities, and is occasionally employed by engineers.

The taper-vice, figs. 840 and 841, is made principally of cast-
iron, and to include within itself the base whereon it stands, that
has at the back two small iron trucks or rollers, so that when
the vice is supported upon them alone, it may be easily rolled
from place to place notwithstanding its weight.   The front limb
of the vice moves on the joint *a*, the back on the joint *b*, so as to

Figs. 840.   841.

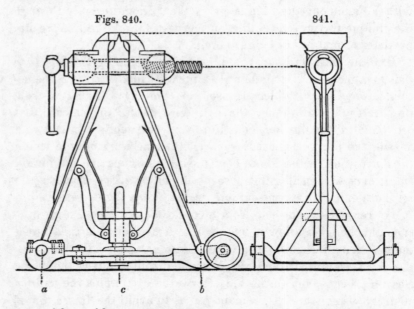

grasp either wide or narrow pieces; but it is by this arrangement
adapted alone to objects that are parallel, which condition, it is
true, is more usually required.   But in the present apparatus, if
the jaws are closed upon a *taper object*, a form that frequently
occurs in steam-engines and similar works, the two parts of the
vice swivel horizontally on a joint, the axis of which is on the
dotted line *c*, so as to place the jaws at an angle corresponding

with that of the work; in fact, the lower part or pedestal of the vice is jointed somewhat like the front axletree of a carriage.

Under ordinary circumstances however, the screw and nut of such a vice would bear very imperfectly upon the moving parts, owing to their obliquity; but this objection is met by cutting a spherical recess in the outside of each half of the vice, and making the collar of the screw, part of a sphere to constitute a ball-and-socket-joint, and also by making the nut a perforated sphere, adapted to a spherical cavity or seat, but with a feather to prevent it from turning round. The two bearings of the screw thus accommodate themselves at the same time, both to the horizontal and vertical obliquities of the jaws. To constrain the two parts of the vice to open in an equal degree, there are two links that are jointed to a collar that slides freely on a cylinder, which latter is in fact the continuation of the joint pin c; and to the collar are also attached the two springs that open the limbs of the vice when the screw is relaxed. This useful apparatus is well adapted to its particular purpose, such as the larger pieces of steam engines, and similar machinery.

The ordinary tail-vices, or standing-vices for heavy engineering and large works, sometimes exceed 100 lbs. in weight; but the average weight of tail-vices, for artizans in general, is from 40 to 60 lbs., and of those for amateurs, from 25 to 35 lbs.

The bench for the vice usually extends throughout the length of the engineer's shop, or vice-loft, and is secured against the windows. The tail-vice is strongly fixed to the bench at the required height, and the tail that extends downwards is fixed in a cleet nailed to the floor, or against one of the legs of the bench, which latter mode is desirable, as the vice is then in better condition to resist the blows of the chisel and hammer, which give rise to much more violence than the act of filing.

Amateurs sometimes employ portable vice-benches, having nests of drawers for containing the files and other tools ; or the vice is attached to the right hand side of the turning-lathe; less frequently the tail-vice is attached to the planing-bench, but it is then requisite it should admit of ready attachment and detachment, to leave the planing-bench at liberty for its ordinary application.

Fig. 842 represents a very convenient mode of mounting the tail-vice upon a tripod stand of cast-iron, which indeed, is in many cases preferable to the wooden benches; as although small, it is sufficiently heavy to ensure firmness, especially as from having only three points of support, all are sure to touch the ground. The tripod readily admits of being shifted about to suit the light, and also of temporary change of height, by lifting-

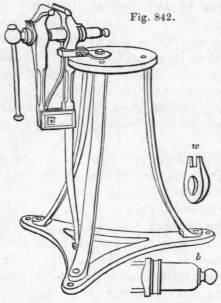

Fig. 842.

pieces added to the feet, when the work is required to be nearer to the eye of the operator. The tripod pedestal serves additionally for the occasional support of a small anvil (when not required for forging,) and also for a paring-knife, (fig. 8, page 26, Vol I.,) when an appropriate wooden cutting-block is added to the tripod.

The table-vice mostly used by watch-makers and similar artizans, resembles that shown in figs. 843 and 844. It is attached to the table by a clamp and screw, which are armed with teeth to give a secure hold; but it is usual to glue a small piece of wood on the table to receive the teeth, and also to prevent the lodgment of small pieces of the work at that part, and the work-table has also a ledge around it, to prevent the work or tools from rolling off. It will be also perceived, that the clamp is surmounted by a small square projection *a*, used as a stake or anvil; and that the jaws of the vice have center holes on one or both sides for the employment of small center drills, that are too delicate for the breast-plate, after the mode described in page 553 of the present volume.

It is in all cases desirable that the jaws of vices should be exactly parallel, both with the edge of the bench and with the ground, in order that the position of the work may be instinctively known; but the tail-vice and bench-vice are liable to various objections that arise from their opening on a center, or as a hinge; for although the jaws are almost parallel when closed, or then nip in preference at the upper edge, when opened widely, the radial position of the jaws causes the lower edges alone to grasp the work, and as in addition, the front jaw moves in a

Fig. 843. | *a*   844.

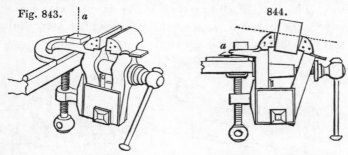

circular arc, a wide object, on being fixed, is necessarily thrown out of the horizontal into an inclined position; each of which imperfect conditions is shown in fig. 844.

The inclination of the two limbs of the vice, likewise depreciates the contact of the screw and nut; this is sometimes remedied by a modification of the ball and socket already described. A more simple mode is the employment of a washer of the form represented at *w*, fig. 842, which is placed beneath the screw; the fork embraces the lower extremity of the curved jaw of the vice, and the washer being thickest in the center, rolls, so that the flat side always touches the entire surface of the shoulder of the screw, and the central and bulged part of the washer touches the limb of the vice, and causes the pressure to be nearly central upon the screw, instead of, as in fig. 844, against the upper edge of the collar of the screw, which is then liable to be bent and strained. The box or internal screw, *b* fig. 842, in which the screw-pin works, has also a power of adjustment or hinge-like rotation, which ensures, here likewise, centrality of pressure. This mode is extremely simple, and worthy of general adoption.

The inconveniences common to vices opening radially on a joint pin, are completely removed in those opening on straight slides; these are called *parallel vices*, because the surfaces of their jaws or chaps, and also the bearings of their screws and nuts, always retain their parallelism; consequently whether the work be wide or narrow, it is always firmly grasped by the chaps, provided the work be itself parallel. One of these vices is represented in fig. 845. The front jaw is forged in continuation of the body of the vice, the whole being of a rectangular form, and receiving at its upper parts the extremities of the pinching screw, which has a semi-cylindrical cover to protect it from the file-dust. The back or sliding jaw of the parallel vice fits accurately upon the upper surface of the principal bar at *a*, and also upon a square bar *b*, placed above it.

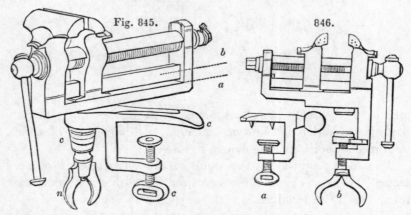

Fig. 845.   846.

Parallel vices are sometimes attached to the table or bench, by clamps that only allow them one fixed position, namely, with the jaws parallel with the bench, as in the bench-vice, fig. 843; but more generally the clamp of a parallel vice, *c c c*, fig. 845, has a vertical socket or hole, and the principal piece of the vice terminates in a round stem that fits the socket, and has a nut *n*, by which means any horizontal inclination may be given to the jaws; they are represented inclined, or they may even be placed at right angles to the bench.

Some parallel vices are attached to the table by ball and socket joints, as shown detached in fig. 846; and various similar schemes have been proposed. The screw-clamp is attached to the table by a thumb-screw *a*, and the clamp terminates in a portion of a sphere; the lower part of the vice has two shallow spherical cups adapted to the ball, so that by turning the thumb-screw *b*, the ball is grasped between the two cups. It is true this kind of parallel vice may be inclined both horizontally and vertically, and therefore, offers much choice of position; but it is too unstable in any to serve for more than very light works, which require but a small application of force.

The jaws of vices are faced with hardened steel and cut like files, so as to hold securely; but works that are nearly finished would be injured by the indentation of the teeth, and are therefore, protected by various kinds of shields or *vice-clamps*, as they are generally called; several of these are shown in figs. 847 to 857.

Vice-clamps, such as fig. 847, are often made of two detached pieces of stout sheet-iron, brass, or copper, of the length of the chaps of the vice, and nearly as wide. The two pieces are pinched between the jaws, and then bent closely around the shoulders of the vice to mould them to the required form, and make them easily retain their positions when the work is removed from between them.

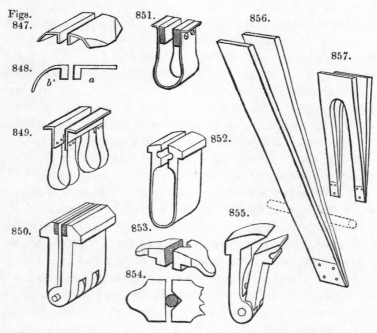

Figs. 847. 851. 856. 857. 848. 849. 852. 850. 853. 855. 854.

Sometimes sheet lead an eighth of an inch thick is used; but such clamps answer better when cast in the rectangular form, as in *a*, fig. 848, and then bent as at *b*; the lead should be hardened with a little antimony, to resemble a very soft type metal (Vol. I., page 277,) and, previously to bending the clamps, they should be heated to about 300° to 400° Fahr., to avoid fracture. This alloy, although harder than lead, is still sufficiently soft to adapt itself to irregularities in the objects held, and the clamps being thick, last longer, and more readily admit of being restored to form by the hammer or rasp, than those made of sheet lead.

Spring or jointed clamps of the several forms, figs. 849 to 857, are also made.   Fig. 849 represents two stout rectangular pieces of metal, united by two springs which pass on the sides of the vice-screw; these open to a considerable distance, and from the flexibility of the springs, readily adapt themselves either to thick or thin pieces.

The clamp, fig. 850, is made in two pieces of cast or wrought iron, jointed like a wide door hinge, and with a spring to separate the two parts to a small extent; this clamp has a piece of soft steel or iron attached to each half, to make a fine close mouth, suitable to delicate works and thin plates.

Fig. 851, is a narrow spring clamp made of one piece of steel, to which are attached pieces of wood or brass, that may be renewed when worn out of shape; the clamp, fig. 852, is made of one piece of steel, and formed with a crease to hold small wires horizontally; 853 and 854 are detached clamps, one plain the other with an angular notch, that serve for holding round and other pieces vertically; 852 and 853 are each useful in holding round bars whilst they are being tapped, and not unfrequently their inner edges are cut with file teeth, after which they are hardened and tempered.   As shown in fig. 855, some of the vice-clamps are made with jaws inclined at about 30 degrees to the perpendicular, to serve for holding chamfer bars for slides, and various bevelled works; these clamps have the effect of placing the chamfered edge nearly horizontal, which latter is the most convenient position for the act of filing.

Fig. 856 are the long sloping clamps, consisting of two pieces of wood bevelled at their extremities, and united by an external strap of sheet iron or steel, which is riveted to them; should they fail to spring open sufficiently, a stick is thrust between the two parts, as shown by the dotted lines; fig. 857 are upright wooden clamps, which are forked so that the tails proceed vertically, one on each side of the screw of the vice.   The sloping wood clamps commonly used by gun-makers, are made long enough to rest upon the floor, and when the one end of the gun-barrel is pinched between them, the other end is supported either by a vertical prop, called a *horse*, or by a horizontal wooden horse, fixed to the bench at about the same height as the jaws of the vice.

Wooden clamps, although of great convenience, are open to a

drawback that is sometimes acutely felt, as when small pieces are briskly filed whilst held in wooden clamps, owing to the slow conducting power of the wood, the works become so hot as to be inconvenient to be held in the fingers, but which is continually required, as it is necessary at short intervals to remove the work from the vice, for the purpose of testing, by the straight edge, square, or other measuring instruments, the progress made. Sometimes the work is grasped between slips of leather or card, that are simply held to the vice by the penetration of its teeth. Leather and card are however, partly open to the same objection as wood clamps, from which the metal clamps, owing to their superior power of conducting heat, are nearly free.

A great number of small works are more conveniently filed, whilst they are held with the left hand, the file being then managed exclusively with the right; this enables the artizan more easily to judge of the position of the file. In such cases, a piece of wood *f*, fig. 858, called a *filing-block*, is fixed in the table or tail-vice, and square, round, and similar pieces, are rested in one of several notches made in the block with a triangular file. If the works are rectangular, or have flat surfaces, they are held quite at rest; if they are circular, they are continually rotated, as will be explained, and if they are wide and flat, they are laid on the flat surface of the filing-block *f*, against a ledge or projection represented on the *lower* side of the block, which is then placed upwards.

Pieces that are sufficiently long and bulky, are held upon the filing-block by the hand unassistedly; but small and short works are more usually fixed in some description of hand-vice, and applied in the position shown in fig. 858, and the vice being larger than the work, serves as a handle, and affords a better grasp.

For works of larger size the hand-vices are progressively larger, as in 859 and 860; some of them have wooden handles. Almost all the hand-vices have fly nuts to be twisted with the fingers, but the most powerful, which sometimes weigh as much as about three pounds, have square nuts that are fastened by a key or spanner *s*. Occasionally, to ensure a strong grip, one ear of the ordinary fly-nut is pinched in the tail-vice, whilst the hand-vice is twisted bodily round; but unless due caution is used, either the vice may be strained, or the screw broken, from the great purchase thus obtained.

Hand-vices are not however, in all cases employed ; but small wires and other pieces are also held in a species of pliers, fig. 861, called *pin-tongs*, or *sliding-tongs*, which are closed by a ferule that is drawn down the stem. Fig. 862 shows another variety of this kind, that has no joint, but springs open by elasticity alone when the ring *r* is drawn back.

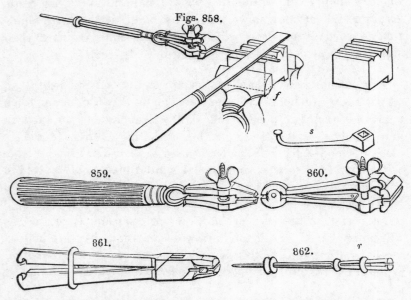

Figs. 858.

The small pin-vice, fig. 858, is used by watchmakers in filing up small pins and other cylindrical objects, the jaws are not united by a joint, but are formed in one piece with the stem of the vice, the end that constitutes the jaws being divided or forked ; the screw and stem are each perforated throughout, that the ends of long wires may be filed ; and the stem is octangular that the pin-vice may be readily twisted to and fro between the fingers and thumb of the left hand, whilst the file is reciprocated by the right hand, and in this manner a considerable approach to the cylindrical form is obtained.

Independently of the rapid movement of the hand-vice to and fro on its axis, simultaneously with the strokes of the file, the two hands being moved together, the hand-vice is thrown progressively forward with the fore-finger about a quarter of a turn at nearly every alternation, so as to bring all parts of the work alike under the operation of the file. But as it is in this case important that the work should be pinched exactly central in the vice, or so that the axis of the work may pass through the axis or central line of the vice, a central angular groove is frequently made in each jaw of the hand-vice to give the work, without trial, a nearly axial position. This is more usual in the narrow vices, fig. 859, known as *dog-nose* or *pig-nose* hand-vices, than in those with wide or *cross chaps*, 858 and 860.

Many circular works that were formerly thus filed, are now, from motives of expedition and accuracy, more commonly executed in the turning-lathe, since the great extension in the use of this machine, which has become nearly as general as the vice or the file itself; but frequent occasions still remain in which the hand-vice and file are thus employed, and it is curious to see how those accustomed to the rotation of the different kinds of hand-vice with the wrist, will in this manner reduce a square or irregular piece to the circular section.

In the pin-tongs, fig. 862, besides the facility of turning the instrument round with the fingers, from the reverse end having a center and pulley, the same spring tongs serve conveniently as forceps for holding small drills to be worked with the drill-bow, and also for other purposes in watch-work.

Numerous flat works are too large, thin, and irregular in their superficies to admit of being fixed in the various kinds of bench and table-vices that have been described, and if so fixed, there would be risk of bending such thin pieces by the pressure of the vice applied against the edges of the work, consequently, different methods are employed in fixing them.

The largest flat works are simply laid on the naked surface of the work-bench, and temporarily held by half a dozen or more pins or nails driven into the bench. The pins should be as close to the margin as possible, and yet below the surface of the work, so as not to interfere with the free application of the file; it is frequently necessary to lift the work out of its temporary bed for its examination with measuring instruments, and advantage is taken of these opportunities for sweeping away with a small brush (like a nail-brush for the dressing-table,) any loose filings that may have got beneath the work, and prevent it from lying flat.

For thin flat works of smaller size, the filing-board, fig. 863, is a convenient appendage, it measures six or eight inches square, and has a stout rib on the under side, by which it is fixed in the vice. Such thin works are required to be frequently corrected with the hammer, and also to be turned over, in order that their opposite sides may be alternately filed, so as to follow and compensate for, the continual changes they undergo in the act of being filed. In some instances the work is held down with one or more screw clamps or hand-vices as represented; this is needful when pins would bruise the margins of nearly finished works, and a card or a few thicknesses of paper are then interposed to protect the object from the teeth of the vice.

Figs. 863.   864.

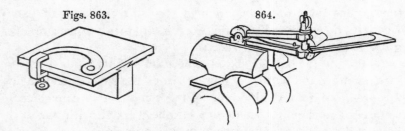

In filing thin flat works, such as the thin handles or scales of penknives and razors, and the thin steel plates used in pocket knives, the Sheffield cutlers generally resort to the contrivance represented in fig. 864, and known as a *flatting-vice*. A hand vice is fixed, in the ordinary tail-vice or table vice, by the one jaw with the screw uppermost, so that the jaws of the hand-vice are horizontal. The thin scale to be filed is then placed on a flat piece of metal not less than a quarter of an inch thick, and the two are pinched together by the one corner, so that all the remaining surface may be free to the action of the files, and the work is readily shifted about to allow all parts to be successively operated upon. The facility of changing the position is particularly useful in working on pieces of tortoiseshell, buckhorn, and other materials of irregular form and thickness, to which the filing boards with pins or clamps would less conveniently apply.

As before observed, the one face of the small filing-block *f*, fig. 858, is also used for very small thin works, and which are prevented slipping from the file by the wooden ledge, or by pins driven in.   In many instances, also, thin works are held upon a piece of cork, such as the bung for a large cask, beneath which is glued a square piece of wood, that the cork may be held in the vice without being compressed.   The elasticity of the cork allows the work to become somewhat embedded by the pressure of the file, between which and the surface-friction, it is sufficiently secured for the purpose without pins.

SECT. IV.—INSTRUCTIONS FOR FILING A FLAT SURFACE, UNDER THE GUIDANCE OF THE STRAIGHT-EDGE, AND OF THE TRIAL-PLATE, OR PLANOMETER.

In following out the subject of the instructions for the use of the file, it is proposed, first to explain that which may be called the manual process of producing a true or plane surface on a piece of cast iron of moderate dimensions, say four or five inches wide and eight or ten inches long; and although the entire routine is only required for surfaces of the most exact and finished kind, the same general treatment, when discontinued at certain stages, is equally suited to various other works in mechanism, that only demand by comparison an inferior degree of precision: the routine is also nearly the same for surfaces larger or smaller than that referred to.

Before any effective progress can be made in filing flat works, the operator must be provided with the means of testing the progressive advance of the work, he should therefore possess a true straight-edge, and a true surface-plate.   The straight-edges used by smiths are generally of steel, and although they have sometimes a nearly acute edge, it is much more usual to give them moderate width; thus, in steel straight-edges from one to four feet in length, the width of the edge is from one-sixteenth to one-fourth of an inch, and in cast-iron straight-edges from six to nine feet in length, the width is usually two to three inches.

The straight-edge is used for trying the surface that is under correction, along its four margins, across its two diagonals, and at various intermediate parts, which respective lines, if all exact, denote the surface to be correct; but the straight-edge alone is a tedious and scarcely sufficient test, and when great accuracy is desired, it is almost imperative to have at least one very exact plane metallic surface, or surface-plate, (the *plano-mètre* of the French,) by which the general condition of the surface under formation may be more quickly and accurately tested at one operation : and to avoid confusion of terms, it is proposed in all cases, when speaking of the instrument, to employ the French appellation *plano-mètre* or rather planometer, which is exact and distinctive.

The flat piece of cast-iron, intended to be operated upon, having been chipped all over, as described in page 850, a coarse hand-file, of as large dimensions as the operator can safely manage is selected, and in the commencement, the rough edges or ridges left by the chipping-chisel are levelled, those parts however being principally filed, that appear from the straight-edge to be too high.

The strokes of the file are directed sometimes square across as on a fixed line, or obliquely in both directions alternately ; at other times the file is traversed a little to the right or left during the stroke, so as to make it apply to a portion of the work exceeding the width of the file. These changes in the applications of the file are almost constantly given, in order that the various positions may cross each other in all possible directions, and prevent the formation of partial hollows. The work is tried at short intervals with the straight-edge ; and the eye directed on a level with the work to be tested, readily perceives the points that are most prominent. After the rough errors have been partially removed, the work is taken from the vice, and struck edgeways upon the bench to shake off any loose filings, and it is then inverted on the planometer, which should be fully as large or larger than the work. As, however, it cannot be told by the eye which points of the work touch the planometer, this instrument is coated all over with some colouring matter, such as pulverised red chalk mixed with a little oil, and then the touching places become coloured.

In all probability the work will at first assimilate so imperfectly with the planometer, that it will only rest thereon at its two highest points, most likely at the two corners of the one diagonal, and when pressure is applied at the two other corners alternately, the work will probably ride or rock on the two points of temporary support. The work is slightly rubbed on the surface-plate, and then picks up at its highest points some of the red matter; it is refixed in the vice, and the file is principally used in the vicinity of the coloured parts, with the occasional test of the straight-edge, and after a short period the work is again tried on the planometer.

Should the same two points still become reddened, they are further reduced with the file, but it is probable the work may be found to rest upon larger portions of its surface, or upon three or four points instead of two only; and if so, all the marked places are reduced in a small degree before the succeeding trial. This process is continually repeated, and if watchfully performed, it will be found that the points of contact will become gradually increased, say from two to four, to six or eight, then to a dozen or more, and so on.

In this, or rather an earlier stage of the work, the smith's plane for metal is often advantageously used in connexion with the file. The general structure of the plane is shown by the figure and description on page 483, and it is employed much after the manner of the joiner's plane, but it may be used at pleasure lengthways, crossways, or diagonally, without any interference from grain or fibre as in wood work. The grooved or roughing-out cutter is employed in the commencement because it more readily penetrates the work, and a few strokes are given to crop off the highest points of the surface, the furrows made by the serrated cutter are then nearly removed with the file, which acts more expeditiously although less exactly than the plane, and in this manner the grooved plane iron and the coarse file are alternately used. In the absence of the planometer, the metal plane assumes a greatly-increased degree of importance.

As the work becomes gradually nearer to truth, the grooved cutter is exchanged for that with a continuous or smooth edge, a second-cut, or bastard file, hand is also selected, and the same alternation of planing aad filing is persevered in, the plane serving as it were to direct the file, until it is found that the plane iron acts too vigorously, as it is scarcely satisfied with merely scraping over the surface of the cast-iron; but when it acts it removes a shaving having a nearly measurable thickness, and therefore, although the hand-plane may not injure the general truth of the surface, it will prevent the work from being so delicately acted upon, as the continuance of the process now demands;

a smoother hand file is consequently alone employed in furthering the work.

If the piece of cast-iron should have been turned in the lathe, or planed in the planing machine, instead of having been wrought entirely with the chipping-chisel, plane and file, the former instructions would be uncalled for, as the remaining steps alone would remain to be followed. Unless indeed the work had been so imperfectly fixed, as to have been at first strained, and thence become distorted on being released from the machine: on the latter supposition the grosser errors would probably require correction with the bastard file, before the smooth file could be judiciously used.

The necessity of the convex form of the file will now be rendered most striking, as were the file absolutely flat on its face, it would be scarcely possible to reduce with it any small and isolated spot that might become coated with the red chalk from off the planometer; but as the file is a little rounded, any precise spot on the work may be acted upon, as the end of the file may be pressed with the fingers of the left hand on the exact spot to be reduced, whilst the remainder of the file is held just out of contact with the rest of the surface.

When however the points of bearing become numerous, the file cannot even thus be managed with sufficient discrimination, and notwithstanding the best efforts it will act on too large a part, and thereby lengthen, or it might be said altogether to prevent the complete correction of the work, because the file is not sufficiently under control. Before the file has assumed this questionable tendency, it is politic and usual as a measure of economy, to discontinue the use of the file, and to prosecute the work with a scraper, which having a sharp *edge*, instead of a broad and abrading *surface*, may be made to act with far more decision, on any, even the most minute spot or point. A worn-out triangular file, ground at the end on all the faces, so as to make thin keen edges, is generally used as the scraper; this should be keenly sharpened on an oil-stone, so as to act without requiring much pressure, which would only fill the work with striæ or utters.

The continual reduction of all the points, which are sufficiently prominent to pick up the colouring matter from the planometer, is now persevered in with the scraper instead of the file, and precisely in the same manner, except as regards the change of the tool; and if the process have been carefully performed throughout, it will be found at the conclusion that if the work and planometer are both wiped clean, and rubbed hard together, that the high points of the work will be somewhat burnished, giving to the work a finely mottled character.

In producing metallic surfaces, the constant effort should be to reduce all the high places with as much expedition as circumstances will admit, but avoiding, on the other hand, that energetic use of the tool, which may too hastily alter the condition of the surface, and in expunging the known errors, induce others equal in degree but differently situated. Throughout the work, attempt should be made to keep the points of bearing, whether few or many, as nearly equidistant as may be, instead of allowing them to become grouped together in large patches.

In respect to the tools there should be a gradual diminution in their cutting powers, and also of the vigour with which they are used, as although energy is wise at the commencement of the work, it should gradually subside into watchfulness and caution towards the conclusion. The periods of alternation between the hand-plane and the file, and also the times when these are successively rejected, in favour of the scraper as the finishing tool, must be in great measure left to the judgment of the operator.

There should be a frequent examination of the work by means of the straight-edge and planometer, which latter should at all times be *evenly* tinted with the colour. At the commencement it is necessary the coating of red stuff on the planometer should be moderately abundant, so as to mark even those places which are minutely distant, but with the continued application of the work, the colouring matter will be gradually removed from the planometer, and which is desirable, as towards the conclusion the quantity of red should be small, so as but faintly to mark the summits of each little eminence, the number and equality of which are dependent on the perfection of the planometer, and the steady persevering watchfulness of the operator.

It is not to be supposed that it is in every case needful to proceed in the careful and progressive mode just described, as the parts of different works require widely different degrees of perfection as to flatness. For instance, in many it is only necessary they should be clean and bright, and have the semblance of flatness, with such even the straight-edge is little if at all used as a test. Those surfaces by which the stationary parts of framings are attached, require a moderate degree of accuracy, such as may be comparable with the perfection in the hewn stones of a bridge or other massive edifice, which require to be flat, in order that they may bear fairly against each other, as without a certain degree of truth the stone might break from the unequal strain to which it would be exposed.

The flat parts of metallic works, if similarly imperfect, would bend, and perhaps distort the remainder; but although it is of great importance that bearing surfaces should be out of winding, or not twisted; it is by no means important that such bearing surfaces should be continuous, as a few equally scattered bearing points frequently suffice. Thus it was the common practice before the general introduction of the engineer's planing-machine, to make fillets or chipping places around the margins of the bearing surfaces of castings, which fillets alone were corrected with the chisel and coarse file, for the juxtaposition of the larger pieces or frame work of machines, the intermediate spaces being left depressed and out of contact. This mode sufficed, provided the pressure of the screw-bolts could not, by collapsing the hollow places, distort the castings, with which view chipping places were also generally left around the bolt-holes of the work, this method greatly reduced the labour of *getting up* such works by hand; but fillets and chipping places are now in a great measure abandoned. Smaller and more delicate works, requiring somewhat greater accuracy than those just described, are left from smoother files, but in most cases without the necessity of scraping; but the rectilinear slides and moving parts of accurate machinery, and the trial or surface-plates of the mechanician, require beyond all other works, the most dexterous use of the file and other means, from which it is again repeated, grinding should be entirely excluded.

Until very recently, when the points of bearing had been so multiplied by the file and scraper, as not to exceed about half an inch in average distance, and that a still higher degree of accuracy was desired; it was the ordinary practice to attempt the obliteration of these minute errors by the method of grinding. Supposing only one piece or surface to have been required, it then became necessary to grind the work upon the planometer itself, but to avoid the necessity of so injurious a practice, it was usual, when practicable, to make three similar pieces at one time, in order that, when all three had been separately filed and scraped to agree pretty nearly with the straight-edge and plano-meter, the three pieces might then be mutually employed in the correction of one another, by grinding the faces successively together with emery-powder and water.

The one piece was laid down horizontally, wetted all over with water, and then strewed with emery powder, after which, one of the other surfaces was inverted upon it, and rubbed about in various ways with longitudinal, lateral, and curling or circular strokes, on the supposition that as the two pieces came into contact respectively at their highest points, these highest points became mutually abraded, with a tendency to reduce them to the general level. After a short period, the top surface was removed, fresh emery and water were applied, and the third surface was rubbed upon the first ; after which, all three were variously interchanged, by placing every one in succession as the lower surface, and rubbing the two others upon the lower, until it was considered from the uniform but deceptive grey tint thus produced, that the errors in all were expunged, and that the three surfaces were all true.

It is however, considered quite unnecessary to enter more into detail on a process that may be considered to be nearly obsolete, as regards the production of plane metallic surfaces, especially as at a future part of this Volume, the practice of grinding will be noticed, in reference to surfaces requiring inferior exactness, and consisting of materials that do not admit of the employment of the file and scraper.

That two surfaces which are *very nearly accurate*, if ground together for a *very short time*, do in some degree correct each other, is true, but it has been long and well known, that a con-tinuance of the grinding is very dangerous, and apt to lead the one surface to become convex, and the other concave in a nearly equal degree, and on this account, three pieces were usually operated upon that the third might act as an umpire, as although two pieces possessing exactly opposite errors may appear quite to agree, the third cannot agree with each of these two, until they have all been made alike, and quite plane surfaces.

But the entire process of grinding although apparently good is so fraught with uncertainty, that accurate mechanicians have long agreed that the *less grinding* that is employed on recti-linear works the better, and Mr. Whitworth has recently shown in the most satisfactory manner,* that in such works grinding is *entirely unnecessary,* and may with the greatest advantage be dispensed with, as the further prosecution of the scraping process is quite sufficient to lead to the limit of attainable accuracy ; the only condition being, that the mode of continually referring the work to the planometer, and scraping down the points sufficiently high to be coloured, should be steadily persevered in, until the completion of the process, and works thus treated, assume a much higher degree of excellence than is attainable by grinding.

Mr. Whitworth stated a further and equally important advantage to result from the discontinuance of grinding, as regards the slides and moving parts of machinery.   Some of the grinding powder is always absorbed in the pores of the metal, by which the metallic surfaces are converted into species of laps, so that the slides and works carry with them the sources of their depreciation and even destruction.   The author's previous experience had so fully prepared him for admission of the soundness of these views, that in his own workshop he immediately adopted the suggestion of accomplishing all accurate rectilinear works by the continuance of scraping, to the entire exclusion of grinding.

SECT. V.—INSTRUCTIONS FOR ORIGINATING STRAIGHT-EDGES AND TRIAL-PLATES, OR PLANOMETERS.

The remarks hitherto offered on producing a flat surface were based upon the supposition that the operator is in possession of a good straight-edge, and a good surface or planometer, and which is usual under ordinary circumstances ; but it may be considered necessary that the more difficult case should be placed before the reader, of originating the planometer itself, by which alone can he render himself independent of external assistance ; the previous observations will greatly abridge the description.

* In a Paper read before the British Association for the Advancement of Science. Glasgow, 1840.

First, to originate a straight-edge.—In originating a straight-edge, it is judicious to prepare the ground, so far as possible, with the means possessed by every joiner ; and accordingly, three pieces of hard straight-grained mahogany should be first planed as straight as possible with the joiner's plane.   Calling the three pieces, for distinction, A B and C, when they are compared, A and B may appear to agree everywhere, even when one of them is changed end for end: this shows A and B to be either both straight, or else the one concave, the other convex ; but C may be unlike either of them.   C is then adjusted also to A, and will therefore become a duplicate of B ; but when the duplicates B and C are compared, it may be found that they touch in the middle, and admit light between them at the ends, showing each to be convex.   The central parts both of B and C, which are erroneous in the *same direction*, are then each reduced in a nearly equal degree, until in fact, the transmission of light is prevented throughout their length, even when they are reversed, and by which the condition of each will be somewhat improved.

Next, to ascertain whether B and C, when thus improved, are each pretty near to the truth.   The third, or A, is fitted to B, making A and B as nearly as may be, counterparts of one another ; and if A, when thus altered, should also agree with the third or C, all are true : but this can scarcely yet be strictly the case.   And the routine is therefore continually repeated of reducing in an equal degree the two which may show evidence of being nearly alike, (either both convex, or both concave,) and then by fitting the third to one of the corrected two, as a test by which to try, if they not alone agree with each other but likewise agree with the third, or the test; as the work can only be perfect when all three admit of being compared, without any want of contact being observable in any of the three comparisons.

If the trying-plane is carefully manipulated, the three pieces will, in three or four repetitions of the series of operations, become as nearly accurate as the nature of the tools and of the method will admit ; and then, either the best of the three wooden straight-edges, or all three of them, may be used as the preliminary test in making the steel straight-edges. *

---

* The more common practice of the joiner is to operate upon only two pieces, each of which is first planed until they agree together when placed *edge to edge* in the ordinary manner, or in one plane.   The two pieces are now placed *side by*

Sometimes the metal straight-edges are wide strips cut off from a sheet of steel of hard quality : if forged from a bar of steel, the hammering should be continued until the metal is quite cold, to render it hard and elastic; and in some instances, the straight-edge, when partly finished, is hardened and tempered before its edges are completed.   In all cases, if the one edge is to be chamfered, this should be done in an early stage, as it is very apt to throw the work crooked ; and the sides are always filed, or otherwise finished, before any great progress is made in correcting the edges.   When three straight-edges are made at one time, the three are generally united by temporary pins through their ends, to make one thick bar, and are then corrected in the mass as the first stage.

The work having been thus far prepared, the wooden straight-edge is rubbed with a dry lump of red chalk, that it may leave evidence of the points of contact.   A coarse file is first used, and it may for a time be assisted by the hand-plane; the size and length of the file are gradually decreased, and after a time, it will be found that the wooden straight-edge is no longer sufficiently delicate to afford the required test.   When all three of the steel straight-edges have been brought collectively to a state of approximate truth, they are separated, and wrought the one from the other, precisely in the same order that was described in reference to the wooden straight-edges; but as on the steel a very small and smooth file may be used, the process of correction may be carried with the file much higher upon steel straight-edges, than upon metallic surfaces.   In addition to the mode of examining straight-edges by the transmission of light, they are also compared by laying them two at a time upon a true bench or surface, and rubbing them together without colouring matter ; the high places will then mutually rub each other sufficiently to

---

side, and their edges are placed in agreement at the extremities, so that the fingers, passed tranversely across their ends, cannot feel any want of continuity of surface ; in other words, cannot feel the joint. If, whilst thus placed, the joint is also inappreciable to the sense of touch at various intermediate parts of the length of both pieces, the work is correct, and the two are straight.

From the very precise action of the trying-plane, the wooden straight-edge may perhaps be equally well produced by the methods requiring either two or three to be made ; but the method of making three at once is given in the text, because it is always followed in metal works, in consequence of the different nature of the working tools, and of the abstract superiority of the method.

leave a small degree of brightness, that may be easily observed on a careful scrutiny; and as both edges of every straight-edge are commonly wrought, the investigation becomes amplified and improved, from there being six comparisons instead of three.

A little grinding is sometimes resorted to in completing steel straight-edges: it is less objectionable with steel, than with cast iron and other metals which are softer and also more porous than steel, but the process of grinding being very difficult of control is not desirable; and as very small files may be used, and with nice discrimination, in correcting straight-edges, the scraper although useful here likewise, does not present the same importance as in correcting wide surfaces or planometers.

Secondly, to originate a surface-plate or planometer.—This process requires that the operator should be in possession of at least one very good straight-edge; one of a series of three that have been accurately tested in the manner just described. The present case also demands, like the last, that three pieces should be operated upon, in order that the same correctional method may be brought into effect.

The planometer should be a plate of hard cast-iron, having ribs at the back to prevent its bending, either from its own weight, or from taking an unequal bearing on the bench or other support. Generally a deep rib extends around the four margins of the planometer, and one, two, or more intermediate and shallower ribs are added, which divide the back into rectangular compartments, as in fig. 865; this planometer would rest upon the bench around its edges, or on four prominent points at the corners represented black. It has been recently proposed by Mr. Whit-

Figs. 865. 866. 867.

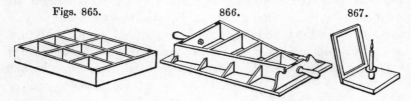

worth, that the ribs should be placed obliquely and made to converge to three points of bearing, as in fig. 866, which is a much better plan, as the planometer is then at all times supported on precisely the same points, notwithstanding the inequality of the bench, which can scarcely be the case when four feet are used.

The handles are added at the ends, that the planometer may be readily inverted; in order that it may be applied upon such heavy works as it would be inconvenient to lift, and then immediately replaced on its feet when returned to the work-bench.

In the absence of the planing-machine, the three castings for the planometers would be chipped all over and roughly filed, and in this case the smith's plane for metal would render most important service for a considerable period. A good wooden straight-edge is now convenient, as when rubbed with red chalk it denotes the high places very effectively, and should be applied at various parts of the length and width, and also obliquely; and indeed a small thick block of beech-wood or mahogany, planed very flat as a surface and rubbed with chalk, will serve to hasten the process of obliterating the coarser errors.

In due time, the plane, the coarse file, and the wooden straight-edge, would all be laid aside, and the work would be prosecuted with a smoother file, under the direction of a metal straight-edge, and which if coloured must be also greased to make the red matter adhere. This part of the work may be carried to no mean degree of perfection, as a very correct judgment of a plane surface can be obtained from a good straight-edge applied in all directions, as the eye readily measures the comparative width of the line of light transmitted, and the fingers also appreciate, when the straight-edge is slightly rotated or rubbed sideways, which points of the work are the highest, and give rise to most friction.

One surface, which may be called A, having been corrected very carefully with the file and straight-edge, may be now smeared with red stuff and oil, and employed to hasten the correction of the second piece, or B, and the third, or C, until these two are about as near to truth as the first, or A; the three are afterwards mutually operated upon under the guidance of colouring matter. At this stage of the work it will soon become necessary to discard the file in favour of the scraping-tool, in using which it will be found very convenient to remove by a paper screen, the glare of the bright metallic surface, so as to enable the little patches of colour to be more readily observed. The screen, fig. 867, consists of a small frame of wood, eight to ten inches square, covered with writing-paper, and attached to a small board; the paper is inclined some ten degrees towards the operator, and at night a short piece of candle is placed in the center of the board or pedestal as shown.

The three plates having been, as before observed, brought into nearly the same preparatory state, it is to be now judged of by the straight-edge, whether all three are nearly alike, or *lean to the same kind of error.*   Thus, supposing the pieces A and B to have a tolerably equal disposition to convexity, or that when placed in contact they rest in the center, but fail to touch around the margin, then A and B are each a little reduced in the middle until the tendency to rotate on the center is gone; A and B will be then each a shade nearer to truth than before.   The third piece, or C, is fitted to A, after which, supposing for a moment A and B to be each a true, or a plane surface, C would become also a plane surface, and the task would be then completed. Perfection is not, however, nearly so easy of attainment, and it is almost certain that although A and B may be *counterparts*, they will not be *planes ;* presuming therefore that C has been fitted to A, it is almost certain that C will not fit B.   (This may be called routine One.)

Considering, therefore, that now A and C are the two most nearly alike, or that both are proved to be convex, these are the two upon which an equal amount of correction is this time attempted, until they become counterparts, or fit well together ; and the third piece, or B, becomes the arbiter in this stage of the work. (This may be called routine Two.)

We will lastly assume that B, when altered until it fits C, does not quite fit to A, but that B and C present an equal departure from truth, and are still both convex; then B and C are altered in an equal degree until they appear to be perfect counterparts, and this time A, when fitted to one of them, shows whether the whole three are planes, or that two of the pieces are convex and one concave. (This may be called routine Three.)

The method of comparison will probably be rendered somewhat more evident, by the following tabular view of the processes.

Routine One.	Routine Two.	Routine Three.
A. B. Counterparts.	A. C. Counterparts.	B. C. Counterparts.
C. Arbiter.	B. Arbiter.	A. Arbiter.

The inspection of the letters in three routines will farther show, that every one of the three surfaces admits of comparison with the two others, and that the abstract method is to fit together those two which *appear to have the same error*, by altering those two in an equal degree, after which, the third piece, when fitted to one of the other two pieces, incontestably proves whether all three are planes ; as this cannot be the case until all three agree together in every comparison. The attainment of true planes will be found to require several repetitions of the three routines, but towards the conclusion increasing care will be continually required, in order that no degeneration may insidiously occur, to disappoint the hope of the progress towards perfection being steadily on the increase.

This correctional process, which is precisely analogous to the mutual correction of three straight-edges, is somewhat familiar to mechanicians, but the process is obviously very much more tedious than the origination of straight-edges, on account of the great increase of the surface to be operated upon, and the circumstance that the quantity taken in excess from any part, must be amended by reducing every other part of that surface in an equal degree.

For the sake of simplicity it has been supposed throughout the description that the two *convex* pieces were in each case selected for correction ; but this is immaterial, as the result would be the same if the two *concave* pieces were wrought, or the one and other pair alternately, as circumstances may accidentally suggest.

The three planometers having been made as perfect as the skill and patience of the operator will admit, one of them should be carefully laid aside, and only used in the most guarded manner in the reproduction of other planometers, or the correction of those in general use ; which latter process will be found occasionally requisite, but the less frequently so, if the instrument is equally worn by rubbing the work to be examined, at *all parts* of the planometer, instead of upon the *central part* alone. And a true surface or standard having been once obtained, it should be most scrupulously preserved, as it will be found very considerably less troublesome to copy a good standard, than to originate the three standards themselves from which the one is to be reserved.

SECT. VI.—INSTRUCTIONS FOR FILING RECTILINEAR WORKS, IN WHICH
SEVERAL OR ALL OF THE SUPERFICIES HAVE TO BE WROUGHT.

The former instructions have been restricted to the supposition that only one of the superficies of the work was required to be made plane or flat; but it frequently happens in rectangular works, such as the piece A B C, fig. 868, that all six surfaces, namely, the top and bottom A, *a*, the two sides B, *b*, and the two ends C, *c*, all require to be corrected and made in rectangular arrangement, (the surfaces *a*, *b*, *c*, being necessarily concealed from view,) and therefore some particulars of the ordinary method of producing these six surfaces will be added; and the former remarks on pages 500 to 503 on squaring thick and thin works in wood may be also consulted.

The general rule is first to file up the two largest and principal faces A and *a*, and afterwards the smaller faces or edges B *b*, and

Figs. 868.

869.　870.

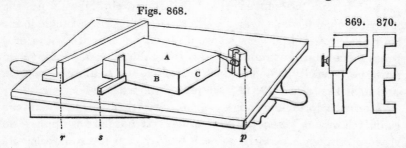

r　　*s*　　　　　　　*p*

C *c*. The principal faces A *a*, especially when the pieces are thin, must be proceeded with for a period simultaneously, because of the liability of all materials to spring and alter in their form with the progressive removal of their substance, and on this account the work, whether thick or thin, is frequently prepared to a certain stage at *every* part, before the final correction is attempted of any *one* part.

The straight-edge and surface-plate are required, to prove that each of the faces A and *a* is a plane surface, and the callipers or a similar gage is also needful, to prove them to be in parallelism. Callipers, unless provided with set screws, are very liable to be accidentally shifted, and it is needful to use them with caution, otherwise their elasticity, arising from the length of their legs, is apt to deceive. There are gages, such as fig. 869, with short parallel jaws that open as on a slide, and are fixed by a side screw; and a still more simple and very safe plan, is to file two rectangular notches in a piece of sheet-iron or steel, as in fig. 870, the one notch exactly of the finished thickness the work is required to possess, the other a little larger to serve as the coarse or preliminary gage.

Sometimes the one face of the work, or A, having been filed moderately flat, a line is scored around the four sides of the work with a metal marking-gage, the same in principle as the marking-gage of the joiner, fig. 342, page 487. At other times the corrected face A, is laid on a planometer larger than the work, as represented, (neglecting the inversion,) and the marginal line is scribed on the four edges, by a scribing point p, fig. 868, projecting from the sides of a little metal pedestal that bears truly on the surface-plate.

Chamfers or bevelled edges are then filed around the four edges of the face a, exactly to terminate on the scribed lines, the central part of a, can be reduced with but little watchfulness, until the marginal chamfers are nearly obliterated. This saves much of the time that would be otherwise required for investigating the progress made; but towards the last, the callipers and planometer must be carefully and continually used, to assist in rendering A and a, at the same time parallel and plane surfaces.

The two principal edges, B b, are then filed under the guidance of a square ; the one arm of the square is applied on A, or a, at pleasure, as in joinery work ; or if the square have a thick back, it may be placed on the planometer, as at s, fig. 868 ; if preferred, the work may be supported on its edge B upon the planometer, and the back square also applied, as at s, in which case the entire length of the blade of the square comes into operation, and the irregularities of the plane B, are at the same time rendered obvious by the planometer.

Another very convenient test has been recommended for this part of the work—namely, a stout bar, such as r, fig. 868, the two neighbouring sides of which have been made quite flat and also square with each other. When the work and trial-bar, (or rectangulometer,) are both laid down, the one side of the bar presents a truly perpendicular face, which may, by the intervention of colouring matter, be made to record on the work itself, the points in which B differs from a rectangular and vertical plane. *

When the edge B has been rendered plane and square, the opposite edge b, may in its turn be marked either with the gage or scribing-point at pleasure ; the four edges of b may be then chamfered, and the entire surface of b is afterwards corrected, (as in producing the second face a,) under the guidance of

* See Smith's Panorama of Science, Vol. I., page 30.

the square, callipers, rectangular bar, and surface-plate, or some of these tests.

The ends C c, now claim attention, and the marginal line is scribed around these by the aid of the back square alone; but the general method so closely resembles that just described as not to call for additional particulars.

Should one edge of the work be inclined, or bevelled, as in the three following figures, in which the works are shaded, to distinguish them from the tools, the rectangular parts are always first wrought, and then the bevelled edges, the angles being denoted by a bevel instead of a square; either with a bevel having a movable blade, as in fig. 871, or by a bevelled templet made of sheet-metal, as in figs. 872, or 873, which latter cannot get

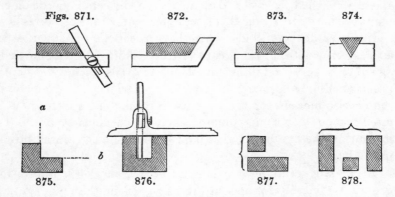

Figs. 871.　　　872.　　　873.　　　874.

875.　　　876.　　　877.　　　878.

misadjusted. The bevelled edge of the work, is also applied if possible on the planometer; in fact the planometer and bevel are conjointly used as the tests. Bevelled works are either held in the vice by aid of the chamfer-clamps, fig. 855, page 859, or they are laid in wooden troughs, with grooves so inclined, that the edge to be filed is placed horizontally. Triangular bars of equilateral section are thus filed in troughs, the sides of which meet at an angle of 60 degrees, as in fig. 874.

The succeeding examples of works with many plane surfaces are objects with rebates and grooves, as represented in figs. 875 to 878. Pieces of the sections 875, and 876, supposing them to be short, would in general be formed in the solid, either from forgings or castings, as the case might be; the four exterior and more accessible faces would be filed up square and true, and afterwards the interior faces, with a due regard to their

parallelism with the neighbouring parts, just after the mode
already set forth. The safe-edge of the file is now indispensable; as in filing the face *b*, the safe-edge of the file is allowed
to rub against the face *a* of the work, and which therefore serves
for its guidance; and in filing the face *a*, the side *b* becomes the
guide for the file. The groove in fig. 876 requires a safe-edge
square file.

When however pieces of these sections, but of greater
lengths, have to be produced by means of the file alone, it is more
usual to make them in two or three pieces respectively, as shown
detached in figs. 877 and 878; and which pieces are first rendered parallel on their several edges, and are then united by
screws and steady pins; or rather, they are united before being
actually finished, in order that any little distortion or displacement occurring in fixing them together may admit of correction.

In works of these kinds, which have rebates, grooves, internal
angles, or cavities, the square, with a sliding blade, shown in
fig. 876, is very useful, as the blade serves as a gage for depth,
besides acting as a square, the one arm of which may be made of
the precise measure of the edge to be tried. This instrument is
often called a turning-square, as it is particularly useful for
measuring the depth of boxes, and other hollowed works turned
in the lathe.

In making straight mortises, as at *s s*, fig. 879, unless the
groove is roughly formed, at the forge, or in the foundry, it is
usual to drill holes nearly as large as the width of the mortise, and

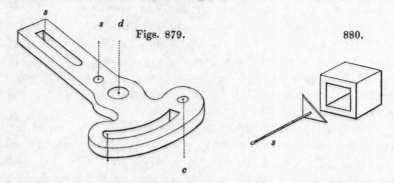

Figs. 879.   880.

in a straight line; the holes are then thrown into one another by a
round file, or a cross-cutting chisel, and the sides of the mortise
are afterwards filed square and true.

For a circular mortise *c c*, the mode is just the same, with the exception that the holes are made on a circular line; and that, instead of a flat file being used throughout, a half-round or a crossing file, is used for the concave side of the mortise.

Short rectangular mortises, or those which may be rather considered to be square holes, as in fig. 880, would if large be prepared by forging or casting the material into the form; and then the six exterior faces having been corrected, the aperture would be filed on all sides under guidance of some of the various tests before referred to. And in such a case, it is convenient to employ a small square *s*, in the form of a right-angled triangle to which is attached a wire that may serve as a handle, whereby the square may be applied at any part within the mortise without the sight of the workman being intercepted by his own fingers. Sometimes also, a cubical block filed truly on four of its faces to the exact dimensions of the aperture, is used as a measure of the parallelism and flatness of the four interior faces.

These miscellaneous examples of filed works with plane surfaces, will be concluded by others of somewhat frequent occurrence, and in which different tools are judiciously employed in conjunction with files. The method first to be described, is one that is considerably used in thick pieces of metal, for making holes differing from the circular form, such as square, hexagonal, triangular, elliptical, and other holes, by first drilling a round hole, and then enlarging and changing the section of the circular hole by a taper punch, better known as a *drift*, which tool is made of steel, and exactly of the same section as that required in the hole; the drift is hardened and tempered before use.

The drift for a taper square hole is made as in fig. 881, or simply as a square pyramid, considerably longer than the hole required; a round hole is first drilled in the work, just large enough to admit the small end of the drift, which is then driven in, its angles indent and force out the metal, making it first like the magnified line *m*, and ultimately exactly square, unless by mistake the hole were drilled too large, when the circular parts would not be quite obliterated. If admissible, the endlong blows on the drift are mingled with a few blows on the sides of the work, as at *b b*, or parallel with the sides of the drift, which cause the metal to adapt itself more readily to the tool. The drift must not however be used too violently, for as it acts as a wedge, it may burst open the work, and which latter is therefore mostly left strong and rough before being drifted ; and generally, when the angles have been somewhat indented, they are partly filed out, and completed by the alternate employment of the file and drift, the marks made by the latter serving continually to indicate the parts to be removed with the file.

Taper square holes, such as those in the chucks for drills, are made with some facility. The chuck is first drilled on its own mandrel, and the drift is put in the four different ways in succession, that the errors incidental to its form may be scattered and lost; the chuck is also placed on the mandrel at intervals, with the drift in its place, that the drift may show as it revolves, whether or not the hole is concentric. When it is required that the drifted hole should be parallel instead of taper, the drift is made as in fig. 882 ; that is, parallel for a short portion in the middle of its length, and the extremities alone are tapered so as to make the tool smaller at each end ; the work is therefore first gradually enlarged to admit the largest part of the drift, and the parallel part is then driven through the work, and renders the inner surface of the same a true counterpart of the drift, if proper care have been taken. In some few cases, the sides of the drifts

Figs. 881.   882.   883.   884.

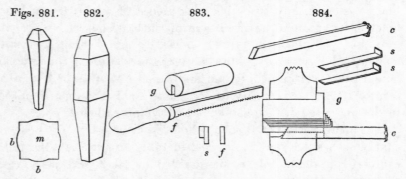

are notched with a file, so as to act as teeth; but this is not general.

When drifts are used, the process of working is often reversed, or the interior surfaces are completed before the exterior. The holes are first drifted whilst the work is larger than its intended size, and afterwards the exterior part is filed or turned, as the case may be, *from the hole*, that is, the hole, (sometimes filled with the drift,) is made the basis of the measurement of the exterior portions of the work. Frequently, as in a square washer, the drift itself, or else a square arbor of similar form, with a center hole at each end, is made to serve as the chuck by which the work is placed in the turning lathe for completion.

In the concluding example of this section, that of making by hand the key-ways in the round holes of wheels, it is to be observed, that it is common to turn a cylindrical plug exactly to fill the hole, and to make a notch in the plug as wide as the intended key-way and parallel with the axis ; the plug is shown at g, fig. 883. A piece of steel f, is then filed parallel, and exactly to fit the notch, and its edge is cut as a file, and used as such within the guide-block, the latter being at the time inserted in the hole of the wheel. In this case, the block becomes the director of the file, and the notches in any number of wheels are made both parallel and axial, and the only precaution that remains to be observed is in the depth of the notches, and this is not always important; the depth may however be readily determined, by making the grooves at first a little shallower than their intended depth, and then, the plug having been removed from the hole, a stop is attached to the side of the file, parallel with its edge, as at s, to prevent its penetrating beyond the assigned depth.

The method of cutting key-ways in large wheels, that was frequently employed prior to the introduction of machinery for the purpose, was as follows. Supposing the wheel to have been bored with a three-inch hole, and to have required a key-way half-inch wide and half-inch deep. The guide-block g, fig. 884, of three inches diameter, would have had a groove say half-inch wide and one inch deep, and a cross-cut chisel c, exactly to fill the groove, would have been made. The chisel having the same section as the groove, when driven through would produce no effect ; but if a piece of sheet steel s, $\frac{1}{16}$ thick, were laid at the bottom of the groove, the chisel would then cut a groove half-inch wide and $\frac{1}{16}$ deep ; and if two, three, four, and ultimately eight such strips were successively employed together, as in the section and detached views, fig. 884, the hole would be accurately *chiselled* out by the repetitions of the process. The hole would require to be finished with a parallel thick file, called a key-way or cotter-file, which has already been described on page 822—3,

SECT. VII.—INSTRUCTIONS FOR FILING CURVILINEAR WORKS ACCORD-
ING TO THE THREE ORDINARY MODES.

The curvilinear surfaces of works are commonly of less importance than the plane surfaces, neither do they in general
require the same skilful use of the file, especially as the more
important curved lines and surfaces in machinery are circular,
and are therefore produced in the turning lathe; and of the remaining curves the majority are introduced either to give a more
pleasing outline to the works than would be obtained by straight
lines, or to obliterate the numerous angles that would be inconvenient to the hands.

In filing works that are *convex*, flat files are always used, and
the file is necessarily applied as a tangent to the curve; and in
filing *concave* works round and half-round files are used, and in
some cases they are selected, nearly or exactly as counterparts of
the hollows to be wrought.

The manipulation of the file upon curvilinear works is entirely
different from that required to produce a plane surface, in which
latter case the work is held at rest and the hands are moved as
steadily as possible in right lines; but in filing curved works an
incessant change of direction is important, and so far as practicable, either the file, or the work, is made to rotate about the axis
of the curve to be produced.

A semicircular groove of half-an-inch radius, as in fig. 885,
would be most easily filed with a round file of nearly the same

Figs. 885.   886.   887.

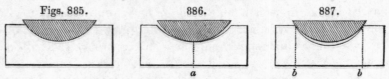

curvature, and the correspondence between the file and work,
and consequently of their axes likewise, would render the matter
very easy; but the file, from the irregularity of its teeth, would
leave ridges in the work, unless in every stroke it were also
twisted to and fro axially by the motion of the wrist, and occasionally in the reverse direction, so that the furrows made by the
teeth might cross each other. If the groove to be filed had a
diameter of three or four inches, although the file might be
selected to correspond in curvature with the groove, as it would
not embrace the entire hollow, the twisting and traversing of the

file would be imperative in order to arrive at all parts of the work.

Under ordinary circumstances it is certainly best that the curvature of the file and work should agree as nearly as possible; but it is obvious that the file if more convex than the work, can only touch the latter at one part, as at *a*, fig. 886, whereas, if the file is less convex, or flatter, than the work, it will act at two places, as at *b b*, fig. 887.   The Sheffield cutlers, in filing out the bows of scissors, and which they do with great rapidity, always avail themselves of this circumstance, and until nearly the conclusion, use files flatter or less convex than the work.

In filing concave works, there is but little choice of position, as the file is always parallel with the axis of the curve, as in the dotted line in fig. 888, but in convex works such as fig. 889, the file may be applied either parallel with the axis as at *p p*, or transversely thereto as at *t t*.   In general however the work would be fixed obliquely as in fig. 890, and the file would be first

Figs. 888.   *t*   889.   *p*   890.

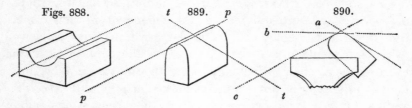

used transversely for some one or two strokes, at an inclination of about 30 degrees with the horizontal line, as at *a*, so as nearly to agree with the straight side of the object, the file would be successively raised to the horizontal, and depressed in the same degree on the other side, in fact proceeding through the positions *a b c*, fig. 890, at some eight or ten intervals, and which would tend to make as many insignificant ridges upon the work.   The ridges would be then melted together by swinging the hands from the position *a* to *c* in every stroke, to be repeated a few times; but as the entire semicircle could not be embraced at one stroke, the work would be re-fixed in two or more positions, so as to divide the operation into about three stages.

A more exact although less energetic method would be to place the file parallel with the axis as on *p p*, fig. 889, and to sweep round the curve principally by the twisting motion of the wrist, which joint can be more readily moved, and also with less fatigue, than the two hands conjointly. A third mode, frequently adopted in such small pieces as can be held upon the filing-block with the hand-vice, is to swing the work upon its axis, and to use the file with the right hand, as if on a flat surface, a mode explained in fig. 858, page 862.

Some works are curvilinear in both directions, such as curved arms and levers with rounded edges ; many of these kinds are completed by draw-filing them, or rubbing the file sideways or laterally around the curve, instead of longitudinally as usual ; but the changes consequent thereupon do not require any especial notice.

The success of all the modes of filing curved works, will be found very much to depend on the freedom with which the several twisting and excursive motions of the hands are performed, and the work should be frequently examined, in order that the eye may judge of the parts in excess and that require to be reduced, in order to produce a pleasing outline.

Having considered the general manipulation of the file in respect to curved works, it remains to be noticed that curvilinear objects are filed up in different modes, dependent on their respective forms and characters. Thus the great majority of curved works are moulded and formed *prior* to the application of the file, which is then principally used to smooth and brighten them—other works are shaped almost entirely with the file, assisted by outlines drawn on the pieces themselves—and again other works are shaped with the file, under the guidance of templets or pattern-plates of hardened steel. Some observations will be offered on all three of these modes.

Firstly, curved works that are moulded or formed prior to the application of the file.—The methods employed in the preparation and figuration of materials into curvilinear and other forms, by founding and forging, have been largely considered in the first volume, and from which remarks it will have been seen, that the perfection of cast works greatly depends on the perfection of the foundry models or patterns, and these latter greatly depend on the facilities offered in pattern-making by the turning-lathe, and the joiner's planes ; and although such castings in many cases do not admit of being finished in the lathe, the perfection of the pattern is a great source of embellishment and economy, in the configuration of the works made by moulding and casting.

In respect to filing up metal works that have been accurately shaped by founding or forging, little or nothing remains to be added to the remarks on the last page, as the only object is to act on every part of curvilinear surfaces in the most expeditious and commodious manner, with the general aim of reducing any trifling errors of form that may already exist in them, and avoiding the introduction of new ones; which circumstances call for the frequent scrutiny of the eye, and an incessant yet judicious variation in the position of the hands.

Secondly, curved works that are moulded or formed almost entirely with the file.—These are blocked out square, and the outlines of the curves are drawn on the ends and sides of the pieces, to guide the file in a manner analogous to the routine pursued by carpenters, masons, and other artizans. For instance, to form a bead, as in fig. 891, the work is prepared of a nearly rectangular form, and the half-circle having been drawn at each end, the angles of the works are coarsely removed at about 45

Figs. 891.   892.   893.

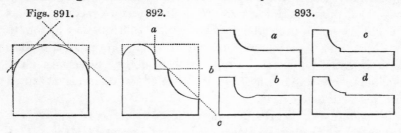

degrees, making the end a semi-octagon; sometimes the four angles are farther reduced, giving to the work eight facets, prior to their being thrown together in making the general curve. If these sides are made with only a very moderate degree of exactness, they will greatly tend to preserve the uniformity of section throughout.

Many workmen, when they have removed the two principal angles at 45 degrees, will make a chamfer entirely around the semicircle at each end, to guide the file in hastily reducing the principal bulk of the material, until the chamfers are nearly obliterated, after which the curve is finished, in exact agreement with the lines, with a smooth file. It is also desirable that the straight-edge should be frequently applied along the axis of the curve, at various parts, during the progress of the work.

Should the entire piece, fig. 892, have to be made from a solid block, two cuts *a* and *b*, made with the saw, would remove the corner, and a little filing would then suffice to complete the internal angle. The round part of the bead would be made as before, and previous to filing the hollow, it would be chamfered on the line *c*; a half round file, of less curvature than the hollow itself, would be first sunk in the middle of the chamfer, and the hollow would be deepened and extended sideways, always maintaining an easy curve, until it reached the marginal lines where the hollow meets the plane surfaces. This mode is better calculated to avoid the accidental obliteration of the angles of the work, than if the file were sunk at each margin.

Where hollows run on to right lines as at *a*, fig. 893, there is some risk of making a break in the junction, either from the curve sinking below the right line, as at *b*, or from the straight line, as at *c*, advancing too far and breaking in upon the curve. On this account a break or fillet is usually made at the part as at *d*, or else it is usual primarily to give that form, by filing the flat first, and then sinking down the hollow just to meet it, and at the conclusion letting the half-round file run a little way on to the right line. Some however prefer the opposite course, or that of sinking the hollow to its full depth, and then filing down the remainder with the flat file, but which mode is certainly attended with more risk.

Thirdly, curved works that are shaped with the file under the guidance of templets or pattern-plates of hardened steel.—This mode is much followed in works of two principal kinds, namely, thin works required in great numbers and precisely of one form, and in a variety of works that require to be exactly circular, although they may not admit of being so fashioned in the lathe.

Many thin works of the first kind are stamped or punched out of the sheet-metals, as for instance the washers for machinery, the links of jointed chains, steel pens, parts of locks for joinery, and numerous other thin works; but many objects of larger kinds, and that are not wanted in such large numbers, are not stamped, but are either cast, or cut out with the shears, and afterwards filed between templets. Instances of such works are occasionally met with in the numerous class of machines for spinning and weaving, cotton, silk and wool, and also in lace and stocking machinery. The mathematical instrument makers likewise employ the mode to a considerable extent in works that require much repetition.

The snail-wheel of a striking clock, fig. 894, is frequently thus formed, by means of a templet: it has an edge formed in twelve steps, arranged spirally, the positions of which determine the number of strokes of the hammer on the bell. In this case, which will serve as a general example, a piece of sheet-steel is cut out, flattened, and smoothed on one side, to receive the drawing of the snail-wheel, and a second piece is also prepared. The two are first drilled together with a central hole, and another hole as distant from the center as admissible. The two plates are then united by two pins, and the outline of the work having been drawn on one of them, they are next filed in steps carefully to the lines, and square across the edges, and they are afterwards hardened and slightly tempered to lessen their liability to fracture on being pinched in the vice. The dozen or more snail-wheels having been cast, or cut out of sheet-brass, and flattened with the hammer, two or three at a time are pinched alongside one of the templets, whilst the two pin-holes are made with the breast-drill or in the lathe, with a drill that exactly fits the holes in the templets. It only remains to place the dozen plates between the templets, keeping them in position by two pins extending through the whole number, and then all the notches are filed in the brass plates, until the file *very nearly* touches the steel patterns, as absolute abrasion on the steel itself would greatly injure the files. In this mode the several brass plates become very exact copies of the pattern.*

A different application of templets is sometimes met with in filing up numerous similar parts in the same object, as the arms or crosses for the wheels of clocks and other machines. The exact

---

* Templets are as much used for setting out and producing series of holes in any special arrangement, as in filing works to any particular form : the most complex example of the kind that occurs at the moment to the author, of templets being used in this manner, is in drilling the side-plates of harps intended for the arbors and link-works, used in temporarily shortening the strings. The respective positions of the holes in these side-plates require a most exact arrangement, any departure from which, would prevent that precise shortening of the string required to produce the semitones with critical accuracy, and would also cause an unbearable jar, unless the cranks of the harp were severally in true position, or on the lines of centers, so as firmly to support the tension of the strings under all circumstances.

pattern of one spoke is filed up as a templet, which is shaded in
fig. 895, and serves for the similar configuration of every spoke ;
the position of the templet being given by a central pin, aided by
any little contrivance which catches into the 3, 4, 5, or 6 equi-distant teeth corresponding with the number of arms.   Many other
equally available cases of the use of templets might be cited, but
we must now proceed to works of the second kind, or those of an
outline partially circular.

It frequently happens that certain forged, cast and other
works have parts, known as bosses, swells, collars and knuckles,
that are pierced with holes, which require their flat surfaces and
also their margins to be made partially or entirely concentric
with the holes.   When such parts occur as bosses, they often

Figs. 894.   895.   896.

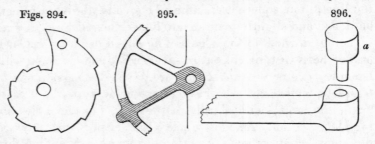

project from a flat surface, and after the central hole is drilled,
some of the pin-drills drawn on page 550, or analogous tools
used in drilling machines, are employed in finishing the margins :
thus figs. 482 and 484 serve for facing the extremities of the holes,
483 and 485 for the external faces of cylindrical bosses or collars,
used in the guidance of arms jointed concentrically with the
holes, and figured cutters 485 serve for bosses with mouldings
intended for ornament.

When the circular margins are discontinuous, files and templets are more or less required : thus the extremity of a forged
arm, such as fig. 896, is drilled, and in the configuration of the
remaining parts, if but one or two such pieces are to be made,
a boss or plug of wood is turned like a, that shall fit the hole ; the
shoulder of the wood is then rubbed with red chalk to mark that
part of the surface which is not at right angles to the hole, and
the circular edge of the boss serves for the guidance of the file in
finishing the exterior margin ; visually rather than obstructively,
as the wooden boss would be reduced instead of the file being

checked. If therefore many such objects had to be filed, two bosses or templets would be made of hardened steel, and used one at each extremity of the hole, and they would be held in position by grasping the three pieces collectively in the tail-vice. The same general method is very largely and more rigorously followed in making joints or hinges, of which three examples will be quoted in conclusion of this section.

The brass and steel plates fig. 897, used for the joints of carpenters' rules are filed up to templets in all respects after the manner described in reference to the snail-wheel, fig. 894, and the joint-plates are inlaid by means of the file, saw, chisel, and plane, by modes that do not require to be noticed.

The joints of drawing-compasses are made somewhat differently, and mostly as follows. The solid knuckle a, fig. 898, is first

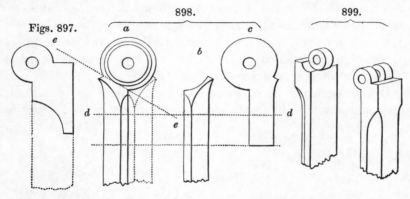

Figs. 897.   898.   899.

drilled and made circular by aid of a templet c, and the hollow side b is filed to correspond exactly with a; the two are then pinched together in the vice on the line $d\,d$, and the parallel notches for the steel joint-plates are made in each with the saw fig. 712, page 729, as deep as the line $e\,e$. The parts a and b are then separated, the notches in b, are completed with the frame-saw, and the bottom of the notches in a, are rendered circular with the joint-saw, fig. 713, as there explained. The middle plates, when filed a little larger than the templets c, are inserted in b, and soldered in their places; the two parts are smoothed on their various internal surfaces, and united by a temporary joint-pin, and any little irregularities in the external or circular curves, (which are left purposely a trifle too large,) are mutually detected by their want of agreement when the joint is opened to different distances; any parts in excess are very carefully reduced with a small smooth file, principally by draw-filing, after which the screw-pin with its brass cheeks or bosses is added.

The pin-drill, fig. 475, p. 547, is commonly used for cutting out the concave parts that extend to the side of small compass-joints, such as are represented in fig. 899, and also for inlaying the heads of small countersunk screws.

Larger joints with wider knuckles, such as fig. 900, are in many instances cast from patterns closely resembling the finished works. In such cases the first process is generally to remove any little external errors with the file, and to clear the angles with a small chipping chisel; the faces of the knuckles are then smoothed and inserted within one another very tightly. The joint-hole is afterwards drilled throughout all the knuckles, and which are filed up externally, sometimes under the guidance of templets put at the ends, but principally by the reduction of those high parts which get scratched or rubbed by the opposite parts, and thereby show their excess of height.

But if such joints are required to be made more accurately, the holes are first drilled in each piece separately, and rather too

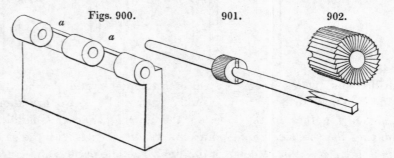

Figs. 900.   901.   902.

close in the corners; the holes are broached with a parallel broach, so as exactly to admit a steel cylinder fig. 901, which has a square end for the brace; this rod is intended to receive the cutters, shown on a larger scale in fig. 902, which are cylindrical pieces of steel bored to fit the rod, and cut with teeth on the outer cylindrical part and on one flat surface; a pin is inserted through both the cutter and bar, so that the two may be united after they have been placed within the joint to be worked; sometimes the back face of the cutter has only a diametrical notch to receive the driving-pin, which pushes the cutter before it as it revolves. A recess must first be cleared for the cutter with a chisel and hammer, or by a wide-joint saw or cutter, such as fig. 713 ; and the hollowed parts at *a a* fig. 900, are then cut throughout their length with the cutter, that afterwards serves to flatten the faces of the knuckles in exact parallelism throughout, and at right angles to the central hole.

The two halves of the joint. having been separately hollowed, and faced until the knuckles will penetrate some distance into one another, the external parts of the joint are next separately filed under the guidance of hard steel rings, or templets, of the same diameter as the cutter, and placed on the cylindrical rod ; after which, the two parts of the joint are put together when yet slightly too large, and the central pin is inserted, in order that the rubbing of the knuckles against the corresponding hollows may denote the parts that are still too high or full; and by cautiously removing all the parts that are abraded, the joints may be made to fit very closely and accurately, and yet to move with great smoothness.

Many joints that are at the same time wide and small, as in hinged snuff-boxes, could not be drilled, as above described, with safety, and are therefore made quite differently, by means of small tube, called joint-wire, the mode of drawing which was explained in vol. i., page 429.

For instance, in making a snuff-box, the rims for the top and bottom are fitted and jointed together before the top and bottom plates are soldered in, and the joint is thus constructed. Supposing that five knuckles are required for the bottom, and four for the top, the nine pieces of joint-wire are cut off, and filed square at the ends ; the rims for the top and bottom having been fitted so as to form the rebate, are placed together, and carefully filed out with a semicircular recess, or groove, by means of a parallel round file, or a joint-file, exactly of the diameter of the joint-wire, which therefore leaves a hollow equal to the fourth part of the circle in each rim.

Five of the joint-pieces are then strung on a wire, inserted in the hollow of the rim for the bottom of the box, and tied therein with fine binding-wire ; the intervals between these five knuckles are regulated by inserting the other four between them for the moment, while the binding-wire is being fastened; after which this first series of knuckles, is soldered in with moderately hard silver solder, which is usually fused with the blow-pipe. The lid is then treated in the same manner, and the bottom part of the box now serves as the gage for regulating the distance between the knuckles in the top rim. The same plan is also used by mathematical instrument makers and others, who however more generally turn the joint-pieces in the lathe, as the draw-bench forms no part of their ordinary supply of tools; and the wide joint pieces or knuckles in mathematical works are usually larger than could be produced in that manner.

SECT. VIII.—COMPARATIVE SKETCH OF THE APPLICATIONS OF THE FILE, AND OF THE ENGINEER'S PLANING-MACHINE, ETC.

The general aim of this present section, is to show, by way of contrast, how several of the pieces advanced as illustrations of works executed with files, in sections IV. to VII. are produced by the planing-machine and analogous contrivances.

The comparison of the modes of producing flat and rectilinear works with the file and with the planing-machine, is greatly in favour of the latter method, in respect to facility, expedition, and accuracy; and the modes are besides entirely different.

For instance, the laborious and tedious mode of *filing* a flat surface has been spoken of at some length, and it will be remembered the work is *fixed*, and the tool is *moved* in a variety of directions upon the surface to be filed.

So far as the action of the smith's hand-plane for metal, (page 483,) and carpenters' planes may be brought into comparison, they are used in many respects as the files, but are applied generally parallel with the one side of the superficies that is being wrought.

But the engineer's mode of planing works in metal is entirely different from either of the above, and is strictly analogous to the mode of turning works in the lathe with a slide rest, if we consider the *axial* motion of the lathe to be replaced by the *rectilinear* motion of the planing-machine, as was briefly explained in general terms in the introductory chapter to the present volume, more particularly in reference to the "*guide principle,*" see pages 468 and 469.

The work to be planed, is there briefly described as fixed on a carriage or sledge, that is made to move to and fro in a true right line, as upon a very accurate railway; whilst the cutting-tool, which is just like those used in the turning-lathe, was supposed to be affixed to a bridge, standing across and at right angles to the railway. Such a fixed tool would plough a furrow in the work, which furrow would be as accurately straight as the railway or guide from which the work itself received its direction of motion.

If the reader will only conceive the work to be continually moved to and fro upon the slide or railway, a distance equal to its own length; and that by a subsidiary contrivance, or another slide placed horizontally, the tool between each reciprocation of the work were moved a small distance to the right continually, a series of grooves would be ploughed, all individually right lines; and these grooves would shave off all the asperities and irregularities of the work, leaving it finely grooved in parallel furrows. Or provided the end of the tool were flat, and ever so little broader than the small interval between the successive strokes, the tool would leave a plane or smooth surface; and the perfection of this surface would mainly depend, on the railway or the cutting-slide, and the horizontal or position-slide, being each truly rectilinear.

Supposing now, by means of a third slide placed exactly perpendicular, the tool were depressed the tenth of an inch, and the process were entirely repeated, the surface would be reduced with perfect uniformity, one-tenth of an inch all over, and the new surface would be mathematically parallel with that existing immediately previous. Pursuing this idea, let it be further supposed that the surface just planed is the upper surface of the carriage or sledge of the planing-machine, technically known as the *bed* or *table*, upon which the work that is to be planed is fixed by screw-bolts and clamps.

It will now be shown how the piece represented by A, B, C, in fig. 868, page 879, would be treated in the planing-machine, in order to make its sides strictly parallel, in pairs, and also at right angles to each other, in short, to convert it into a true parallelopipedon.

The side A, of the piece, would be first placed uppermost and correctly planed; afterwards the side A would be inverted, and placed on the bed of the machine, care being taken that no shavings intervened to prevent their coming into absolute contact; and the second face, or *a*, would be planed strictly parallel with A, and that without any especial care on the part of the operator.

Next, to plane the edge B, it would be necessary the third slide of the planing-machine should be placed truly vertical, and that between each reciprocation of the bed of the planing-machine on its railway, the tool should be depressed a small quantity by the vertical slide, so as in the end to make it slowly descend, by intermittent steps, down a vertical and right line, exactly equal to the perpendicular height of the side B.

All things now remaining fixed as before, if the tool were traversed horizontally until it touched the second edge or *b*, this edge of the work would, on pursuing the same gradual depression of the tool, be planed also vertical and in strict parallelism with its opposite, or B.

Continuing the same order of work as in the hand process, the ends C, *c*, would require the work to be released from the bed of the machine, shifted just 90 degrees, and then refixed, when the ends C, *c*, would be treated exactly as B, *b*, had previously been, and would thence be made parallel and square.

In some instances, indeed, the analogy to the railway is strictly maintained for a farther stage of the work, as such a piece as A, B, C, fig. 868, would sometimes be mounted, as it were, upon one of the turn-plates by which the railway-carriage is twisted one quarter round, preparatory to moving it from off the principal to an adjoining line. In the planing-machine, the turn-plate on which the work is fixed, is a supplementary circular bed having a horizontal or azimuth motion, so that by leaving the tool unaltered, except in its vertical path, the several edges of any regular polygon, whether a square plate, or a triangle, pentagon, hexagon, &c., may be planed with strict accuracy. The sides of any irregular polygon, may be also planed, by moving the tool so much on the transverse or horizontal slide, as the differences in the radial distances of the sides of the unequal polygon, from the center of the turn-plate.

Supposing the piece ABC, fig. 868, to be bevelled or chamfered on one or all of its edges, the slide which had been previously fixed in the vertical line, or perpendicularly, would be inclined the precise number of degrees required, so as to produce the chamfered edge with as much facility as the square or vertical edge.

The more convenient course in small and long works of sections resembling figs. 871 to 874, is to place upon the bed of the planing-machine two headstocks or lathe-heads, the one furnished with a dividing-plate, and so arranged that the axis of the headstock is strictly parallel with the path of the railway or main-slide of the planing-machine. In this case the planing-tool is almost always made to traverse horizontally, and which indeed is the most generally convenient. The triangular prism fig. 874 would be planed with great facility and truth by placing it in three successive positions, one-third of the circle or 120 degrees asunder, by means of the dividing-plate; and if the axis of the headstocks were inclined vertically, a triangular *pyramid* or *wedge,* instead of a triangular *prism,* would be produced. The headstocks, if horizontal and shifted four times, or ninety degrees each time, would plane square or rectangular prisms, and of course also the rectangular faces of the pieces, 871, 872, and 873; and again if instead of constantly shifting the headstocks ninety degrees, as for the rectangular parts, the changes were thirty, forty-five, or sixty degrees, according to the angles respectively required in the objects represented, the bevilled or chamfered edges would be obtained with great facility and accuracy.

The planing-machine almost entirely prevents the necessity for building up work in a dissected state, as in the figures 877, and 878, as such grooves may be sunk, and any fillets may be planed, upon the upper surfaces of works, the vertical or lateral surfaces, and even the lower or inferior surfaces, by bending the tools into appropriate forms, so as to reach into the parts, after the manner of fig. 439, page 534; as such contortions of the instruments, do not in any respect interfere with the paths of the slides in which the tools are fixed and guided.

And consequently, many parts of machinery that if worked by hand would be very difficult of access, and also very difficult of proof in respect to their accuracy, are accomplished in the planing-machine with a degree of facility most satisfactory to the mind, as regards their abstract truth and the parallelism of their various parts, however strangely situated, and also most satisfactory, as regards the relative economy of the method; indeed the planing-machine may be truly considered to have effected a most enor-

mous and beneficial revolution in the art of metallic construction
generally.

The key-grooves in wheels, for the keys or wedges by which
they are attached to their shafts, when made by machinery, are
cut out by a modification of the planing-machine invented by
Mr. Richard Roberts, of Manchester; it is designated the *key-
groove engine*, and may be presumed to have been derived from
the mortising-engines in Brunel's block-machinery, (*ante*, 505-6.)

The cutter used in the key-groove engine resembles a strong
mortise-chisel, and is reciprocated in a vertical line by means of
a crank or excentric, whilst the wheel to be grooved is placed
horizontally on a slide, and traversed towards the cutter until it
has entered to the required depth. To make the groove taper to
the same angle as the key or wedge, the slide is tilted some one
or two degrees; and if two or three key-ways are wanted instead
of one only, then the wheel is mounted on a species of turn-plate
with notches cut on its edge, by means of which the grooves
are placed at exactly equal distances, as in planing squares,
hexagons, &c.

An offspring of the key-groove engine, called the *paring* or
slotting-machine, is also commonly used to fulfil many of the
works hitherto performed with the file. The tool of the slotting-
machine resembles in all respects that used in cutting key-ways,
but the slotting-machine has two horizontal slides at right angles
to each other, and a circular adjustment or turn-plate, all three
used in shifting the position of the work beneath the cutter, and
all three fitted with apparatus for mechanically *feeding the cut*,
as it is technically called, or for moving the respective slides a
minute quantity between every stroke of the reciprocating cutter,
thus making the machine *self-acting*.

In such a slotting and paring-machine, the piece, fig. 879, on
page 882, could be produced without the intervention of filing.
The central hole *d*, and the holes at the one extremity of each
mortise *s s*, and *c c*, would be first drilled; the work would be
guided by a pin in the center of the turn-plate, fitted into the
center hole *d*. The hole *s* would be elongated into the straight
mortise by a chisel of the same width, the work being traversed
beneath it by one of the straight slides. The other hole *c*, would
be elongated into the circular mortise by the gradual adjustment

of the turn-plate, which would swing the work round on its axis d. The turn-plate moving on d, would also serve for paring the outer edges parallel with the circular mortise, and the straight slides would enable the exterior straight lines of the work to be pared.

Even the small semicircles around the ends of the circular mortise, in fig. 879, might be shaped, if before the formation of this mortise, the piece were chucked with c, c, successively in the centre of the turn-plate; or a clever workman, by moving the two slides by hand, or independently of the self-acting feed, would follow any such outline with tolerable regularity; removing the bulk of the metal, and leaving the parts square on the edge, and pretty nearly perfect in form, so that a little filing would complete them satisfactorily; and thus, by the manual adjustment of the slides, many irregular curves are pared out, to any particular outline previously drawn on the work, by that method which the mathematician would perhaps call the method of double ordinates.

Another modification of the planing-machine, called the *shaping-machine*, and which may be considered to have grown out of the paring-machine last alluded to, is much used in correcting the forms of the circular and other parts of large works of the character of figures 897 to 900, pages 893, 894. In such works, the central hole is first bored out; the object is then chucked on a spindle, or arbor, which may be almost considered as the mandrel of a turning-lathe; the tool is next traversed *above* the work, and in a line parallel with the axis of the mandrel, whilst, at every stroke, the mandrel is slightly moved on its axis; so that, in the end, the whole of the circular arc is accurately shaped.

These shaping-machines have also generally two rectilinear slides, at right angles both to each other and to the axis of the mandrel, either of which, or the revolving arbor, can be set to feed itself; so that, by a little dexterity of manipulation, all the edges of a piece, such as fig. 897, could be shaped, even including the hollow, as the cutting-tool is placed at the end of an arm, or radius, of some three to six inches, so as to be applicable to the cutting of *inverted* arcs.

In this manner, with the preparatory aid of the turning-lathe, every part of the cross head, figs. 903 and 904, may be wrought mechanically. The work is first chucked in the lathe between centers on the line *a a*, whilst the whole of the contour in the side view, fig. 903, is turned, and also the bearings *e e*; it is then fixed transversely on the face-chuck of the lathe to bore out the center hole *b b* for the piston-rod, and to turn the central flat surface. After this the lines seen in the plan, fig. 904, may be completed in the shaping or paring-engine; the

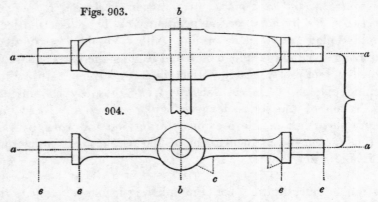

Figs. 903.

904.

central convex part, by the twisting of the work on the general center; the concave parts by the twisting of the tool on the centers *c c*; and the straight parts, by the movement of the horizontal slides; and these several changes may be so nicely managed, as to render the joinings of the several lines scarcely distinguishable.

The method followed in making such works is not always as above described, as in many such pieces, especially in those of large size, the planing-machine is brought into requisition, and sometimes also boring machinery, by which likewise the hollows *c c* may be shaped out. The artist has altogether omitted the transverse mortise, for the key which fixes the piston-rod, and which mortise is made in the key-way or paring-engine, leaving, in fact, nothing to be accomplished by hand-labour.

Many of the varieties of machines for planing and shaping metal works with a single pointed tool, and various other machines of similar effect, in which circular cutters are used, might be here noticed, and in which numerous machines, objects that were formerly always shaped by filing, are now worked by machinery; but it is hoped enough has been shown to satisfy the reader that almost any solid with plane or circular surfaces, however numerous or combined, and also many irregular or arbitrary surfaces, are in the present day, most effectively produced by means strictly mechanical. But it will be borne in mind, that the detailed investigation of these matters appertains more strictly to the proposed fifth volume, to be devoted to the " Principles and Practices of Mechanical Engineering," and in which it is proposed this trifling sketch should be filled up and elaborated.

The author cannot however conclude this chapter on files, their applications, and certain relative topics, without adverting to the revolution as regards filing, consequent on the introduction of the planing-machine and its descendants : a revolution more especially felt in regard to the larger classes of machinery.

The obvious effect, of the large and economic accession of engineers' tools which act by cutting, has been to lessen in a proportionate degree, the employment of files and of manual processes generally, amongst engineers and those occupied in the construction of large machinery. It necessarily follows as a result, that amongst such artizans the practice of filing, from being less required, is far less generally learned by the present race of workmen; and consequently, many of the latter, when deprived of the refined machinery of the workshop, and thrown upon their own handicraft or manual efforts with the simpler and earlier tools, are certainly less skilful than their predecessors.

The art of filing is however still largely employed, and will probably continue to be fostered as much as ever amongst artizans who work on smaller objects, and those to which machinery of the kind referred to, is less applicable than the file and its more simple congenitors, by means of which alone, when employed with skilful manipulation, highly elaborate and accurate works have been and may still be produced, although in many instances, at a greater cost.

In justice to the file it is also right to state, that in many cases it is indispensable that works produced in the planing and other machines, should be finished and adjusted by means of smooth files ; and further that the machines referred to, are unavailable in many small works, which can only be produced by individuals who have been long and delicately skilled in the use of the file.

CHAPTER XXIX.—SHEARS.

SECT. I.—INTRODUCTION : CUTTING NIPPERS FOR WIRES.

SHEARS are instruments of a character quite different from any of those hitherto described, as the cutting edges of shearing tools are always used in pairs, and on opposite sides of the material to be sheared or severed. In many cases the shears are constructed after the manner of pincers and pliers, or as two double-ended levers united at the fulcrum by a pin, but other modes of uniting the two cutting parts of the instruments are also employed, as will be shown.

The general form and position of the cutting blades of shears, was adverted to in the elementary diagram fig. 316, at the beginning of this volume, and the sections of some varieties of this instrument are represented by a, b, c, of the annexed fig. 905, from which it will be seen that the edges of shears and scissors meet in lateral contact, and pass close against one another, severing the material by two cuts, or indentations, or thrusts, which take place in the same plane as that in which the blades are situated and are moved.

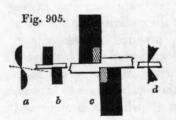

Fig. 905.

Some of the largest shearing tools of the kinds used by engineers, such as c, serve to divide bars of iron, 4, 5, or 6 inches wide, and 1 to 2 inches thick, then requiring the greatest possible solidity and freedom from elasticity.

On the other hand some of the finest scissors of the section a, such as are used by ladies in cutting lace, will cut with the greatest cleanness and perfection, the most flexible thread or tissue of threads, or the finest membranes met with in animal or vegetable structures. But this latter kind of shears, unlike the engineer's shears, is altogether useless unless possessed of a considerable share of elasticity, to keep their edges in accurate contact at that point in which the blades at the moment cross each other, as will be explained, otherwise such thin materials are folded down between the blades instead of being fairly cut. The transition from the elastic to the inelastic kinds of shears is not, as may be supposed, by one defined step, but by gradual stages, making it as difficult in this, as in other classifications, to adopt any precise line of demarcation.

In addition to the above, or to shears properly so considered, there are a few tools known as cutting pliers or nippers, in which the blades meet in direct opposition, but do not pass each other as in the legitimate kinds of shears; this kind is represented by the section d, fig. 905, and it is proposed to consider these several tools as nearly as may be under four heads, namely,—

Sect.　I. Cutting nippers for wires.

　,,　II. Scissors and shears for soft flexible materials.

　,, III. Shears for metal, worked by manual power.

　,, IV. Engineer's shearing tools, generally worked by steam power.

Cutting pliers, if they admit of being classed with shears, are certainly the most simple of the group, and are used for cutting asunder, small wires, nails, and a few other substances. Their edges are simply opposed wedges, exactly as shown in the above diagram at d; and as respects the remainder of the instruments by which their wedges are compressed, the most simple kind exactly resembles carpenters' ordinary pincers for drawing out nails, except that the cutting pincers are made with thinner edges; and figs. 906 to 909, overleaf, represent different kinds of cutting pliers and nippers.

When cutting nippers are compressed upon a nail or a piece of wire, they first indent it on opposite sides, and when from their penetration, the surfaces of the wedges exert a lateral pressure against the material, the latter eventually yields, and is torn asunder at the moment the pressure exerted by the wedges exceeds the cohesive strength of the central metal yet uncut. Consequently the divided wire shows two bevilled surfaces, terminating in a ridge, slightly torn and ragged. The quantity of the material thus torn instead of being cut, will be the less, the softer the metal and the keener the pliers, but experience shows an angle of about 30 to 40 degrees to be the most economical for the edges of such tools.

Little remains to be said on the varieties of cutting pliers; most of these used by general artizans and clockmakers, are smaller than carpenters' pincers, and the extremities of the jaws are bevilled as in *watch-nippers*, fig. 906, that they may cut pins

Figs. 906.

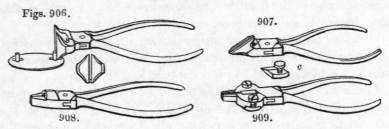

907.

908.

909.

lying upon a flat surface. Other cutting pliers called *side-nippers* are oblique as in fig. 907; those used for the dressing-case, and known as *nail-nippers*, are concave on the edge to pare the nails convex; and another kind known as *nipper-pliers, bell-hanger's* or *bottler's-pliers*, have flat points at the end for grasping and twisting wires, and cutters on the sides for removing the waste ends, as shown in fig. 908.

Surgeons also employ cutting nippers, for dividing small bones, such as those of the fingers and toes, and for removing splintered and dead portions of bone. They assume the forms already explained, and also some others as will be seen on consulting the work before quoted in the foot note, pages 801, 2, namely, *Seerig's Armamentarium.*

The edges of cutting nippers are apt to be notched, if used upon hard wires, or if wriggled whilst the cutting edges are buried in the wire, and they scarcely admit of being reground or repaired. This inconvenience led to a modification of the instrument fig. 909, by the enlargement of the extremities, to admit of loose cutters fitted in shallow grooves being affixed by one screw in each, as shown detached at *c*, so that the cutters may admit of removal and restoration by grinding, which end is effectually obtained although somewhat to the prejudice of the instrument, by increasing its bulk.*

---

* H. Bursill, a youth only 12 years old was rewarded for this contrivance by the Society of Arts in 1845.

SECT. II.—SCISSORS AND SHEARS FOR SOFT FLEXIBLE MATERIALS.

The scissors and shears to be described in this and the succeeding section, act on a very different principle from the nippers recently spoken of. The nippers have edges of about 30 to 40 degrees, meeting in direct opposition, but yet leave ragged edges on the work; whereas the shears have edges commonly of 90 degrees, seldom less than 60 degrees, these edges pass each other and leave the work remarkably keen and exact.

Let the edges of scissors be ever so well sharpened, they act very imperfectly, if at all, unless the blades are in close contact at the time of passing; and this imperfection is the more sensible the thinner and more flexible the material to be cut, as it will then fold down between the blades if they do not come in contact. Whereas when the blades exactly meet, the one serves to support the material whilst the other severs it; or rather this action is reciprocal, and each blade supports the material for the other, rendering the office of a counter-support, or of the bench, stool or cutting-board, used by the carpenter with the paring chisel.

On a cursory inspection of a pair of ordinary scissors, it may be supposed that their blades are made quite flat on their faces, or with truly plane surfaces like the diagram fig. 910 overleaf, representing the imaginary longitudinal section of the instrument, the two blades of which are united by a screw, consisting of three parts differing in diameter, namely the *head*, the *neck*, and the *thread;* the bottom of the countersink that receives the head of the screw is called the *shelf* or the *twitter-bit.* If however the insides of scissors were made flat, and as carefully as possible, they could scarcely be made to cut slender fibrous materials, or if at all, then for only a short period, and additional friction would accrue from the rubbing of their surfaces.

The form which is really adopted, more resembles the exaggerated diagram fig. 911; the blades are each sloped some 2 or 3 degrees from the plane in which they move, so that their edges alone come into contact; instead of the blades being straight in their length they are a little curved so as to overlap; and close behind the screw-pin by which they are united, there is a little triangular elevation, insignificant in size but most important in effect, which may be considered as a miniature hillock or ridge,

sloping away to the general surface near the hole for the screw.
This enlargement or bulge is technically called the "*riding part*,"
and as there is one on each blade, when the scissors are opened
or that the blades are at right angles, the points or extremities
only of the riding parts come into contact, and the joints may
then have lateral shake without any prejudice.   But as the
blades are closed, first the bases or points of the riding parts, and
lastly the summits or tops, rub against each other, and tilt the
blades beyond the central line of the instrument; the effect of
which is, to keep the successive portions of the two edges in contact throughout the length of the cut, as by the time the scissors
are closed, the points of the blades are each sprung back to the
central line of the scissors, which is dotted in the diagram.

Although scissors when in perfect condition for work, may be
loose or shake on the joint when fully opened, (and thereby
placed beyond their range of action,) they will be always found

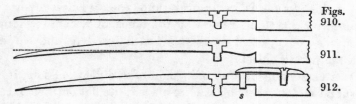

Figs.
910.

911.

912.

to be tight and free from shake, as soon as the blades can begin
to cut the material near the joint, and so to continue tight until
they meet at the points.   That all scissors do exhibit this construction may be easily seen, as when they are closed and held
edgeways, between the eye and the light, they will be found
only to touch at the points and at the riding parts, or those just
behind the joint screw, the remainder being more or less open
and gently curved ; and their elastic action will also be experienced by the touch, as whilst good scissors are being closed,
there is a smoothness of contact which seems to give evidence of
some measure of elasticity.

Fig. 912, represents the section of the one blade of a pair of
scissors registered in July 1841, by Mr. G. Wilkinson of Sheffield, and in which the elastic principle is differently introduced.
These scissors are made without the riding part, but instead
thereof, immediately behind the screw which unites the blade
as usual, the one blade is perforated, for the purpose of admit-

ting freely, a small pin or stud fixed to the end of a short and powerful spring, so that the stud *s*, from acting on the opposite blade throws the points of both towards each other, so as to give them a tendency to cross, but which being resisted by the edges of the blades touching one another, keeps them very agreeably in contact throughout their motion, and causes them to cut very well.

If further evidence is wanted of the elastic principle in scissors, it is distinctly shown in sheep shears, which besides their ostensible purpose of shearing off the fleece, are used by leather dressers and others.   It is well known that sheep shears, fig. 919, page 915, are made as one piece of steel, which is tapered at each end to constitute the cutting edges, is then for a distance fluted and straight to form the semi-cylindrical parts for the grasp, and that in the center or opposite extremity, the steel is flattened and formed into a bow by which the blades are united and kept distended; sheep shears consequently require no joint pin, and the hands have only to compress them as they spring open for themselves. If sheep shears are examined when fully opened, or when partially closed by tying round the blades a loop of string, it will be found that the blades have a tendency to spring into contact, as after having been pressed sideways and asunder, the cutting edges immediately return into exact contact the moment the distending pressure is removed.

The construction of scissors with the riding place as adverted to in fig. 911, is that which ordinarily obtains in most scissors, from the finest of those used by ladies, to the heavy ponderous shears for tailors, which sometimes weigh above six pounds, and are rested on the cutting board by one of their bows, that are large enough to admit the whole of the fingers.

The peculiar form of the insides of the blades is in all cases of paramount importance, and in the manufacture of fine scissors is attended to by a person called a ' *putter-together*,' whose province it is to examine the screw-joint, and see to the form of the riding-places, and lastly to set the edges of the scissors, which for general purposes are sharpened on an oilstone at an angle of about 40 degrees, but for the fine scissors more nearly upright or at 30 degrees from the perpendicular.

So important indeed is the configuration of the inner face of scissors, that they should never be ground or meddled with at that part, but by a person fully experienced in their action, and scissors may with careful usage be kept in order for years, without being ground, if the edges are occasionally set on the oil-stone at the inclination above referred to. It will frequently happen that well-made scissors which appear to grate a little when closed, merely do so from dirt or dust, which if removed by passing the finger along the edges, will restore the scissors to their smooth and pleasant action.

It seems quite uncalled for to enter into the separate description of various instruments known as button-hole scissors, cutting-out, drapers', flower, garden, and grape scissors, horse trimming scissors; hair, lace, lamp, nail, paper, pocket, stationers', and tailors' scissors, and many others; nor of the large shears for the garden such as pruning, trimming, and border shears, the distinctions between which varieties are sufficiently known to those who use the several kinds, but the author will merely notice such of them as present any peculiarity of structure.

Button-hole scissors are notched out towards the joint screw as in fig. 914, so as to enable the instrument to make an incision

Figs. 913.   914.

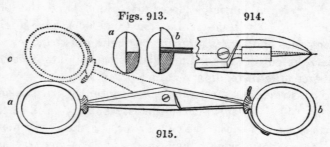

915.

a little distant from the edge of the material; the joint must be made stiff, so as to prevent the points catching against each other.

Flower and grape scissors assume the section of fig. 913, so that they first cut the stem, and then hold it like a pair of pliers, the one blade requires to be made in two parts riveted together; when entirely closed they present an elliptical section *a*; and *b* shows how the stem of the flower is grasped, the blades are rounded at all parts that they may not injure the plants.

Lamp scissors have the one blade very broad, and with a little rim to prevent the snuff of the lamp falling on the carpet.

Nail scissors for the dressing-case, are made very strong and with short blades. In using scissors formed in the ordinary mode, the fingers and thumb of the right hand, have naturally a tendency to press the blades together, in that position in which they are intended to cut; but the left hand on the contrary has a tendency to separate the blades and defeat the principle on which scissors act. Therefore nail scissors are made in pairs, and formed in opposite ways, or as "rights and lefts," so that they may suit the respective hands.

Pocket scissors have blades which admit of being locked together in the form represented in fig. 915, as the point of the one blade catches into a small spring near the bow of the other; and the instrument cannot be opened until the spring or catch is released with the nail. When closed for the pocket, the bows stand on one line as at *a b*, when opened for use as at *a c*.

Surgical scissors are of many forms, but have generally short blades and long straight slender handles, that the hand may not impede the vision. In some of the surgical scissors the blades are curved as scimitars, and others are curved sideways, these kinds are difficult to make, as the elasticity of contact in the blade is required nevertheless to be maintained.

Many of the shears and scissors used in gardening, only differ from scissors and shears in general in their size, and the adaptation of their handles, some of which are of wood, and placed at an angle of 40 or 50 degrees, as in the letter Y inverted. Other garden shears used in trimming borders, have handles a yard long and inclined about 80 degrees to the blades, which may therefore lie on the ground whilst the individual stands nearly erect. Some of the border shears have rollers to facilitate their movement along the ground.

In pruning shears and scissors, two peculiarities of form are judiciously introduced. In the more simple of the two kinds, which is shown in fig. 916, the one part of the instrument terminates in a hook, with a broad and sometimes a roughened edge, to retain the branch from slipping away, the other part of the instrument is formed as a thin cutting blade, the edge of which is convex. Theoretically it should be part of a logarithmic spiral, in which case the edge of the cutter would present a constant angle to the work throughout its action, and slide laterally through the incision made by itself, or make a sliding cut, whereas if the edge of the blade were radial, it would make a direct cut without any sliding, as in a paring chisel. The spiral blade cuts more easily, and will therefore remove a larger branch, with an action precisely analogous to that of the oblique cutters in some of the planes, although differently produced.

Some of these instruments when a little modified in form, are mounted on poles from 6 to 10 feet long, and are actuated by a catgut; this tool which is known as the *Averuncator*, is very efficient for pruning at a considerable distance above the head.

The other pruning shears represented in fig. 917, are denomi-

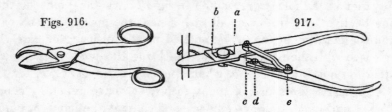

Figs. 916.   917.

nated *sliding shears*, the pin that unites the two parts, fits in a round hole in the one blade and a long mortise in the other, and a link or bridle-rod *c e*, is attached by a screw to each lever; in consequence, when the instrument is fully opened the pin or fulcrum is at the end *a*, of the mortise, whereas, on the shears being gradually closed, the cutting blade slides downwards upon the pin until the fulcrum is near the opposite end *b*. In this modification of shears the sliding action is produced to a much greater extent than with the spiral blade, but the construction is a little more expensive; and as the instrument is not provided with bows for the fingers, the spring *d e*, is added to throw it open.

Before dismissing this section, two modifications of shears will be briefly adverted to; those used by card makers, and the revolving shears employed in manufacturing woollen cloth.

Card paper is prepared in large sheets; when dried and pressed it is cut into square pieces of the required sizes by means of long shears, the one blade of which is fixed at the end of a table, and has the joint at the farther extremity, whilst the cutting blade has a handle in front, and moves through a loop to keep the blade in its position, as in some chaff-cutting machines; there is also a stop fixed parallel with the blades, and as distant as the width of the slips into which the card is first divided, and these slips are then cut again the lengthway of the cards. The shears are moved so rapidly, that the action sounds like that of knocking at a door, and still the cards agree most rigidly in size.

Revolving shears or *"perpetual shears"* are used for shearing off the loose fibres from the face of woollen cloths. For narrow cloths the cylinders are 30 inches long and 2 in diameter, eight thin knives are twisted around the cylinders, making $2\frac{1}{4}$ turns of a coarse screw, and are secured by screws and nuts which pass through flanges at the ends of the axis : formerly the cylinders were grooved and fitted with several thin narrow plates of steel 6 or 8 inches long. The edges of the eight blades are ground so as to constitute parts of a cylinder, by a grinder or *strickle* fed with emery, passed to and fro on a slide parallel with the axis of the cylinder, which is driven at about 1200 turns in the minute.

In use, the cylinder revolves about as quickly, and in contact with the edge of a long thin plate of steel, called the *ledger blade*, which has a very keen rectilinear edge, measuring 40 to 50 degrees, the blade is fixed as a tangent to the cylinder, and the two are mounted on a swing carriage with two handles, so as to be brought down by the hands to a fixed stop. The edge of the ledger blade is sharpened, by grinding it against the cylinder itself with flower emery and oil, by which the two are sure to agree throughout their length.

The cloth, before it goes through the process of cutting, is brushed so as to raise the fibres, it then passes from a roller over a round bar, and comes in contact with the *spring bed*, which is a long elastic plate of steel, fixed to the framing of the machine, and nearly as a tangent to the cylinder, this brings the fibres of the cloth within the range of the cutting edges, which reduce them very exactly to one level. The machine has several adjustments, for determining with great nicety, the relative positions of the cylinder, ledger-blade and spring-bar, but which could not be conveyed without elaborate drawings. Formerly the cloth was passed over a *fixed* bed having a nearly sharp angular ridge, but which mode was far more liable to cut holes in the cloth than the spring-bed.

Broad cloths require cylinders 65 inches long, and machinery of proportionally greater strength. In Lewis's patent cross-cutting machine, the cloth is cut from *list to list*, or transversely, in which case the cloth is stretched by hooks at the two edges,

3 N

and there are two spring beds; the cylinder in this machine is 40 inches long, and the cloth is shifted that quantity between every trip until the whole piece is sheared. The perpetual shears are also successfully applied to coarse fabrics including carpets.*

A modification of the above revolving shears, made in a much less exact manner for mowing grass lawns, is fitted up somewhat as a wheel-barrow, or hand truck, so that the rotation of the wheels upon which the machine is rolled along, gives motion to the shears, which crop the grass to a level surface.

SECT. III.—SHEARS FOR METAL WORKED BY MANUAL POWER.

When metals are very thin such as the latten brass used for plating and other purposes, they may be readily cut with stout scissors; and accordingly we find the weakest of the shears for metal, are merely some few removes in strength, beyond the strong scissors for softer substances.

It is however to be observed, that as common scissors are sharpened to an angle varying from about 50 to 60 degrees, they may fairly be considered to *cut* the materials submitted to their action; but shears for metal have in general *rectangular* edges, as they are seldom more acute than 80 degrees, and therefore instead of cutting into the material, they rather *force* the two parts asunder, by the pressure of the two blades being exerted on opposite sides of the line of division.

It was recently stated to be of the utmost importance, that the blades of the weaker or elastic kind of shears should be absolutely in contact, or else thin flexible materials would be folded down between their blades without being cut.

And it may now be urged as of equal importance, that the blades of the shears for metal should be also exactly in contact, not that rigid plates or bars of metal could be bent or folded down between their blades, even if these were a little distant; but the resistance to the operation of cutting would be then enormously increased, because the force exerted to compress the shears, would not be then exerted in the line of their greatest resistance, which is strictly the case when the edges truly meet in one plane.

---

* Messrs. Sugden and Son, of Leeds, makers of machinery for the manufacture of cloth, kindly furnished the author with the information from which the above remarks were gathered.

If the blades were distant as in fig. 924, from the want of direct support, the bar or plate would be tilted up, and become jammed, this would tend further to separate the blades, and the shears would be strained or perhaps broken without dividing the bar, whereas all these evils are avoided if the shears close accurately in one and the same plane, as if the lower blade were shifted to the dotted line, and in which case they require the least expenditure of power and act with the best effect.

Having now in accordance with the general method of this work, noticed the principles on which the shears for metal act, the author will proceed to describe some of the ordinary forms of the instrument.

Hand shears which are the smallest of these tools, are made of the form represented in fig. 920, and vary from about four to nine

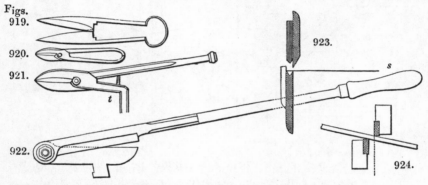

Figs.
919.
920.
921.
922.
923.
924.

inches in total length, they are much used by tinmen, coppersmiths, silversmiths and others who work in sheet metals, and are often called *snips*, to distinguish them from bench shears ; sometimes however they are fixed by the one limb in the table or tail vice, and then become essentially bench shears, and this enables them to be used with somewhat increased power.

Bench shears of the ordinary form are represented in fig. 921, the square tang *t*, is inserted in a hole in the bench, or in a large block of wood, or else in the chaps of the bench vice itself; a less usual modification is seen in fig. 922, with the joint at the far end, and the cutting part between the joint and the handle.

Bench shears vary in total length from about one foot and a half to four feet, and the blades occupy about one fifth of the length, sometimes to increase the power of these shears, the handle is forged thicker at the end to add weight, so that when the instrument is closed with a jerk, it may by its momentum cut thicker metal than could be acted upon by a simple thrust, but when considerable power is required, it is better to resort to the shears next described.

Purchase shears which are represented in fig. 925, are in every respect more powerful than those previously noticed, the framing is much more massive, and the cutters are rectangular bars of steel inserted in grooves, to admit of their being readily sharp-

Fig. 925.

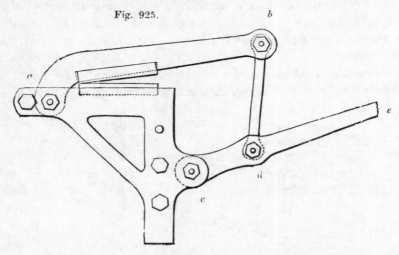

ened or renewed. Instead of the hand being applied on the first lever or *a, b,* a second lever *c, d, e,* is added, and united to the first by the link *b, d,* and but for the limit of the paper the hand lever *c, d, e,* would have been represented of twice its present length.

As the length of the part *a, b,* is three to four times the length of *c, d,* the hand has to move through three to four times the space it would if applied directly to the shear lever, and consequently the purchase shears have three to four times the force of common shears, supposing the manual lever to be of equal length in each kind. There is usually at the back of the moving blade, a very powerful spring or *back stay*, to keep the two edges in contact, and still further behind a *stop* to determine the lengths or widths of the pieces sheared off.

Before using shears, in those cases where the stop is not employed to determine the width, it is usual to mark on the work the lines upon which it is intended to be sheared, the shears are then opened to the full, and the extremity of the line is placed in the angle formed by the jaws; if the work is short, it is also observed whether the opposite end of the line lies exactly on the edge of the lower blade, but if the work is long, the guidance is less easy.   When the blades are closed the work will probably slip endlong, notwithstanding the resistance of the hand, until the angle at which the blades meet is so far reduced that they begin to grasp the work, when the extreme edge will be first cut through, and then the incision will be extended to the full length of the blades.

As however each successive portion is severed, the two parts are bent asunder to the angle formed by the blades, and both pieces become somewhat curved or curled up; provided the cut is through the middle of the sheet so that both are equally strong, the two parts become curved in the same degree, but when a narrow and consequently weaker piece, is removed from the edge of a wide sheet, the curling up occurs almost exclusively in the narrow strip on account of its feebleness.   In long pieces it is sometimes necessary to increase the curvature in order that as the work is sheared off, the one part may pass above, and the other below the rivet or screw by which the halves of the shears are united.

When from use or accident the joint becomes loose, so as not to retain the two parts in contact, in order to make the shears cut, the moving half must be pressed against that which is fixed to the pedestal or tail vice.   Sometimes the sway of the blades of jointed shears is prevented, by allowing the moving arm to pass through a loop or guide which may retain it in position.

Such a guide is mostly used in the light shears with which printers cut their space line leads, or those thin slips of metal inserted between the lines of type, to separate them and make the printing more open.   The leads are cast in strips about a foot long, and are cut into pieces of the exact width of a page, by laying them in a trough having at the end a pair of shears, and beyond these a stop to determine the precise length, so that any number of the leads may be cut exactly to the length required.   Before adverting to the powerful shears used by engineers, two modifications of those already described will be noticed.

Fig. 923, page 915, represents the section through the blades of a pair of shears invented by Mr. Collett, by which the tags or tin ferrules at the end of silk laces are cut and bent at one process, the general aspect of the tool being that of fig. 921, page 915. The shearing blades are shaded obliquely in fig. 923, and to the lower, which is fluted on the edge, is attached a stop that determines the width of the piece removed from the strip *s*, to make the tag. The upper shear blade, which is ground more acutely than usual, carries a ridge piece, (shaded vertically,) which compresses the strip as it is cut off, into the fluted edge of the lower blade, and thereby throws it into a channelled form; and by the employment of a pair of hollow pliers, or else a light hammer and a hollow crease, the bending is readily completed, and the tag attached to the cord.*

A nearly similar machine, but constructed more in accordance with the printers' space line shears, is used for cutting slips of thin latten brass, into the channelled pens used in stationers' machines for ruling the blue and red lines on paper for account books, &c. The one side of a slip of brass $1\frac{1}{2}$ inch wide, is thus cut and channelled at intervals suited to every line; the sides of every channel are closed to form a narrow groove, and the intervening pieces are removed with hand-shears. The compound pen is fixed on a hinged board, and a strip of thick flannel laid at the top of the pen, is saturated with ink which flows steadily down all the channels, whilst the paper is moved horizontally under the pens, by two or three rollers and tapes, somewhat as in the feeding apparatus of printing machines, and thus the whole page is ruled one way and very quickly.

Shears of the above kinds, with rectilinear blades, are not suited to cutting out curvilinear objects, such for example as the sides of callipers *a* fig. 950, page 933. The outline of such callipers is first of all marked on the sheet of steel from a templet, and with a brass wire which leaves a sufficient trace; the outline is followed with a hammer and chisel upon an anvil, the chisel having a rounded or convex edge. Detached cuts running into one another are made around the curve, and the work is finally separated by pinching it in the tail vice successively at all parts of the curve, and wriggling the other edge of the sheet with the hand until it breaks.

The vice is often also used for cutting off straight pieces, which

---

* See Transactions of the Society of Arts, London, 1826, vol. xliv. page 76.

are then fixed with the line of division exactly flush with the chaps, and an ordinary straight chisel is so applied, that the chamfer of the tool rests on the chaps of the vice, and the edge lies at a small angle to the work, and after every successive blow, the chisel is moved a little to the left without losing its general position.

SECT. IV.—ENGINEERS' SHEARING TOOLS; GENERALLY WORKED BY
STEAM POWER.

The earliest machines of this class were scarcely more than a magnified copy of the bench shears shown on page 915, but made very much stronger, thus fig. 926, represents a shearing and squeezing tool used in some iron works and smithies. It has one massive piece that is fixed to the ground, and jointed to it is the lever, which carries at a, a pair of shearing cutters situated exactly on two radii struck from the center of motion; this

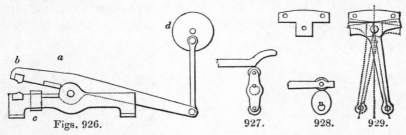

Figs. 926.   927.   928.   929.

machine has also two squeezers b, for moulding pieces of iron when red-hot to the particular forms of the dies. The longer end of the lever is united by a connecting rod to an excentric stud in the disk d, which is made to revolve by the steam engine.

The late Mr. Penn of Greenwich moved his shears by means of an axis carrying two rollers, placed at the extremities of a diametrical arm, as in fig. 927. The one roller acts on the radial part of the shear lever in the act of cutting, and the curved part then allows the lever to descend by its own weight rapidly, yet without a jerk, by the time the other roller comes into action for the succeeding stroke of the machine, which by this double excentric makes two reciprocations for every revolution of the shaft.

It is however more usual to employ cams, as in fig. 928, and in this case the part of the cam which lifts the shear lever is usually spiral, so as to raise it with equal velocity; the curve of

the back is immaterial, provided it forms a continuous line so as
to prevent the lever descending with a jerk.

Fig. 929 represents the double shears contrived by the late Sir
John Barton for the Royal Mint, the one part, shown also
detached, presents two horizontal but discontinuous edges with
the axis in the center, this piece is fixed to a firm support; the
other or the moving part somewhat resembles the letter T or a
pendulum, to the lower end of which, and beneath the floor
is jointed a connecting rod, that unites the pendulum with an
excentric or crank driven by the engine.   The machine is
double, or cuts on either side, and has two pairs of rectangular
cutters of hardened steel, which may be shifted to bring the
four edges of all of them successively into action.

Boiler makers have great use for powerful shears for cutting
plate iron from $\frac{1}{4}$ to $\frac{1}{2}$, and sometimes $\frac{3}{4}$ inch thick; and the next
stage of their work is to punch the rivet holes by which the plates
are attached.   The two processes of shearing and punching are
so far analogous in their requirements, that it is usual to unite

Fig. 930.

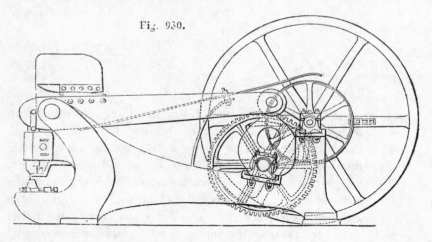

the two processes in one machine; and as it sometimes happens
the boiler maker's yard is at a distance from the general factory,
it then becomes necessary to work the shears by hand with a
winch handle, and which is effected in the manner shown in
fig. 930, by the introduction of only one wheel and pinion.   The
wheel is fixed on the cam shaft, the pinion on the same axis that
carries the heavy fly-wheel employed to give the required
momentum; this mode of working the shearing and punching

engine is perfectly successful, but of course less economical than steam or water power, the agency of which the machine is also adapted to receive.

When shears that move on a joint and have radial cutters as in fig. 926, are employed for thick bars, owing to the distance to which their jaws are opened, they meet at a considerable angle, and therefore from their obliquity they do not grasp the thick bar, but allow it to slide gradually from between them, to prevent which a rigid stop is added at the part *c*, fig. 926, when, as the bar can no longer slide away it becomes severed. The shears with radial cutters, are also liable from their very oblique action to curve the plates, neither do they serve for making long cuts, as the joint then prevents the free passage of long work.

All these inconveniences however are obviated in the shearing machines with slides, in which the edges approach in a right line instead of radially, and are also nearly obviated in the very massive and powerful shearing and punching tool with jointed lever, designed by Mr. Roberts of Manchester, and represented in fig. 930, which occupies an entire length of eleven feet, and serves for cutting plates not exceeding $\frac{3}{4}$ inch thick, cutting 12 inches in length at a time, and punching holes of $1\frac{1}{4}$ inch diameter in $\frac{3}{4}$ inch iron. The shearing cutters are in this machine 15 inches long and raised above the center of motion, as they lie on a chord instead of a radius, the longest pieces may therefore be cut without interference from the joint, and the cutters have the further advantage of meeting at a much smaller angle than if fitted radially.

The portable punching and shearing machine shown in front and side elevation in figs. 931, and 932, was also designed by Mr. Richard Roberts, it will serve for a general example of such machines, as the differences in the several constructions are only those of form and arrangement, and not of principle.

This machine stands upon a base of a triangular form, and has in front a strong chamfer slide, which is reciprocated in a vertical line, by an excentric that is concealed from view, it being immediately behind the slide, and upon the same axis as the excentric is the toothed wheel. The pinion that takes into this wheel, is on the shaft that carries the fly wheel, and one of the arms of the latter, receives the handle by which the machine is

usually worked; or if it is driven by power, fast and loose
pulleys are then fixed on the same axis as the fly wheel.

The upper part of the slide carries a shearing cutter, which is
about 7 inches wide, and meets a similar cutter that is fixed to
the upper and overhanging part of the casting. The cutters
although ground with nearly rectangular edges, are bevilled to

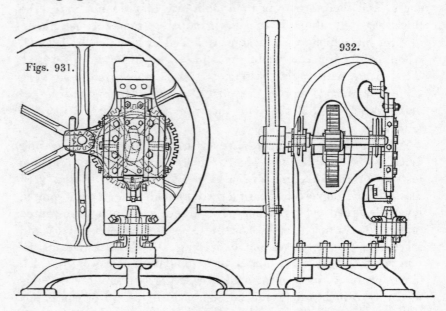

Figs. 931.   932.

the extent of about three-fourths of an inch in the direction of
their length, that they may commence their work on the one
edge, and therefore more gradually than if the entire width of the
cutter penetrated at the same instant; this degree of obliquity
does not cause the work to slide from the shears, neither does it
materially curl up the work ; and as the blades are quite clear of
the framing, a cut may be extended throughout the longest works,
provided the cut is not more than five inches from the edge of
the plate, the distance of the cutters from the framing of the
machine.

The above machine which measures in total height about five
feet, makes 12 or 15 strokes per minute, shears $\frac{1}{2}$ inch iron
plates, and punches $\frac{3}{4}$ holes in iron $\frac{1}{2}$ inch thick. A larger
machine makes 10 or 12 strokes per minute, shears $\frac{3}{4}$ inch plate,
and punches $1\frac{1}{4}$ inch holes in iron $\frac{3}{4}$ inch thick ; and a still
heavier machine working at 8 or 10 strokes in the minute, shears

1 inch plates, and punches 2 inch holes in iron 1 inch thick. Some of these are provided with railways by which the work is carried to the shears or punches as will be described; and Mr. Roberts' bar-cutting machine, having only shearing cutters at the bottom, and the excentric at the top of the slide, is used for cutting bars not exceeding 6⅜ inches wide by 1⅜ thick, or bars 2 or 2½ square, but he thinks these dimensions of the works performed might if required be greatly exceeded in heavier machines.

A patent has been recently granted to Mr. G. B. Thorneycroft, for a shearing machine for cutting wide plates of sheet iron. This machine which is used in the manufacture of wrought iron, has two wide cutters of steel fixed to the edges of thick plates of cast iron; the lower cutter is at rest and quite horizontal, the upper cutter bar is fitted in grooves at the end of the frame, so as to be carried up and down vertically, by a shaft or spindle immediately above the cutter and parallel with it, this shaft has an excentric at each end, and one in the center, and three connecting links, which attach the cutter frame to the excentrics, and give it a small reciprocating motion. The upper cutter is a little oblique so as to begin to act at the one end, and in removing the strips curls them but very little.*

Nasmyth, Gaskell and Co.'s vice for cutting wide pieces of boiler plate, is based on the mode of cutting thin slips of sheet metal over the chaps of the ordinary tail vice as described on page 918-9. The jaws of the machine are about six feet long, faced with steel, and powerfully closed by two perpendicular screws and nuts, one at each end, which also secure the machine to the ground.

The plate of iron is therefore fixed horizontally and with the line of division level with the jaws. A strong rod chisel struck with sledge hammers, is applied successively along the angle formed between the work and the vice, and after the iron has been indented the whole length, the blows of the sledges directed on the overhanging piece of iron complete the separation. †

Fig. 933, represents the plan, and fig. 934, the partial vertical section, of a "hydraulic machine for cutting off copper bolts,"

---

* Thorneycroft's Patent, sealed 31st January, 1843, is described in the Repertory of Patent Inventions, Vol. ii, Enlarged Series, page 129.

† Nasmyth, Gaskell and Co.'s cutting vice is figured in plate 49 of Buchanan's Mill Work, edited by Sir G. Rennie, F.R.S., 1841.

devised by Mr. A. M. Renton, and constructed for the Government Dock Yards, by Messrs. Charles Robinson & Son. This machine is actuated by the hydro-mechanical principle discovered by the celebrated predecessor of the firm, Mr. Timothy Bramah.

The circle in fig. 933, represents the cylinder of a hydrostatic press, which is flattened to the width of the rectangular bar that is fixed alongside the cylinder, the two being enveloped in the external casting which is shaded in the section fig. 934, and resembles a stunted pillar three or four feet high. The whole of the parts are traversed by nine sets of holes suitable to bars from $\frac{3}{8}$ to $2\frac{1}{2}$ inches diameter, the holes where they meet on the lines $b\ b$, are furnished with annular steel cutters, and are enlarged outwards each way to admit the work more easily.

The rod $r\ r$, to be sheared, is introduced whilst the holes are directly opposite or continuous, and the men then pump in the injection water through the pipe w, it acts upon the annulus or shoulder intermediate between the two diameters of the cylinder,

Figs. 933.   934.   935.   936.   937.

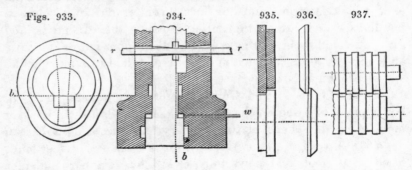

causes the descent of the latter with a pressure of about 100 tons, and forces the bar asunder very quietly, and from the annular form of the cutters without bruising it. When the bar has been cut off, the injection water is allowed to flow out from beneath the cylinder, and the latter is raised by a loaded lever beneath the floor ready for the next stroke. The machine is far more economical in its action, than the old mode of cutting off the copper bolts, with a frame saw used by hand, and the storekeeper in charge of the bolts, can if needful perform the entire operation unassistedly, although usually four men work the pair of one inch injection pumps, by a double-ended lever as in a fire engine.

In concluding this chapter it is proposed to speak of the rotary shears for metal, which have continuous action like rollers and are pretty generally used. In the best form of the instrument, two spindles connected together by toothed wheels of equal size, have each two thin disks of different diameters, which are opposed to each other, that is, a large and a small in the same plane, as in the diagram fig. 935, the larger disks overlap each other and travel in lateral contact, and therefore act just like shears, and the two disks in each plane meet, or rather nearly meet, so as just to grasp between them, after the manner of flatting rollers, the two parts of the strip of metal which have been severed, and by carrying these forward they continually lead the yet undivided part of the metal to the edges of the larger disks, which in this manner quickly separate the entire strip of metal into two parts.

The machine requires that the spindle carrying the disks should have an adjustment for lateral distance, as in flatting rollers, to adapt their degree of separation to the thickness of the metal to be sheared. One of the spindles should also have an endlong adjustment to bring the disks into exact lateral contact, and the machine requires in addition a fence or guide, fixed alongside the revolving shears to determine the width of the strips cut off. Sometimes the two smaller disks are omitted, and the larger alone used, as in fig. 936, the circular shears are then somewhat less exact in their action, but perform nevertheless sufficiently well for most purposes.

Circular or rotary shears, are very useful for shearing plates not exceeding one eighth of an inch thick, and one of the advantages which the rotary possess over the common shears, is the facility with which curved lines may be followed, on account of the small portion of the disks that are in contact, whereas the length of rectilinear shear blades prevent their ready application to curves. Of course the speed at which the machines may be driven depends on the nature of the work, and if the cuts are straight and the plates light, the velocity of the shears may be considerable.

As remarked on page 188 of the first volume, the circular shears, or splitting rolls used in the works where wrought iron is manufactured, are composed of steeled disks of equal thickness, but of two diameters, arranged alternately upon two spindles as in fig. 937, so as at one action to split thin plates of iron of about 6 inches in width, into very narrow pieces known as nail rods, and into strips from half to one inch wide designated as bundle or split iron. Of course different pairs of rolls are required for every different width of the strips thus manufactured.

CHAPTER XXX.—PUNCHES.

THE title of the present chapter, may at the first glance, only appear to possess a very scanty relation to the tools used in mechanical manipulation, as the ostensible purpose of a punch may be considered to be only that of making a round or square hole in any thin substance. But it frequently happens that the small piece or disk so removed by the punch, is the particular object sought, and some of the very numerous objects thus made with punches, assume a very great importance in the manufacturing and commercial world, as will perhaps be admitted when a few of these are referred to in the course of the present chapter.

The general character of a punch, is that of a steel instrument the end of which is of precisely the form of the substance to be removed by the punch, and which instrument is forcibly driven through the material by the blow of a hammer. When the subject is entertained in a moderately extended sense, it will be seen that much variety exists in the forms of the punches themselves, and also in the modes by which the power whereby they are actuated is applied.

So far as relates to the actual edges of the punches by which the materials are severed, they may be classed under two principal divisions, namely duplex punches, and single punches. The duplex punches have rectangular edges and are used in pairs, often just the same as in shears for metal. The single punches have sometimes rectangular but generally more acute edges, the one side being mostly perpendicular.

The single punches require a firm support of wood, lead, tin, copper, or some yielding material, into which the edge of the punch may penetrate without injury, when it has passed through the material to be punched. Consequently many of the tools the author has ventured to consider as single punches, might be classed with chisels, and many of the duplex punches might be classed with shears, analogies which it is not worth while either to pursue or refute.

The following classification has been attempted, as that best calculated to throw into something like order, the miscellaneous instruments that will be more or less fully described in this chapter, namely,

Section I. Punches used without guides.

„ II. Punches used with simple guides.

„ III. Punches used in fly presses, and miscellaneous examples of their products.

„ IV. Punching machinery used by engineers.

It is proposed in all the sections to commence with those punches having the thinnest edges, and which are used for the softest materials.

It would be hardly admitted, that a carpenter's chisel driven by a mallet through a piece of card could be considered as a punch, still the circular punch used with a mallet on a block of lead, for cutting out circular disks of cards for gun-wadding, is indisputably a punch, and yet scarcely more than a chisel bent round into a hoop. The gun-punch is formed as in fig. 938, over-leaf, and is turned conical without and cylindrical within, or rather a little larger at the top that the waddings may freely ascend, and make their way out at the top through the aperture; when however annular punches exceed about 2 inches in diameter, it is found a stronger and better method, to make them as steel rings, attached to iron stems or centers spread out at the ends to fill the rings, as in fig. 939, but holes are then required to push out the disks that stick into the punch, as shown by the section beneath the figure 939.

The punch used in cutting out wafers for letters is nearly similar, it being formed as a thin cylindrical tube of steel, fitted to the end of a perforated brass cone having at the top two branches for the cross handle, by which it is pressed through several of the farinaceous sheets, and as the wafers accumulate in the punch they escape at the top. Confectioners use similar cutters in making lozenges, and frequently the thin steel cutter is fixed to a straight perforated handle of wood. The lozenges are cut out singly and with a twist of the hand.

When the disk is the object required, the punch is always chamfered exteriorly, as then the edge of the disk is left square and the external or wasted part is bruised or bent; but the punch is made cylindrical without, and conical within, when the annulus or external substance is required to have a keen edge. And when pieces such as washers, or those having central holes, are required in card or leather, the punches are sometimes constructed in two parts as shown separated in fig. 940, the inner being made to fit the outer punch, and their edges to fall on one plane; so that one blow effects the two incisions, and the punches may then be separated for the removal of the work should it stick fast between the two parts of the instrument.

Punches of irregular and arbitrary forms, used for cutting out paper, the leaves for artificial flowers, the figured pieces of cloth for uniforms and similar things, are made precisely after the manner of fig. 938, and also of fig. 939, except that they are forged

Figs. 938.   939.   940.   941.   942.

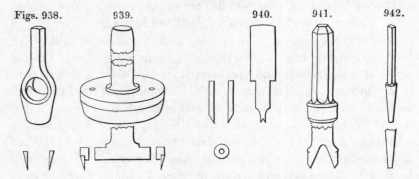

in the solid, or without the loose ring.   These irregular punches are however much more tedious to make, than the circular, which admit of being fashioned in the lathe.

Figured punches of much larger dimensions, have been of late used for cutting out the variously formed papers used in making envelopes for letters.   The punch or cutter is sometimes made in one piece, as a ring an inch to an inch and a half deep, or else in several pieces screwed around a central plate of iron, and when the punch is sharp it is readily forced through three to five hundred thicknesses of paper, by the slow descent of the screw press in which it is worked.   Army clothiers use similar instruments for cutting out the leather for shoes and various other parts of military clothing, and several of these punching or cutting tools are often grouped together.

Proceeding to the punches used for metal, those having the thinnest edges are known as hollow punches; they are turned of various diameters from about ¼ to 2 inches, and of the section fig. 941, they are always used on a block of lead, and sometimes for two or three thicknesses at a time of tinned iron, copper or zinc. Punches 942, smaller than ¼ inch are generally solid, quite flat at the end, and are also used on a block of lead, which although it gives a momentary support, yields and receives into its surface the little piece of metal punched out by the tool.

Fig. 944, represents the punch used by smiths for red hot iron, the tool is solid and quite flat at the end, and whether it is round, square, or oblong in its section, as for producing the holes represented, it is parallel for a short distance, then gradually enlarged, and afterwards hollowed for the hazle rod by which it is surrounded to constitute the handle (see foot note, page 202, vol. i.) Various practical remarks on the application of the smith's punches are given on pages 215—217 of vol. i., it will be thence seen that the smith's punch is frequently used along with a bottom or bed tool known in this case as a *bolster*, and which has a hole exactly of the same area as the section of the punch itself.

Punches when used in combination with bolsters, are clearly similar in their action to the shears with rectangular edges, as will be seen on comparing figs. 943, and 944, the only difference

Figs. 943.   944.   945.

946.

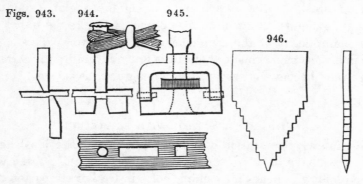

being that the straight blade of the shears, is to be considered as bent round into a solid circle for a circular punch, or converted into a square, rectangle, or other figure as the case may be ; but every part of the punch should meet its counterpart or the bolster in *lateral contact*, the same as formerly explained in reference to shears. This supposes the tools to be accurately made and correctly held by the smith, but which is somewhat difficult,

3 o

because, the bolster, the work, and the punch, are all three simply built up loosely upon the anvil, and the eye can render but little judgment of their relative positions, the punch is consequently apt to be misdirected so as to catch against the bolster and damage both tools. The mode sometimes used to avoid this inconvenience is represented in fig. 945, in which a guide is introduced to direct the punch, but agreeably to the proposed arrangement, this figure will be more fully explained in the next section, when some other tools of a lighter description have been spoken of.

Previously however to concluding this present section, attention is requested to fig. 946, which shows a punch used by harp-makers and others, in cutting long mortises in sheet metal. The punch is parallel in thickness, and has in the center a square point from which proceed several steps, this punch is used with a bolster having a narrow slit, as long as the width of the punch. A small hole is first drilled in the center of the intended mortise, the first blow on the punch converts this into a square, the next cuts out two little pieces extending the hole into a short mortise, and each successive blow cuts out a little piece from each end, thereby extending the mortise if needful to the full width of the punch. From the graduated action, the method entails but little risk of breaking the punch or bulging the metal, even if it should have but little width. Sometimes, to make the punch act less energetically at the commencement of its work, the steps at the point are made smaller both in height and width; the serrated edge then becomes curved instead of angular, as shown.

SECT. II.—PUNCHES USED WITH SIMPLE GUIDES.

Beginning this section with the tools having the most acute edges, we have to refer to the punch pliers, fig. 947, fitted with round hollow punches for making holes in leather straps and thin materials; some pliers of this kind have a small oval punch terminating in a chisel edge, for cutting those holes that have to be passed over buttons; and pliers have been made with circular, square, and triangular punches, for the cruel practice of marking sheep in the ear. In all these tools the punch is made to close upon a small block of ivory or copper, so as to ensure the material being cut through without injuring the punch.

Another example of slender chisel-like punches, is to be seen in Mr. Roger's machine for cutting the teeth of horn and tortoiseshell combs (see page 130, vol. i.). The punch or chisel is in two parts, slightly inclined and curved at the ends to agree in form with the outline of one tooth of the comb, the cutter is attached to the end of a jointed arm, moved up and down by a crank, so as to penetrate almost through the material, and the uncut portion is so very thin that it splits through at each stroke, and leaves the two combs detached.

The little instrument called a pen-making machine, is another ingenious example of punches moving on a joint, it is represented of half its true size, and ready to receive the pen, in fig. 948, and in fig. 949, the two cutters are shown of full size and

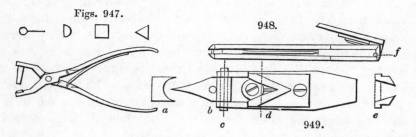

Figs. 947.

948.

949.

laid back in a right line; although in reality it only opens to a right angle. The lower half has a small steel cutter b, pointed to the angle of the nibs of the pen, and fluted to the curve of the quill as at a, the upper cutter d, is made as an inverted angle with nearly vertical edges as seen at e, which exactly correspond with the lower cutter, so as between them to cut the shoulders of the pen. The upper tool also carries a thin blade or chisel, which penetrates nearly through the quill and forms the slit.

The quill having been pared down to its central line, is inserted through the hollow joint, on the line f, and the cutters being very near the joint, the lever on being closed gives abundant power for the penetration of the punches. The pen requires to be afterwards nibbed, and for which purpose another cutter is attached to the instrument which has likewise an ordinary pen-blade, so as to be entirely complete in itself.

This method of producing a pen was introduced in a somewhat different form, in the late Mr. Timothy Bramah's patent machinery for making portable quill pens, the barrel of the quill was in that case cut into two lengths, and each length being split longitudinally into three parts, and shaped at each end in a small fly-press with cutters of the above character, converted every quill into six double-ended pens, many thousand boxes of which were made ; they may be considered to have opened the path to the present truly enormous manufacture of steel pens, which consumes many *tons* of steel annually.

Passing from the punches with guides obtained by means of joints, and actuated by the pressure of the fingers, we will return to fig. 945, on page 929, which with its simple guide becomes a very effective tool sometimes known as the *hammer press*, in contradistinction to the *screw*, or *fly-press* to be hereafter spoken of.

The guide in the contrivance fig. 945, is a strong piece of iron attached to the bottom tool, and sufficiently above it to admit the work between the two. Each part is pierced with a hole of exactly the same size, and accurately formed as if they were interrupted portions of the same hole. The punch is made exactly to fit either hole, so that from the upper it receives a correct guidance, and it therefore cuts through the material, and penetrates the lower piece, with a degree of precision and truth scarcely attainable when the tools are unattached, and are used simply upon the anvil as before described.

As however the punch mostly sticks tight in the work, it is needful to turn the instrument over, and drive out the punch with a drift a little smaller than the punch, and on which account punching tools of this kind are often made of two parallel plates of steel firmly united by screws or steady pins, yet separated enough for the reception of the work, and frequently contrivances are added to guide the works to one fixed position, in order that any number of pieces may be punched exactly alike.

Thus in punching circular mortises, as in the half of a pair of inside and outside callipers *a*, fig. 950, the punch *c*, is first used to produce the central hole, and this punch is then left in the bed *b*, to retain the work during the action of the second punch *m*, by which the mortise is cut. The punch *m*, is very short to avoid the chance of its being broken, and it is also narrow so as to embrace only a short portion of the mortise, which is then completed, with little risk to the tool, at three or four strokes, whilst the punch *c* serves as a central guide.

Occasionally also punches of this simple kind, but on a larger scale, have been placed under drop hammers, falling from a considerable height through guide rods, somewhat as in a pile-driving machine. This mode of obtaining power, is not suited to the action of punches used in cutting out metals, amongst other reasons, because the punch sticks very hard in the perforation it has made, and requires some contrivance for pulling it out, which is not so easily obtained in this apparatus as in fly-presses, that are suited alike to large and small works.

The drop hammer, or as it is more commonly called *a force*, is however very much used at Birmingham in the manufacture of stamped works, or such as are figured between dies, of which an example is described at length in pages 409 & 410 of vol. i. Compared with a fly-press of equal power, the force is less expensive in its first construction, but it is also less accurate in its performance.

Fig. 951, is a very simple yet effective tool which may be viewed as a simplification of the fly-press, it consists of one very strong piece of wrought iron, about one inch thick and four

Figs. 950.

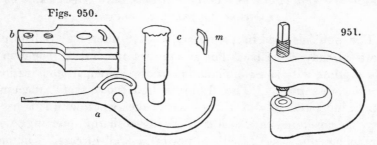

951.

or five inches wide, thickened at the ends and bent into the form represented, the one extremity is tapped to receive a coarse screw, the end of which is formed as a cylindrical pin, or punch, that is sometimes made in the solid with the screw, but more usually as a hardened steel plug inserted in a hole in the screw. Immediately opposite to the punch is another hole in the press, the extremity of which is fitted with a hardened steel ring or bed punch. When the screw is turned round by a lever about three feet long, it will make holes as large as ¾ inch diameter in plates ⅜ inch thick, and is therefore occasionally useful to boiler makers for repairs, and also for fitting works in confined situations about the holds of ships, and other purposes. When this screw is turned backwards the punch is drawn out and relieved from the work, but the screwing motion is apt to wear out the end and side of the punch, and therefore to alter its dimensions.

A very convenient instrument of exactly the same kind, is used in punching the holes in leather straps, by which they are laced together with leather thongs, or united by screws and nuts, to constitute the endless bands or belts used in driving machinery. In this case the frame of the tool is made of gun-metal, and weighs only a few ounces, the end of the screw is formed as a cutting punch, and it is perforated throughout, that the little cylinders of leather may work out through the screw, which only requires a cross handle to adapt it to the thumb and fingers.

In this case the screwing motion is desirable, as the punch in revolving acts partly as a knife, and therefore cuts with great facility, as the leather is supported by the gun metal which constitutes the clamp or body of the tool.

SECT. III.—PUNCHES USED IN FLY-PRESSES, AND MISCELLANEOUS EXAMPLES OF THEIR PRODUCTS.

The punches used in fly-presses, do not differ materially from those already described, but it appears needful to commence this section, with some explanation of the principal modifications of the press itself. The fly-press is a most useful machine, which, independently of the punch or dies wherewith it is used, may be considered as a means of giving a hard, unerring, perpendicular blow, as if with a powerful well-directed hammer. The precision of the blow is attained by the slide whereby the punch is guided, the force of the blow by the heavy revolving fly attached to the screw of the press. When the machine is used, the fly is put in rapid motion, and then suddenly arrested by the dies or cutters coming in contact with the substance submitted to their action. The entire momentum of the fly, directed by the agency of the screw, is therefore instantaneously expended on the work to be punched or stamped, and the reaction is frequently such as to make the screw recoil to nearly its first position.

The bare enumeration of the multitude of articles that are partially or wholly produced in fly-presses, would extend to considerable length, as this powerful and rapid auxiliary, is not only employed in punching holes, and cutting out numerous articles from sheets of metal and other materials, but also in moulding, stamping, bending or raising thin metals into a variety of shapes, and likewise in impressing others with devices as in medals and coins.

Fig. 952, represents a fly-press of the ordinary construction, that is used for cutting out works and is thence called a cutting press, in contradistinction to the stamping or coining presses. It will be seen the body of the press, which is very strong, is fixed upon a bed or base that is at right angles to the screw, the

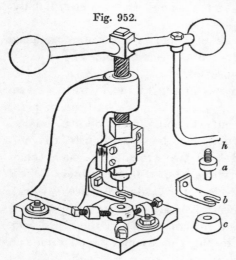

Fig. 952.

latter is very coarse in its pitch, and has a double or triple square thread, the rise of which is from about one to six inches in every revolution. The nut of the screw is mostly of gun-metal, and fixed in the upper part or head of the press. The top of the screw is square or hexagonal, and carries a lever of wrought iron, terminating in two solid cast iron balls, that constitute the fly, and from the lever the additional piece *h*, descends to the level of the dies to serve as the handle, so that the left hand may be used in applying the material to be punched, whilst the right hand of the operator is employed in working the press.

The screw is generally attached to a square bar called the *follower*, which fits accurately in a corresponding aperture, and is strictly in a line with the screw; and to the follower is attached the punch shown detached at *a*. The punch is sometimes fitted into a nearly cylindrical hole, and retained by a transverse pin or a side screw, but more generally the die is screwed into the follower, like the chucks of some turning lathes; the bed or bottom die *c*, which is made strictly parallel, rests on the base of the press, and is retained in position by the four screws, that pass through the four blocks called *dogs*, these screws which point a little downwards, allow the die to be accurately adjusted, so that the punch may descend into it without catching at any part, and thereby inflicting an injury to the tools.

The piece *b*, which rests nearly in contact with the die, is called the *puller off*, it is perforated to allow free passage to the punch; when the latter rises, it carries up with it for a short distance the perforated sheet of metal that has been punched through, but which is held back by the puller off, whilst the punch continuing its ascent rises above the puller off, and leaves behind the sheet of metal so released ; the sheet is again placed in position whilst another piece is punched out, and so on continually.

Before proceeding to speak of some of the works produced in stamping presses, it is proposed to describe some of the points of difference met with in fly-presses.

The body of a cutting press is in general made with one arm as represented in fig. 952, because the sheet of metal can be more freely applied to the die, but stamping and coining presses, which are used for pieces that have been previously cut out, require greater strength and have two arms, or are made somewhat as a strong lofty bridge with the screw in the center.

The fly of the press is frequently made as a heavy wheel, which may be more massive and is less dangerous to bystanders than the lever and balls, and in large presses there are two, three, or four handles fixed to the rim, as many men then run round with the fly, and let go when the blow is struck.

Fly-presses are variously worked by steam power; thus in the Royal Mint the twelve presses for cutting out the blanks or disks for coin, are arranged in a circle around a heavy fly-wheel, which revolves horizontally by means of the steam-engine. The wheel has one projecting tooth or cam, which catches successively the twelve radial levers fixed in the screws of the presses, to cut the blanks, and twelve springs immediately return the several levers to their first positions, ready for the next passage of the cam on the wheel.

The fly and screw are also worked by power, in some cases by an excentric or crank movement fixed at a distance, a long connecting rod then unites the crank to an arm of the wheel, or to a straight lever, and gives it a reciprocating movement.

At other times, in place of the crank motion are ingeniously substituted a piston and cylinder worked after the manner of an oscillating steam engine, if we imagine the boiler to be superseded by a large chamber, exhausted by the steam engine nearly to a vacuum, thus constituting an air engine, the one side of the piston being opened for a period to the exhausted chamber, whilst the other receives the full pressure of the atmosphere. This mode is adopted in several Mints, constructed by Mr. Hague, of London, for foreign countries, and the author believes it is also employed for the stamping or coining presses of our national Mint.*

In the manufacture of steel pens, (see page 942-3,) it is important to have an exact control over the punches which cut the slits, and those which mark the inscriptions, as by descending too far they might disfigure the steel, or even cut it through. Accordingly Mr. Mordan introduced between the head of the press and the lever, an adjustable ring which acts as a stop, and only allows the punches to descend to one definite distance; until in fact the ring is pinched between the press and lever.

The screw of the fly-press, is sometimes superseded by a contrivance known both as the toggle joint, and as the knee joint. The two parts a, b, and b, c, fig. 953, are jointed to each other at b,

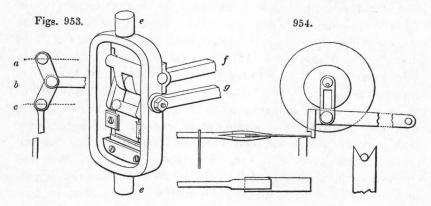

Figs. 953.   954.

the extremity a, is jointed to the upper part of the press, and c, to the top of the follower. When the parts a, b, and b, c, are inclined at a small angle the extremities a, and c, are brought closer together, and raise the follower, but when the two levers are straightened, a and c separate with a minute degree of motion, but almost irresistible power, especially towards the

* See Encyclopædia Metropolitana, part Manufactures, article Coining.

completion of the stroke.   The bending and straightening of the toggle joint, is effected by the revolution of a small crank, united to the point b, fig. 953, by a connecting rod b, f.

Presses with the toggle joint are perfectly suited to cutting out works with punches and bolsters, provided the relative thickness of the work and tools are such, as to bring to bear the strongest point of the mechanical action, at the moment the greatest resistance occurs in the work; but as the fly-press with a screw is in all cases powerful alike, irrespective of such proportions, provided alone that there is sufficient movement to create the required momentum, the fly-press is more generally useful.

The cut 954 refers to a lever press worked by an excentric, and used in cutting brads and nails, which will be again alluded to when this manufacture is briefly noticed.

It is now intended to describe a few examples of works executed in fly-presses, giving the preference to those appertaining to mechanism.

The round disks of metal for coin are always cut out with the fly-press, and are then called blanks, the punch being a solid cylinder, the bed or bolster a hollow cylinder that exactly fits it. In the gold currency, more especially, great care is taken to make these punches as nearly as it is possible mathematically alike in diameter, and the sheets of gold also mathematically alike in thickness, by aid of the drawing rollers or rather drawing cylinders referred to in vol. i., page 428; but notwithstanding every precaution the pieces or blanks when thus prepared do not always weigh strictly alike.   This minute difference is most ingeniously remedied, by using the one error as a compensation for the other.   Trial is made at each end of every strip of gold, and by cutting the thicker gold with the smaller punches, the adjustment is effected with the needful degree of accuracy, so that every piece is made critically true in weight, without the tedious necessity for weighing and scraping, otherwise needful.

Buttons are made in enormous quantities by means of the fly-press.   That metal buttons should be thus cut out with tools and stamped with dies, will be immediately obvious to all, but the fly-press has been also more or less employed in making buttons of horn, shell, wood, *papier-maché* and some other materials. Amongst others may be noticed the silk buttons called, Florentine buttons, each of which consists of several pieces that are cut out in presses, then enveloped by the silk covering, and clasped together at the back, (in the press,) by a perforated iron disk, the margin of which is formed into 6 or 8 points that clutch and hold the silk, whilst the cloth by which the button is sewed on, is at the same time protruded through the center hole in the back plate of the silk button; details that may be easily inspected by pulling one of them to pieces. Indeed great ingenuity has been displayed, and many patents have been granted, for making this necessary article of dress, a button.

Round washers that are placed under bolts and nuts in machinery, are punched out just like the blanks for coin; although in punching the larger washers, that measure 5 and 6 inches in diameter and $\frac{1}{4}$ inch thick, with the ordinary fly-presses, the iron requires to be made red hot.

The round or square holes in the washers are made at a second process with other tools, and to ensure the centrality of the holes, some kind of stop is temporarily affixed to the lower tool. The more complete stop is a thin plate of iron hollowed out at an angle of from 90 to 120 degrees and screwed on the top of the bed, as this may be set forward to suit various diameters. But the more usual plan, is to drill two holes in the bed, to drive in two wires, and to bend their ends flat down towards the central hole as also shown in fig. 955 overleaf, the ends of the wires are filed away until, after a few trials, it is found the blank when held in contact with the stops by the left hand, is truly pierced; the whole quantity may be then proceeded with as rapidly as the hands can be used, with confidence in the centrality of all the holes thus produced.

Chains with flat links that are used in machinery are made in the fly-press. The links are cut out of the form shown at a, fig. 956, the holes are afterwards punched just as in washers and one at a time, every blank being so held that its circular extremity touches the stops on the bed or die, and thereby the two holes become equidistant in all the links, which are afterwards strung together by inserting wire rivets through the holes.

The pins or rivets for the links, are cut off from the length of wire in the fly-press, by a pair of cutters like wide chisels with square edges, assisted by a stop to keep the pins of one length; or by one straight cutter and an angular cutter hollowed to about

60 degrees; or by two cutters each hollowed to 90 degrees. In the three cases, the wire is respectively cut from two, three, or four equidistant parts of its circumference; semicircular cutters are also used. The straight cutters first named, are moreover very usefully employed in the fly-press for many of the smaller works, that would otherwise be done with shears.

Sometimes the succession of the links for the chain, is one and two links alternately as at *b*, fig. 956; at other times 3 and 2, or 4 and 3 links, as at *c*, and so forth up to about 9 and 8 links

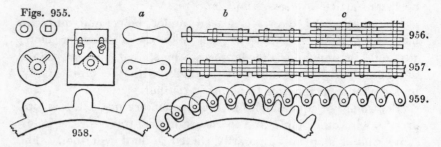

Figs. 955.

alternately, which are sometimes used, and the wires when inserted are slightly riveted at the ends.

The pin is generally the weakest part of the chain and gives way first, but in the chains with 8 and 9 links, the pin must be cut through at 16 places simultaneously, before the chain will yield.

Chains are sometimes intended to catch on pins or projections, around a wheel of the kind shown in fig. 958, to fulfil the office of leather bands, without the possibility of the slipping, which is apt to occur with bands when subjected to unusual strains.

Such chains are made after the manner shown in fig. 957, to constitute the square openings that fit over the pins of the wheel, the central links are made shorter, by which means the apertures are brought closer together than if the longer links were used throughout. Fig. 959, shows a different kind of chain, that has been used for catching in the teeth of an ordinary spur wheel with epicycloidal teeth, the author believes this chain to have been invented by the late Mr. John Oldham, Engineer to the Bank of England.

Chains for watches, time-pieces, and small machinery, are too minute to be made as above described, therefore the slip of steel is first punched through with the rivet holes required for a number of links, by means of a punch in which two steel wires are inserted; the distance between the intended links is obtained, (somewhat as in file cutting,) by resting the burrs of the two previous holes, against the sharp edge of the bed or bolster. The links are afterwards cut out by a punch and bolster of the kind already noticed, but very minute, and the punch has two pins inserted at the distance of the rivet holes, the slip of steel being every time fitted by two of the holes to these pins, all the links are thereby cut centrally around the rivet holes.

The tools are carried in a thick block having a perpendicular square hole, fitted with a stout square bar, the latter is driven with a hammer, which is supported on pivots, raised by a spring, and worked by a pedal; but when the links measure from $\frac{1}{4}$ to $\frac{1}{2}$ an inch in length, such tools are worked by a screw.

The punches are fitted to the side of the square bar, in a projecting loop or mortise, and secured by a wedge. They are drilled with holes for the pins, and across each punch there is a deep notch to expose the reverse ends of the pins, in order that when broken they may be driven out and replaced. The pins are taper pointed, that they may raise burrs, instead of cutting the metal clean out, and being taper, no puller-off is required, and the bed tools are fitted in chamfer grooves in the base of this old yet very efficient instrument.

A large chain for a pocket chronometer now before the author, measures nearly 14 inches in length, and contains in every inch of its length 22 rivets and also 33 links, (in three rows); the total number of pieces in the chain is therefore 770, and its weight is $9\frac{1}{2}$ grains. A chain for a small pocket watch, measures 6 inches in length, and has 42 rivets and 63 links in every inch, in all 630 pieces, and yet the entire chain only weighs one grain and three quarters.

The square links of chains for jewellery are often cut out with punches, the exterior and interior being each rectangular; after which each alternate link is slit with a fine saw for the introduction of the two contiguous links, and then soldered together so that the gaps become filled up. Other chains are drawn as square tubes, and cut off in short lengths with a saw, these after having been strung together are often drawn through a drawplate with round holes, to constitute chains which present an almost continuous cylindrical surface like round wire; a very neat manufacture invented in France.

The teeth of saws are for the most part cut in the fly press. Teeth of the forms figs. 643 to 647, page 684, whether large or small require but one punch, the sides of which meet at 60 degrees. Two studs are used to direct the edge of the blade for the saw to the punch, at the required angle depending on the *pitch* or inclination of the teeth, and an adjustable stop determines the *space* or interval from tooth to tooth, by catching against the side of the last tooth previously made. Gullet teeth, figs. 650 to 653, and the various other kinds shown, require punches of their several compounded figures, and of different dimensions for each size of tooth.

The teeth of circular saws are similarly punched out by mounting the perforated circular disk on a pin or axis, but in cutting the last six or eight teeth, it is needful to be watchful so as to divide the remaining space into moderately equal parts.

In cutting the teeth of circular saws not exceeding 12 inches diameter, Holtzapffel and Co. have been in the habit of mounting the steel plates on a spindle in a lathe with a dividing plate, and using a punch and bed fitted to a square socket, fixed horizontally in the ordinary rest or support for the turning tool, the punch being driven through the plate by one revolution of a snail or cam, by means of a winch handle, and thrown back by a spring. In this arrangement the dividing plate ensures the exact dimensions and equality of the teeth, which are rapidly and accurately cut.

The copper caps for percussion guns are punched out in the form of a cross with short equal arms, or sometimes in a similar shape with only three arms, and the blanks, after having been annealed, are thrown into form by means of dies, which fold up the arms and unite them to constitute the tubular part, whilst the central part of the metal forms the top of the cap, that receives the composition, and sustains the blow of the hammer.

Steel pens are another most prolific example of the result of the fly-press, they pass through the hands many times, and require to be submitted to the action of numerous dies, to five of which alone we shall advert. The blanks are cut by dies of the usual kind so as in general to produce a flat piece of the exterior form of fig. 960, page 944, the square mortise at the bottom of the slit is then punched through, the next process is usually to strike on the blanks the maker's name.

The slit is now cut by a thin chisel-like cutter, which makes an angular gap nearly through the steel, from that side of the metal intended to form the inner or concave part of the pen, and the act of curling up the pen into the channelled form, brings the angular sides of the groove into contact, rendering the slit almost invisible. The slit which is as yet only part way through the pen, is in general completed in the process of hardening, (see vol. i. page 249,) as the sudden transition into the cooling liquid, generally causes the little portion yet solid to crack through, or else the slit remains unfinished, until the moment the pen is pressed on the nail to open and examine its nibs.

Larivière's perforated plates for strainers, lanterns, meat safes, colanders and numerous other articles, exhibit great delicacy and accuracy in the mode in which they are punched out; the tools are illustrated by the enlarged sections, fig. 961 overleaf. The punch consists of a plate of steel called the punch plate, which is in some cases pierced with only one single line of equidistant holes, that are countersunk on their upper extremities. Every hole is filled with a small cylindrical punch made of steel wire, the end of which is bumped up, or upset to form a head, that fills the chamfer in the punch plate, so that the punch cannot be drawn out by the work in the ascent of the press. The bed punch or matrix has a number of equidistant holes corresponding most exactly with the punches. In this case the holes in the work are punched out one line at a time, and between each descent of the punches, the sheet of metal is shifted laterally by a screw slide, until it is in proper position to receive the adjoining line of holes.

At other times the tool instead of having only one line of punches, is wide and entirely covered with several lines, so as to punch some hundreds or even thousands of holes at one time. For circular plates the punches are sometimes arranged in one radial line, but more usually, the whole of the punches required for the fourth, sixth or eighth part of the circular disk are placed in the form of a sector, and the central hole having been first punched, is made to serve as the guide for the four, six or eight positions, at which these beautiful tools are applied.

Many of the thin plates thus punched require to be strained like the head of a drum to keep the metal flat, in which case the metal is grasped between little clamps or vices around its four edges, and then stretched by appropriate screws and slides with which the apparatus is furnished, and the same mechanism prevents the metal from rising, and therefore fulfils the office of the puller-off commonly used with punches.

The construction of the tools above described, calls for the greatest degree of precision, the drill employed to pierce the punch and matrix is of the kind fig. 474, page 547, and of exceedingly small size in the finest perforated works, as it is said

Figs. 960.   961.   962.

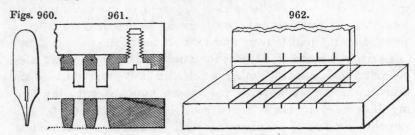

so many as six or seven hundred holes have been inserted in the length of six inches, which, considering the intervening spaces to be half as wide as the diameter of the holes, would make the latter of the minute size of only six thousandths of an inch diameter. Such finely perforated metal appears to offer nearly the transparency of muslin, and is a manifest proof of the great skill displayed in the construction of the instruments and in conducting the entire process.*

Mr. Julius Jeffery's Patent Respirator, or breath-warming apparatus, for persons having delicate lungs, presents another very neat example of punched works. Most persons will have had an opportunity of seeing, that the apparatus consists of about a dozen very thin plates of metal, punched out with several rows of large rectangular holes, leaving the metal like a delicate lattice. These lattices are severally wound round with fine wire and then assembled together between perforated covers. The exhalation of the breath amidst the interstices of the wires, warms the instrument, and the instrument in return, warms the air that is inhaled by the wearer.

To return to the operation of punching the lattices, it is to

---

* M. Marc Larivière's patent was granted 28th Nov., 1825, and is described in the Repertory of Patent Inventions, vol. iii. 3rd Series, page 182. Some other particulars are to be found in Gill's Technical Repository, vol. ix. 1826, page 375. translated from the Bibl. Univ., for Dec., 1824.

be observed these measure from center to center, half an inch in length and one fifth of an inch in breadth, the bed punch which is represented in fig. 962, is a piece of steel about $\frac{3}{4}$ inch thick, having a central aperture, $3\frac{1}{2}$ inches long, and 18 hundredths of an inch wide, as the long bars of the lattices are two hundredths wide. Six transverse notches, one eighth of an inch deep and half an inch asunder, are then made across the bed with a circular saw three hundredths of an inch thick, the grooves are fitted with slips of hardened steel, after which, the whole is ground to a level surface. The punch is a plate of steel $3\frac{1}{2}$ inches wide and ·18 thick, across which six notches about $\frac{1}{4}$ inch deep, are also made with the circular saw at intervals of $\frac{1}{2}$ inch.

The press has a puller-off or stop much as usual, and at the back it has a long screw of five threads in the inch, the nut of which has two square pins exactly like the two exterior portions of the punch. The copper, which measures about one hundredth of an inch thick, is cut in long wide strips, and one row of holes having been punched, the piece is hooked on the two pins of the nut, and when the screw has moved once round under the governance of a spring catch, a second row of holes is punched exactly one fifth of an inch from the former, and so on. When five rows have been punched, the screw is moved two turns to leave a wide rib, and another series of five rows is punched, and so on alternately, and afterwards the lattices are separated through the wide ribs with a pair of shears. Some of the lattices of small respirators have only six rows in the long and four in the narrow direction, and others five rows by three, thus making three distinct sizes with the same tools, and all present a most beautiful regularity and slenderness.*

All the foregoing examples of punched works, suppose the punch to have been *fixed* to the follower of the press, and the matrix to the base of the same, in which case the bed punch requires to be very exactly adjusted by the set screws or dogs of the press. But it remains in concluding this section, to advert to a different arrangement in which the cutting tools are quite *detached*, and are far less liable to accident or fracture, even

---

* Patent granted to Mr. Julius Jeffreys, for his improvements in curing or relieving disorders in the lungs. Sealed, 23rd January, 1836. Published in Repertory of Patent Inventions, Vol. vi. fourth series, page 211. The patent respirator is very fully described, but not so the machinery.

when the punches are of very large area and complicated figure, than when constructed in the ordinary manner with a shank by which they are united to the follower of the press. In this present case, the press has merely two flat surfaces six or eight inches in diameter, or square and of similar size, thereby more nearly resembling a hammer and anvil, of a very powerful and exact kind, to which the fly press was first compared.

Punches to be used in this manner, for works with various detached apertures requiring any especial arrangement, and for various straggling and complicated objects, are constructed as shown in figs. 963 to 965. There are two steel plates somewhat larger than the work, and from $\frac{3}{16}$ to $\frac{3}{8}$ thick, the plates are hinged together like the leaves of a book, but are placed sufficiently distant, to admit between them the work to be stamped out, and which is pinched between them by a thumb screw a. The two plates whilst folded together, are perforated with all the apertures required in the work, which perforations may be either detached, continuous, or arranged in any ornamental design that may be required. To all the apertures are fitted punches, which in length or vertical height, are about one eighth of an inch longer than the thickness of the upper plate, so as to stand up one eighth when resting on the material to be punched, as seen in the partial section 965, in which the work is shaded obliquely and the punch vertically.

As it would be difficult to fit the punches in one single piece to the ornamental or straggling parts of some devices, and as moreover such large and complicated punches, would be almost sure to become distorted in the hardening, or broken when in use, the difficulty is boldly met, by making the punch of as many small pieces as circumstances may render desirable, but which pieces, must collectively fill up all the insterstices of the plate.

In using these punching tools, it is only necessary first to fix between the plates the metal to be pierced, then to insert all the punches into their respective apertures, and lastly to give the whole one blow between the flat disks of a powerful fly press, this drives all the punches through the work, and leaves them flush with the upper surface. The whole is then removed from the press, and placed over an aperture in the work bench, and with a small drift and hammer the punches are driven out of the plates into a drawer beneath, and on the plates being separated, the work will be found to be exactly perforated to the same design as that of the tool itself; or with any part of the design instead of the whole, if part only of the punches were inserted in their respective places. The punches are selected from amidst the corresponding pieces of brass, which latter are laid on one side, and the routine is recommenced.

It is by this ingenious application of punches that buhl works are stamped, as referred to in the foot note page 737 of this volume. If a honeysuckle should be the device, the piece of brass is first placed between the plate and punched out, and provided the punches are of the same length, the honeysuckle

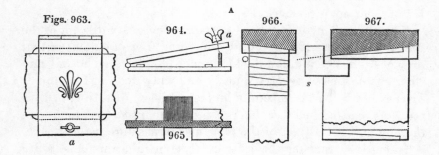

Figs. 963.   964.   A   966.   967.   965.

is removed in *one* piece although the punch may be in *several;* the wood is afterwards inserted, and is punched to exactly the same form, so that the brass honeysuckle will be found to fit in the most perfect manner as it is an exact counterpart of the removed wood.

The process is very economical and exact, but is only suited to large designs, because of the injury it would otherwise inflict on the wood, and on account of the expense of the tools, the mode is only proper for those patterns of which very large numbers are wanted; whereas the buhl saw is not liable to these limitations, but is of universal, although less rapid application.

Cut brads and *nails* or those which instead of being forged, are cut out of sheet iron by machinery, constitute the last example it is proposed to advance in this section.

Brads of the most simple kind as in fig. 966, have no heads, but are simply wedge form, and are cut out of strips of sheet iron, equal in width to the length of the brads, these strips are slit with circular shears, *transversely* from the ends of the sheets of iron so that the fibre of the iron may run lengthways through the nails.

When such brads are cut in the fly press, the bed has a rectangular mortise shown by the strong black line in fig. 966, the punch is made rather long and rectangular so as exactly to fill the bed, but the last portion of the punch, say for half an inch of its length, is nicked in, or filed back exactly to the size and angle of the brad, as shown in the inverted plan, in which the shaded portion shows the reduced part or tail of the punch.   The punch is never raised entirely out of the bed, in order that the strip of metal may be put so far over the hole in the bed, as the tail of the punch will allow it, and also in contact with a stop or pin fixed to the bed, and in the descent of the punch its outer or rectangular edge removes the brad.

The strip of metal is turned over between every descent of the press, so as to cut the head of the one brad from the point of that previously made, and the double guides afforded by the tail and stop, enable this to be very quickly and truly done.   The upper surface of the bed is not quite horizontal but a little inclined, so that the cutting may commence at the point of the brad, and thereby curl it less than if the tools met in absolute parallelism.

In cutting brads that have heads, the general arrangements are somewhat different as explained in the diagram fig. 967, in which as before, the rectangular aperture in the bottom tool is bounded by the strong black line, the tail of the punch is shaded, the stop s, is situated as far beyond the aperture in the bed, as the vertical height of the head, and it is so made that the small part which extends to the right, overhangs the slip of iron that is being cut, after the manner of a puller-off; but the overhanging part only comes into action when the slip is tilted up, either by accident, or from being so short as to give an insufficient purchase for the hand.   It is also to be observed that the width of the point of the brad, is just equal to the projection of its head.

On the end of the strip of iron being first applied, a wedge-form piece is cut off, exactly equal to the difference between the tail of the punch and the bed, and a little projection is left near s, and which projection, after the iron is turned over, rests against the tail of the punch, as shown in the figure, so that the succeeding cut removes the one brad and forms the head of the following; the tail of the punch being inclined to the precise angle drawn from the point to the head of the brad, as denoted in the diagram.

When, as it is more usual, brads are cut out by steam power, the cutters are not worked in a fly press, but the moving cutter is commonly fixed at the end of a long arm which is moved rapidly up and down by a crank; the strip of metal is held in a spring clamp, terminating in a long iron rod which rests in a Y or fork, so that the boy who attends the machine, can turn the metal over very rapidly between every alternation of the machine; these particulars are shown in fig. 954, page 937.

The machine fig. 954, may be used for brads either with or without heads, it is however, always necessary to turn the iron over between every cut; but in the toggle press fig. 953 on the same page, and which acts much more quickly, it is not requisite to reverse the metal, as the entire press is moved on its pivots *e e*, by the rod *g*, so as to incline the press alternately to the right and left, to the angle of such nails as are simply wedge-form, or have no heads, as in fig. 966, page 947.

In some machines resembling fig. 954, the nail as soon as cut off is grasped in a pair of forceps or dies, whilst a hammer, also moved by the machine, strikes a blow that upsets the metal, and constitutes the flat head in the kinds known as cut nails, and tacks.*

---

* The first patent for making nails that the author has met with, was granted to John Clifford, 17th July, 1790 (see Repertory of Patent Inventions, 1st Series, Vol. vii. p. 217). The mode preferred by the patentee, was to employ two rollers of iron faced with steel, in which were sunk impressions of the nails, half in each roller. The indentations were arranged circumferentially with the heads and tails in contact, so as to extend the grooves around the roller, and roll the whole rod of iron into a string of nails, which required to be separated from each other with shears, nippers, or other usual means. Sometimes many grooves were cut around the rollers, and a sheet of iron was then converted into several strings of nails that required to be separated nearly as before.

The same inventor took out a second patent, about six months later, for a method of making nails by punching. The plates of metal were forged or rolled taper to the angle of the nails, and were then cut up by a punch and bed, each made taper, and also to the angle of the nail. Nails that required heads were afterwards put into a heading tool or bed, having a taper hole of corresponding form, that left a small piece of the thick end projecting; and the head was upset with a punch or die, just after the manner now practised in making solid headed pins. This second patent was sealed on the 4th of Dec., 1790, and is described in the 377th page of the volume before referred to.

Subsequently to this period not less than thirty to forty patents have been granted for making brads and nails, and some three or four of them have been very successfully worked.

SECT. IV.—PUNCHING MACHINERY USED BY ENGINEERS.

After the remarks offered on pages 919 to 923, on shearing tools, little remains to be said in this place on the punching machinery used by engineers, as it was there stated that the cutters for shearing and the punches, were most usually combined in the same machine ; the punch being placed either at the outer extremity of the jointed lever, or at the bottom of the slide in those machines having rectilinear action. The punch is fixed to the slide or moving piece, the die is secured to the framing by means of four holding and adjusting screws just as in fly-presses, and the puller-off, or stop is likewise added, all which details are represented in the woodcuts on pages 920 and 922.

The principal application of the engineer's punching engine, is for making the rivet-holes around the edges of the plates of which steam-boilers, tanks and iron ships are composed. Another important use, and in which the punches trench upon the office of the shears, is in cutting out curvilinear parts and apertures or panels in boiler work, to which straight bladed shears cannot be applied. In this case the round punch is used in making a series of holes running into one another, along the particular line to be sheared through, or in other words the punch is used as a gouge, by which the hole that has been first formed, is extended by cutting away crescent-form pieces, thus leading the incision in any required direction.

This employment of the punch to shearing curved lines, is also much used in cutting out the side plates of the framings of locomotive engines, which consist of two pieces of stout boiler plate, (the technical name for iron in sheets from $\frac{1}{4}$ to $\frac{3}{4}$ inch thick,) riveted alongside a central piece of wood, that is sometimes also covered above and below with iron, all the parts being united by rivets. The punching engine serves admirably for cutting out all the curved lines in these side plates, also the spaces where the bearings for the wheels are situated, and various apertures.

Messrs. Maudslay Sons & Field introduced, many years back, a very great improvement in the punching engine, as applied to making boilers and tanks, in which the rivet-holes are usually required to be made in straight lines, and at exactly equal distances, so that holes in two pieces punched separately may exactly correspond.

The plate was fixed down upon a long rectilinear slide or carriage, and during every ascent of the punch, was advanced by the machine itself, the interval from hole to hole, the moment after the punch was disengaged from the work. Subsequently 2, 3, or 4 punches were fixed at equal distances in the vertical slide, but the punches were made of unequal lengths, so that they came successively into action, thereby dividing the strain, and the horizontal slide was consequently shifted every time a distance equal to 2, 3, or 4 intervals. This machine which displayed much ingenuity of invention served as the foundation of the more simple punching engines that are now met with.*

This volume will be concluded by the account of two sets of experiments in punching. The first " An account of some experiments to determine the force necessary to punch holes through plates of wrought iron and copper by Joseph Colthurst."†

" These experiments were performed with a cast iron lever, 11 feet long, multiplying the strain ten times, with a screw adjustment at the head, and a counterpoise."—" The sheets of iron and copper which were experimented upon, were placed between two perforated steel plates, and the punch, the nipple of which was perfectly flat on the face, being inserted into a hole in the upper plate was driven through by the pressure of the lever."

" The average results of the several experiments, (which are given in a detailed tabular form,) show that the power required to force a punch half an inch diameter through copper and iron plates is as follows :

---

* Messrs. Maudslay contrived their machine, in order to manufacture in a short space of time, a very considerable number of water tanks for the Royal Navy ; the machine is carefully engraved in plates 51 and 52 of Buchanan's Treatise on Mill Work, edited by G. Rennie Esq., F.R.S.

Other punching engines some of them with shears are also engraved on pages 48, 50, and 52ᵃ of the same valuable work.

The plate 52ᵃ contains the section and elevation of a steam punching machine by Mr. Cavé, of Paris, it is in effect a combination of the punching machine with the high pressure steam engine. This machine may carry either punches or shearing cutters at pleasure, but although apparently more costly than those actuated as usual by a simple crank movement, it does not appear to be so convenient, neither would it be politic to construct every machine in a factory, so as to include a steam engine for its own especial use.

† Extracted from the Minutes of Proceedings of the Institution of Civil Engineers for 1841, pages 60-1.

Iron plate   0·08 thick, required a pressure of   6,025 Pounds.
———————— 0·17 ———————————————— 11,950 ————
———————— 0·24 ———————————————— 17,100 ————
Copper plate 0·08 ——————————————— 3,983 ————
———————— 0·17 ———————————————— 7,883 ————

" Hence it is evident, that the force necessary to punch holes of different diameters through metal of various thicknesses, is directly as the diameter of the holes and the thickness of the metal. A simple rule for determining the force required for punching may be thus deduced. Taking one inch diameter and one inch in thickness as the units of calculation, it is shown that 150·00, is the constant number for wrought-iron plates, and 96·000 for copper plates. Multiply the constant number by the diameter in inches, and by the thickness in inches; the product is the pressure in pounds, that will be required to punch a hole of a given diameter through a plate of a given thickness."

" It was observed that the duration of pressure lessened considerably the ultimate force necessary to punch through metal, and that the use of oil on the punch reduced the pressure about 8 per cent." A drawing of the experimental lever and apparatus accompanied the communication.

The second experiments were by Mr. Hick of Bolton, who by means of a hydrostatic press having four cylinders in combination, punched through various pieces of iron; the thickest of them measured $3\frac{1}{2}$ inches thick, and from which was punched out a disk of 8 inches diameter, with a pressure of 2000 tons.

The removed piece was rather thinner than the remainder and a little taper, which arose from the circumstance of the bolster having been purposely made with a flat bottom, and a little larger in diameter than the punch, so that the disk when removed was a little spread or flattened out.

It is curious that experiments so distant from one another in their scale of proportion, should yet agree so nearly; by Mr. Coulthurst's formula

The computed force is . . $150·000 \times 8 \times 3\frac{1}{2} = 4·200·000$ lbs.

The actual force was . . . $2000 \times 20 \times 112 = 4·480·000$ lbs.

———————

END OF THE SECOND VOLUME.

APPENDIX.

During the period in which the Second Volume of this Work has been passing through the press, various new and additional matters having relation both to the first and second volumes have come under the author's notice ; the more important of these additions are here given. By inserting in the body of the first edition of the work references as follows:—see Appendix note H,—note I, &c., at the pages respectively designated, the notes will come under observation at their appropriate places in the text.

Note H, Page 22—To follow the Foot Note.
(Payne's Patent for preserving timber, by the double decomposition of sulphate of iron, and muriate of lime, within the pores of the wood.)

In this process, which is now more resorted to than others for this purpose, several pieces of timber are arranged side by side on a sledge, bound together by hoops and chains, and thus introduced upon a railway into a long cylindrical iron vessel, the cover or end of which is then screwed on air-tight. Steam is now admitted, first to drive out the air, through a valve opened for the purpose, and then to form a vacuum, which partially occurs when a little of the cold solution of *sulphate of iron* is pumped into the vessel, by means of the steam engine, to condense the steam ; the vacuum is then completed by an air pump, the liquid flows in as the air is exhausted, and is ultimately subjected to pressure by force pumps also worked by the steam engine ; this fills all the pores of the wood with sulphate of iron. After a few minutes the sulphate is allowed to flow out of the tank by the re-admission of air, the vessel is again heated with steam, and is similarly filled with *muriate of lime.*

A double decomposition instantly occurs *within the pores of the wood,* as the muriatic acid goes over to the iron, forming muriate of iron, and the sulphuric acid proceeds to the lime, forming solid sulphate of lime or gypsum, the latter remains principally in the pores, whilst the muriate of iron pervades the wood generally. The entire process of preparing the timber, including the filling and emptying of the tank requires from one to three hours, according to the size of the cylinder. The wood becomes much heavier, indisposed to decay, less combustible, darker in colour, and also proof against rot and the ravages of insects.

By certain variations of the process, and the employment of some other salts, the light coloured English woods may be stained in a variegated manner throughout their substance, so as to be available for making ornamental furniture, but the principal application hitherto made of the process, (for which the patent was specified in January 1842,) is for preparing timber for railway purposes, and for building, especially the wood used in piles and wet foundations.

Mr. Payne has a new patent, which will be shortly specified, designed for a different preparation of timber for the sheathing of ships and sea walls.

Note I, Page 25—To follow the Foot Note.
(The Bassŏŏlăh or Indian Adze.)

" By far the handiest instrument, (said the late Sir John Robison,) for blocking either hard or soft wood for the lathe, is the Bassŏŏlăh or Indian adze, with a head of from 1¾ to 2 pounds weight. The eye is conical and made widest at the upper end, so that the handle may be knocked out to allow of the adze being ground."

The Bassōōläh is represented at *d* fig. 318, page 473, of this present volume.

Notes J, K, L, Page 46—To conclude the Page.

Note J.—*Mr. Irving's Carving Machine.*

Since the period at which Messrs. Braithwaite's patent for carving wood by burning was granted in Nov. 1840 (see Note A, Appendix vol. i.) two other important patents have been taken out for carving wood by revolving cutters, and on each of which patents a few words will be now offered.

Mr. Irving's Patent, sealed November 1843, although it may be used for figures in low or high relief, is principally applicable to works in one plane, such as the mouldings of Gothic tracery, whether straight, curved, or undercut, and of all sections ; the work is generally executed from templets or pattern plates.

The revolving drill, or cutter, which is made globular, elliptical, or of the particular section of the moulding, is mounted on a vertical axis at the end of a swinging arm or lever, which is jointed to the solid framing of the machine. The wood or other material to be carved, is fixed towards the edge of a circular table that is free to move on a vertical and central post. The arm with the drill is capable of being adjusted vertically by means of a treadle, to make the tool penetrate more or less deeply into the work,

As therefore the drill may be moved in one arc, say nearly from east to west by swinging the arm upon its axis, and as the work may be also moved in another arc, nearly as from north to south, by swinging the table round upon its axis, and as these two motions may be accomplished simultaneously and in any relative degrees by the two hands, any outline that has been drawn on the work may be readily followed with the drill or cutter. But more usually a perforated templet is affixed upon the work, and the end of the cylindrical spindle or drill socket is allowed to rub against the templet, in order that the drill may cut away all the material between the interstices of the templet, and which latter mode is much the more rapid and exact, especially when many copies of the same work are required.

Many of the mouldings both in wood and soft stone, that are used in the new Houses of Parliament, are in the course of manufacture by this machine, which is now the property of Mr. Pratt, of London.

Note K, to follow note J, on Page 46.

Mr. Jordan's Patent Carving Machine.

Mr. Thomas Brown Jordan's Carving Machine, patented Feb. 17, 1845, is more employed for figures and ornaments than for mouldings, and two copies are generally carved at once, the pattern being placed midway between them.

The model and the wood for the copies are fixed, say exactly 8 or 10 inches asunder, upon a rectilinear slide free to move say from north to south, and which slide moves upon a second rectilinear slide free to move from east to west, these two slides run upon anti-friction rollers, and together support what is called " *the floating table,*" upon which the work is fixed. The two movements of the table are under the guidance of the two hands of the workman, while he controls a third slide with his foot. The third slide, which is vertical to the other two, carries in the center a tracer of globular form, and also at 8 or 10 inches on the right and left of the tracer, cutters of the same globular form, which latter are both set to make about 6000 or 7000 revolutions in the minute. The third slide, which together with the tracer and two cutters forms one entire mass, when left to itself descends with a moderate pressure that sends the two cutters into the two blocks of wood, until the central tracer rests in contact with the model, the cutting then ceases, and the slide is raised from the work by the treadle.

In this manner by a multitude of vertical incisions at different parts, the whole of the material might be cut away until the copies were reduced to the exact form of the model. But it is a more expeditious mode, together with the vertical motion of the drills and tracer, to move the work about horizontally by means of the two slides, as in every such rambling motion, the cutting will cease when the tracer comes in contact with the model. The only conditions are, that the cutter and tracer be exactly alike in form and size, and that the distance between them, and also the distance between the model and copies, whether 8 or 10 inches or other measure, be fixedly preserved throughout the one process.

The above case, in which the work lies always horizontally, is that most usually required ; but when the work has to be carved on all three sides, as for example in brackets or consoles projecting from a wall, although the arrangement of the central tracer and the cutters parallel therewith partaking of a vertical motion in common, remains unaltered, the model and copies are all three adjusted so as at one time all to lie on their backs, at other times all on their right or left sides with the progress of the work. Sometimes this change is effected simultaneously by mounting them on platforms, that are situated on fixed, parallel, and equidistant axes, and shifting all three at one movement, by a simple arrangement derived from the ordinary parallel rule with radius bars.

In the case of figures carved in the round, or on every side, the central model and two copies are built above one wide bar, upon three circulating pedestals or turn-plates with graduations and detents, by which the three objects may be alike twisted round to face any point of the compass ; and as the wide bar upon which the three circulating pedestals are built, has a tilting motion by which the three pedestals may be all alike placed either horizontally, or inclined, to the right or left in any required degree, until nearly vertical, it is clear that these two directions of motion constitute universal joints, and enable any and every similar part, of all three objects, to be presented to the tracer and cutters respectively.

Messrs. Taylor, Williams, and Jordan, of London, employ these carving machines for all the woods, and occasionally for soft stones, marble, and alabaster, and these machines as well as Mr. Pratt's are also contributing largely to the embellishment of the New Houses of Parliament and other buildings now in course of being erected.

Note L.—To follow Notes J and K on page 46.

(Mr. Tomes's Patent Dentifactor, for making artificial Gums, Teeth, and Palates.)

Another variety of carving machine, bearing some analogy to that last described, was invented at about the same time as Mr. Jordan's, we allude to Mr. Tomes's Dentifactor, a machine for carving the artificial teeth, gums, and palates used in dental surgery : patented March 3rd, 1845.

This machine, like the last, is intended to make an exact copy from a solid model, but which in Mr. Tomes's case is a true counterpart of the mouth of the individual, produced by moulding. Thus an impression of the mouth is taken as usual in softened bees'-wax, from this a plaster cast is obtained, and from the plaster a model or impression is made in a fusible though hard composition, principally gum lac combined with a softer gum, which produces an exact reverse or counterpart of the gums ; one that when carefully made fits so exactly to the surface of the mouth as even to exclude the air from between the model and gums, and is therefore capable of being retained in position without springs, simply by atmospheric pressure. The object of the machine is to carve an *exact* fac-simile of the composition model, in hippopotamus or walrus ivory, to constitute the artificial palate to which the teeth are fastened.

As some analogy necessarily exists between Mr. Tomes's machine and that last described, this account will be facilitated by briefly noticing some of the principal points of difference, resulting from the circumstances, that Mr. Tomes moves the work about in a *vertical* plane, and moves the drill in a *horizontal* plane, and usually cuts the material away by parallel cuts, extended laterally over the surface ; whereas in the wood carving machine, it will be remembered the work is *horizontal* the drill *vertical*, and the motion rambling in all directions.

Mr. Tomes's tracer and drill are fixed four inches asunder on one slide, that is moved horizontally towards the work by a weight, and pulled back by a lever ; and the cement model and the ivory to constitute the copy, are clamped on circular plates or disks, also four inches asunder, and which disks are fitted upon the slide plate of a long horizontal slide, moved by a coarse screw with a winch handle, by the traversing of which the series of lines is usually cut. This horizontal slide is mounted upon a vertical slide, having a screw and ratchet movement, so arranged that when one irregular undulating line of the work has been cut, and the drilling slide withdrawn to its full extent, the work is shifted by the ratchet movement, more or less either upwards or downwards, according to the particular nature of the work, and thus, by a succession of parallel cuts, the entire surface is eventually produced, the weight all along supplying one constant pressure to the slide carrying the drill and tracer, to keep them up to their work with the right degree of force; and from the graduated path of this machine, and its perfection of action, the tool-marks are not discoverable in the finished work, as they become completely merged one into the other.

To enable the few undercut parts, that occur in artificial palates, to be carved by the dentifactor, Mr. Tomes now makes the slide that carries the disks not with one flat surface, but to have two inclined and parallel planes, that serve as the foundations for the circular disks, and which latter are connected by one long tangent screw that moves the two upon their axes, similarly and equably ; so as by the angular change of the disks which carry the work and model, to place the few undercut parts successively at the lowest sides of the inclines, or at the bottoms of the hills, when such undercut parts, (unless they exceed in inclination 20 degrees, and which never occurs in this branch of art), slope the reverse way, so as to be conveniently accessible to the revolving cutter.

The dentifactor was constructed in the author's manufactory, and he therefore feels increased pleasure in announcing the complete efficacy of Mr. Tomes's project, which was favorably noticed in the *Minutes of Conversation of the Institute of Civil Engineers*, page 250 ; in the *Medical Gazette*, p. 161, and numerous other publications, and for which invention Mr. Tomes received the *Gold Isis Medal* of the Society of Arts,—all in 1845.

Note M, Page 121.—To precede the last two lines.

(Straightening stag-horn and buck-horn.)

Stag and buck-horn admit of being partially straightened, when in thin pieces or scales, to adapt them to the forms of the handles of pen and pocket knives. To effect this, a dozen pieces of the stag or buck-horn, when reduced nearly as thin as required, are thrown into a vessel of water almost boiling, and on removal one at a time, are flattened or untwisted, by grasping their ends between pliers, and straining them into form, after which they are allowed to cool in the air, or are sometimes dipped in cold water. The under sides of the scales are then filed or rasped upon a strip of iron held in the *flatting vice,* represented in fig. 864, page 864.

Stag-horn and buck-horn are considered to become more brittle from the immersion, which is therefore made as short as possible. Stag-horn, buck-horn, ivory and pearl-shell, especially the first, are somewhat liable to cause rust on the steel works of knives, not so however tortoiseshell, or buffalo and similar horn.

Note N, Page 155.—To follow the first paragraph.

(Isinglass glue.)

"If it be wished to dissolve good isinglass in spirits of wine, it should first be allowed to soak for some time in cold water, when swelled it is to be put into the spirit, and the bottle containing it being set in a pan of cold water may be brought to the boiling point, when the isinglass will melt into an uniform jelly, without lumps or strings, which it is apt to have if not swelled in cold water previously to being put in spirits ; a small addition of any essential oil diminishes its tendency to become mouldy."

"If gelatine which has been swelled in cold water, be immersed in linseed oil and heated, it dissolves and forms a glue of remarkable tenacity, which when once dry perfectly resists damp, and two pieces of wood joined by it will separate anywhere else rather than at the joint. Ordinary glue may be thus dissolved and sometimes a small quantity of red lead in powder is added." *Sir J. Robison.*

Note O, Page 160—161.

(Prosser's patent process for works made of dry clay.)

The first line of the article on clay, which ran as follows : " This material is only worked in the soft and plastic state," is unintentionally erroneous, as the author since learns that Mr. Mencke obtained in 1828 a patent for manufacturing bricks and tiles from dry pulverized clay, containing a quantity of moisture not exceeding one per cent., the clay was pressed forcibly into moulds and immediately baked, without the necessity for its being dried, and from the dense condition of the compressed mass, without the risk of cracking in the fire.

Mr. Rowland Prosser's patent, 1840, is for a similar but superior employment of dry clay, sometimes mixed with colouring matters, for making buttons, rings, knobs, the tesseræ for pavement, and other things. The dry powder is put into a deep mould, that holds just the right quantity, and terminates at foot in the bottom die, the top die is attached to the fly press, descends within the tube, and moulds the object, making the four holes in the button at the same moment. The pieces are released from the mould by a piston or rammer pressed upwards as usual by a treadle or otherwise. This patent is successfully worked by Messrs. Minter of Stoke-upon-Trent.

Note P, Page 191, to precede Section IV.

(Clay's patent process for manufacturing wrought iron.)

The author transcribes from the Minutes of Conversation of the Institution of Civil Engineers for 1843, page 82, a part of the account of this process.

" By the ordinary system of iron-making, the ores are reduced into the state of carburet of iron, and then, by refining and puddling, the metal is de-carburetted, thus making it into malleable iron by a number of processes which are recapitulated :—"

" 1st. Calcining the ore.

" 2nd. Smelting in a furnace, by the aid of blast, either cold or heated, with raw coal, or coke, for fuel, and limestone as a flux.

" 3rd. Refining the ' pig' into ' plate' iron.

" 4th. Puddling, shingling, and rolling, to produce 'merchant' or No. 2. bars.

" 6th. A repetition of the same process to make ' best' or No. 3. bars."

" Seeking to diminish the number of manipulations by the new process a mixture of dry Ulverstone, or other rich ore (Hæmatite,) is ground with about four-tenths of its weight of small coal, so as to pass through a screen of one-eighth of an inch mesh. This mixture is placed in a hopper, fixed over a preparatory bed, or oven, attached to a puddling furnace of the ordinary form. While one charge is being worked and balled, another gradually falls from the hopper, through the crown upon the preparatory bed, and becomes thoroughly and uniformly heated ; the carburetted hydrogen and carbon of the coal, combining with the oxygen of the ore, advances the decomposition of the mineral, while by the combustion of these gases, the puddling furnace is prevented from being injuriously cooled. One charge being withdrawn another is brought forward, and in about an hour and a half the iron is balled, and ready for shingling and rolling."

" The cinder produced is superior in quality to that which results from the common system ; it contains from 50 to 55 per cent. of iron, and is free from phosphoric acid, which frequently exists, and is so injurious in all the ordinary slags : when re-smelted the cinder produces as much as No. 1 and No. 2 cast-iron, and is of as good quality, as the ordinary ' black band' ore of Scotland."

The process was highly commended by the meeting as being simple and scientific, and evidence was advanced to show the iron produced in this mode, to be equal to the best cable iron.

Note Q, Page 196 of Vol. i.—To follow the Foot Note.

(Nasmyth's Patent Direct-action Steam Hammer.)

Since the foregoing pages were printed, a valued friend of the author, Mr. James Nasmyth, of Patricroft near Manchester, has brought into successful operation two very important machines, the one the Direct-action Steam Hammer employed in the place of the old helves or lift hammers, the other a legitimate descendant of the above hammer, a machine invented for driving the piles required for the foundations of buildings and coffer dams. The author is enabled to present to his readers some particulars of these machines, which their inventor has been kind enough to write for these pages.

" Fig. 968 represents a general view of the steam hammer, B is the cylinder in which the piston works, and to the piston-rod which comes out at the *bottom* of the cylinder is attached the hammer A, high-pressure steam is let in under the piston, which raises it together with the hammer A, to any required height within its vertical range of motion, and in which it is guided by two planed guides EE. On the escape of the steam when the valve of the cylinder is opened, the hammer falls on the work that lies on the anvil with the full force due to gravity, and without any loss worth naming from friction ; the instant the hammer has given its blow the steam is again let in under the piston, and the same action is repeated with ease and rapidity."

" When it is desired to lessen the force of the blow, the steam is let in under the piston, *ere the fall is complete*, so that a cushion of steam is then presented to receive the force, and modify it to any required extent ; such is the precision with which this can be done, that the hammer may be arrested in the most soft and silent manner even when within one-tenth of an inch of the anvil. The hammer can be thus set to give any definite blows, by the due adjustment of the lever which closes the valve, for which purpose its position is regulated by two long screws seen in the figure ; the re-opening of the valve is effected by a small cylinder and piston (at B), on the top of which piston steam is made to act as a most perfect spring."

" When, on the other hand, it is desired to increase the energy of the hammer, by making it give blows even more powerful than those due to the highest fall of the hammer by gravity alone, the following simple but effective arrangement is

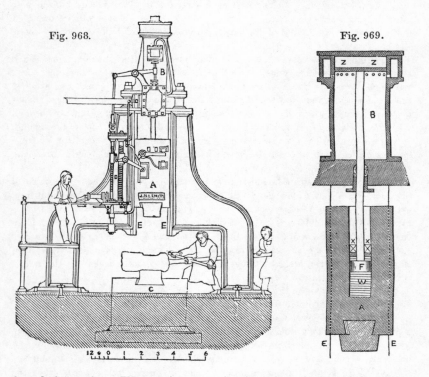

Fig. 968.

Fig. 969.

brought into action. This contrivance consists in making the top of the cylinder quite steam and air tight, so that when the piston passes beyond the holes *o o o o* fig. 969, the old steam or air which is then pent up in the chamber Z Z above the piston, may obtain a reviving energy by the compression it receives from the upward motion of the piston, and this compression is wholly returned in the condition of elastic recoil of the most perfect kind, which recoil added to the simple gravity of the hammer vastly augments the rapidity and intensity of the blows. As soon as the piston re-passes the holes o o o o the old steam or air re-enters with perfect freedom, so as to offer no resistance to the fall of the hammer."

" It may be well to notice in conclusion, the peculiar, elastic, yet firm manner in which the connection between the piston rod and hammer block is made ; this being one of the most important details in the whole arrangement, and without which this invention would have possessed but little practical utility. It will be seen in the enlarged section, fig. 969, that the piston rod has a large end F, forged to it, this goes down into a well inside the hammer block, and rests on several pieces of hard wood placed at W, one or two rings of the same material being placed above the part F, the whole being keyed hard down by two taper keys XX, which are driven in over the wood rings through the body of the hammer ; these cross keys retain all the parts firmly together."

" This attachment while it effectually unites the piston rod and hammer, at the same time presents such an elastic or yielding medium, as to remove all risk of destructive action, which would be otherwise certain to occur, if any hard unyielding substance were placed between the anvil and hammer, or that these two parts were allowed accidently to come in violent contact ; no such concussion can now injuriously affect the piston and hammer. A close resemblance will be observed in this arrangement to that of the cartilage in the joints of animals between bone and bone."

The author of this volume has to add, that several of these steam hammers have been erected in our Government Dock Yards, and at the works of various engineers ; sometimes they have flat-faced hammers and anvils for general purposes ; at other times semicircular tools for swaging round shafts, and in this case peculiar advantage arises from the steam cushion, which prevents the approach of the tools beyond one precise distance, so that the shaft is made of uniform diameter throughout.

The steam hammer has also been employed in manufacturing large copper pans, into the central parts of which the convex hammer then dips with unerring precision, and any particular measure of force.

The largest of the steam hammers as yet made, has been erected in the works of Sir John Guest, Bart., Dowlais, South Wales, for the manufacture of wrought iron, and in this machine the hammer weighs 6 tons, it can be raised 7 feet, and its face measures 4 feet by 2 feet, so as to consolidate at one action, the entire mass of the *blooms* or *uses* for making railway bars, as the hammer face includes the whole surface of the bloom at every blow ; the bed or anvil, perhaps the largest iron casting in the world, weighs 36 tons, and was cast in one mass from the united contents of four great furnaces.

In a former account of the steam hammer, written by Mr. Nasmyth for the Civil Engineer's and Architect's Journal, Vol. VI. page 40, he first describes the *circuitous* mode in which the power was conveyed from the steam engine through intermediate gear and shafting, to the old helves or lift hammers, alluded to in the first volume, some of which lift hammers although weighing upwards of 6 or 7 tons, give by comparison ineffective blows on large masses, because from moving on a joint the rise and fall of the hammer is limited ; and in forging thick works when the strongest blows are required, the hammer has the less space to fall. Mr. Nasmyth then contrasts the above *circuitous* mode, with his own simple and " *direct* " means applied to the same end, under an arrangement in which the *largest* works may with more consistency be made to receive the *strongest* blows.

Another comparison there also instituted is greatly favourable to the patentee, as he adds that although from various practical reasons, the dimensions of the old helves cannot be materially exceeded ; the cylinders and appendages required in the new hammer admit of an almost unlimited increase in their magnitude, in order to meet the continual aggrandizements of engineering requirements.

Note R.—To follow Note Q on Page 196.
(*Mr. Nasmyth's Steam Pile Driving Engine.*)

On this machine Mr. Nasmyth writes—" There are two grand or important features of novelty in this pile-driving engine, compared with all former contrivances for the like purpose. In the first place by the employment of the steam hammer action, the steam is made to act direct in raising up and letting fall the hammer, or *monkey*, without the intervention of any rotative motion, while in the second place another grand feature of novelty consists in the employment of the pile which we are about to drive, as the foundation or sole support of the apparatus A, B, C, fig. 971, so that by its resting on the shoulders of the pile, we have not only the effect produced by the blows of the hammer, (30 cwt. at 80 to 100 three feet falls per minute,) but we have also the entire weight of the apparatus A, B, C, equal to 3 tons assisting in a most important degree to force the pile down into the ground."

" The pile to be driven is raised up and planted in its situation by the machine by means of a windlass worked by a small detached steam engine at H, the apparatus A, B, C, is at the same time raised up and

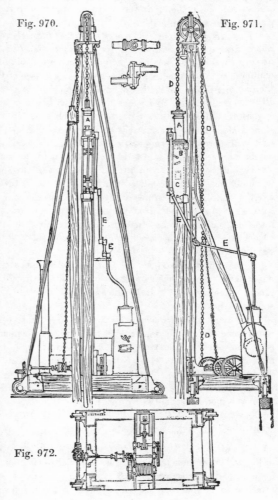

Fig. 970.

Fig. 971.

Fig. 972.

placed on the shoulders of the pile, like an extinguisher on a candle, the chain D, D, is then let free, so that the entire weight of A, B, C, shall rest on the pile ; the steam is now let in from the boiler to the cylinder, by the jointed wrought iron pipe E, E, the hammer then sets to work with great energy, showering down its ponderous blows on the head of the pile at the rate of 80 to 100 per minute, at each blow the pile sinks, and the machinery A, B, C, follows down with it, guided in its descent by clamps which loosely grasp a guide rail fixed on the side of the great upright, and which upright also retains the pile in true position all the way down."

" Some idea of the rapidity with which piles are driven by this machine may be formed, when we state that a pile of 60 feet in length and 14 inches square, can be driven 45 feet into stiff soil down to the rock below in 4 minutes, and such is the good effect resulting from the blows being given by a *great mass*, of 30 cwt. striking *quickly* but with small velocity of actual impact, that the pile head requires no hoop, and presents after being driven a neater appearance than it had when it was first placed under the hammer."

" This is a very important result, and the natural consequence arising *from the employment of mechanical force in the right conditions for the purpose required*, namely in this case, striking a quick succession of blows with a large mass or hammer, but with small velocity of impact, by reason of the small height from which the hammer falls ; the action of the ordinary pile driver being quite the reverse of all these conditions.   By inspecting the figure it will be seen that the entire machine is possessed of locomotive powers, inasmuch as it is mounted on wheels and moves along rails so as to pass onwards as the piles are driven in succession, it may be as well to observe that the apparatus A, B, C, is only raised up by the small fixed steam engine *once per pile*, instead of *once per blow*, as in the case of the ordinary machine."

The author has not had the advantage of seeing Mr. Nasmyth's pile-driving machine, but he understands from eye-witnesses " that its rapidity is such as to excite a smile, from the almost marvellous manner in which this '*jack in the box*,' (the hammer being concealed from view by the frame or casing,) performs its work, as it fulfils in 4 minutes, that which frequently required, by the old machine, a period of 36 hours, presenting a ratio in the time saved as 540 to 1, a ratio most egregious but true withal."

" A pile said to have been driven *home*, or as far as possible by the old pile-driving engine, (as the old ram then rebounded as from a solid rock,) was driven a further quantity of 10 feet by the steam pile driver, until it had indeed met the solid rock beneath."

" The action of the machine is adduced as a most perfect evidence of the high importance of knowing under what modification we should use force in the accomplishment of certain duties ; thus—if you want to split and shatter a pile into lucifer matches, then let fall *cannon balls* upon it from a great height, but if you want to drive the pile, then let the *cannon itself* fall on it, and that from a small height, and as rapidly as it can be effected, say 100 times in a minute, so that it may never give the pile a moment's time to *set fast* in the soil."

Note S, page 202.—To follow the third paragraph.
(*The Oliver, or small lift hammer.*)

Fig. 973 represents a species of lift hammer worked by the foot. The hammer head is about 2½ inches square and 10 long, with a swage tool having a conical crease attached to it, and a corresponding swage is fixed in a square cast-iron anvil block, about 12 inches square, and 6 deep, with one or two round holes for punching, &c. The hammer handle is about 2 to 2½ feet long, and mounted in a cross spindle nearly as long, supported in a wooden frame between end screws, to adjust the groove in the hammer face to that in the anvil block. A short arm, 5 or 6 inches long, is attached to the right end of the hammer axis, and from this arm proceeds a cord to a spring pole overhead, and also a chain to a treadle a little above the floor of the smithy.

When left to itself the hammer handle is raised to nearly a vertical position by

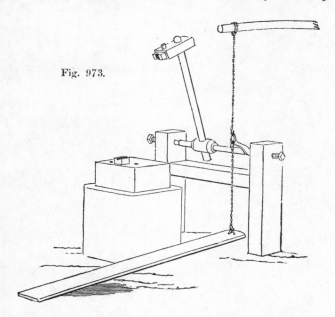

Fig. 973.

the spring, and it is brought down very readily with the foot, so as to give good hard blows at the commencement of moulding the objects, and then light blows for finishing them. The machine was used when the author first saw it, in making long stout nails, intended for fixing the tires of wheels, secured within the felloes by washers and rivetting ; the nails were made very nicely round and taper, and were forged expeditiously.

Note T, page 226.—To follow the fifth line.
(*The Manufacture of Wrought Iron Tubes.*)

The author's attention has been drawn to the contents of pages 225 and 226 of his first volume, referring to the manufacture of wrought iron tubes, associated with a regret, that he had not set forth more fully and historically the progressive steps through which this interesting and important manufacture has arrived at its present state of perfection.

Upon this hint the author requested Mr. Prosser, with whom the suggestion originated, to point out the errors of mode and date that he had committed, and which correction Mr. Prosser has most kindly rendered in the accompanying synoptical table here inserted without alteration.

3 Q 2

SYNOPTICAL TABLE

OF THE

MANUFACTURE OF IRON TUBES.

Drawn up for this Work by Rowland Prosser, Esq., C.E., of Birmingham.

Drawbench introduced into England 1565.

Rolls invented for rolling iron by Cort 1783.

Drawbench and Rolls used for making lead pipes by Wilkinson 1790.

Combination of 2, 3 or more pairs of rolls by Hayledine 1798.

	Benj. Cook.	James and Jones.	Henry Osborne.	Henry Osborne.	James Russell.	Cornelius Whitehouse.	George Royl.	Harvey and Brown.	T. H. Russell.	Richard Prosser.	Job Cutler.	Russell and Whitehouse.
Dates of Patents	1808	1812	1812	1817	1824	1825	1831	1836	1836	1840	1841	1842
WELDING BY												
Hand hammers	1808	..	..	..	..	..	..	..	..	..	..	..
Power hammers	..	1812	1812	..	1824	..	..	..	..	..	..	..
Many holes in two rolls	..	1812	..	1817	..	..	1831	..	..	..	..	..
Many holes in two rolls alternating	..	1812	..	..	..	..	..	..	..	..	..	..
Segment moving on a bed	..	..	1812	..	..	..	..	..	..	..	..	..
Three or four rolls making one hole	..	..	..	..	..	..	..	..	..	1840	..	..
Drawing through holes or tongs	..	..	..	..	..	1825	..	..	..	..	1841	1842
Drawing through rolls	..	..	..	..	..	..	..	..	1836	..	1841	..
FINISHING BY												
Drawbench and holes	1808	..	..	..	..	..	1831	..	1836	..	1841	..
Drawbench and rolls	1808	..	..	..	1824	..	..	..	1836	..	..	..
Drawing over a mandril	..	..	..	..	..	..	..	..	..	..	1841	..
FORM OF MANDRIL.												
No mandril	..	..	1812	..	1824	1825	1831	..	1836	..	..	..
Parallel and in motion	1808	..	1812	..	1824	..	..	..	..	..	..	1842
Taper and in motion	..	1812	..	..	..	..	..	..	..	..	..	..
Enlarged end, and at rest	..	..	..	1817	..	..	..	1836	..	1840	1841	..
FORM OF JOINT.												
Butt (or jump)	..	..	..	..	1824	1825	1831	1836	1836	1840	1841	..
Scarf (or lap)	1808	1812	1812	1817	..	..	..	1836	..	1840	1841	1842

In the first column on the left of the Synoptical Table, are represented little sketches of the principal means employed in the manufacture of welded tubes ; next follow the verbal explanations of the sketches ; and the group of columns on the right are headed with the names of patentees and the dates of their patents. The dates inserted in these columns, in the same horizontal lines as the sketches, are intended to show that such means were employed under the several patents desig nated by the dates.

For example, running the eye down the first date column, it is to be understood that Benjamin Cook's, the first patent for the manufacture of iron tubes, was dated 1808—that by him the tube was welded by the hand hammer—finished by the draw-bench and drawing rolls—that the mandril employed was parallel, and lastly that the tube had a scarf or lap joint—and so with all the others.

This tabular view, although most fascinating for a cursory inspection, could not be made to convey various matters of detail, and points of important yet minute difference, which have existed in the several modes of practice, and which have given rise to many and expensive lawsuits. And therefore, as a brief summary of the entire manufacture, the author subjoins, from the pen of a friend who is professionally and intimately acquainted with the subject, a condensed account, showing the dates, titles, and the main features and processes of the entire series of patents for making wrought iron tubes.

" BENJAMIN COOK, of Birmingham. Patent dated 28th March 1808 for a method of making barrels for fowling pieces, muskets, pistols and other similar fire-arms and ramrods for the same." '

" The Patentee proposed three plans of making barrels, in one only of which was there any welding."

" The first plan consisted of forging or otherwise producing a round bar of iron or other proper metal of a short length as compared with the intended barrel, and then a hole was drilled in the same, and it was proposed to elongate the barrel by draw plates similar to wire drawing but having a mandril in the barrel, or the elongation was to be effected by grooved rollers using a mandril inside the barrel."

" The second plan was to turn a short plate of iron or steel over a mandril or beak iron, and to weld it by hand, then to elongate the barrel so produced by drawing through holes in dies or by grooved rollers as before, using a mandril inside the barrel when elongating it."

" The third plan consisted of taking a circular plate of metal, and then by successively forcing it through a series of holes in a die it was proposed to raise it into the shape of a cup, and then having done so the cup was to be elongated by drawing it through holes in a die or by means of a pair of grooved rollers, using a mandril on the inside of the barrel when elongating it ; none of these plans succeeded, and they never came into public use."

" HENRY JAMES AND JOHN JONES, of Birmingham. Patent granted 26th July 1811, for an Improvement in the manufacture of barrels of all descriptions of fire-arms and artillery."

" There are two methods of welding barrels described in this invention. First the plate of iron was to be turned over into the shape of a barrel, so that the edges should be brought into a position for welding, a part of the barrel being heated to a welding heat, was to be placed on a hollow anvil having several grooves to correspond with the barrel, and then by a series of hammers, worked by machinery, the heated part of the barrel was to be welded ; a stamp or mandril being inserted in the barrel when welding. And secondly, the Patentee proposed to use grooved rollers, the grooves being of the figures of the barrel, and a mandril was to be used. This appears to be the first invention of the use of grooved rollers to weld barrels of fire-arms."

" HENRY OSBORN, of Bordesly, near Birmingham, Sword and Gun Barrel Maker. Patent granted 1st of March 1817, for a new method or principle of producing cylinders of various descriptions."

" The Patentee had a previous patent for turning the plates of iron ready to be welded into barrels or cylinders, and this was done by grooved rollers, the present patent was for using grooved rollers as a means of welding cylinders or gun barrels and it consisted in using similar grooved rollers to those described by James and Jones ; but in this patent a mode of using a mandril was described very different to that suggested by James and Jones, and it is by means of these Inventions that by far the largest proportion of gun barrels have ever since been welded in Birmingham."

" The novelty in using the mandril consisted in this, there was to be a shield fixed on the mandril so as to prevent the mandril being drawn through between the grooved rollers when welding a cylinder or barrel thereon. In using the mandril it was inserted into an unwelded barrel (the barrel being at a welding heat) and conveyed thereon to the rollers, the mandril being retained by stops which prevent the shield passing ; thus the barrel, as it was welded by the rollers, was drawn off the mandril, the mandril keeping the bore open and preventing the iron from being rolled into a solid mass. In this manner was the weld made, and then by repeatedly heating the barrel or cylinder, and passing it between grooved rollers with a succession of mandrils, the barrel or cylinder was drawn out to the desired length."

" JAMES RUSSELL, of Wednesbury, Gas Tube Manufacturer. Patent granted 19th January 1824, for an Improvement in the manufacture of tubes for Gas and other purposes."

"This Patentee proposed to weld iron tubes or barrels by means of a hollow hammer and tool, and it was intended that the tube to be welded should be held in the hollow tool and receive blows by the hollow hammer, and this welding was to be done either with or without the aid of a mandril. And then having welded the tube or barrel it was to be shaped interiorly and exteriorly by means of a pair of grooved rollers and a mandril with a large head, over which the grooved rollers were to move the welded tube or barrel. This Patent failed of success. It was found that the hollow hammer and corresponding hollow tool would, if they embraced the barrel, have no effect on it, and if the barrel was too large in diameter for the hollow, it would only be crushed by the sides of the hammer and the hollow tool."

" CORNELIUS WHITEHOUSE, of Wednesbury, Stafford, Whitesmith. Patent dated 26th February 1825, for certain Improvements in manufacturing Tubes for Gas and other purposes."

" This Invention was the first to suggest that a tube might be formed and welded by simply applying external pressure without internal support, and the inventor described the means of accomplishing the welding and shaping of iron tubes for gas and other purposes, to consist of, first, turning up the plates of iron so that the edges would come together or nearly so, and then about half the length was to be heated to a welding heat, and by means of a draw bench such heated part of the prepared tube was to be drawn through a bell-mouthed die, which might be formed in the shape of a pair of tongs with handles to open or close the two halves of the die, or the two halves might be opened or closed by a screw. The inventor did not confine himself to the particular construction of the dies, and it was held by a Court of Law that grooved rollers capable of giving complete circumferential pressure when no internal support of a mandril was resorted to, was within the claim of the Patentee."

" Such was the great simplicity and utility of this Invention, that notwithstanding the assignee of the Patent, Mr. Russell, had made a very considerable sum of money by the Patent, the Privy Council advised the Crown to extend the period for which the Patent was granted from 14 to 20 years."

" GEORGE ROYL, Walsall, Stafford, Whitesmith. Patent granted 21st March, 1831, for an Improved method of making Iron pipes, tubes, or cylinders."

" This Patentee proposed to use two grooved rollers placed in front of the furnace, so that the prepared tube when it was heated to a proper welding heat should be drawn out and welded by the rollers ; and to facilitate the working, the upper roller was capable of being separated from the under one by which the tube could be moved between the rollers, and when the upper roller was brought to the lower roller and motion communicated to them, the tube was run out of the furnace and welded. The tubes being thus welded, were to be passed through dies, to give them a better shape : this invention was put into use by Messrs. Dixon & Co. of Wolverhampton. This mode of manufacture was declared to be an infringement of Whitehouse's Patent because the welding was by circumferential pressure without any mandril or internal support being employed."

" FREDERICK EDWARD HARVEY, of Tipton, Staffordshire, and JERE-MIAH BROWN, of the same place. Patent granted 3rd February, 1836, for certain Improvements in the process and machinery for manufacturing Metallic Tubes, and also in the process or machinery for forging or rolling metal for other purposes."

" In this invention grooved rollers were employed, and the principal novelty consisted in the mode of supporting the mandril, which was a short instrument placed and fixed in front of the rollers, and in such manner that the enlarged head came just in the pinch of the rollers, and in working, the heated tube was to be forced over the short cranked stem of the mandril, the unclosed seam of the tube being sufficiently open to allow it to pass the fin by which the stem of the mandril was carried."

" THOMAS HENRY RUSSELL, of Handsworth, Warwick, Tube-maker. Patent granted 3rd May, 1836, for improvements in making or manufacturing welded Iron Tubes."

" This Patentee proposed to make welded iron tubes without first turning up the Iron plate from end to end, and the invention consisted of only turning up a few inches of the length and then by apparatus placed in front of the furnace, to cause the plate of iron when in a welding state to be first turned into the shape of a tube, and the welding was simultaneously to go on by means of dies or by rollers in the manner of Whitehouse's Invention before mentioned."

" RICHARD PROSSER, of Birmingham, Civil Engineer. Patent dated 27th March, 1840, for improvements in machinery or apparatus for manufacturing Pipes.' "

" This Patentee proposed to use a combination of three or four rollers. When four rollers are employed they are formed with grooves all exactly equal to the quadrant of a circle, and with edges bevelled at 45 degrees, so as collectively to make up the entire circle. The four rollers are connected with equal wheels, in order that they may travel with the same velocity. The end of the thin strip of iron is bent to the circle, and when at the proper heat the rollers carry it forward, and depose the welded tube upon a long mandril smaller than the bore of the tube, and placed immediately opposite the rollers : the mandril serves to support the tube whilst in its heated and soft state. Large numbers of tubes have been made in this manner by the four rollers, and when three only are employed they embrace one-third of the circle instead of the fourth."

" THOMAS HENRY RUSSELL, of Wednesbury, Staffordshire, and CORNE-LIUS WHITEHOUSE, of the same place. Patent granted March 7th, 1842, for improvements in the manufacture of welded Iron Tubes."

" This Invention has for its object a mode of welding very thin iron tubes when making lap joints, and the tubes were particularly intended for steam boilers. The invention consisted in using a mandril of small diameter, when compared with the intended diameter of the tube, and the tube was welded by passing the tube with the mandril in it between grooved rollers or through bell-mouthed dies, the hole being of an oval shape : so that when mak-ing the weld the mandril was set fast in the tube throughout its length, but on passing the welded tube through dies with a circular opening, the tube was made cylindrical, thus allowing the mandril to be readily withdrawn in consequence of the smallness of its diameter, when compared with that of the tube. The pressure of the roller or dies was made to act first on the outer edge of the lap joint, then on the inner, and lastly on the central part ; the three processes being accomplished at one heat, and the diametrical line upon which the pressure was applied, became for the time the shorter diameter of the oval."

" JAMES ROOSE, of Wednesbury, Stafford. Patent granted 9th May, 1843, for an Improvement or Improvements in the mode or method of manufacturing welded Iron Tubes."

" This Invention consisted of a mode of using dies, and also rollers with grooves and mandrils, in a peculiar manner which does not appear to have come into use."

" JOHN JAMES RUSSELL, and THOMAS HENRY RUSSELL, of Wed-nesbury, Staffordshire, Tube Manufacturers. Patent granted July 24, 1844."

" This Invention was for the welding of the larger class of tubes for boiler and such like purposes, and consisted of a moving hollow bed on which the prepared tube in an unwelded state was placed ; and the bed with the tube passed under a grooved roller. A fixed mandril being used on the inside of the pipe over which the pipe moved, so as to give support and resistance where the weld was taking place. The end of the tube being fixed to the hollow bed, the movement of the bed necessarily carried with it the tube, and caused it to pass over the mandril and under the pressing or welding roller."

" THOMAS HENRY RUSSELL, of Wednesbury, Stafford, Tube Manufacturer. Patent granted 14th August, 1845, for improvements in the manufacture of welded Iron Tubes."

" This Patent describes an invention for welding iron tubes for steam boilers and other purposes, and it consists of using a long fixed bar or beak iron, supported at one end, on to which a prepared iron tube at the welding heat is placed, the edges of the metal overlapping in order to produce a lap joint, and then the weld is produced by external mechanical pressure, which is shewn to be produced by a grooved roller, situated above the end of the beak iron by drawing it off the beak iron and beneath the roller ; the beak iron must not be less than half as long as the tube, and the latter is welded at two processes.   This invention has come into extensive use in making tubes of large diameter of thin plate iron with lap joints."

In concluding this notice of the manufacture of wrought iron tubes, the author has to observe that the great feature of modern times in the manufacture of tubes, is the being able to dispense with all internal support, and to complete the tube by external pressure alone, such pressure acting on all points of the circumference.

The mandril was quite indispensable, when gun-barrels were forged by means of the lateral blows of hand-hammers upon anvils or swages, and the idea of the necessity for the mandril has been long retained under various modifications, greatly to the prejudice of the entire manufacture of wrought iron tubes, as when the mandril fits tightly it hinders the progress of the tube over it and spoils the work.   The mandril when now used is only employed as a supporting instrument, one that does not fit the tube but only serves as a holder or bracket to carry the tube in its heated and flexible state, and not in any respect as a means of forming or perfecting the bore of the tube.

On this point the strongest yet clearest judgment was pronounced by Baron Parke, in the trial on Whitehouse's patent, namely, " *that the great novelty is the complete circumferential pressure, with motion, leaving out the mandril or any internal support.*"

Another point of great nicety in the manufacture is the reverberatory furnace, which, notwithstanding its length, requires to be heated most intensely yet uniformly throughout; sometimes a blast is used, but the description of Mr. Prosser's furnace will serve as a general explanation.

The furnace requires of course to be of the full length of the longest tube, and it has a door at each end for the entry and removal of the skelp ; on the one side are several stoke holes for the introduction of the fuel, which is mostly coal, sometimes coke, and in the opposite wall, beyond the bridge of the furnace, are corresponding apertures leading into a longitudinal chamber parallel with the fire, and thence into the lofty flue ; the dimensions of the apertures must be determined in some measure experimentally, until the furnace burns with equal intensity throughout its length.

The time the iron is exposed to the intense heat of the furnace likewise requires careful attention, as if accidentally exceeded, the iron is entirely spoiled.

The manufacture of thin tubes has recently obtained a great impulse, from the very general adoption of the tubular system in marine boilers.   These tubes are usually about one-tenth of an inch thick, and as large as three inches diameter, to adapt them to the combustion of coal, the fuel of marine engines ; whereas the tubes of locomotives in which coke is always burned are of only about half the bore of those for marine boilers ; the tubes for locomotives, although more generally of brass are also made of wrought iron.

The tubular constructions of boilers present a very great fire surface, and effect a proportionate saving in the dimensions of the boiler, and consequently in the weight both of the boiler and the water contained therein.   Thick tubes, from their weight, would be altogether inapplicable either to marine or locomotive boilers.

Note U, page 256.—To follow the Foot Note.

(Additional remarks on the late Sir John Robison's Workshop blowpipe.)

" Articles heated in the flame of the workshop or gas furnace blowpipe, (said its inventor,) preserve their polish in the same way as by Mr. T. Oldham's process, *if they have been kept in the flame.* As the whole of the oxygen is taken up by the hydrogen of the gas, none is left free to act on the surface of the steel, and as there appears to be a tendency to a deposition of carbon on glass rods when submitted to this flame, it may be, that this may not only have an influence in saving the steel from oxidation, but may produce some chemical effect on its composition, as work-men suppose that gravers or turning tools hardened from this heat, are more endur-ing than those heated in the muffle or on a bar of hot iron."

As already noticed on page 440 the workshop blowpipe is figured and described in the *Mech. Mag.* for 1842, page 258.

Note V, page 283.—In continuation of the article on SILVER.

(Amalgams used by Dentists for stopping teeth.)

Dentists employ an amalgam containing silver for stopping carious teeth, it is pre-pared by rubbing together in a mortar, or even in the hollow of the hand, finely divided silver and mercury, and then squeezing out all the uncombined mercury, leaving a plastic mass, which feels to grate and crepitate under the fingers. When all the unsound parts of the tooth have been carefully cut away, the amalgam is thrust into the *dry* cavity, that the tooth may be hermetically sealed from the air, and in the course of a few hours the amalgam appears to crystallize, and become considerably harder than lead.

The usual mode of preparation is to dissolve the silver in muriatic acid, and pre-cipitate it as a fine metallic powder, by stirring the solution with a rod of zinc or iron. Some dentists file part of a shilling into dust, under the impression that the copper then also employed makes the amalgam harder, others rub in with the silver a little gold leaf or platinum leaf with the same intention. Precipitated palladium forms with mercury a similar amalgam to that with silver, but with the evolution of heat at the time of combination. These alloys, which have received various high sounding names, are seldom remelted, but then resume for some hours their plastic condition.

Note W, page 323.—To follow the seventh line.

(Babbet's Patent Anti-friction Metal.)

Babbet's anti-friction metal, to be used somewhat after the manner of tin, for the bearings of machinery, is thus described :—

" An excellent compound or alloy for this purpose may be prepared by taking about fifty parts of tin, five of antimony, and one of copper, but other compounds analogous in character may be used."

Tin or compounds like the above used alone, owing to their softness, spread and escape under the superincumbent weight of locomotive engines, and other heavy machinery ; and therefore brasses or bearings are employed under this patent to support the softer metal, but the brasses are made larger in diameter, and with internal fillets that almost touch the axles, so as to prevent the thin lining of the anti-friction metal from spreading and being pressed out.

The brasses are first cleaned and tinned, and an exact iron model of the axle having been turned, the parts are heated, put together in their relative positions, luted with plastic clay, and the fluid anti-friction metal is poured in, which then becomes of the required form and effectually soldered to the brass. The anti-friction metal scarcely appears to suffer from wear, and owing to its unctuous greasy nature, requires much less oil than other metals and alloys used for bearings.

See Letters Patent granted to Wm. Newton, 15th May, 1843, for " Certain improvements in the construction of boxes or axletrees of locomotive engines and carriages, and for the bearings or journals of machinery in general, and also improvements in oiling or lubricating the same. Being a communication, &c."

Note X, page 285, at foot, and 302.—Before " *The palladiumizing process.*"
(*Craufurd's Patent for Galvanized Iron.*)

At the time the author inserted in his former volume the account of Mallett's process for coating iron with zinc and palladium, he accidentally overlooked a previous patent granted to Mr. Henry William Craufurd, April 1837, (and described in the " Repertory of Patent Inventions," Vol. ix, New Series, page 289,) he will now proceed to supply the deficiency ; and also to give some particulars of another method by which iron that has been previously tinned is also coated with zinc.

In Mr. Craufurd's patent, sheet iron, iron castings, and various other objects in iron, are cleaned and scoured by immersion in a bath of water acidulated with sulphuric acid, heated in a leaden vessel, or used cold in one of wood, just to remove the oxide. They are then thrown into cold water, and taken out one at a time to be scoured with sand and water with a piece of cork, or more usually a piece of the husk of the cocoa nut, the ends of the fibres of which serve as a brush, and the plates are afterwards thrown into cold water.

Pure zinc covered with a thick layer of sal-ammoniac is then melted in a bath, and the iron, if in sheets, is dipped several sheets at a time in a cradle or grating. The sheets are slowly raised to allow the superfluous zinc to drain off, and are thrown whilst hot into cold water, on removal from which they only require to be wiped dry.

Thick pieces are heated before immersion in a reverberatory furnace, to avoid cooling the zinc. Chains are similarly treated and on removal from the zinc require to be shaken until cold to avoid the links being soldered together. Nails and small articles are dipped in muriatic acid, and dried in a reverberatory furnace, and then thrown altogether in the zinc covered with the sal-ammoniac, left for one minute, and taken out slowly with an iron skimmer ; they come out in a mass soldered together, and for their separation are afterwards placed in a crucible and surrounded with charcoal powder, then heated to redness and shaken about until cold, for their separation. Wire is reeled through the zinc, into which it is compelled to dip by a fork or other contrivance.

It is to be observed that the zinc is melted in a bath or crucible just a little beyond the point of fusion, and is always covered with a thick coat of sal-ammoniac, both to prevent the waste of the zinc, and further to prepare the metal that is to be zinced. Cast-iron baths or vessels, such as are used for melting tin or pewter, were first employed, but zinc acts very rapidly upon the cast-iron, unites with it, and falls in a granular state to the bottom of the vessel ; therefore an earthen lining of fire brick luted with clay, was, with some difficulty and loss of heat, maintained in the cast-iron vessel, to defend the same from the action of the zinc.

(Craufurd's patent, 1837.)   Now, however, wrought-iron baths welded at the angles are used without the clay lining, (Morewood & Roger's patent, 1841,) as the deterioration both of the zinc and of the vessel are then less rapid, and the process succeeds better than when cast-iron baths are employed.   The spoiled granulated metal, which is only considered to contain about five per cent. of iron, is ladled out and returned to the zinc manufacturers for purification or re-manufacture.

Note Y, page 285, at foot, and 302.—Before " *The palladiumizing process.*"

(*Morewood and Rogers's Galvanized Tinned-iron.*)

Mr. Edmund Morewood's process is different, and is declared in his patent dated 1841—" to consist in tinning the metals to be preserved from oxidation as aforesaid, in the ordinary manner of what is called tinning, and then, in what I call zincing the said tin, so that the external surface may be zinc, placed in such relation with the tin, and the metal to be preserved from oxidation, as that both the said tin and zinc should have a united or combined influence in preserving the said metal." See " Repertory of Patent Inventions," New Series, Vol. xviii. page 170.

The present practice is however different from the above as the iron is covered with tin by a galvanic deposition, as in the electrotype process, and is afterwards zinced in a bath of the fluid metal.   The following is the practice, which is secured by subsequent patents, enumerated further on.

The sheets of iron are pickled, scoured, and cleaned just the same as for ordinary tinning.   A large wooden bath is then half filled with a dilute solution of muriate of tin, prepared by dissolving metallic tin in concentrated muriatic acid, which requires a period of about two or three days, and two quarts of the saturated solution are added to 300 or 400 gallons of the water contained in the bath.   Over the bottom of the bath is first spread a thin layer of finely granulated zinc, then a cleaned iron plate, and so on, a layer of finely granulated zinc and a cleaned iron plate alternately, until the bath is full ; the zinc and iron together with the fluid, constitute a weak galvanic battery, and the tin is deposited from the solution, so as to coat the iron with a dull uniform layer of metallic tin in about two hours.

Whilst the above process is in operation a wrought iron bath containing fluid zinc is prepared, the melted metal is covered with sal-ammoniac mixed with earthy matter, to lessen the volatilization of the sal-ammoniac, which becomes about as fluid as treacle.   Two iron rollers immersed below the surface of the zinc are fixed to the bath, and are driven by machinery to carry the plates through the fluid metal at any velocity previously determined.   The plates are now received one by one from the tinning bath, drained for a short time, and passed at once, whilst still *wet*, through the melted zinc by means of rollers ; the plates thus take up a very regular and smooth layer of zinc, which owing to the presence of the tin beneath, assumes its natural crystalline character, giving the plates an appearance resembling that known as the *moirée metallique*.

When the sheet of metal is dipped vertically into the zinc, the lower edge is much longer in contact with the zinc, than the upper, and from the violent action of melted zinc on iron, this makes the bottom edges of the sheets sensibly more brittle than the upper ; whereas the rollers cause every part of the sheet to be acted upon in the same degree, and which degree may be exactly determined by the velocity given to the rollers.   Consequently by the roller process thinner iron may be zinced than by dipping edgeways and vertically, as no part of the iron need to be immersed longer in the metallic bath than is absolutely necessary for its properly taking the coating of zinc.

In addition to Mr. Morewood's patent dated 1841 for the general process by ordinary tinning and zincing, Messrs. Morewood and Rogers have patents dated respectively 1843 for the rollers, and the electro mode of tinning, in fact for the mode of covering metals by the conjoined processes, first of voltaic deposition, and subsequently of immersion in another fluid metal.——1844 for new fluxes and details of management ;——and 1845 for the manufacture of the galvanized tinned-iron plate into tiles and ridge pieces for roofing and other works, by various processes of stamping.

Craufurd's Patent, (worked by the Galvanized Iron Company,) and Morewood and Rogers's combined patents, have obtained very extensive employment for a great variety of purposes, and both methods are well supported by testimonials. But so far as the author can learn, the galvanized iron covered with pure zinc, is much more suitable to the sheathing of ships, for which it is highly economical, as it is proved to be much cheaper and is expected to prove more durable than copper ; —the galvanized tinned iron-plate is more malleable and may be used for thinner iron, and is therefore more suitable to being wrought, as by the tin-smith, with the hammer, and it is also found to answer thoroughly for roofing ; as it can be bent and soldered with facility. Galvanized iron is now largely used by Government and by public companies for this purpose.

The author is informed that both kinds are open to two curious facts, the first that the chains of tillers and cranes, and objects exposed to much friction, do not lose their coating of zinc ; this is accounted for by the smooth un-oxidized zinc surfaces of the chain moving freely on one another, whereas unprotected iron when covered with rust, (the peroxide used in polishing,) is subject to continued wear ; and it has also been imagined the zinc becomes as it were burnished into the surface of the iron. But it may happen that when moisture is occasionally present, that the worn parts are then continually re-zinced from the neighbouring parts, as explained by the curious fact now to be noticed, and which on its discovery excited great surprise.

The edges of some galvanized iron plates cut with shears so as to expose the central iron, when attached to the piles of the Bell Rock Light House, for the purpose of experiment, became zinced around the cut edges, and at the holes where the nails were driven, and it was also observed that even the nails and fastenings made of *un*-galvanized iron became zinced from their proximity to the galvanized sheets. By the same action, the holes perforated through the sheathing for nailing it to the ship's sides become coated ; and the zinced wires of the Electric Telegraph, where cut through, become coated by the action of the rain water on the galvanized portion of the surface.

Note Z, page 308.—To precede SECTION II.

(*Portable brass furnace.*)

Since the foregoing pages were printed, Holtzapffel & Co. have constructed portable brass furnaces, made of the hexagonal form in sheet iron, lined with Stourbridge clay, and fitted with cast-iron pedestals, tiles, and stout sheet iron pipes complete, so as to be erected on any level spot of ground, and if near a dead wall so much the better.

The smaller sized of these air furnaces serve for about 10 pounds weight of brass or copper, and a large furnace on the same model will melt 20 pounds ; when

favourably managed they have been made hot enough to melt cast-iron. These furnaces have entirely superseded the little blast furnaces formerly made for the
portable forge, shown on page 203 of Vol. I.

Note AA, page 374.—To follow the last Foot Note.

(*Berlin method of moulding delicate complicated objects.*)

" One method said to be followed by the Berlin founders for producing complicated subjects, such as a bouquet of flowers, is to dissect the object to be moulded,
into small parts which may be straightened out or moulded separately, and cast in
fusible metal."

" Having cast all the parts separately in soft fusible composition, these parts are then
bent into the natural forms, and a synthetic operation is commenced, or that of
putting the parts together again by means of soldering, and tying together by
wires. When the whole object has been in this way built up, it is embedded in the
mould, (with proper precautions for the escape of air,) the mould is heated to allow
the fusible metal to melt and escape, and the iron is run in by a descending gait,
which enters the mould at its lowest part, and the fluid metal carries up any impuri-
ties on its surface, expelling the air as it rises through the vents." *Sir John Robison*.

Note AB, page 424.—To follow the paragraph ending " wax is generally used."

(*Fluid for lubricating draw-plates employed in India.*)

" The lubricating matter for facilitating the slipping of wire through draw-plates,
is perhaps not a matter of indifferent choice ; the Hindoo Sonârs, who are noted for
their dexterity in drawing gold wire, uniformly use *Castor oil*, which they allege
prevents waste of gold by friction." *Sir John Robison*.

Note AC, page 410.—To follow the paragraph that precedes SECTION III.

(*Foxall's patent Method of raising Vessels in sheet metal.*)

Notice of the patent granted to Mr. Thomas Foxall Griffith, of Birmingham, for
improvements in stamping and shaping sheet metal. Feb. 3, 1846.

In the paragraph to which this note follows as an appendix, it was stated that works
having lofty and perpendicular sides, such as jelly moulds, could not be produced
by stamping ; but this difficulty has been very cleverly overcome under the recent
patent above cited, in which the processes of stamping and that of burnishing to
form or spinning are successfully alternated. Quoting the words of the specification,
the patentee observes :—

" Heretofore sheet metal has been raised by the simple act of stamping in dies,
by raising and letting fall a succession of forces, and the process of burnishing to
form has been combined with the ordinary process of stamping, whereby sheet metal,
having been raised as far as possible in dies by the processes of stamping, the shaping
has been completed by the process of burnishing the stamped articles on chucks in
a lathe, and to secure such last-mentioned combined processes letters patent were
granted on 15th February, 1834."

" In shaping sheet metal by stamping, as heretofore practised, the sides of the
articles depend materially for the height of the raising on the stretching or extending of the metal ; and to this end the metal at the outer circumference is supported
throughout the process of stamping by a projecting flanch, which rests horizontally

on the upper surface of the dies, such flanch being progressively reduced and the metal thereof stretched or extended, so that, from the bottom to the upper edge, the thickness of the metal is brought thinner and thinner, which is objectionable. At the same time, owing to the severe treatment to which the sheet metal is thus subjected, it requires to be more often annealed, in order to prevent its suffering injury by the successive processes of stamping, and such is the extent to which the metal is stretched or extended by raising, according to the old practice, that the disk or blank of metal employed for raising a vessel of a few inches diameter to a considerable extent, is only about three quarters of an inch larger in diameter than the finished vessel raised therefrom by stamping. Whereas, according to my invention, the blank or disk of sheet metal used for making any particular article when the sides thereof are upright, is of a diameter of about the diameter of the vessel or article added to the depth of the vessel; thus supposing the vessel or article produced by stamping in a die be six inches in diameter and three inches deep, then the die or blank of sheet metal would be about nine inches diameter, and the article when stamped therefrom, if it be cut through the sides and bottom, all parts would be found as nearly as may be of the same thickness, and that thickness the thickness of the original sheet metal."

The figures A to G, reduced from the specification, show the several forms which would be given to the work originally of the diameter aa, by the employment

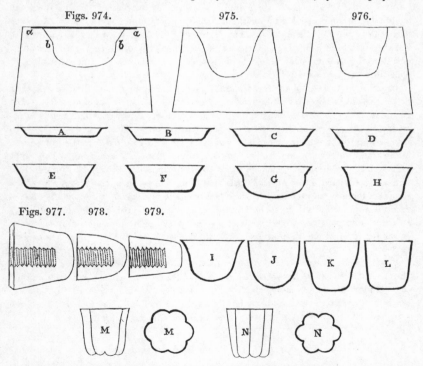

Figs. 974.   975.   976.

Figs. 977.   978.   979.

of a die such as fig. 974, with a second point of bearing at bb. The successive *forces* or top dies that are employed, being so shaped as to bear only on the bottom of the vessel so far as the edge bb, and not on the sloping sides; by which scheme the edge *bb* fulfils in great measure the purpose of a draw-plate, such as would be used for drawing cylindrical tubes.

After having been progressively stamped, to the contour of G, the work is burnished to form on a chuck such as fig. 977. The work is then again stamped in the second die fig. 975, then burnished on the second chuck fig. 978, and is afterwards struck in a third die fig. 976, and then burnished on a third chuck fig. 979, to make the metal proceed through the stages H to L ; of course the work is occasionally annealed, as will be explained.

Fluted works, such as N, are first raised nearly as cylinders with bottoms to the shape of L by the intermittent stages already explained, and the burnishing to form is then discontinued. The flutes require the use of two or more pairs of dies and forces, in which the flutes are gradually developed, but which tools have not been represented. In the first pair of tools for the object N, the flutes are shallow and the die a little bell-mouthed ; in the second pair, the flutes are of the full depth, and as from the sides being almost perpendicular, or exactly counterparts of the burnished object N, the piece when struck holds fast in the die, the latter is perforated and has a central rammer, which is raised by a side lever to force the finished work out of the die ; these particulars are all minutely explained in the specification.

The vessels when cut through present a nearly uniform section, and which may be thus explained as regards the cylindrical vessel. If the disk of 9 inches diameter could have its margin folded up without puckering, it would have a rim of $1\frac{1}{2}$ inches high, the upper edge being of twice the primary thickness, as in fig. 271, page 400, but the stretching from the dies, causes the height of the sides to become 3 inches, and therefore this tapering thickness is gradually drawn out, as in tube drawing, to constitute the increased height.

In proof of the complete efficacy of the mode, it may be stated that vessels may be thus made in sheet-iron (known as charcoal-iron), a material far less tractible than copper and brass. Great difficulty was experienced in carrying out this alternation of the two processes of stamping and burnishing to form, when working with iron, owing to the scaling or oxidation of surface which resulted from the annealing, and which roughness tended to prevent the employment of burnishers. This difficulty was, after various trials, obviated by annealing after the method practised in annealing articles made of malleable cast-iron, (see pages 259, 260,) in which case the ductility and tenacity of the sheet-iron are preserved, and that with a surface quite unimpaired by the firing. The patentee prefers for the annealing mixture, one part of pulverised iron-ore, added to eight of coke or lime, and he gives the preference to that iron-ore which has been once used for annealing cast-iron.

So completely successful are the combined processes, that extinguishers have been thus raised from round disks of sheet-iron, and of course without a seam ; the method of stamping with dies having the bevilled mouth and shoulder *b b*, fig. 974, enables vessels to be raised much higher than by any other method of stamping, even when burnishing to form is not employed in connection with the stamping.

Note A D, page 431.—To follow the first paragraph.

(Drawing taper brass tubes for locomotive engines.)

Some of the brass tubes for locomotives, are made cylindrical without and a little taper within, the metal for them is cast hollow, and drawn on a taper triblet through an ordinary plate. The thick end is placed near the fire box, that the tube may be the longer in wasting away from the action of the fire, and also that cinders capable of entering its smaller end may readily escape at the larger.

Note AE, page 431.—To follow the second paragraph.

(Rand's patent Collapsable Tubes.)

These thin tubes are closed at the one end by a convex disk with a projecting screw ; the screw being perforated for the expulsion of artist's colours or other matters inclosed in the vessels. They were first drawn as tubes, as described in the text, and the ends were cast and soldered in ; but the entire vessel is now made by means of only two blows, in dies of appropriate kinds.

By one blow of a screw press, a thick circular disk of tin of the external diameter of the intended vessel is punched out, made concave, and perforated with a central hole ; somewhat like a washer for machinery.

By a second blow, the blank or button is converted into the finished tube. The bottom tool is a mould with a shallow cylindrical cavity of the same diameter as the button of tin, and terminating in a hollow screw ; the upper tool is a cylinder exceeding the length of the tube, and with a small taper spindle of the diameter of the hole. The cylinder is just so much smaller than the mould as to leave an annular space equal to the intended thickness of the tube —The very soft ductile tin, when submitted to great pressure in the contracted space within the mould, follows the laws of liquids, and may be said literally to *flow* through the annular crevice, and up the cylindrical mandril, as indeed the formation of the tube appears to be instantaneous, and is a beautiful example both of true principle, and accurate workmanship in the means employed.

The tube is released from the mould, first by the ascent of the cylinder, which leaves the tube behind ; and the screwed extremity of the mould is then driven up by a ram and lever from below, and the screwed dies being divided on their diameter, instantly fall away from the vessel thus elegantly produced by a mode which was only attained after repeated variations in the process, respectively secured by patents. Small tubes are thus made in screw presses, and large tubes in hydrostatic presses of proportionate strength.

Note AF, page 433.—To follow the third paragraph.

(Clay props used by the Asiatics instead of binding wire in soldering.)

" The Asiatic goldsmiths seldom use binding wire for light work, they have always beside them a little dish of a tempered mixture of clay and sand or powdered brick, with little portions of which they form connections and supports for the pieces they mean to solder together. Thus if two tubes have to be joined in the form of the letter T, (inverted whilst being soldered,) they first warm the lower piece, and then dab on a little at a time of the mortar, (leaving the joint clean,) until the inclined props of the clay run high enough nearly to touch the upright piece, which being warmed and set in its place, the connection is completed by a further addition of the mortar, which when heated over charcoal, becomes quite firm and supports the pieces whilst the solder is running, even in works of pretty considerable size." *Sir John Robison.*

Note AG, page 444.—To precede Section IV.

(Pumice-stone used by Dentists, instead of Charcoal, as a support in soldering.)

Dentists are much in the habit of using a lump of pumice-stone as the support in soldering the gold work to which artificial teeth are attached. The pumice-stone is usually filed or rubbed to a flat surface, and the work when laid on this incombustible support, and subjected to the action of the blowpipe, receives a more moderate heat than when laid on charcoal; which latter support is less convenient, as it loses its form from burning continually away, and because at the same time, owing to its combustion, it reverberates more heat than is required by the dentists for their particular purpose.

The following Notes in the Appendix refer to the Second Volume.

Note AH, page 482.—To precede the last paragraph.

(Silcock and Lowe's Patent Planes for Joiners, &c.)

Subsequently to the foregoing matter on planes having been printed, Messrs. Silcock and Lowe, of Birmingham, took out a patent in January, 1844, for various kinds of bench planes, constructed in great part of malleable cast-iron. Several of these planes are figured and described in the "Mechanics' Magazine" for 1844, pages 81 to 86, to which the reader is referred. A few lines are however extracted nearly verbatim for the convenience of those readers to whom this journal is not accessible.

"The *first* of these planes is certainly a very remarkable instrument. It is a double fillister plane, which is so constructed that it is capable of filleting boards *of all sizes from about ⅜ths of an inch to about 3 inches*, and may be adapted to the several purposes of *a filleting plane, a side fillister, a sash or back fillister, and a skewed rabbet plane.*"

"When this tool is to be used as a filleting plane, both the right and left side planes are combined together, and fixed at a distance from each other, corresponding to the breadth of the fillet. To use it as a side fillister, the left side plane only is required, with a stop inserted into an appropriate recess. When it is to be used as a sash or back fillister the right side plane only is employed, but with a slight modification in the figure of the fence."

"To use the tool as a skewed rabbet plane, the right hand plane, with its chase and fence are laid aside, and the left hand plane only is employed."

"All the parts are of cast-iron, protected by tinning or zincing from corrosion, with the exception of the stock and the handle and body of the fence, which are of wood, and with the exception also of the screws, the cushion of the travelling screw and the sliding nut, which are all of brass."

"The fore and back parts are cast in one piece. The wood of the handle is not cut across the grain, as usual, but with the fibres running in a direction at right angles to the body of the planes, whereby a considerable increase of strength is gained."

"The *second* instrument described, is a *fluting* or *grooving plough*. In this tool the body is wholly of metal, but in all other respects, as regards the materials and mode of putting them together, it possesses the same peculiarities as the double fillister plane first described."

"The *third* instrument is a *dado-grooving plane*, with which no less than sixteen and more different sizes of work may be executed ; the *fourth* instrument is a *trying plane* suitable both for rough and smooth work ; the *fifth* and last is a *moulding or bead plane.*" The explanation of these peculiar tools cannot however be conveyed without exceeding our limit of space and the introduction of numerous figures.

In addition to the foregoing patent planes, constructed principally in metal, the patentees manufacture all the ordinary wooden bench planes with screws for fixing the irons, instead of the wedges driven by the hammer.

Note AI, page 487.—To follow the third paragraph.
(Mr. Lund's Screw Router Plane.)

Mr. Wm. Lund has constructed the router, fig. 341, page 487, with a screw adjustment to the cutter, as it is mostly necessary this should be set gradually deeper as the work progresses. When a similar but smaller tool is fitted with a perpendicular cutter, he finds it very useful in reducing the level backgrounds of small ivory carvings in bas-relief ; in which case a margin is left around the subject, if only as a temporary guide for the router to run upon.

Note AJ, page 488.—To follow the last paragraph.
(Mr. Falconer's Improved Circular Plough.)

Mr. Falconer's plough rewarded by the Society of Arts in the Session 1846, presents many points of improvement on the banding plane by Mr. Onwin, described in the text. The principles of the plough, fig. 335, page 486, are nearly followed, but instead of a variety of fences being used some concave others convex, the new instrument has a flexible steel fence, attached to the plough by two stays which are jointed to the ends of the elastic fence, whilst to the central part of the same is fitted a screw adjustment, so that the one fence may be made to assume any required curvature, either convex or concave and of course the right line also.

The widths of the grooves are determined as usual by those of the cutters, which are provided with double pointed scorers or nickers, for cutting through such of the fibres of the work as lie transversely, and would otherwise be torn up. The entire construction of this circular plough is very judicious and complete, and the tool may be considered as greatly improved on those previously used for this purpose.

Notes AK, AL, and AM.—To follow the last line of page 495.
(Note AK, Mr. Franklin's Screw Bench Hook for Carpenters.)

A screw bench hook for carpenters, intended to supersede that shown at *a* fig. 353, page 494, was invented by Mr. F. E. Franklin, of Purton, Wilts, and published in the Transactions of the Society of Arts for 1840, vol. 53, p. 92. There is a metal sheath or socket fitted to the bench, within which an iron bar with a side spring, slides up and down under the guidance of an adjusting screw below, the square bar carries two or more steel teeth formed as a separate piece and screwed on. The contrivance although quite effective is rather expensive for ordinary use.

Note AL.—To follow the above on page 495.
(Mr. De Beaufort's Vice or Stop for a Joiner's Bench.)

Figs. 978 and 979 represent the vice or stop for a joiner's bench, for which Mr. H. De Jay De Beaufort, of Perigeaux, received the reward of the Society of Arts in 1841.   There are two double ended levers moving freely on the centers by which they are attached to the bed or foundation piece, so that when a board or piece of

Figs. 978.   979.

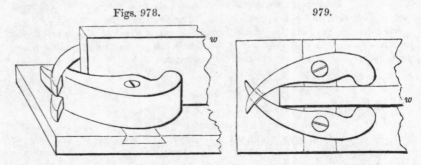

wood w, placed on edge, is inserted between them, it catches between the tails of the levers and separates them until the piece is grasped also by the other ends of the same levers, and therefore at two places at once, as seen in the plan fig. 979. The levers are about one inch thick, and the tail of the one is thinned to enter a cleft on the other, as distinctly shown in fig. 978, to adapt the vice to very thin pieces, and the levers being mounted on chamfered slides, may be fixed wider asunder for very thick pieces.   See Transactions of the Society of Arts, vol. 53, page 86.

Note AM.—To follow Note **AL**, on page 495.

(*Mr. S. Nicholls' Stop or Clamp for a Joiner's Bench.*)

Fig. 980 is a perspective view, and fig. 981 a plan of Mr. S. Nicholls' subsequent contrivance for the same purpose, and rewarded by the same society in 1843. Two inclined and undercut slips of wood a a, are firmly screwed to the bottom board, and between them are loosely fitted two pieces b b, nearly counterparts

Figs. 980.   981.

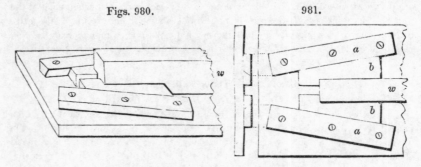

of a a, but with projecting fillets at the end.   When the board w, is inserted between these loose jaws or chaps, they are thrust forward until they reach that contracted part of the angular gap, which compresses them firmly upon the board to be fixed. This mode serves for a much greater range of size in the pieces fixed than the last, and the straight faces of the jaws do not indent the works, as may happen when soft woods are clamped in the vice shown in figs. 978 and 979.   See Transactions of the Society of Arts, vol. 55, page 42.

Note AN, page 504.—To follow the paragraph commencing " The Scale-board plane."

(Messrs. Esdaile and Margrave's Scale-board Machine.)

The scale-board machine used by Messrs. Esdaile and Margrave, at the City Saw Mills, London, has a wide cast-iron slide plate, that works freely in chamfer bars elevated on frame work about six feet above the ground ; the power of the steam engine is applied to the slide by means of a stout leather strap, or rather by two straps for the to and fro movement ; but one is always out of action and loose. The slide is perforated for a cutter upwards of one foot wide, placed beneath the slide, and inclined horizontally about 40 degrees, as a skew rebate plane, but the pitch of the iron or its vertical face, up which the shavings slide, has only half the inclination of the horizontal, or about 20 degrees.

The log of wood, which is preferred wet on account of its superior elasticity in that condition, is held down by heavy weights, whilst the metallic plane slides beneath it and shaves off in an admirable manner one single shaving ; the thickness of the same is determined by the adjustment of the cutter which is principally held by wedges.

Messrs. Esdaile and Margrave recently patented the employment of three cutters situated as above, but one behind the other to remove three scale-boards in immediate succession ; the scheme was effectual in its action, but in the end less economical than the single cutter—and which must be moved by a strap or rope, as although racks and iron chains have been tried, they fail apparently from the want of sufficient elasticity.

Note AO, page 505.—To follow the second paragraph.

(On Machines for Planing Wood.)

Of the machines for producing works in wood, similar to those usually accomplished by hand planes, several have been constructed to act by means of cutters having circular motion. Thus in Paxton's machine, various circular saws or cutters of different diameters and forms are placed on one spindle beneath which the sash bar is traversed. In machines for planing mouldings from 2 to 8 inches wide, for house joinery, picture frames, &c., two figured cutters of the entire width of the moulding are screwed to a rectangular block fixed on the revolving spindle, by which means the cutters are presented at the proper pitch or inclination of 60 or 70 degrees to the face of the moulding. Circular cutters were also used in the earlier experiments with Burnett and Poyer's machine, some of them with only 4, 5, or 6 edges or teeth constructed very nearly on the principle of ordinary plane-irons.

But circular cutters were abandoned by Messrs. Burnett and Poyer from two motives ; first, the difficulty of constructing and sharpening them, and secondly, that notwithstanding the rapidity at which the cutters might be driven, they still left marks upon the work because there is a distinct though small interval of time, between the passage of the one cutting edge and that next following, and during which small interval, the uninterrupted advance of the work allowed certain portions, to be less reduced, or left as little hills and ridges slightly above the general surface. The wood only becomes absolutely smooth, when its traverse is so far diminished, that one point of the cutter, (or probably the highest point of the entire series,) is enabled to touch every individual portion of the work, and which requires a much greater reduction in the feed or traverse, than might be expected, thus mostly leaving something to be smoothed off or removed by hand tools.

Messrs. Burnett and Poyer from these circumstances ultimately rejected revolving in favour of *fixed* cutters, and thus in planing mouldings, they employed a stock which contained from twelve to twenty cutters, every one figured and secured by a separate wedge, so that the first cutter penetrated but little into the moulding, and that every succeeding tool removed a shaving of its own ; all the cutters gradually assimilated more and more to the last of the series, which was sharpened exactly to the form of the moulding.   Under this arrangement the machine was enabled to work mouldings in pine wood, at the enormous velocity of 70 lineal feet per minute, and still the work had all the smoothness of that produced by the joiner's hand planes as usual.

Note AP, page 505.—To follow the former note having the same reference.
(*Mr. Antonio Mayer's Patent Splint Cutting Machine.*)

The production of an article of apparently minor importance, has led to the invention of a very effective and important machine allied to the planes, namely, the splint-cutting machine for cutting the wood for chemical matches.

It is necessary to premise that when these useful matches were first introduced, they were mere shavings cut from blocks of deal, by the plane previously used in preparing the chips of willow and other woods from which ladies' bonnets are woven.   This plane had at the front, a series of lancet-like knives which scored the wood in shallow parallel furrows, and immediately behind the knives was fixed an inclined plane iron of very low pitch which cast off a shaving, thus producing several splints at once from the edge of a board about one inch thick.

When the same splint plane was used for the stronger and less flexible matches nearly one-tenth of an inch square now used, the splints were found to be broken or disrupted in their fibres, by the comparatively abrupt angle at which they were removed from the block of wood, notwithstanding that the plane had a very thin iron sole and a cutter of very low pitch.   This defective action of the hand plane led to the invention of Mr. Mayer's Patent Splint Cutting Machine, used exclusively at the celebrated works of the Messrs. Esdailes and Margrave of London.

The splint-cutting machine has a metal slide, which travels parallel with the ground, but in a vertical plane, by means of a crank and connecting rod that give it 60 strokes in a minute.   The slide carries first a series of 30 lancet-like knives, half sloped on the upper surface, the other half on the lower, these penetrate the wood about one-tenth of an inch, and are immediately followed by the cutter or plane iron, the broad flat side of which rests directly against the wood to be cut, (no sole being used,) the edge of this knife is very much inclined, namely, to 70 degrees, and is ground with a very long bevel, 2 inches wide, giving to the edge the acute angle of 12 degrees, and which, combined with the great obliquity of the knife, causes the splints to be only bent from the wood at the insignificant angle of about 4 degrees, so as to be entirely removed by *cutting*, and not by *splitting* or rending.

The wood used for making the splints consists of whole deals 10 inches wide, 3 inches thick, cross cut into blocks 5 inches long.   Three of these blocks are placed together, constituting a length of 15 inches, sufficient for six splints or matches ; and as there are thirty lancet knives, every traverse of the machine produces 180 splints ; this at 60 strokes a minute makes 648,000 an hour, or 1,648,000 in a day of ten hours.   There are two such machines constantly at work, and these, notwithstanding their prolific production of upwards of three millions of splints a day, furnish another proof that in some processes, machinery cannot overpower hand labour ; as the larger proportion of the splints used in this country are nevertheless obtained from the hand cutters and foreign importations.   The hand-cut splints although cheaper are inferior to those cut by the machines in question.

Note AQ, page 533.—To follow the last line but one.
(On grinding some of the tools for turning iron.)

When the tools 431 or 432 p. 533 are used in both directions, that is if sometimes moved towards the right hand, at other times to the left, it is then necessary the chamfer or upper face of the point should be ground square across to serve for either direction of motion.   But when the tool is used exclusively from the right hand towards the left, the chamfer should be so ground that the left side is the higher, as this from being then the entering angle of the tool, works much more freely from being sloped some 30 degrees from the horizontal, as already explained.

On the very same principle an efficient side-cutting tool for iron to be used in the *slide* rest, is derived from the triangular tool, page 521, and represented in three views in the annexed figure 982.   A bar of steel is drawn down at the end, to about half its thickness, the width, or rather the vertical height remaining unaltered, this narrow part is chamfered on its outer face, so as to be a little inclined from the perpendicular, and is then ground on its upper surface to make a ridge parallel with the side of the tool.   The ridge which is sloped about 30° from the horizontal, is sometimes on the right, sometimes on the left, as the tools are made in pairs ; and as they will readily remove a shaving an inch or more wide, a cylinder of six inches diameter may be reduced to four inches or less at one cut, in a lathe having proportionate power.

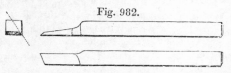

Fig. 982.

Note AR, page 538.—To follow the paragraph ending, " for general purposes."
(On lubricating metal turning tools with water.)

When water is used for lubricating the tools in turning iron with hand tools, the most simple plan is to dip the tool occasionally into a small vessel containing the fluid.   A more effectual way employed in turning by hand or with the slide-rest, is to make a small mop, of a bit of rag surrounded by a loop of wire, the ends of which are twisted together to form a handle, as in a bottle brush, with which the work is occasionally moistened.

In turning with the slide-rest or self-acting lathe, practical men often fix a drip-can to the slide-rest, that the water may fall on the work close by the tool ; or in the best mode a flexible hose is used that leads from a cistern above, the discharge of water being regulated by a small tap.   These two modes require that metal pans should be placed beneath the work to catch the water that runs away, and also that some vigilance should be exerted to keep the lathes from becoming rusty.

Notes AS, AT, AU and AV.—To follow the last line of page 538.
(On the Principles of Tools for Turning and Planing Metals.)

The formation of the tools used for turning and planing the metals is a subject of very great importance to the practical engineer, as it is indeed only when the mathematical principles upon which such tools act, are closely followed by the workman, that they produce their best effects.   With a full conviction of the advantages which result when theory and practice are thus associated, the author has to congratulate himself on being able to present to his readers, two original papers, respectively written on the subject of the principles of tools for turning and planing metals, by Charles Babbage, Esq., F.R.S., &c., and Professor Willis, A.M., F.R.S., &c., both distinguished by their high mathematical attainments, and their intimate practical experience in the use of tools.

Note AS.—(*Paper on the Principles of Tools for Turning and Planing Metals, by Charles Babbage, Esq., F.R.S., &c. &c.*)

Steel of various degrees of temper and under various forms, is almost universally employed for cutting metals. Before deciding on the forms of the different tools it is desirable to inquire into the principles on which their cutting edges act, and to assign special names to certain angles on the relations of which to each other, and to the metals upon which they are used their perfection mainly depends.

In fig. 983, *c* is a cylinder of steel or other metal, and T is a planing or turning tool acting upon it at the point *a*. A *c* is a horizontal line passing through the center *c*, and the cutting point *a*. B *a*, is a line passing through the cutting point *a* and along the upper plane *b a*, of the cutting tool T. C *a*, is a line passing through the cutting point *a* and along the front plane *e a*, of the cutting tool. D *a*, is a line from the cutting point *a*, at right angles to the radius *c a*.

The angle D *a* C, may be called the *angle of relief*, because, by increasing it, the friction of that face of the tool upon the work is diminished.

The angle C *a b*, may be called the *angle of the tool*.

The angle B *a* A, may be called the *angle of escape*, because the matter cut away by the tool escapes along it.

The forces to be overcome in cutting a thin shaving of metal from a cylinder or from a flat surface are of two kinds,

1st. It is necessary to tear along the whole line of section each atom from the opposite one to which it was attached. The force required for this purpose will obviously be proportioned to the length of the cutting edge of the tool, and dependent on the nature of the metal acted upon. But it will be quite independent of the thickness of the part removed.

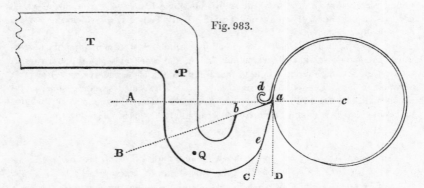

Fig. 983.

2nd. The shaving cut off by the tool must in order to get out of its way, be bent or even curled round into a spiral. This second force is often considerable, and when thick cuts are taken, is usually far larger than the former force. If the bending were of small extent, then the force to be exerted would vary as the square of the thickness of the shaving multiplied by some constant, dependent on the nature of the metal operated upon. But the bending very frequently proceeds to such an extent that the shaving itself is broken at very short intervals, and some shavings of iron and steel present a continued series of fractures not quite running through, but yet so complete, that it is impossible even with the most careful annealing to unwind the spiral. This partial severance of the atoms in the shaving itself, will require for its accomplishment a considerable exertion of force. The law by which this force increases with the thickness most probably embraces higher powers than the first and second, and may be assumed thus

$$\text{force} = a + b\,t + c\,t^2 + d\,t^3 +$$

For the present illustration it is unnecessary to consider more terms than those already more particularly explained, namely the constant force, and that which varies as the square of the thickness of the shaving.

If therefore t, be the thickness of the shaving, and A and B two constants, we shall find amongst the forces required for the separation of the shaving the two terms.

$$\text{A} + \text{B}t^2$$

where A, and B, depend upon the nature of the metal acted upon.

We may learn from this expression, even without being acquainted with the values of the constants A and B, that the force required to remove the same thickness of metal, may vary considerably according to the manner in which it is effected.

For example. If a layer of metal of the thickness of $2\,t$, is to be removed. It may be done at two successive cuts, and the force required will be equal to

$$2\,\text{A} + 2\,\text{B}t^2$$

But the same might have been accomplished at one cut when the force expended would have been

$$\text{A} + 4\,\text{B}t^2$$

Now the force required for the two cuts, will always be less than the force required for making one cut, if $t^2 > \dfrac{\text{A}}{2\,\text{B}}$

For let $t^2 = \dfrac{\text{A}}{2\,\text{B}} + v$ then

Force for two cuts $= 2\,\text{A} + 2\,\text{B}\left(\dfrac{\text{A}}{2\,\text{B}} + v\right) = 3\,\text{A} + 2\,\text{B}\,v$

Force for one cut of twice the thickness $\left.\right\} = \text{A} + 4\,\text{B}\left(\dfrac{\text{A}}{2\,\text{B}} + v\right) = 3\,\text{A} + 4\,\text{B}\,v.$

which former is always smaller than the latter force by the quantity $2\,\text{B}\,v$

In the same manner it may be proved that if

$$t^2 > \dfrac{\text{A}}{n\,\text{B}} \text{ or } t^2 = \dfrac{\text{A}}{n\,\text{B}} + v$$

it will always require less force to make n separate slices, than to cut one slice of n times the thickness for

Force for n slices $= n\,\text{A} + n\,\text{B}\left(\dfrac{\text{A}}{n\,\text{B}} + v\right) = (n+1)\,\text{A} + n\,\text{B}\,v$

Force for one slice of n times the thickness $\left.\right\} = \text{A} + n^2\text{B}\left(\dfrac{\text{A}}{n\,\text{B}} + v\right) = (n+1)\,\text{A} + n^2\text{B}\,v$

which former force is always less than the latter by the quantity of $(n^2 - n)\,\text{B}\,v$.

The angle of relief should always be very small, because the point a will in that case have its support nearly in a line directly opposed to that force acting upon it.

If a tool either for planing or for turning is defectively formed, or if it is presented to its work in such a manner that it has a tendency to dig into it ; then a very small angle of relief, in addition to a long back $a\ e$, will in some measure counteract this defect.

The smaller the angle of the tool, the less will be the force necessary for its use. But this advantage of a small angle is counterbalanced by the weakness which it produces in the support of the cutting point. There is also another disadvantage in making the angle of the tool smaller than the escape of the shaving requires ; for the point of the tool being in immediate connection with a smaller mass of metal, will not so quickly get rid of the heat it acquires from the operation of cutting, as it would if it formed part of a larger mass.

The angle of escape $A\ a\ B$ is of great importance and it varies with the nature of the material to be acted upon. If this angle is very small the action of the tool is that of scraping rather than of cutting, and the matter removed approaches the form of a powder. If however the material is very flexible and cohesive, in that case shavings may be removed. The angle I have found best for cutting steel is about 27^0, but a series of experiments upon this subject is much required.

After the form of the cutting tool is decided upon, the next important point to be considered is the manner of its application. The principle which is usually stated for turning tools is, that the point of the tool should be nearly on a level with the axis of the matter to be turned, or rather that it should be very slightly below it. This rule when applied to the greater number of tools and tool-holders is calculated to mislead. Before applying the correct rule it is necessary to consider in each tool or tool-holder, what is the situation of that point around which the cutting point of the tool will turn when any force is put upon the tool. Let this point be called the center of flexure. Then the correct rule is, that the center of flexure should always be *above* the line joining the center of the work and the cutting point.

On looking at fig. 983 A c, is the line joining the cutting point a and the center of the work c. By making the tool weak about Q that point becomes the center on which the point a will bend when any unusual force occurs. On the occurrence of any such unusual force arising from any pin or point of unequal density in the matter cut, the point of the tool a, by bending around the center Q will dig deeper into the work and cause some part of the apparatus to give way or break.

If on the other hand the point P is that around which the point of the tool when resisted tends to turn, then since this point is above the line joining the cutting point and the center of the work, the tendency of the additional strain on the point is to make it sink less deeply into the work, and consequently to relieve itself from the force opposed to it.

Fortunately the position of this point can always be commanded, for it is always possible, by cutting away matter, to make one particular part weak. This is indeed a circumstance too frequently neglected in the construction of machinery. Every piece of mechanism exposed to considerable force is liable to fracture, and it is always desirable to direct it to break at some one particular point if any unexpected strain occurs. In many cases where danger may arise from the interference of the broken part with the rest of the machinery this arrangement is essential. In all cases it is economical, because by making the breaking, if it occur, at a selected spot, provision may be made of duplicate parts and the delay arising from stopping the machine be avoided.

The results of the preceding inquiry would lead to considerable changes in the forms of tools generally used in cutting metals, and as the time employed in taking a cut is usually equal whether the shaving be thick or thin, the saving in power by taking thin cuts separately would be accompanied by a considerable expense of time. This however need not be the case if proper tool-holders are employed, in conformity with the following several conditions : thus

The tool-holders should be so contrived as to have several cutters successively removing equal cuts.—The cutting edges should be easily adjusted to the work.— The steel of which the cutters are formed should be of the best kind, and after it is once hardened should never again be submitted to that process.—The form and position of the cutter should be such that it may, when broken or blunted, be easily ground, having but one or at the utmost but two faces requiring grinding.—It is desirable that when being ground it should be fixed into some temporary handle, in order that it may always be ground to the same cutting angles.—The cutters should be very securely, but also very simply tightened in their places.—The center of flexure of the cutter should, in turning, be *above* the line joining the center of the work and the cutting point ;—whilst in planing the center of flexure should be in *advance* of a line perpendicular at the cutting point to the surface of the work planed. Examples of some tool-holders of this kind will be given subsequently.

The effects of such improved tools would be to diminish greatly the strain put upon lathes and planing machines, and consequently to enable them to turn out better work in the same time and at a less expense of power : whilst the machines themselves so used would retain their adjustments much longer without reparation.

Note AT.—To follow Note AS at foot of page 538.

(*The author's description of Tools and Tool-holders for turning and planing metal, constructed by C. Babbage, Esq., F.R.S.*)

In the course of the investigation which led Mr. Babbage to write the foregoing paper, he constructed various experimental tool-holders, a part of the more successful of which I shall now attempt to describe, beginning with those in which a single

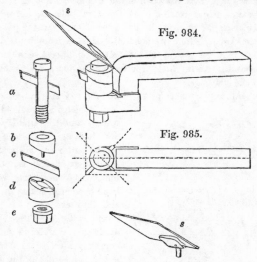

Fig. 984.

Fig. 985.

cutter is used. The figures are one-fourth of the size of the actual tools, but the proportions of which may of course be enlarged or reduced according to circumstances.

Fig. 984 represents the perspective view, fig. 985 the plan, and a b c d e the details of Mr. Babbage's tool-holder, for the general purposes both of turning and planing metal: the tool itself c, being simply a short rectangular piece of steel cut off from the end of a long bar, and ground at the end with one chamfer at about 60 degrees with the length of the blade. The stock is cast of gun-metal and of a cranked form, as seen in fig. 984, the end being pierced with a vertical hole, in which is fitted the bolt a, having a long diametrical mortise to admit the tool freely as shown, and a nut and washer e, below to bind all the parts together. The bolt a, passes through two circular wedges b and d, inclined at the angle 27^0 on their internal faces, and loosely united by steadying pins; the lower circular wedge has a diametrical inclined mortise to serve as the seat for the tool, and which is grasped by the margins or walls of the wedges, when the bolt and nut are tightened.

Sometimes the cutter lies centrally to the shaft of the holder, as shown in fig. 984, and also by the central dotted line in the plan, the vertical branch of the holder is pierced with a mortise, then to receive the superabundant length of the steel cutter; but at other times the cutter is inclined about 45^0 in either direction, as represented in the plan, fig. 985, and the cutter then just escapes the stock through a little notch filed for the purpose.

The one inclined position has been represented in the plan, fig. 985, and in this case the point of the cutter lies in a very favourable position for turning either cylindrical or plane surfaces, as the cutter stands in advance of the stock, and may proceed into an internal angle, such as the joining of a mass composed as it were of two cylindrical blocks of different diameters. The tool when simply bevelled, or ground with one chamfer, will not perfect the inner angle of the work on both faces, but which may be done if the tool is ground with two faces, or as a pointed tool meeting at an angle a little less than 90^0.

The figure also represents a very useful addition, applicable to all the tool-holders and slide-rests for metal turning, namely a little eye-shade, which is no more than a small piece of window glass, attached either to the tool-holder or any part of the rest, in a spring clamp which retains it at about an inclination of 40 or 50 degrees, so as to be nearly at right angles to the line proceeding from the point of the tool to the eye of the workman, which it effectually shields from injury. This simple contrivance, which may be readily added to any slide-rest, enables the workman narrowly to inspect the course and progress of the tool, and yet defends his eye completely from the shavings.

Fig. 986 represents the perspective view, and fig. 987 the end view, (full size,) of Mr. Babbage's tool holder for internal works, and the small parts are shown detached, also full size.

Fig. 986.

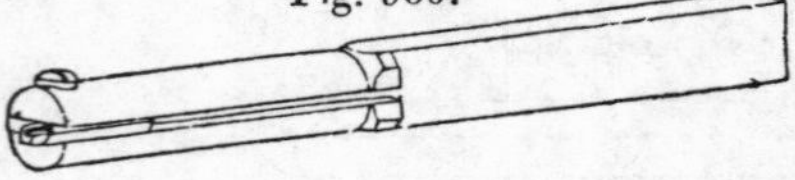

Fig. 987.

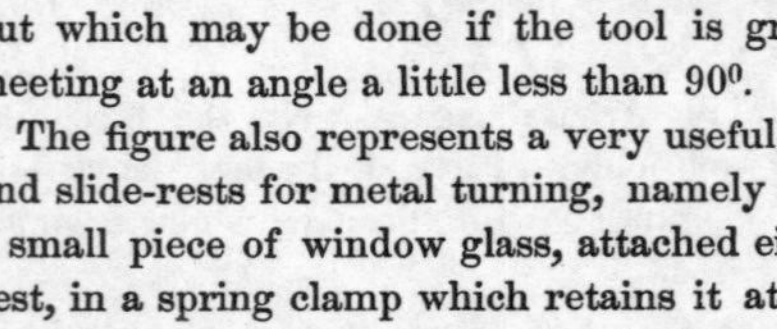

The cutters c are short pieces cut off from a bar of steel, fluted in the planing machine, to give that which Mr. Babbage has described as the angle of relief, and they are sharpened almost exclusively at the end, nearly square across or slightly chamfered or rounded at the corner. This tool-holder is made of steel, the end is turned cylindrical, and a cleft is sawn with a thick circular cutter or saw, down one side nearly to the axis, and entirely across the end to the depth of about one diameter and a half.

In the end view fig. 987, c represents the cutter, b the block against which the cutter rests, and s the screw that passes through b, and holds the several parts in contact. The tool may be made to cut on the right or left hand side at pleasure, as c and b each reverse. To enable the cutter to resist being drawn out, by the force of the cutting action, the small square wire, represented black, is added, this square wire fits a groove planed out in the tool holder, and lies in the flute of the cutter so as to secure it.

In this internal cutting tool as in all others of similar kind, a hole must be drilled or otherwise made in the work to admit the shaft of the tool, before it can be used, and from the contracted measure of the tools used for turning the inner surfaces of small apertures, the most suitable angles cannot be generally given to the internal tools.

Figs. 988 and 989 represent in the entire and dissected states, one of several tools contrived by Mr. Babbage, for turning wood by means of the slide rest. A small part of the end of the gun metal tool holder is inclined to the stem, and the extreme end is filed convex to fit the concave side of the gouge c, which is ground on the outside, exactly as usual with a gouge used by hand. The cutter is retained by means of the strap d, which embraces the cutter, and also two little blocks a, and b fitted together with a chamfered joint, so that the middle piece, which is carried down by the central binding screw, acts as a powerful wedge, and fills out the space within

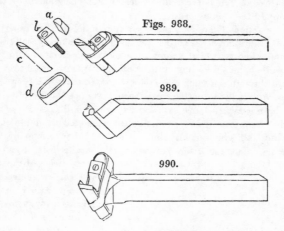

Figs. 988.

989.

990.

the loop, consequently the tool is grasped with considerable firmness against the rounded end of the holder, even when the pressure of the screw is very moderate. The screw requires a groove below its head, and the wedge b, a corresponding pin or key, that it may be raised to release the tool when the screw is unwound.

In some of these tools the cutter is circular as a gouge, in others straight as a chisel, or angular as a pointed tool, and of these three varieties, some have bent shafts the ends of which not only dip downwards, as shown in the side views figs. 988 and 989, but are also inclined horizontally at an angle of 45° as in fig. 990, in order to produce the same effect as the inclined position of fig. 985, and enable the same tool to serve alike for turning cylindrical or plane surfaces at the one fixing. The whole of these cutters for wood act in a vigorous and efficient manner.

I shall now say a few words on Mr. Babbage's notions of the employment of cutting tools with many points, so that the work may be equally divided among all the points.

The most simple case quoted by Mr. Babbage, is that of the screw tap, in which to carry out his principle, he cuts 6 or 7 longitudinal grooves instead of three only, the faces of which grooves are undercut or inclined to the radius, although not fully to the approved angle of 27°, they more resemble those taps called by workmen original taps, shown in figures 550 and 551, page 591, but they nevertheless answer for tapping and screwing the finer class of work, as they produce true threads and work freely. The circular tops of the threads are as usual a little cleared with the file, unto near the cutting points, and in the larger sizes of these taps the flutes are undercut to admit of their being sharpened on a revolving lap.

Another example quoted by Mr. Babbage is that of Messrs. Whitworth's key-way cutter, for making the internal grooves in the holes of wheels, for the keys by which they are fixed upon their cylindrical shafts. The cutter is a cylindrical rod of steel, through which are made about ten or a dozen rectangular mortises, placed at equal distances and in a right line. Every mortise is fitted with a small steel cutter, the sides of which are made exactly true in the engineer's planing machine; the first cutter is sharpened so as scarcely to project beyond the surface of the cylindrical bar, the second projects a little more than the first, and so on to the last, the projection of which equals the full depth of the key-way. When used, the bar is first put into the hole of the wheel, and which it should exactly fit, and the bar is steadily pushed quite through the hole of the wheel or pulley, by aid of the steady movement of an appropriate screw press.

This mode of action always cuts the key-way parallel and not taper as frequently wanted. From the subdivision of the work amongst the many cutters, the work is well done, and almost without injury to the cutters, which should be sufficiently close together, that the succeeding cutter may enter the groove, before the previous one has passed through the same; in other words, the interval between the cutters should be always less than the thickness through the boss of the wheel. The cutters after having been sharpened, are set forward by aid of little screws fitted in a thin bar, inlaid in a chamfered groove extending the whole length of the cutters.

Figs. 991 and 992, represent Mr. Babbage's tool holder with many blades for the planing machine. This tool holder consists of two parallel bars of gun-metal, united to cross pieces at the ends, so as to form a narrow central cleft; the side bars are pierced with several holes which receive as many pins, that constitute the centers upon which a series of short parallel blades are jointed to the holder. When in use, the blades are separated by parallel slips of brass, and at the left extremity is a block to which is given the inclination of 27°, and the end screw being fastened the whole of the blades are fixed at that angle; Mr. Babbage says in making another tool holder of this kind he would cast the holder in one piece, and tighten the cutters by the method of the screw and wedge *a*, *b*, fig. 988.

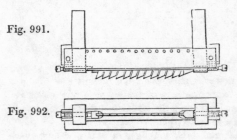

Fig. 991.

Fig. 992.

In order to sharpen the cutters, the brass separating pieces and the angle block at the end are removed, and all the flat pieces then fall down so that their chamfered ends lie in a straight line; when thus fixed by the end screw, their chamfers are all ground at once upon a lap; on the re-insertion of the brass plates, the tools bristle up like so many saw teeth after the manner shown. The tool is fixed in the planing machine at such an inclination, that the first cutter penetrates but a little way, and every succeeding cutter penetrates more and more unto the required degree, owing to the inclined position of the tool-holder ; the difference in elevation or projection of its two ends, being exactly equal to the intended thickness of the shaving to be removed, and the two tails of the tool-holder enable each end of the same to be securely grasped in the planing machine. (See first paragraph, page 982.)

Fig 993, a face-cutter for the lathe, is the last of these tools which Mr. Babbage's occupations have given him leisure to devise. The circular block is screwed to the lathe as an ordinary chuck, and on its cylindrical surface are cut 10 wedge-form grooves or notches, the one side of every notch is exactly on a diameter, the other side of the notch is inclined a few degrees, and fitted with a parallel steel blade, and a gun metal wedge ; the several wedges are sent forward by tail screws, tapped through a ring screwed on the back part of the chuck or otherwise attached.

To sharpen the blades they are removed from the chuck and placed in the rhomboidal cavity of a tool-holder shown in perspective in fig. 995, and in plan in fig. 996 ; the sides of the cavity are parallel and in pairs, but inclined in both directions to the angles at which the cutters are ground upon a revolving lap ; the horizontal

Figs. 993.   *d*   994.   995.

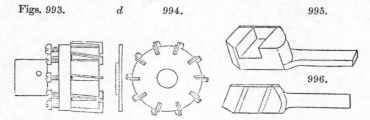

996.

angle seen in 996 is 24 degrees, the vertical is 16. By means of this holder the chamfered ends of the cutters are all thrown into one plane, and the sides of the cutters into another plane, and secured by two equal or folding wedges, the ends and sides of all the cutters are then ground *en masse*.

When replaced in the chuck a distance plate *d* with a central projection or boss, is first fixed to the end of the chuck, the cutters are allowed to rest in contact with this plate, and on the screws being tightened, every cutter becomes fixed by its wedge, and the distance plate ensures the ends of the cutters lying on one plane, and as much in advance of the end of the chuck, as the space between the chuck and the reduced margin of the distance plate.

This circular cutter with removable blades, may be viewed as a miniature and refinement, of some of the large boring tools and cutters with loose blades, figs. 516 and 517, pages 569 and 571 ; and the tool here shown has been extensively used by Mr. Babbage in facing all kinds of rectilinear pieces, which are at the time fixed in the slide rest, or in a universal chuck with screw jaws attached to the slide rest, by means of which the works are carried past the end or face of the slowly revolving cutter, which serves for several of the metals including steel, but the most effectively for brass and gun metal.

Note AU.—To follow note AT at the foot of page 538.

Paper on the Principles of Tools for Turning and Planing Metals, by the Rev. Prof. Willis of Cambridge, A.M., F.R.S., &c.

Let FGHK, fig. 997, represent a rough cylinder of metal running in a lathe between the centers M and L, and suppose that this is subjected to the action of the tool

DBE, which in the figure is supposed to have travelled from A to B, for the purpose of turning the surface of the cylinder. The tool is fixed in a slide rest by
which it is carried in a direction parallel to the axis of the cylinder ; it moves at
such a rate that during each revolution of the cylinder, the point B of the tool is
carried onwards through the space B *b*. The proportions of the figure are greatly
exaggerated for the purpose of showing the effect proposed to be illustrated, for
in practice, as is well known, although it is true that the effect produced by the
tool in turning a cylinder, is to trace a screw upon the surface, yet the thread of
that screw is either so fine from the slow motion of the tool, that it appears as a
mere roughness of surface, or else it is so flattened as to disappear from sense.* In
this figure the screw must be considered as an exaggeration for the sake of explanation.

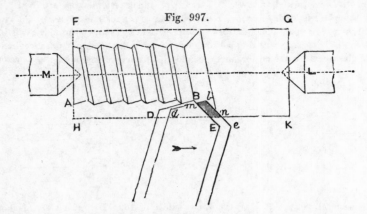

Fig. 997.

Since DBE and *dbe* represent the two successive positions of the tool, at the beginning and end of one rotation of the cylinder, a little consideration will show that the
shaded space between them, namely, *mbn*, is the section of the spiral shaving which
runs off the work during the process of turning. In this diagram *bn* is the breadth
of the shaving, and *bm* its thickness ; but by varying the position or angles of the
tool, and its relative motion to the work, it may happen that the reverse may be the
case ; that is to say, that *bm* may be the breadth, and *bn* the thickness. In all
cases, however, the two cutting edges of the tool are employed in detaching the
shaving, the one, (as BE in this figure,) separating its breadth from the solid, and the
other, (as DB,) separating its thickness, or *vice versâ*.

In adjusting the position and angles of a tool for turning or planing a given piece
of work, it appears to me essential that its action, as shown by such a diagram as
this, should be well foreseen and investigated, and I can only regret that the narrow
limits within which I am at present circumscribed, prevent me from explaining the
consequences of this principle by a variety of figures.

For example. In practice, if a tool were used in the position of fig. 997, the
motion would be slow, and the space B*b* or *mb*, which is the thickness of the shaving,
would be much less than in the diagram. It would be usually argued, that BE was
the real cutting edge, and that the shaving would come off without the assistance
of the other edge BD. Nevertheless, the action of this edge BD, is the only one

---

* In fig. 997 the thread of the screw, is inadvertently drawn, so as to incline in the
wrong direction. In fact the figure now shows the *lower surface* of the work seen trans-
parently, instead of the upper as it ought to have done.

which is left upon the surface of the work, and if the shaving be torn off edgewise by neglecting the action of this edge, the surface will necessarily be left rough.

By placing the edge BD still more nearly, or even exactly parallel to the axis of rotation, and rounding off the corner D * to prevent it from catching the surface, the screw form may be wholly obliterated, and if the edge BD be carefully sharpened a finished surface will result ; for it is clear, that thus the edge BE is wholly occupied with the hard work of separating the breadth of the shaving, and that the surface which it leaves at each turn is wholly removed in the next, whereas the edge BD has the lighter work of separating the shaving edgewise, and the surface which it leaves, is in fact the visible surface of the work when completed.

Let us now examine the angles that may be given to the tool edges. Fig. 998 shows the pointed tool in its simplest form, AB and AC are its cutting edges. The stem of the tool may be of various shapes for convenience, but the cutting portion of the instrument is bounded by three planes, namely, two *side planes*, one of which only, S, is shown in the figure, and a third or *upper plane* U. The intersection of this upper plane, with the two side planes respectively, produces the *cutting edges* AB, AC, and the intersection of the two side planes produces the line of the front angle AD.

By a proper management of the inclination of these planes to each other, we obtain the desired form of the point of the tool, and the proper acuteness of the cutting edges. This is the subject to which I wish in the next place to direct attention.

The front angle upon AD determines the form of the point of the tool in plan, and also the section of the shaving, as already explained. As to the cutting edges, a greater or less inclination of the upper plane U of the tool to the horizon, (always supposing the tool to rest on a horizontal bed,) will produce a greater or less degree of acuteness in these cutting edges.

If the upper plane be horizontal the cutting edges will plainly be square, whatever be the front angle of the tool. But if not, then the angle of the edges will vary conjointly with the front angle of the tool, and the inclination of the upper plane.

Different metals, and qualities of metal, require different degrees of acuteness in the cutting edges, which have not been as far as I know exactly determined. In the present case I will assume, that wrought iron requires an edge of 60°, cast iron of 70° ; that brass may be roughed out with an edge of 80°, and finished with one of 90°. These angles I believe to be very near to the best ; probably a variation of a degree or two is of little consequence. But as the finishing of some kinds of work requires that the edge of the tool should endure through a long process, without giving way and requiring fresh grinding, it is of some importance that the angles of the edges should be carefully investigated.

In grinding a tool of this form it is convenient to consider only the angle which the upper plane U makes with the line of the front angle AD. In other words, the angles of the cutting edges AB AC being equal, if we suppose a vertical plane to pass through AD and make equal angles with the side planes S, it will clearly intersect the upper plane in a line Ak, bisecting the angle BAC, and the upper plane will be perpendicular to this vertical plane. A rough goniometer† will enable us to grind this upper

---

* In fact, there is no occasion to round off the corner D, because the edge BD is, in most cases, inclined downwards, and the corner D carried thereby clear of the surface of the work, except in face turning.

† By this term is meant a frame attached to a grinding machine, capable of being set at different angles, so as to ensure that the tool, which rests upon it during the process, shall receive its proper form. A *goniostat* would be a better name.

plane at any desired angle kAD, and thus to ensure that the cutting edges shall be alike.

But this angle kAD is not the same as that of the cutting edges, and the question to be answered in every case is the following :—*Given the front angle of a tool (i.e. the plan of its point,) and the cutting edge required by the metal which it is to cut, to find the angle of inclination kAD of the upper plane.* This is an affair of trigonometrical calculation, and for practical purposes is best resolved into the form of a

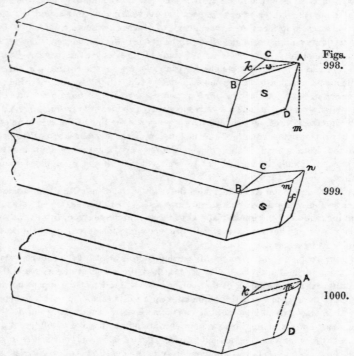

Figs.
998.

999.

1000.

short table which I will give, simply remarking that I have not thought it necessary to state the results nearer than to the next half degree, which is indicated in decimals when it occurs as 69·5.

TABLE OF THE ANGLES k A D									
FRONT ANGLE UPON A D	CUTTING EDGE.								
	85°	80°	75°	70°	65°	60°	55°	50°	45°
150°		80°	74·5	69·5	64	59°	54°	48·5	43
140°		79·5	74	69	63	58	52·5	47	41·5
130°		79	73·5	68	62	56·5	51	45	39
120°	84·5	78·5	72·5	67	60·5	55	49	42	35·5
110°	84	78	71·5	65·5	59	52·5	46	38·5	30
100°	83·5	77	70	63·5	56·5	49·5	42	33	23
90°	83	76	68·5	61	53	45	36	25	0
80°	82	74·5	66	58	49	39	27	0	
70°	81	72·5	63	53·5	42	29	0		
60°	80	70	58·5	47	33	0			
50°	78	66	52	36	0				
40°	75	59·5	40	0					

To use this table, take the column which corresponds to the required cutting edge. The degree placed opposite to the front angle of the tool will show the inclination of the upper plane U to the front angle, namely, the angle kAD. Thus to obtain cutting edges of 70° for a tool whose front angle is 90°, the plane U must be ground to an angle of 61° with the line of the front angle AD.

By means of this table several curious results may be obtained. For example, I have often seen tools for turning iron, in which the front angle AD has been made 60°. Now referring to the table in the column for 60°, (the proper cutting edge for iron,) we find zero opposite to the front angle 60°, indicating that the desired form is impossible ; that is to say, that it is impossible to place the upper plane of the tool at an angle that will cause it to make the desired cutting edges of 60°. The same front angle of 60°, under a cutting edge of 65°, gives the angle kAD equal to 33°, which is still too acute for the required strength, and even a cutting edge of 70° requires the weak angle kAD of 47°. In short, no proper edge can be given to an iron turning tool whose front angle AD is not greater than 60°.

To produce a stronger point the front angle of the tool is sometimes ground flat as at f in fig. 999, so as to make a short intermediate cutting edge m n. It is clear that the angle of this new cutting edge m n is the same as kAD in fig. 998, in the table, which table will therefore serve for this new form. This shows the impossibility of making the front cutting edge m n, with the same angle as the other two, for the former will be much more acute than the latter, except they be all square edges. If it were not for this circumstance, this form would give a strong and effective tool, so that it is worth while to examine the amount of the objection.

Supposing the front angle of the tool (which in this case is the angle at which the two side planes *would meet*,) to be 90°, the table shows that if the lateral cutting edges are 60°, the front edge m n will be 45°. As this is too acute to stand, let the front edge be made 60°, this will give about 70° for the side edges. For iron and steel tools then, this form is bad, because the difference between the angles of the cutting edges is too great. The best form for these metals appears to be one in which the front angle of the point is made as obtuse as possible, and both the cutting edges alike.

For example, the front angle may be made equal to 135°. This corresponds by the table for a cutting edge of 60°, to a vertical angle kAD of 57°, and produces a very strong tool, similar in form to the part of fig. 999, which is included between the planes S and f, but having both its cutting edges of the same degree of acuteness.

The same remarks apply, but not perhaps so forcibly, to the case of tools for cast iron, in which the cutting edge should be about 70°. Thus if we give to the form fig. 999 lateral cutting edges Bm Cn of 70°, (supposing as before that its side planes are inclined at 90°,) the front edge m n will be only 61° ; and if we make this front edge 70°, the lateral edges will be about 76°. Thus the difference is much less than in the former example, but still the form of fig. 998 is preferable, and the more obtuse the front angle is made the stronger will the point of the tool be. An angle of 150° may be given to the front angle AD.

Sometimes tools are made nearly like fig. 999, but in which the front is rounded off, as in fig. 1000, instead of being blunted by a plane as at f. These are liable to the same objection as the form fig. 999 ; namely, the impossibility of giving an equal angle to all the cutting edges. For, comparing fig. 999 and fig. 1000, it is clear that the vertical angle kAD is the same in both, and that in the round point this angle passes through all degrees of acuteness, between that at A and that at m, instead of abruptly changing from one to the other at m, as in fig. 999.

Besides this, a shaving which is separated by a round tool, and which, conse-quently, has a curved section, cannot roll itself off the work with the same ease·that a ribbon-shaped shaving does. It thus opposes greater resistance to the edge of the tool, and blunts it sooner. Also, a round-pointed tool is more difficult to keep in order than a tool whose edges are formed by planes alone.

On the whole, then, I am inclined to recommend the obtuse pointed tool for cylinder turning and the planing of flat surfaces; but the tool should terminate in an *angular* and not in a *rounded* point, and the edge BD (see fig. 997,) *should be set nearly or quite parallel with the path of the tool*, as from A to B, in turning a cylinder, or planing a flat surface. For more complicated figures, of course, different forms must be adopted, as for planing into corners or turning projections; but the same principle of keeping the front angle AD fig. 998, as obtuse as possible, may always be recollected with advantage.

There is yet another point to be remarked. In the above pages, the tool being assumed to rest upon a horizontal plane, the side planes S may be supposed to be vertical, and, consequently, the line of the front angle AD vertical also.

But Mr. Nasmyth has well explained the necessity of inclining these planes to an angle of about 3° from the vertical. This produces in AD an inclination from the vertical which varies according to the amount of the front angle of the tool, but which must be taken into the account in the construction of the *goniostat*. For the angles given in the table above, are the angles kAD, and not the angles which the upper plane makes with the horizontal platform of the slide rest upon which the tool is seated. The following table, therefore, is given to show the angle which AD makes with the vertical line Am, under different angles of the front, always supposing the plane S to make an angle of 3° from the vertical, according to Mr. Nasmyth's statement.*

Front Angle ..	150°	140°	130°	120°	110°	100°	90°	80°	70°	60°	50°	40°
Vertical Angle mAD.	3° 5′	3° 10′	3° 17′	3° 27′	3° 38′	3° 53′	4° 12′	4° 44′	5° 11′	6°	7°	8° 39′

The above remarks are offered, in the hope that some one with the proper oppor-tunities will be induced to make experiments upon the best form and edge of tools for different materials.

The relative angular positions of the planes of the tool point, and the different kinds of edges produced, may be made clear to persons not familiar with geometrical notions, by large wooden models, in which the three principal planes being cut, the resulting edges may be measured with a goniometer.

Note AV.—To follow Note AU at the foot of page 538.

A Paper on a new form of tool-holder, with detached blades for turning or planing metal, and on a new mode of fixing down tools upon the slide rest, by Professor Willis, A.M., &c.

Instead of making the cutting portion and the stem of a tool in one piece of steel, the cutting part is sometimes formed out of a small piece of steel, and the stem is furnished with some convenient contrivance for grasping it.

This principle has several advantages, especially for amateur workmen, who can

---

* Mr. Nasmyth's tool gauge for showing this angle is described and figured on page 534 of the text.

shape and temper a small piece of steel, but who may not be provided with a forge and apparatus necessary for the construction of a complete tool. Besides, the process of tempering can be more effectually carried out with a small piece than when we have to deal with the end of a large lump. I do not know the history of this contrivance. Mr. Holtzapffel has had for many years on sale a tool on this principle, and I have also seen it in other factories.*

I will proceed to describe the form into which I have put it, for the purpose of experimenting upon the angular forms of the tool edges deduced in the preceding pages. As the cutting extremity of the tool is bounded by three planes, the piece of steel may be arranged with respect to those planes, in different ways, according to the purpose required.

Thus a triangular prism of steel may be adopted of which the front sides, S fig. 1001, make the same angle with each other as that of the side planes of the proposed

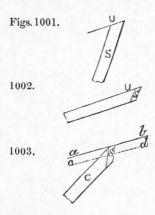

Figs. 1001.

1002.

1003.

tool. The stem of the tool must grasp the prism so that these planes may make an angle of 3° from the vertical, and the upper plane U only must be ground from time to time at the proper angle ; the prism being, of course, raised in its clamp, so that the point shall always coincide with the level of the axis of the lathe. This is the arrangement of Mr. Holtzapffel's tool. It does not allow of different angles being tried for the side planes, because the grasping part of the stem is so fitted to the angles of the prism as not to admit of prisms of different front angles being inserted. And, indeed, this would not be practicable, for, according to the second table which I have given, it appears that the angle of inclination of the prism would be different for different front angles. But when the best front angles are determined, this arrangement will probably be found very effectual.

Another method is to clamp the steel prism at such an angle, that its upper surface U, fig. 1002, may coincide with the upper plane of the tool, and in this case the side planes S can be ground at any desired angle, but the angle of the upper plane remains fixed.

I have found it convenient to choose an angular position for the prism, that shall, as in fig. 1003, lie between the mean place of the upper planes of the tools and the places of the side planes. Thus if C, fig. 1003, be the prism inclined at an angle of 55° to the horizon, side planes S may be ground at its upper end, and also an upper plane ab.

The section of the prism being thus independent of the relative angular positions of the three planes that form the cutting extremity, may be determined solely from considerations of convenience, for facility of shaping and fixing. I have employed round steel wire of the largest diameter usually kept in the shops, (namely, Lancashire bright steel wire,) and filed slightly flat on the upper surface, as shown in the succeeding figures. When the side planes have been formed, the grinding may take

---

* The author believes that tool-holders, with small detached cutters, were first used in the block machinery at Portsmouth, and since 1830 he has largely employed various kinds of these tool holders in his manufactory. See text, pages 535—6, where some of the tool holders are described and figured.

place on the upper plane alone for some time; thus beginning at *ab*, we may grind down to *cd*, then we may grind the side planes afresh, and so on.

I will now describe the stem and clamping apparatus, figs. 1004, 1005 and 1006. A bar of iron ABCDE, shewn in elevation in fig. 1004, serves as the foundation of the instrument. It is straight and square from A to B, which portion is the stem of the tool, by means of which it is fixed in the tool-holder of the slide rest. The form of the part BCDE, which receives the steel wire PQ, is given in the elevation. It is bounded, however, by the same vertical planes as the stem AB.

An angular notch is filed at DE for the reception of the wire. The axis of the wire when clamped into the notch, should lie in a vertical plane parallel to the sides of the stem, and should make an angle of 55° with the horizon. The section of the notch is shown in fig. 1005, which is a plan of the tool, or rather projection upon a plane perpendicular to the axis of the wire. The inner side of the notch is sunk

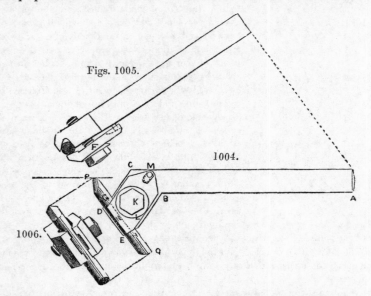

Figs. 1005.

1004.

1006.

perpendicularly to the side of the tool, so that the flat side of the wire may lie upwards. The wire is clamped into the notch by means of a piece F. The form of this piece is shown in fig. 1004, and is very nearly the same as that of the extremity of the stem piece. The screw K tapped into the stem piece, presses F into contact with the wire along one extremity GH, and with a short pin M, (fixed into the stem of the tool) at the other extremity. To ensure the firm grasp of the wire the following arrangements are made :—

The first requisite is that the clamping piece F should be left at liberty to take a secure bearing upon the wire. If the latter were perfectly straight and cylindrical, and the under surface of F perfectly flat, this bearing would take effect along the line GH, which is the line of contingence of the said plane and cylinder.

But in practice a rounded or twisted surface would defeat this object, and therefore the middle of the bearing surface of the clamp is filed away as shown in the front view, fig. 1006, so as to ensure a pinch at or near each extremity of the line GH. (For the same reasons the notch in the stem piece should be filed away in the middle as also shown.)

The bearing at the other extremity M of the clamp, is upon a round-headed, short, hard steel pin, driven tight into a hole in the stem piece. The head of this pin is received freely into a notch filed lengthwise in the tail of the clamp, as shown by the dotted lines. This allows the clamp to settle itself freely upon this bearing point, and at the same time prevents it from turning round and shifting its proper position upon the stem.

Thus the pressure of the screw K is distributed upon the three points G, H and M ; and, by the well-known principles of statics, if N be the bisection of GH, and if the center of K lie in the straight line joining N and M, then will the pressure of the screw be equally divided upon G and H, whatever be the angle GNM. Further, if MK be equal to twice NK, the pressure of the screw upon all three points will be equal. However, it is better to throw M as far from the screw as possible, for thus less pressure is exerted upon M, and therefore more upon G and H.

Finally, to ensure the free transmission of the pressure of the screw to the clamp without jamming or wedging, a spherical washer L is interposed between the head of the screw and the clamp, and is received into a corresponding cavity turned in the clamp. If this be thought too expensive an arrangement, the lower part of the head of the screw may be made spherical, and received into a conical or countersunk cavity. Care must be taken to make the hole in the center of the clamp F, through which the screw passes, considerably larger than the diameter of the screw ; else all these arrangements to enable the clamp to settle itself freely upon its bearing points may be defeated, by its being driven laterally against the screw. A short wire spring, coiled loosely round the screw between the clamp and the stem piece and touching the clamping piece between K and N, serves to press this piece outwards against the spherical washer, and also keeps it in contact with M, and thus prevents it from hanging loosely when the wire is withdrawn.

(A new Tool-holder for the Slide rest.)

In the ordinary tool-holder or contrivance by which the tool is secured to the table of the slide rest, no provision is made for placing the tool in various angular positions. The stem must lie parallel, or very nearly so, with one side or the other of the table, or in other words, we have but the choice of two directions for its stem. If it be desired to present the point of a tool in an oblique direction, it can only be effected by bending the tool itself. I am aware that contrivances have been proposed to enable the tool to be fixed angularly, as for example " Mr. Parsson's Improved Box for a slide rest," (described in the Society of Arts' Transactions, Vol. xlviii., page 240,) which is, I believe, but little used, and in principle of construction is entirely different from mine.

The contrivance I am about to describe I constructed in the spring of 1842, and have had in use ever since, and it was also immediately adopted by Mr. Holtzapffel, by whom it has, I believe, been found perfectly effective.* It enables the tool to be fixed at any required angular position upon the table of the slide rest, and is besides capable of being entirely removed from the table, so as to leave it free for the reception of other contrivances, as for drilling, cutting wheels, &c. The tool-holder is shewn in plan in fig. 1008, and in elevation (partly sectional) in fig. 1007.

In this tool-holder the tool is secured in its position by the action of a single nut A, which is tapped to a strong screw pillar BC. This screw has a round shoulder

---

* Nearly all the sliding rests in the author's manufactory have been fitted with Mr. Willis's apparatus for grasping the tools, and which answers so completely as to be always adopted in sliding rests for metal turning now made therein.

below, which bears upon the surface of the table ; beneath this shoulder is a short portion of screw C, which is tapped into a hole in the table.   The screw pillar can therefore be removed or replaced by means of a key applied to flat faces filed upon the shoulder.   The pressure of the nut A is transmitted to the upper surface of a triangular clamping piece DEF fig. 1008, through the interposed spherical washer G, which works freely in a corresponding cavity in the triangular clamp, as shown in the section fig. 1007.

Two short rounded studs of hard steel D, E, are driven into the lower side of the triangle, and rest upon the upper surface of the stem of the tool.   At F a screw is tapped stiffly into the triangle, and its lower end being rounded like those of the studs D and E, it follows that when the nut A is brought into action, its pressure upon the triangle is resolved upon the three bearing points below, namely upon the two, D E, which press upon the tool, and clamp it to the surface of the table, and upon the third at F which presses upon the table through the intermediate piece H, which is principally interposed to save the table from bruises.

If the nut be loosened the tool and triangle are set at liberty, and the latter may be placed in any required angular position, when a turn of the nut at once fixes it

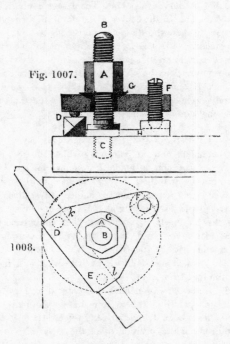

Fig. 1007.

1008.

completely.   But as it is necessary that the tool should be under the studs D, E, and therefore always at the same distance from the center of the screw, the intermediate piece H is contrived also to answer the purpose of guiding the stem of the tool readily to this distance.

The outline of this piece is exactly the same as that of the triangle under which it lies, with the exception of the side which is parallel to the tool.   This side is made at such a distance from the center of the screw that when the tool rests against it, it is set in the proper position to receive the pressure of the studs D, E, of the triangular clamp. The dotted line k l fig. 1008, is the boundary of the lower piece, and at the opposite extremity of this piece a thick lump is formed in which a notch or groove is filed in a direction pointing to the center of the screw pillar. This groove receives the end of the screw F as already explained. The form and thickness of the lump and the position of the groove are shown by the dotted lines in the figures.

The triangle and washer are drawn in section in the upper figure, to explain the adjustment of the washer G. As the upper surface of this washer is always horizontal, the hole need be no larger than is sufficient to pass freely up and down the screw pillar. But the case is different with the triangle D E F, for as that is required to accommodate itself to irregular thicknesses of the tool, that may throw it out of the horizontal position, the hole through which the screw pillar passes, should be large and slightly conical as shown in the section. In fixing the position of the screw pillar, upon the table of the slide rest, it should be placed at such a distance from the two edges, that the bearing points D, E, F of the triangle, may not hang over the edges in any position, but that the tool may be always clamped within the limits of the table ; the dotted circle in the plan explains this sufficiently.

A circular hole in the middle of the piece H fits loosely the shoulder of the screw pillar, and as the end of the screw F is received freely in the groove of the intermediate piece, which latter is thereby kept in its proper place below the triangle, it follows that the whole combination of tool, triangle, and intermediate piece, may be swung round the central pillar, without escaping from their proper relative positions.

The screw F is introduced to allow of adjustment for tools of greatly differing thickness. But if it be necessary to put thin wedges under either end of the stem of the tool in order to raise or depress its point, the spherical washer allows of this by transmitting freely and centrically the pressure of the nut notwithstanding that the upper surface of the triangle becomes inclined from the horizontal position. It must be also observed that the tool may be placed either to the right or left of the screw pillar at pleasure and a spiral spring may be introduced below the triangle, to prevent it from falling down when the tool is withdrawn.

The triangle should be made of such a size, that the distance between its bearing pins D E, may be the same as that which would be given to the binding screws of an ordinary tool-holder.

Note AW, to follow the first paragraph page 542.

(*Mr. Franklin's Expanding Center Bits.*)

This modification of the center bit fig. 457, page 541, enables a series of three tools, to bore all holes intermediate between half an inch and two inches in diameter, and that with very little interference in the general principle of the tool.

In figure 1009 the two parts of the instrument are separated beyond the distance at which they are used, in order to show the construction, and from which view it will be seen that the part a, of the expanding bit, which is squared at the end to fit the carpenter's brace, is extended at the other end, to form the central pin d, by which the tool is guided. The moveable part carries the scoring cutter or nicker e, and this piece admits of adjustment of diameter, it being attached to the main stem by the rivet near b, and fastened thereto by the binding screw c, that passes through the mortise in the moveable piece ; this latter part is formed to constitute the lateral cutter f, by which the shavings are as it were swept out of the hole that is being made.

When the center bit is contracted to serve for its smallest diameter as in fig. 1010, the radii of the nicker and cutter are just alike, but it is found that the radius of the nicker may be increased above one-fourth as in the dotted position, and that still

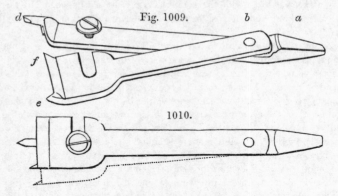

the cutter acts fairly, as the shavings become readily disengaged.   These expanding bits are not intended to supersede the ordinary center bits of fixed sizes, but to serve for occasional works ; and they are extremely well suited to the wants of amateurs.

Note AX, to follow the paragraph page 544, commencing "another Screw Auger."
(*The American Screw Auger.*)

The American screw auger fig. 466 page 543, was patented by Mr. Wm. Ash of Sheffield, and is described in the " Practical Mechanic and Engineers' Magazine," Glasgow 1842, Vol. 1, page 108.

This description speaks of a different modification of the screw auger, from that described in the text, and in which a piece called a *guide* is employed instead of the worm usually soldered to the shaft.   The guide consists of two thin rings, united concentrically by two fins situated on a diametrical line, leaving two large semi-annular spaces between them.   The outer ring is made as a short conical screw, the inner embraces the central stem of the auger, upon which it fits loosely behind the cutter.

The auger first bores a shallow hole, into which the loose guide ring is screwed to serve for the guidance of the instrument, by the central ring or *thimble* which fits the auger shaft, and the shavings have to escape through the annular spaces betwixt the two rings.   This part of the contrivance appears however to be far less practical than that described in the text.

Mr. Phineas Cooke was rewarded by the Society of Arts in 1771 for the invention of the screw auger fig. 463, page 543, but the difficulty and expense attending its first construction, appear long to have withheld it from general use.—See also Smith's Panorama of Science, Vol. 1, p. 113.

Note AY, page 554, to follow the paragraph ending, " without figures."
(*Freeman's Registered Drill Tool.*)

This is a very useful substitute for the drill bow, it consists simply of a flat strip of wood, from about 8 to 16 inches long, by $\frac{3}{4}$ to $1\frac{1}{2}$ wide, with an appropriate handle, and on one side of the wood is cemented a strip of sheet india rubber or caoutchouc. The pulley of the drill or drillstock is made of wood and cylindrical, the diameter and length being about equal, and the extreme angles slightly rounded. The contact between the wooden pulley and the caoutchouc will be found quite sufficient for the working of small drills, and as the tool is simply used as a violin bow, the tedious process of coiling on the string of the ordinary bow is entirely avoided.

Note AZ, page 557, to follow the paragraph ending " for reciprocating drills."
(Mr. MacDowall's Archimedean Screw Drillstock.)

Mr. MacDowall's improved drillstock fig. 1011, is a very useful instrument, acting by reciprocating motion, and which was rewarded in 1845 by the Society of Arts. It consists of a rod of the so-called pinion wire, (the formation of which is noticed on page 426 and fig. 294 of vol. 1.) The one end of the wire is bored up to serve as a socket for receiving the drills, the other end is formed into a center point and contained within a handle or socket, by which the instrument is guided towards and pressed into the work ; the remainder of the instrument consists of a slider or nut fitted to the ribs of the pinion wire, and possessing a handle having an universal joint.

If the grooves of the pinion wire were straight like the flutes of a column, the nut might be slid up and down without giving any motion to the drill, but as the

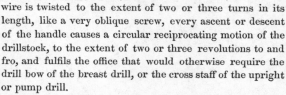

Fig. 1011.

wire is twisted to the extent of two or three turns in its length, like a very oblique screw, every ascent or descent of the handle causes a circular reciprocating motion of the drillstock, to the extent of two or three revolutions to and fro, and fulfils the office that would otherwise require the drill bow of the breast drill, or the cross staff of the upright or pump drill.

The instrument as above described answers beautifully for very small holes, but the ingenious inventor was again rewarded in the following year, for additions by which the power of this drill tool is much increased. He first added a transverse or diametrical arm at the foot, carrying two balls to serve as a fly and give momentum; but inconvenience then occurred from the weight having to be suddenly started and stopped. This defect was judiciously remedied by introducing a little catch wheel or ratchet in the nut by which, as in the Brequet watch key, and also in the ratchet drill page 561, the catch slips over the teeth of the ratchet wheel in the ascent, and only moves the drill in the descent; thus allowing the fly to act uninterruptedly and impel the drill with continuous motion in the one direction only, and with increased force. With the improved instrument registered under the name of the *" Continued Revolving Archimedean Drill,"* holes can be pierced of fully twice the diameter of those which could be made with the former and more simple Archimedean drill having a reciprocating action.

Note BA.—To follow the Note A, Z, on page 557.
(Mr. MacDowall's Rectangular Archimedean Drillstock for Dental Surgery.)
This tool, which is represented in fig. 1012, is an offshoot of the reciprocating Archimedean drillstock. The parts *a, b, c* to *d*, of the succeeding figure are precisely

analogous to the corresponding parts in fig. 1011, except that from *b*, to *d*, extends a straight bar that firmly unites these two parts. From *d*, to *e*, is a socket or tube carrying at *e*, a small drill socket or hollow mandrel, at right angles to the length of the instrument, and within the tube are concealed two very small bevel pinions, the one fixed on the drill socket, the other on the end of the reciprocating drill shaft *b d*, which is continued within the tube so far as *e*, the bevel pinions therefore transfer the motion of the reciprocating shaft to the drill.

The tube which extends from *d*, to *e*, may be moved round in the collar at *d*, and fixed in any required position by the thumb-screw, so that the drill may be directed upwards, downwards, to the right, or to the left, according to the position of the hole the dentist has to drill in the tooth of his patient.

Note BB.—To follow the Note B, A, on page 557.
(Capt. G. D. Davison's Rectangular Drillstock for Dental Surgery.)

Fig. 1013 represents an instrument for the same purpose as the foregoing, and which was invented at about the same time as fig. 1012, by an officer of the British Army, engaged in the Ahmednuggur Survey in India. It consists of two slender

Figs. 1012.

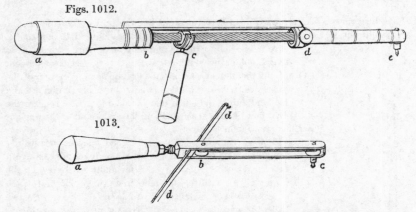

1013.

bars of steel united at both extremities, and inserted by the one end into a wooden or ivory handle *a* ; at *c*, is a small spindle for the drills with an appropriate pulley situated between the two side bars, and at *b* is a similar pulley. The catgut line by which the drill is moved passes entirely round the pulley of the drill-socket at *c*, the two ends then run parallel with the stem of the tool, make each a quarter turn in opposite directions over the guide pulley *b*, and then proceed to the extremities of the drill bow *d d*, which passes through the space between the side bars of the instrument. If the pulley *c*, is situated close to the end of the instrument, and the drill-bow nearly fills out the space between *b* and the steel frame, the cord will then be retained in the grooves of the pullies with little or no risk of its being accidentally detached. This instrument, like the last, may be used in all the required positions.

Note BC, page 563.—To precede Section IV.
(Mr. George Scott's Apparatus for Boring and Tapping Cast-iron Main Pipes for Water and Gas.

Fig. 1014 represents Mr. George Scott's apparatus for drilling gas and water pipes, and which was rewarded in June, 1846, by the Society of Arts. The parts are all grouped together as if in use, but the pipe itself is represented in dotted lines, in order that the point of the drill and the apparatus generally may be better seen : *a*, is a semicircular iron strap that embraces the pipe *b b*, *c c*, is a cross piece with a screwed central hole attached to the curved strap by the nuts *d d*, and *e*, is a tube screwed into *c c*, and which tube carries the revolving socket *f*, terminating in the drill *g*. When the parts are all united and fixed to the pipe as in the figure, the drill-socket *f g*, is handed round by means of a spanner about 2 feet long, applied to the square at *f*, and whilst the hole is being pierced, the drill is set gradually deeper, by a screwed nut which is extended so as to constitute the handles *h h*, by the movement of which at intervals, the drill is gradually forced deeper into the hole it is in the act of boring.

When the hole is completed the socket and drill *f g*, are removed from the cross-piece *c c*, and the screw tap, shewn separately at *i*, is inserted into the same hole, and the threads of *c c*, and *i*, being alike in diameter and pitch *c c*, serves to guide the tap

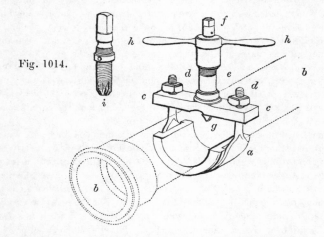

Fig. 1014.

very truly into the hole previously made. By introducing different saddle-pieces of wood, that lie between the strap *a*, and the pipe, and by using smaller drills and screw taps of the same thread, the same apparatus may be made available for smaller pipes ; it is very efficient for its intended purpose, and a decided improvement on former methods. The principal part of the tap *i*, is left with the thread entire, to serve for the guidance, and the end alone is tapered and cut with several notches almost as a conical countersink, and which fully suffice for tapping the thin metal of the pipe.—See also text, page 558.

Notes BD—BE—BF—BG—BH and BI.—To follow the text, pages 564 to 567.

On Drills and Boring Bits used in Lathes and Boring Machines.

Six tools of this class have come to the author's knowledge since the foregoing pages were printed, they will be now figured and described by way of appendix to the text. Three of these tools are intended to maintain their several diameters unaltered, the other three admit of adjustment for size within certain limits. To the best of the author's belief, they are all quite separate and independent inventions applied to one nearly common purpose.

Note BD.—To follow the text, pages 564 to 567.
(*Mr. Collas's lathe drill.*)

A lathe drill described as the invention of Mr. Collas, of Paris, Engineer, is figured in page 171, of the Engineers' and Machinists' Assistant, Glasgow, 1846. The instrument for greater perspicuity is here represented in perspective in fig. 1015. This drill is turned as a cylinder, and perforated to the extent of three or four diameters, with a hole of about one tenth of the exterior size.   Exactly one-third the

Fig. 1015.

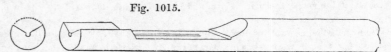

cylindrical end is removed, so as to form a longitudinal incision extending to the center and having radial sides ; the extremity of the drill is ground somewhat as in the half round bit fig. 507, page 565, to make the one edge cut ; behind the angular part a further portion is reduced to the diametrical line, and the remainder is either cylindrical or square, and terminates in a center for the popit head.

The work having been chucked in the lathe, and a shallow recess turned out to admit the end of the bit, the latter bores the hole in the *solid metal* to any depth that may be required ; as the core or the small portion opposite the central hole extends up the drill shaft, (which it is considered to guide,) and the core breaks off in small pieces as the drill progresses into the solid metal.

The ordinary half round bits, fig. 507, may also be employed for boring holes in the solid metal, but which is not their common application, and when exactly semi-circular they remove the whole of the metal not leaving a core, but as usually ground they leave the bottom of the hole as a very obtuse cone ; to make the bottom of the hole quite flat, the half-round bits may be ground square across on the cutting side, and bevelled on the opposite to clear the bottom.   But the nearly rectangular edges of the half-round and similar bits, require more power and work less freely, in drilling holes in fibrous metals, than the ordinary fluted drills fig. 478, page 548, and are more troublesome to enter.

The author considers the central hole in Mr. Collas's drill not to be required for the purpose of guiding it, which office is performed by its exterior surface, and he sees no reason why the cutting edge should not, as in the half-round bit, proceed beyond the center and remove the whole material, as in making a flat-bottomed hole, in this case the central pin left by Mr. Collas's drill requires after removal.

Note BE.—To follow the text, pages 564 to 567.
(*C. Holtzapffel's boring bit with changeable cutters, derived from the half-round bit.*)

This was contrived for boring holes in models of guns, howitzers, and mortars, to avoid the expense of the many long boring bits required in making a series of these models.

The stock is constructed as shown entire in fig. 1016, and detached in fig. 1017.   The end of the stock is turned cylindrical, and has a notch across the extremity extending below the diametrical line, and also a longitudinal groove on the underside.   The notch receives the cutter *c*, which embraces the flattened edges of the stock, and is held by two small screws, the groove receives the bearing piece *b*, which is fixed by two other screws, that are countersunk.

The outer parts of c, and b, are turned to the cylindrical form and hardened, the cutting angle c, being allowed to be always more prominent than the two other parts.

One stock was thus made to serve for various diameters from $\frac{7}{8}$ of an inch to $1\frac{3}{16}$, (or ·882 to 1·169,) another for sizes between $1\frac{1}{4}$ inch to $1\frac{5}{8}$, (or 1·297 to 1·66,) so as between them to answer for boring models of the entire series of Ordnance employed by the British Government, when constructed on the scale of one-sixth their true sizes.

For drilling the preparatory holes below $\frac{7}{8}$ diameter, the system of three tools described in the first paragraph, page 567, was employed, so as to ensure the exact

Figs. 1016.

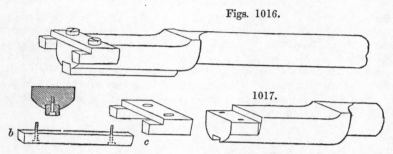

1017.

centrality and straightness of the bore ; and in forming the curved chambers in the various models, different cutters with tail screws, were inserted in a hole tapped in the axis of a long boring bar, also used in the lathe. The entire scheme was quite successful, and is perhaps the smallest example of, (virtually,) half-round bits with loose cutters.

Note BF.—To follow the text, pages 564 to 567.
(*The Cornish bit with loose cutters.*)

The Cornish bit is a useful lathe drill, apparently derived from the boring bar, fig. 514, page 569, and like it, is adaptable to holes of certain fixed diameters. As seen in fig. 1018, the stock which is cylindrical throughout, (except where it is squared for the hook wrench,) is enlarged at the one end, and has a diametrical mortise, fitted with a cutter c, notched out at the one end to embrace the flattened sides of the bar, and secured with the wedge w, as in fig. 514. But as the Cornish bit is used in the lathe, and is therefore only supported by the work at the one end, and the popit-head at the other, a bearing piece b is fitted in a longitudinal chamfer groove on the

Fig. 1018.

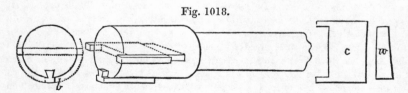

under side of the stock, as seen in the end view, in order to keep it central. The three edges, of the cutter and bearing piece respectively, are all turned in their places. The cutter is bevelled and rounded so as to cut at the front only, after which the parts are hardened.

The Cornish bits are not made for holes smaller than about $1\frac{1}{2}$ inch in diameter, and by means of additional cutters and bearing pieces, every stock may admit of an increase of size of fully one-half its minimum diameter, or say from about $1\frac{1}{2}$ to $2\frac{1}{4}$ inches, and larger sizes in proportion. This is a very effective tool, and is in general use amongst engineers.

Note BG.—To follow the text, pages 564 to 567.

(Messrs. Maudslay's boring bits, with loose cutters for boring the bosses of wheels, pumps and small steam cylinders in the lathe.)

Boring Bits of the kind represented in fig. 1019, ranging from about 3 to 12 inches in diameter, and with a power of variation in size, were many years back introduced by Messrs. Maudslays, and employed for boring the bosses of wheels, small cylinders, pumps, &c. The stocks of the smaller sizes of these tools are made in wrought-iron, those of the larger in cast-iron, the cutters rest in contact with a fillet made on the stock exactly at right angles to the axis, and are held down by screws which pass through mortises in the cutters, to enable these to be set out to various

Fig. 1019.

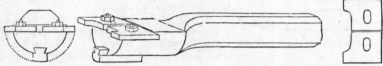

diameters. The bearing pieces beneath, although generally fitted in a chamfer groove, are also made to admit of packing pieces by which they may be set out, to make the three points of bearing to fall in a circle of the exact diameter of that to be bored. The larger of these tools, the cutters of which are $\frac{3}{4}$ inch thick, are now very much less used, since the boring bars with sliding heads or blocks, referred to in pages 569 to 572 of the text, have obtained such general employment for boring cylinders and pumps.

Note BH.—To follow the text, pages 564 to 567.

(Mr. Stivens' Registered Lathe Drill.)

This instrument is represented in perspective in fig. 1020, and in plan with the top plate removed in fig. 1021, it has two cutters which are adjustable for various diameters ; the tool is intended to be used after the manner of figs. 509, 510, and 511, page 565, that is with the loop fig. 511. The two cutters $c\ c$, lie in oblique grooves, the ends of which are at an angle of 45 degrees, and between the cutters is placed a wedge $w\ w$, the long shaft whereof extends through the entire length of the drill shaft, and has the hollow center for receiving the pressure of the popit-head. When this long wedge is set forward, by a tail screw and nut, (not represented,) it throws out the two cutters in any required degree, so that the bit for holes of one inch in diameter, may be thus enlarged for any size not exceeding about $1\frac{1}{4}$ inch, and so with the larger tools.

The cap piece, or plate $p\ p$, which is represented removed, and is attached by three screws, has a shallow circular recess within which the two pins fixed in the cutters are loosely contained, to prevent them from being accidentally lost. The cutters are rounded at the ends, and sharpened precisely like the bit fig. 509, and the two edges of the shaft from a to b, are made symmetrical and with rectangular edges, in order to stick into the sides of the loop such as fig. 511, from which this

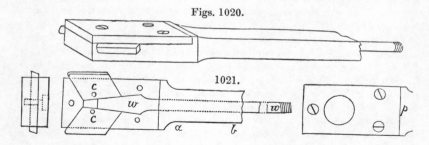

Figs. 1020.

1021.

drill receives its axil guidance, in the manner already explained on page 566 ; but it appears objectionable that the guiding loop should from necessity be so far removed from the cutting edges of this expanding drill, which is proposed to be made as large as eight inches in diameter.

Note BI.—To follow the pages 564 to 567.
(*Mr. Kittoe's Expanding half-round bit.*)

In this instrument, three parts instead of two only are made to adjust radially and equally ; from the one point only being sharpened, and from there being a bottom bearing upon the surface of the hole that is bored, the instrument is used in all respects as the common half-round bit, and without the necessity of the loop or guide, (fig. 511, page 565), required with Mr. Stivens' expanding drill, and of which latter, Mr. Kittoe had not the least knowledge when he constructed the present tool.

Fig. 1022 is the perspective view of the boring bit when in condition for work, fig. 1023 is a section of the same through a horizontal plane ; and a to k, fig. 1024, are

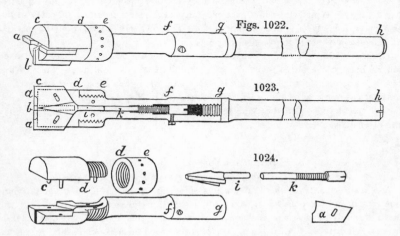

Figs. 1022.

1023.

1024.

the parts shown separately, the same letters being attached to the same parts throughout. The part from c to g is of brass, and contains all the mechanism, g to

3 T

h is an iron rod screwed into the brass to serve as the shaft of the tool, and which is made of any required length. The portion from *c* to *e* is constructed in two pieces, which separate nearly on their diameter, and are united jointly by steady pins and the screwed nut *d e*, the division being made for the purpose of introducing the two bits *a a*, one of which only is made to cut ; *b* the bottom bit is inserted in a similar but vertical cleft.

The three bits are simultaneously and equally advanced by the central wedge *i*, shown also detached, which resembles a cone, reduced so as to form three fins at right angles to one another, that enter the grooves for the bits ; the wedge *i*, is set forward by the tail screw *k*, there is a side screw, which prevents the unintended movement of the set screw *k*, to arrive at which latter it is necessary to remove the socket *c g*, from the stem of the instrument *g h*.

If the wedge with its three fins were considerably advanced beyond its present position, it would stand before the cutter, and prevent the tool from proceeding to the extremity of a flat-bottomed hole ; in order to avoid this, Mr. Kittoe has made the back edges of the cutters at the same angle as the wedge, so that the act of setting forward the wedge also sets forward the cutters to keep them in advance of the point of the wedge. The cutters have oblique mortises which pass over the retaining pins fixed in the semicircular piece, and prevent the cutters from being accidentally lost.

It is the intention that every instrument constructed on this mode should possess various sets of the bits *a*, *b*, so proportioned in size that the smallest instrument should be capable of being expanded to the smallest size of the second instrument, the second to the third, and so on, in order that a few of the boring bars, or stocks, may serve for a considerable range of sizes.

Note BJ.—To follow foot note on page 572.

(*Mr. George Wright, inventor of the modern system of boring large Cylinders.*)

The author is informed by John Taylor, Esq., F.R.S., &c., that the mode of boring steam engine cylinders, by means of a revolving bar with a traversing cutter block and cutters, as slightly explained in fig. 517, page 571, was invented by Mr. George Wright, whilst in the employment of Messrs. Boulton & Watts, of the celebrated Soho Works, near Birmingham. This admirable contrivance has proved of immense advantage to practical engineers.

It may be added that Mr. Nasmyth constructs his heaviest boring bars with three longitudinal grooves fitted with adjustable chamfer bars, and that sustain the pressure of the cut against those faces of the chamfer bars which are radial to the bar. The vertical position seems now to be rather preferred to the horizontal for this class of boring machines, so that the cylinders may be bored in the position in which they are afterwards erected.

Note BK.—To follow the text on page 580.

(*Mr. Mallett's method of describing regular and irregular spirals.*)

We transcribe from the " Mechanics' Magazine" for 1844, page 55, the commencement of a very useful paper by Mr. Mallett of Dublin :—

" For many purposes of the arts, a simple and rapid method of tracing spirals upon a cylindric surface is important ; carvers, wood-turners, &c., often want such, and in larger works, such as some particular branches of mill-work and engineering, it is also frequently wanted. The usual method, by dividing the cylindric surface into equal portions in circumference and length, and drawing lines diagonally, is tedious."

" The following method, believed to be new, is simple and ready, and sufficiently exact for most purposes. Two straight edges of equal length and width, and about ⅝ths of an inch in thickness each, are to be secured on a table, parallel to each other, standing on their edges, and distant from each other by nearly the length of the cylinder upon which the spiral is to be marked. Between these there is also to be secured, in a diagonal direction, stretching from one to the other, a third straight edge, formed of two slips of deal glued together, with a slip of straight thick Bristol board between them projecting ⅛th of an inch at one edge."

" The entire height of the diagonal straight edge when standing on the table, must be a *shade* more that that of the two other straight edges. The three pieces being then thus arranged, the edge of Bristol board is charged with printer's ink. Then, on causing the cylinder to roll over the edges of the two parallel straight edges in the direction of their length, the diagonal slip of inked Bristol board will trace a spiral upon the surface of the cylinder with very considerable accuracy."

Mr. Mallet then goes on to describe that by substituting a *curved edge* for the inclined *straight edges* variable screws will be described, following any particular condition set out in the developed surface of the screw as represented by the curve ; this he considers useful in setting out the variable screws or those of increasing pitch for propellers, and he further shows that spiral lines may be thus drawn on cones, prisms, &c.

Note BL, page 696, to follow the paragraph ending " a convenient bed for the file."
(*On Sharpening the teeth of Saws by means of Grindstones.*)

A peculiar mode of sharpening the teeth of large circular saws by means of grind-stones, the author is informed is followed by Mr. James Boag, of Johnston, Scotland, Manufacturer of Casks and various works in wood.

A small grindstone, mounted on a spindle, and turned on the edge with a narrow ridge suited to the form of the teeth, is made to revolve by the steam engine ; the circular saw is placed upon the surface of a slide, having a center pin to fit the axis of the saw, and a stop to determine how nearly it shall approach the grindstone ; the platform or slide is inclined agreeably to the angle at which the stone should meet the saw plate, and there is a detent or hook, which by catching against one of the teeth, holds the saw plate in the positions successively required for every other tooth, around its circumference.

The grindstone from its rapidity of action is constantly employed when much has to be removed, as in depthening the gullets, when but little is required to be done to the saw, the file is employed as usual.

Sometimes also the saw remains at rest except as regards the change from tooth to tooth, and the grindstone is mounted on a swing frame and brought down every time to a stop.

Note BM, referring both to the Table on Rectilinear Saws, page 699, and to the Table on Circular Saws, page 784.
On the Gages at present used, for measuring the thicknesses of sheet metals and wires, and proposals for a new system of Gages, founded on the decimal subdivision of the Standard Inch.

In setting out the Tables of the Dimensions of Saws, the author could only express their several thicknesses, in the measure always employed for that purpose, namely in the sizes or numbers of the "*Birmingham wire gage*," and to render these measures intelligible to the general reader, the author then determined to introduce in this Appendix—first, the exact values of the principal gages in use for sheet metals and wires, a subject he believes to have been hitherto overlooked ; and secondly, a proposal he has long desired to see carried out, namely an easy and exact system of gages for sheet metals, wires, and general purposes, founded on the decimal division of the inch ; and in which system the nomenclature should be so completely associated with the actual measures, as to convey to the mind, even in the absence of the gages themselves, a very close idea of the several spaces of the gage, or of the thicknesses or sizes of the works measured thereby.

It is to be observed at the outset, that the gages for measuring wires and sheet metals, are usually thick plates of steel of several sizes and forms, around and near the edges of which are first drilled various holes, the next step is to saw a notch from the edge into every hole, saws of the widths of the several notches being used ; and lastly, little parallel plates of steel, called *drifts*, which are hardened and tempered, are driven into the notches, in order to smooth the sides of the same and render them of uniform width, after the manner of various other applications of drifts, explained at pages 883 to 885.

It should be further observed that the Birmingham and other gages seem to have been originated in great measure accidentally, or almost by the eye alone, and without any attempt at system, either as regards the values of the intervals between the successive measures or numbers, or their correspondence with the subdivisions of the inch. And as moreover gages, nominally the same, have been made by various manufacturers with insufficient aim at unity of measures, some irregularity thence exists amongst the gages in common use, notwithstanding that they may be nominally alike.

In ascertaining the precise measures of the principal gages, the author has had the valuable co-operation of Messrs. Stubs of Warrington, who manufacture a large number of these gages, and who tested the drifts they employ, by means of a sliding gage constructed by Holtzapffel & Co., for reading off quantities to the thousandth part of an inch, by means of a vernier ; the results of these admeasurements are stated in the three sections of the accompanying table.

The three series of measures or gages particularized in the annexed table, have no relation whatever to one another ; for example, the numbers 10 of the table are respectively different and undefined quantities, or are neither aliquot nor direct fractional parts of the inch, as the number 10 notches, are severally ·134, ·024, and ·190 of an inch wide ; and other similar numbers are also unrelated.

The approximate measures of any one of these three series may, perhaps, be moderately familiar to those artizans who use that particular gage, but these same artizans will probably be as little informed of the two other gages, as the generality of individuals, to whom the whole of these, and other arbitrary ill-defined measures are vague and confused ; because their nomenclatures have no relation whatever, either to one another, or to our general standard of such quantities, namely, ordinary linear measure ; or, in other words, the standard foot and inch.

The following explanatory remarks on the three gages specified in the table, and certain other gages derived from them, will show the complicated and uncertain nature of the subject of measures, for wires, sheet metals, and various small works.

VALUES OF GAGES

FOR

WIRE AND SHEET METALS IN GENERAL USE,

EXPRESSED IN DECIMAL PARTS OF THE INCH.

SECTION ONE. Birmingham Gage for Iron Wire, and for Sheet Iron and Steel.		SECTION TWO. Birmingham Gage for Sheet Metals, Brass, Gold, Silver, &c.		SECTION THREE. Lancashire Gage for round Steel Wire, and also for Pinion Wire. The smaller sizes distinguished by Numbers. The larger by Letters, and called the Letter Gage.					
MARK.	SIZE.	MARK.	SIZE.	MARK.	SIZE.	MARK.	SIZE.	MARK.	SIZE.
0000	·454	1	·004	80	·013	40	·096	A	·234
000	·425	2	·005	79	·014	39	·098	B	·238
00	·380	3	·008	78	·015	38	·100	C	·242
0	·340	4	·010	77	·016	37	·102	D	·246
1	·300	5	·012	76	·018	36	·105	E	·250
2	·284	6	·013	75	·019	35	·107	F	·257
3	·259	7	·015	74	·022	34	·109	G	·261
4	·238	8	·016	73	·023	33	·111	H	·266
5	·220	9	·019	72	·024	32	·115	I	·272
6	·203	10	·024	71	·026	31	·118	J	·277
7	·180	11	·029	70	·027	30	·125	K	·281
8	·165	12	·034	69	·029	29	·134	L	·290
9	·148	13	·036	68	·030	28	·138	M	·295
10	·134	14	·041	67	·031	27	·141	N	·302
11	·120	15	·047	66	·032	26	·143	O	·316
12	·109	16	·051	65	·033	25	·146	P	·323
13	·095	17	·057	64	·034	24	·148	Q	·332
14	·083	18	·061	63	·035	23	·150	R	·339
15	·072	19	·064	62	·036	22	·152	S	·348
16	·065	20	·067	61	·038	21	·157	T	·358
17	·058	21	·072	60	·039	20	·160	U	·368
18	·049	22	·074	59	·040	19	·164	V	·377
19	·042	23	·077	58	·041	18	·167	W	·386
20	·035	24	·082	57	·042	17	·169	X	·397
21	·032	25	·095	56	·044	16	·174	Y	·404
22	·028	26	·103	55	·050	15	·175	Z	·413
23	·025	27	·113	54	·055	14	·177	A 1	·420
24	·022	28	·120	53	·058	13	·180	B 1	·431
25	·020	29	·124	52	·060	12	·185	C 1	·443
26	·018	30	·126	51	·064	11	·189	D 1	·452
27	·016	31	·133	50	·067	10	·190	E 1	·462
28	·014	32	·143	49	·070	9	·191	F 1	·475
29	·013	33	·145	48	·073	8	·192	G 1	·484
30	·012	34	·148	47	·076	7	·195	H1	·494
31	·010	35	·158	46	·078	6	·198		
32	·009	36	·167	45	·080	5	·201		
33	·008			44	.084	4	·204		
34	·007			43	·086	3	·209		
35	·005			42	·091	2	·219		
36	·004			41	·095	1	·227		

1. *The first column of the table* refers to the gage used for most kinds of wire, and is thence called for the sake of brevity, the "*Wire gage*," although it is also known as the "*Birmingham wire gage*," the "*Birmingham iron Wire gage*" and the "*Sheet iron gage*." This gage which is specified in the column of the table headed section one, is the most common of the three principal kinds, and is employed not only for iron wire, as its name implies, but also for brass and other wires, for black steel wire, also for sheet iron, sheet steel, and various other materials, and likewise for some manufactured works, including screws for joiners' use.

On reference to the table, it appears the largest notch of the Birmingham iron wire gage, is marked 0000, and measures 454 thousandths of an inch, or $4\frac{1}{2}$ tenths of an inch nearly ; and further, that the smallest notch, marked 36, measures 4 thousandths, or the 1-250th part of an inch. Although this gage seems only to possess 40 terms, in reality not less than 60 sizes of wire are made, as intermediate sizes are in many cases added ; and occasionally, although the sizes are retained, their numbers are variously altered ; thus.

The sizes of wires drawn for manufacturing needles correspond with some of the ordinary wire sizes, but the numbers are different ; thus No. 1, of the needle wire, agrees with $18\frac{1}{2}$ of the Birmingham wire gages as here shown :—

Needle wires,   Nos. 1.   2. $2\frac{1}{2}$.   3.   4.   5. and thence to 21.

And Birmingham wire gage, Nos. $18\frac{1}{2}$. 19. $19\frac{1}{2}$. 20. 21. 22. and thence to 38.

Are respectively alike.

Sometimes half-sizes of both series are interpolated, and the manufactured needles when bought and sold are designated by another series of numbers unrelated to either of these wire sizes.

In the wire used for the strings of piano-fortes, the sizes now commonly used, are known as Nos. 6 to 20, and these agree very nearly with the sizes and half-sizes of some of the notches of the Birmingham wire gages, as follows :—

Music wires,   Nos. 6. 7.   8. 9.   10. 11.   12. 14. 16. 18. 20.

And Birmingham wire gage, Nos. 26. $25\frac{1}{2}$. 25. $24\frac{1}{2}$. 24. $23\frac{1}{2}$. 23. 22. 21. 20. 19.

Are respectively alike.

The number 6, or the thinnest music wire now commonly used, measures about the fifty-fifth part of an inch in diameter, and the No. 20, or the thickest, measures about the 25th of an inch.

Piano-fortes were formerly always strung with brass wire, but steel is now alone employed, and they are "*strung much heavier*," or thicker wires are employed, from which cause the numbers 1 to 5 have probably fallen into disuse. The covered

Numbers of the Screws.	Numbers of the Wire Gage.	Numbers of the Screws.	Numbers of the Wire Gage.	Numbers of the Screws.	Numbers of the Wire Gage.	Numbers of the Screws.	Numbers of the Wire Gage.
25 —	0000	14 —	3	7 —	9	1 —	15
23 —	000	12 —	4	6 —	10	0 —	16
22 —	00	11 —	5	5 —	11	00 —	17
21 —	0	10 —	6	4 —	12	000 —	18
17 —	1	9 —	7	3 —	13		
16 —	2	8 —	8	2 —	14		

strings are of steel, upon which a fine copper wire is spirally wound ; and in very short strings, as those of Mr. Pape's Console Piano-fortes and some others, two covering wires are used, that the bulk of the doubly-covered strings may compensate for their want of length.

The manufacturers of the patent screws made from iron wire for joiners' use, also give the intervals of the wire gage a new system of numbers. Thus in the annexed table, the left hand columns shew the number of the screws, the right hand the numbers of the wires from which they are respectively made.

Examples of other and similar conversions of the numbers might be shown, but which would only serve further to illustrate the irregularity, and arbitrary nature of gages, used in the mechanical and other arts.

----

2. *The second column of the table,* page 1013, refers to the gage employed for most of the sheet metals, (excepting iron and steel,) namely, copper, brass, gilding-metal, gold, silver, platinum, &c. This gage is called the " *Birmingham metal gage,*" and for brevity, simply the " *Metal gage,*" or the " *Plate gage,*" in contradistinction to the " *Wire gage* " specified in the first column of the table.

The intervals in the metal or plate gage, are closer or smaller than those of the wire gage. Thus the No. 1, which in this series is the *smallest* sized notch, is 4 thousandths or the 250th part of an inch wide, whilst the largest notch or 36, measures 167 thousandths, or is evidently meant for the sixth part of an inch.

When thicker metals are wanted, their measures are sought in the Birmingham wire gage, thus the 36 on the plate gage, nearly agrees with the 8 on the wire gage, and therefore the numbers 7, 6, 5, to 0000 of the latter, are then employed for thicker metals than can be measured by the plate gage. Frequently the plate gage ends at 24, which number agrees with 14 of the wire gage, and then the numbers 13. 12. 11. to 000 of the latter are similarly resorted to for thicker metals. These combinations of different series of numbers, running in reverse orders, are evidently liable to lead to confusion.

The method in which sheet metals are commercially described, also present much variation, for instance zinc has a gage thus constituted—

Sheet zinc   Nos. 6. 7. 8. 9. 10. 11. 12. 13. 14. 15. 16 ⎫ are nearly alike.
B. Plate gage Nos. 4. 4½. 5. 6. 7. 8. 9. 10. 11. 12. 13 ⎭

These thin sheets of zinc, which measure only from one to about four hundredths of an inch thick, are principally used for gutters, roofs, and small works manufactured with the hammer.

Thicker zinc plates, or those from about 5 to 18 hundredths thick, and which are used for zincography, door plates, and engraved works, are commonly made to the notches, 18 to 7 of the Birmingham Wire Gage, without alteration of the numbers, but which run the reverse way of those of the other series used for zinc.

Several of the metals are estimated by the weight of every superficial foot, and that the more especially when the value of the material in the sheet, exceeds the value of the labour afterwards expended upon it in converting the metal to its intended purpose; thus

Cast and milled lead are both described as of from 4 to 12 pounds to the superficial foot, the variation being one pound to the foot.

Coppersmiths and braziers, do not acknowledge the plate gage at all, but reckon their metal as from about 3 to 56 pounds to the sheet; the sheet measures 2 feet by 4 feet, and therefore contains 8 superficial feet.

The precious metals, are sometimes estimated as of so many ounces or pennyweights troy to the superficial foot; and it will be hereafter shown, how by aid of the proposed scheme, derived from the decimal subdivision of the inch, the correspondence between the relative weights and thicknesses of metals, may be critically arrived at with great simplicity.

The third, fourth, and fifth column of the table, page 1013, constitute one series of gages, employed exclusively for the bright steel wire prepared in Lancashire, and the steel pinion wire for watch and clockmakers.

The smallest notch of this series is called No. 80, and measures 13 thousandths of an inch, or about the 120th of an inch; and the first part of this series continues unto No. 1, which measures 227 thousandths, or nearly one quarter of an inch.

The steel wire gage apparently ended at this size in the first instance, but has since been extended by a second series to the diameter of 494 thousandths, a measure doubtless intended for half an inch. In order to avoid the confusion attendant upon two series of numerals, meeting at zero in the midst, the larger sizes are distinguished by the letters A to Z, and these terms are then continued under the denominations A 1, B 1, C 1, D 1 to H 1, which latter size is the largest and measures 494 thousandths of an inch, as shown by the table. This second part of the Lancashire wire gage, is called by way of distinction, the " *Letter gage.*"

Many other gages of arbitrary characters came to the author's knowledge in this inquiry, several of which are applicable alone, to particular trades; amongst these may be mentioned, the rod iron gage, the nail rod gage, the button maker's gage, others used in watchwork, and the gage used by gun makers for the bores of guns and rifles; three of which gages alone will be described.

The rod iron gage, employed by Messrs. Bradleys, and some other iron masters, and also by Messrs. Stubs, for steel, has measures derived from the division of the inch into 8ths and 64ths as follows—

MESSRS. JOHN BRADLEY & CO.'S ROD IRON GAGE.

No.	Inch.	No.	Inch.	No.	Inch.	No.	Inch.
00	$\frac{1}{8}$	5	$\frac{5}{16}$	11	$\frac{1}{2}$	17	$1\frac{1}{8}$
0	$\frac{5}{32}$	6	$\frac{11}{32}$	12	$\frac{9}{16}$	18	$1\frac{1}{4}$
1	$\frac{3}{16}$	7	$\frac{3}{8}$	13	$\frac{5}{8}$	19	$1\frac{3}{8}$
2	$\frac{7}{32}$	8	$\frac{13}{32}$	14	$\frac{3}{4}$	20	$1\frac{1}{2}$
3	$\frac{1}{4}$	9	$\frac{7}{16}$	15	$\frac{7}{8}$		
4	$\frac{9}{32}$	10	$\frac{15}{32}$	16	1		

MESSRS. JOHN BRADLEY & CO.'S NAIL ROD GAGE.

No.	Inch.	No.	Inch.	No.	Inch.	No.	Inch.
00	$\frac{1}{8}$	$1\frac{1}{2}$	$\frac{13}{64}$	4	$\frac{9}{32}$	7	$\frac{3}{8}$
$00\frac{1}{2}$	$\frac{9}{64}$	2	$\frac{7}{32}$	$4\frac{1}{2}$	$\frac{19}{64}$	8	$\frac{13}{32}$
0	$\frac{5}{32}$	$2\frac{1}{2}$	$\frac{15}{64}$	5	$\frac{5}{16}$	9	$\frac{7}{16}$
$0\frac{1}{2}$	$\frac{11}{64}$	3	$\frac{1}{4}$	$5\frac{1}{2}$	$\frac{21}{64}$	10	$\frac{15}{32}$
1	$\frac{3}{16}$	$3\frac{1}{2}$	$\frac{17}{64}$	6	$\frac{11}{32}$	11	$\frac{1}{2}$

It will be perceived that the intervals, from $00\frac{1}{2}$ to $3\frac{1}{2}$ are the 64th of an inch, from 4 to 11 the 32nd, and above 13, the differences are $\frac{1}{8}$ of an inch. This mode although systematic, is objectionable, as there is no evident relation between the numbers and their corresponding measures, and therefore both have to be impressed upon the mind.

In guns of most kinds, the weight of the balls determine the denominations of their respective sizes. Thus it is well known that heavy guns or ordnance are named 6. 9. 12 to 68 pounders, from having bores respectively suited to iron shots of those respective weights, the bore is always $\frac{1}{20}$th larger in diameter than the shot, the difference being known as *windage*. The sizes of the bores of Mortars and modern guns intended for hollow shot, are designated in inches, as 8, 10, 12 inch mortars, &c.

In rifles and fowling pieces, the diameters of the bores, designated as No. 1. 2. 3. 4. 5. &c., are the diameters respectively of leaden bullets or spheres, of which 1. 2. 3. 4. 5. &c. weigh exactly one pound avoirdupois ; and as the subject may have an interest for some of the readers of this volume, the following particulars of the weights of the balls in grains, and of the diameters both of the balls and of the barrels in hundredths of an inch, are transcribed from Mr. Wilkinson's gage, which he has constructed with great care.

MR. WILKINSON'S GAGE FOR RIFLES AND FOWLING-PIECES.

Number.	Diameter of Bore in Hundredths.	Weight of Leaden bullet in Grains.	Number.	Diameter of Bore in Hundredths.	Weight of Leaden bullet in Grains.	Number.	Diameter of Bore in Hundredths.	Weight of Leaden bullet in Grains.
5	·98	1400	15	·70 +	$466\frac{2}{3}$	25	·60 +	280
6	·93—	$1666\frac{2}{3}$	16	·69—	$437\frac{1}{2}$	26	·59 +	$269\frac{3}{13}$
7	·89	1000	c 17 p	·67 +	$411\frac{13}{17}$	27	·59	$269\frac{7}{27}$
8	·85—	875	18	·66	$388\frac{8}{9}$	28	·58 +	250
9	·81—	$777\frac{7}{9}$	19	·65 +	$368\frac{8}{19}$	29	·58—	$241\frac{11}{29}$
10	·79	700	20	·63 +	355	30	·57	$233\frac{1}{3}$
m 11 p	·77—	$636\frac{4}{11}$	21	·63	$333\frac{1}{3}$	31	·56 +	$225\frac{25}{31}$
12	·75 +	$583\frac{1}{3}$	22	·62 +	$318\frac{2}{11}$	32	·56—	$218\frac{3}{4}$
13	·74—	$538\frac{6}{13}$	23	·61 +	$304\frac{8}{23}$			
m 14 s	·72—	500	24	·61	$291\frac{2}{3}$			

From the perusal of the foregoing particulars of numerous gages, employed in different branches of mechanical art, it will have been seen that little analogy, on the one hand, but great confusion on the other, exist in such of the gages as have been referred to ; and the author will now briefly state the remedy he would suggest to obviate the difficulty in the most simple and inexpensive manner.

The remedy proposed to remove the arbitrary incongruous system of gages now used, is simply and in every one of the cases above referred to, and also in all others requiring minute measures, *to employ the decimal divisions of the inch, and those under their true appellations.*

Thus for most purposes the division of the inch into one hundred parts would be sufficiently minute, and the measures 1. 2. 5. 10. 15 or 100 hundredths, would be also sufficiently impressive to the mind ; their quantities might be written down as 1. 2.

5. 10. 15 or 100 hundredths, as the decimal mode of expression might if preferred be safely abandoned, and the method would be abundantly distinct for common use if the word " *Hundredths* " were stamped upon the gage, to show that its numerals denoted hundredths of the inch, quantities which could be easily verified by all.

It does not follow that the entire hundred notches should be at all times used, as in many cases it might suffice that below 20 hundredths, every size should be employed ;—from 20 to 50 hundredths, every alternate size,—from 50 to 100 hundredths every fifth size. As at present also, the upper or lower part of the series of terms might be omitted to any desired extent, in those cases where they were beyond the particular wants of the artizan or the particular branch of trade, in order to lesson the bulk and expense of the gage.

It may be objected to this scheme, that for the more valuable metals, and the more minute purposes, the quantity of the one hundredth of an inch is too coarse a difference. Two facile modes of remedy may be here applied. The first to make half sizes : thus $8\frac{1}{2}$ or 8·5 would of course denote the medial interval between 8 and 9 hundredths. Or secondly, and preferably, below one tenth of an inch, a finer scale might be substituted for the more minute and delicate purposes, namely a gage based in precisely the same manner, on the *thousandth* of the inch as the unit, which would give a much finer degree of subdivision than is afforded by any of the arbitrary gages in general use ; in this case the intervals being derived from the thousandth of an inch, the word *"Thousandths,"* should be stamped on every such gage.

In practice no difficulty could be seriously felt even without this precaution of marking the gages respectively with the word *Hundredths* or *Thousandths ;* as we should not more readily mistake 5 thousandths for 5 hundredths, then we should, 5 tenths or half an inch, for 5 whole inches, or 5 entire inches for as many feet.

Neither is it to be admitted that no such gages are attainable as may be read off in hundredths or thousandths. The demand would immediately create the supply, and there could be no more difficulty in constructing the gages of the customary forms, with notches made to systematic and *defined* measures, *that may be easily arrived at or tested,* than with their present unsystematical and *arbitrary* measures, *which do not admit of verification.*

Besides, for those who desire to possess them, several very correct decimal gages already exist, amongst which may be cited the decimal sector gages long since recommended, and published by the Society of Arts, Edinburgh, and various sliding gages with verniers some to read off in hundredths, and finer ones in thousandths, of the inch, all of which have been long and constantly used in the author's manufactory.

To these may be added—La Rivière's gage, modified and enlarged from that used for the balance springs of watches amongst the Geneva watchmakers.—Chater and Hayward's gage for sheet metals and glass.—Walker's gage for sheet iron.—Whitworth's micrometer gage and others—which may be severally read off to the thousandth of the inch, and even more minute quantities, and amongst which kinds sufficient choice exists for almost every purpose.

The advantages offered by this proposed application of decimal measures, appear to be numerous and considerable, the more especially in those cases of small measures, where the ordinary wire gages on the one hand, and the coarse division of ordinary foot rules on the other, are obviously insufficient for accurate purposes. Amongst these advantages may be enumerated the following :

The proposed decimal scheme would introduce one universality of system, intel-ligible alike to all, instead of the numerous and irregular measures now used, which are but partially and indifferently known and lead to frequent mistakes.

It would give a superior idea of particular magnitude, and enable the theoretical and practical man to proceed with so much more decision in their respective communications.

In conveying verbal or written instructions, the system would be in every way superior to the usual methods, as being almost free from the chance of misunder-standing; more especially as some of the decimal sliding gages are so small as hardly to take up more room in the pocket than an ordinary penknife, and might be therefore continually within reach for reference.

When certain objects are required to be so proportioned as to constitute a series; the intervals between the decimal measures would be far more easily arranged and appreciated, than those of vulgar fractions; and if calculation were referred to, the decimal figures, especially when divested of the decimal point, and the zeros to the right of the same, would be immediately intelligible to the least informed, from being then no more in fact than simple numerals.

Quantities expressed decimally would be more easily written down, and more exactly defined than the compound fractions such as $\frac{3}{8}$ and $\frac{1}{16}$ of an inch—or than the still more obscure method, of $\frac{3}{8}$ of an inch *full* or *bare* as the case might be, which latter nearly sets all attempts at exactness at defiance.

The smaller aliquot fractions of the inch such as the $\frac{1}{20}$ $\frac{1}{22}$ $\frac{1}{24}$ $\frac{1}{26}$ $\frac{1}{28}$ $\frac{1}{30}$ &c., of an inch although in themselves very precise, do not from their nature, so readily admit of definition or comparison, as the quantities 2. 3. 4. 5. 6. 7. 8. 9. or 10 hundredths of an inch; because, in the vulgar fractions every one has a *specific* relation to the inch, whereas the decimal terms have one *general* relation, decimals being sometimes considered as the numerators of fractions, all having the constant deno-minator unity, or 100, 1000, &c. : and therefore the latter, or the decimal terms, constitute a simple arithmetical series, or one in which the intervals are alike, but this is not the case with vulgar fractions.

It would bring all foreign measures within reach of our workshops. For example, in the United States of America and Russia, English measure is employed, and no difficulty would be felt in reference to these countries. And as most of the National Foot measures, are more than 11 inches English, and less than 13, even if they are considered for the time as equal to our own foot, and without any adjustment being attempted, the average error would not exceed about five per cent. And further, when two of Holtzapffel and Co.'s engine-divided scales, the one of the particular foreign measure, and the other of English inches, are laid side by side, they show visually, as on a slide rule, the correspondence between any quantity of such foreign measure with our own, as more fully explained in the author's pamphlet " On a New System of Scales of Equal Parts," in which this and numerous other employ-ments of scales of equal parts are treated at length.

The decimal scheme would allow the exact weight in every superficial foot of sheet metals and other substances to be readily arrived at.—Thus, as a cubic foot of water weighs 1000 ounces troy, the specific gravities of lead, copper, silver, &c., denote at the same time how many troy ounces are severally contained in one cubic foot of the same. The specific gravity divided by 1200, gives the weight of a plate or film, the one hundredth of an inch thick, and thence a table may be readily computed, *by addition alone*, to show the weight of plates of any thickness in *troy* ounces.

These calculations would be correct at once for gold and silver, as these metals are estimated by troy weight; but for other substances requiring avoirdupois weight, the numbers expressing the specific gravities of the substances must be previously altered by one of the usual methods, namely, either by multiplying them by 192, and dividing the product by 175, numbers which represent the ratio between troy and avoirdupois ounces; or else instead thereof, the specific gravities of substances may be multiplied by the decimal constant usually employed for effecting the same end.

In this method also, constant multipliers may be readily found for thus determining from the specific gravities of the several materials, the exact *thicknesses* of plates or sheets of the same, which shall precisely *weigh* one ounce or one pound, either troy or avoirdupois as may be required. This has already been done by Mr. Hayward as regards crown glass; for assuming its specific gravity to be 2·52, when the glass is of the thickness of ·1525, (or one tenth and a half nearly,) it weighs 32 avoirdupois ounces to the superficial foot and thence by Mr. Hayward's calculation are obtained the following numbers—the first line denotes the weight of crown glass in ounces, in every superficial foot, the second line the corresponding thicknesses in thousandths of the inch, ranging from about 5 to 152 thousandths—

Crown glass of 1   2   4   8   12   16   20   24   28   32 ounces.
Measures ·00476 ·0095 ·019 ·038 ·0571 ·0762 ·0952 ·1333 ·1429 ·1524 inch.

The above and the intermediate terms are sometimes engraved on Messrs. Chater & Hayward's gages, alongside of the line of graduations which denotes thousandths: and at other times, instead of the weight per foot are engraved divisions indicative of the 8th, 9th, 10th, 11th, 12th, &c. of the inch; which quantities are of course obtained by simply dividing 1000 by those respectives numbers.

Tables might in the above manner be very readily computed, that would show the weights in every superficial foot of the metals and other materials for all defined thicknesses; and also other tables for showing how thick the metals should be, in order to weigh exactly so many ounces to the superficial foot. These matters could be also arrived at by the employment of scales of equal parts, laid down in the proportions of the specific gravities of the substances; and in the opinion of the author they could be worked out with even greater simplicity and universality, by a *decimal proportional instrument* he has some time since contrived, which is applicable to the visual development of all ratios that have reference to decimal arithmetic, including those of interest, discount, profit, and other calculations to which the term *Per Cent.* is applied.

In conclusion, the author begs to add that he does not suggest any alteration whatever, as regards those measures for which the division of the foot-rule into eighths and sixteenths may be found sufficiently precise and minute. But he would ask whether for more minute measurements, greater convenience and distinctiveness would not result, from the general employment of measures expressed in hundredths of the inch, than from the employment of the many gages for specific uses, the sizes and numbers of which are entirely devoid of system, and which gages may be considered as unknown beyond the particular trades in which they are employed.

How confusing would it be, if the measures by which broad cloths, linens, cottons, silks, velvets, carpets, and other textile fabrics, are manufactured and sold, were all different instead of being uniformly the yard measure; and yet this incongruity fully applies to the various articles whose measurements are described under the mystical names of *Number, Size, Gage,* and other appellations, which assume *different* values in *different* branches of manufacturing art; as for example, in the various kinds of sheet metals, various kinds of wires, in tubes, joiners' screws, and vast numbers of small manufactured articles, the various sizes of which are arbitrarily designated as Nos. 1. 2. 3. 4. &c.

Why not in all these branches of trade, describe every thing measuring $\frac{1}{10}$th of an inch, as No. 10 ; those of $\frac{3}{10}$ths inch, as No. 30 ? and then in sets of objects required to be nearly alike, the succeeding numbers could be 31. 32. 33. 34. 35. 36. &c. ; or if fewer and wider variations were wanted, the series might be 32. 34. 36. 38. 40. ; or else 35. 40. 45. 50. 55. Every trade could select any portion of the series it might require, both as regards general magnitude, and the greater or less intervals between the sizes, and with the power of adding to, or subtracting from, the scale first selected, as circumstances might suggest.

But there should be one common understanding that the *commercial* numbers or sizes, when different from the measures of the foot-rule, should be always understood to be hundredths of the inch, (in some rare instances thousandths,) as then from the unity of system no confusion or difficulty could possibly arise.

It may be true that some of the proposals having reference to the weights of materials in the superficial foot, the correspondences with foreign measures, and some of the projects principally intended for the purposes of science, may not be required in every-day practice ; but still much remains in the system, that in the opinion of the author, would admit of very easy introduction, and most general and satisfactory employment.

In respect to the practical application of the method of decimal divisions, as regards mechanical construction, the author can speak most satisfactorily from some years' experience in his own manufactory, as he has found it to be most readily followed by his workpeople, and also that it has avoided frequent and vexatious misunderstandings, to which, before its adoption he was frequently subjected, from the want of a more minute and specific system of measure, than is afforded by the common foot-rule and wire gages.

Therefore, from conviction of the usefulness and practicability of the decimal system of measures for small quantities, he would most strongly urge its general, or indeed universal, adoption, as above proposed ; the more especially as it is a change that would be attended with very little temporary inconvenience or expense, circumstances which greatly retard all attempts at generalization.

Note BN.—To follow the paragraph ending the *ribbon saw*, p. 751.
(*Mr. Bodmer's Patent Tires for Locomotive Wheels.*)

Mr. Bodmer's Patent mode of constructing the inner and outer tires of locomotive wheels, and other annular objects, might possibly serve for making in one piece the riband saws spoken of at page 751, and also the crown saws represented and described fig. 797, pages 802—3.

In making the tires of locomotive wheels, the first course is to prepare a mass of wrought iron of the *appropriate weight* and with a central hole ; this rude annular piece of iron when raised to the welding heat, is inserted between a pair of rollers that overhang the bearings in which they work. The one roller is placed within and the other without the piece of iron, which, however irregular, is soon thereby reduced to an equal section throughout when the rollers are set in motion ; and a third roller, placed in the path of the nascent hoop or tire, gives it a form almost as truly circular as if it had been turned in a lathe. The three rollers ensure circularity in the tire upon the same principle that is employed in the three bending rollers, *see* fig. 232, page 389, Vol. I.

Note BO, page 803.—To follow the third paragraph.
(*Mr. Harvey's Patent Curvilinear Saws.*)

Mr. Harvey took out a patent in June 1845, for an adaptation of the cylindrical or crown saws, described in pages 800 to 803, by which they may be applied to works of indefinite length. The hoop constituting the saw, is attached to a disk mounted on an axis, but the disk only extends over $\frac{2}{3}$ of the circumference, leaving $\frac{2}{3}$ exposed for the passage of the wood; And the saw instead of receiving continuous circular motion, as before, is now reciprocated by a crank through a few degrees only of the circle, so that the wood sawn off may proceed through the aperture between the saw and the disk; which aperture somewhat resembles the space between the spokes of a wheel having three arms and a very thin flat rim.

The square log fig. 1025 is mounted on centers, upon a drag or slide, fitted with rack, pinion, ratchet and detent as usual for feeding the cut, so that the log is presented with its four angles successively; and the extreme edges having been first sawn off with an ordinary circular saw, also attached to the machine, the four

Fig. 1025.   Fig. 1026.

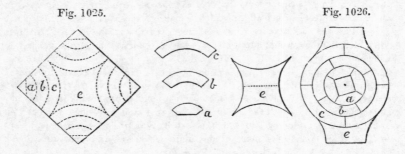

annular sections *a a a a*, are first removed from the four angles, then four larger *b b b b*, with a saw of greater diameter and afterwards four others *c c c c*, the nucleus *e*, is then sawn in two, and the several pieces when recombined produce the mast of the section fig. 1026, which is said by the Patentee to be much stronger than any mast or spar consisting of a single piece of timber.

The inventor also proposes to apply the saws to short works such as chair backs and brushes, but which may be apparently better produced in the old drum saw, which acts more rapidly from receiving continuous motion—he also proposes to cut pieces of double curvature or of the ogee form, by the employment both of the inner and outer surfaces of the cylindrical saws according to circumstances. See Mechanics' Mag. 1846, Vol. 44, p. 18.

The reader is referred to Note BN, which suggests a new mode of constructing cylindrical or crown saws.

Note BP, page 827, to follow the paragraph ending " fast by each foot."
(*Cutting the teeth near the ends of files.*)

To this paragraph it should have been added, that in cutting the *ends* of the files, which parts must necessarily be laid at the time *upon* the anvil, the opposite end of the blank is supported upon a *wooden prop* of the same height as the anvil, and the straps are placed in the middle of the length of the file.

Note BQ, to follow the first paragraph, page 839.
(Mr. Michael Kelly's Quannett.)

Mr. Michael Kelly's Quannett represented in figs. 830 and 831, was rewarded by the Society of Arts in 1845 ; and the instrument has been successively applied to scraping zinc plates for the process denominated Anastatic Printing, invented in Germany, and Patented in England by Mr. Joseph Woods. By this ingenious art impressions may be made, by the *transfer process*, from any, even the earliest printed works and engravings, provided any portion of the oil still remains in the ink.

Note BR, page 841, to follow the paragraph ending "are not at present used."
(Inventors of various file cutting machines.)

Since the article on File Cutting Machines was written, the author finds that Thiout was not, as he had supposed, the inventor of the first machine for cutting files ; as in the Memoir on the subject by M. de Montigny, read before the Committee of Commerce in 1778, the following were noticed as the more important of the machines invented for cutting files—namely, that constructed by Duverger in 1699 —by Fardouet 1725—by Thiout 1740—by Brachat et Gamain 1756—and by Vaucher 1778.

To these machines are to be added those subsequently made by Raoul in 1800— and by Ericcson in 1836. See Article *Limes*, (Vol. 12, p. 289, of the) *Dictionnaire Technologique des Arts et Metiers, Paris*, 22 vols. 8vo. and 2 vols. Atlas 1822—1835.

Note BS.—Referring to page 299 of the First Volume.

During the period in which the last sheet of this appendix was being printed, Mr. T. Taylor kindly pointed out to the author that in the table for converting decimal proportions into divisions of the pound avoirdupois, inserted on page 299 of the first volume, a clerical error had been committed from the subdivisions of the avoirdupois ounce having been considered to consist of 8 drams, as in apothecaries' weight, instead of 16 as in avoirdupois weight.

The author much regrets this oversight, which arose from the circumstance of the avoirdupois ounce, being rarely subdivided in common use more minutely than into halves or quarters, and he inserts overleaf the corrected table, which Mr. Taylor has been kind enough to calculate for this work.

TABLE FOR CONVERTING DECIMAL PROPORTIONS

Into Divisions of the Pound Avoirdupois.

Decimal.	oz.	dr.	Decimal.	oz.	dr.	Decimal.	oz.	dr.	Decimal.	oz.	dr.
·39		1	12·89	2	1	25·39	4	1	37·85	6	1
·78		2	13·28	2	2	25·78	4	2	38·28	6	2
1·17		3	13·67	2	3	26·17	4	3	38·67	6	3
1·56		4	14·06	2	4	26·56	4	4	39·06	6	4
1·95		5	14·45	2	5	26·95	4	5	39·45	6	5
2·34		6	14·84	2	6	27·34	4	6	39·84	6	6
2·73		7	15·23	2	7	27·73	4	7	40·23	6	7
3·13		8	15·62	2	8	28·13	4	8	40·62	6	8
3·52		9	16·01	2	9	28·52	4	9	41·02	6	9
3·91		10	16·41	2	10	28·91	4	10	41·41	6	10
4·30		11	16·80	2	11	29·30	4	11	41·79	6	11
4·69		12	17·19	2	12	29·69	4	12	42·19	6	12
5·08		13	17·58	2	13	30·08	4	13	42·54	6	13
5·47		14	17·97	2	14	30·47	4	14	42·97	6	14
5·86		15	18·36	2	15	30·86	4	15	43·36	6	15
6·25	1	0	18·75	3	0	31·25	5	0	43·75	7	0
6·64	1	1	19·14	3	1	31·64	5	1	44·14	7	1
7·03	1	2	19·53	3	2	32·03	5	2	44·53	7	2
7·42	1	3	19·92	3	3	32·42	5	3	44·92	7	3
7·81	1	4	20·31	3	4	32·81	5	4	45·31	7	4
8·20	1	5	20·70	3	5	33·20	5	5	45·70	7	5
8·59	1	6	21·09	3	6	33·59	5	6	46·09	7	6
8·98	1	7	21·48	3	7	33·98	5	7	46·48	7	7
9·38	1	8	21·88	3	8	34·37	5	8	46·87	7	8
9·77	1	9	22·27	3	9	34·69	5	9	47·27	7	9
10·16	1	10	22·66	3	10	35·16	5	10	47·66	7	10
10·55	1	11	23·05	3	11	35·55	5	11	48·05	7	11
10·94	1	12	23·44	3	12	35·94	5	12	48·44	7	12
11·33	1	13	23·83	3	13	36·33	5	13	48·83	7	13
11·72	1	14	24·22	3	14	36·71	5	14	49·22	7	14
12·10	1	15	24·61	3	15	37·11	5	15	49·61	7	15
12·50	2	0	25·00	4	0	37·50	6	0	50·00	8	0

Application of the Table.

The Chinese Packfong, similar to our German silver, according to Dr. Fyfe's analysis, p. 279, is said to consist of—

40·4 parts of Copper		equivalent to	6 oz. 7 drams, full.
25·4 — Zinc			4 — 1 — full.
31·6 — Nickel			5 — 1 — nearly.
2·6 — Iron			7 — nearly.

| 100·0 Parts. | | | 16 oz. 0 — Avoirdupois. |

Note BT.—To follow the notes J. K. L, on page 46 of Vol. I.
(*Mr. Joseph Gibbs' Patent Carving Machine.*)

Mr. Joseph Gibbs' patent for "improved machinery for cutting marble, wood, and other substances," sealed 12 Nov., 1829, was inadvertently overlooked by the author, when he wrote the notes J. K. L of this appendix, on the carving machines subsequently patented by Irving, Jordan, and Tomes, described on pages 954—7 ; he now proposes to supply the omission.

A general idea of Mr. Gibbs' carving machine will be conveyed, by imagining the model and the copy, to be placed on two separate horizontal platforms, situated one above the other ; the drill and tracer are each exactly vertical, and in one and the same line ; but of course in an interrupted line, as between them lies the platform with the model. The tracer is at the top of all, and rests on the model, the drill is below the model and rests upon the copy, that it is in the act of producing.

It is next to be explained how the tracer and drill, are simultaneously and equally moved in all directions, over the model and copy which lie at rest ; and this is accomplished by building them in one vertical line at the outer edge of a double swing frame, consisting of two frames or panels which move on joints, somewhat as a folding door that consists of two leaves jointed in the center ; a construction which also resembles that of the double swing frame, used in Brunel's cross cutting saw-machine, see fig. 789, page 796.

The two leaves of the swing frame—to borrow the words of the former description,—give respectively the powers of moving the tracer and drill simultaneously from north to south, and from east to west. In addition to these two motions is a third; for the entire mass of the swing frame is movable vertically, as it slides through fixed circular bearings, and is supported on a treadle which allows the drill gradually to penetrate the work, until the further descent of the machinery is arrested, from the tracer coming into contact with the model to be copied. As in Brunel's saw machine and some others, the motion of the prime mover, is communicated by belts or straps, reeved on pulleys situated at the two axes of motion, so that the rambling of the tool does not affect the tension of the bands.

One great application of this machine was to the cutting of the wooden letters used for shop fronts, several in one pile, and in which case a metal templet was used. The machine presented all the elements required for the purposes of carving, and was used for that purpose ; but the duplication of the swing frame enfeebled the construction, and gave rise to more vibration than exists in the subsequent machines of Irving, Jordan, and Tomes, which all more or less resemble Gibbs' original machine in principle, although severally different in construction, and more efficient in use.

END OF THE APPENDIX TO THE SECOND VOLUME.

Eccentric Chuck.

Oval Chuck.

Segment Engine.

Rose Engine.

IBBETSON'S *Geometric Chuck.—Parts First, Second, and Third.*

IBBETSON'S Compound Eccentric Chuck.

Straight Line Chuck.

Two Eccentric Movements.

One Oval and one Eccentric Movement.

HOLTZAPFFEL & Co.'s *Compound Oval and Eccentric Chuck.*